T3-BID-598

579.3
B82
63991
Braun.
Bacterial genetics.

Date Due

APR 6 '66			
OCT 11 '67			
NOV 2			
NOV 22 '67			
OCT 23 '68			

The Library
Nazareth College of Rochester, N. Y.

PRINTED IN U.S.A.

BACTERIAL GENETICS

By

WERNER BRAUN
INSTITUTE OF MICROBIOLOGY
RUTGERS, THE STATE UNIVERSITY

Second Edition
Illustrated

1965

W. B. SAUNDERS COMPANY
PHILADELPHIA & LONDON

WITHDRAWN

NAZARETH CO!LEGE LIBRARY

Bacterial Genetics

63991

© 1965 by W. B. Saunders Company. Copyright 1953 by W. B. Saunders Company. Copyright under the International Copyright Union. All rights reserved. This book is protected by copyright. No part of it may be duplicated or reproduced in any manner without written permission from the publisher. Made in the United States of America. Press of W. B. Saunders Company. Library of Congress catalog card number 65-12318.

PREFACE TO THE SECOND EDITION

Progress in the field of bacterial genetics has been so rapid and extensive that a mere updating and revision of the 1953 version of *Bacterial Genetics* proved impractical. To a very large extent, therefore, this is really a new book, especially as far as Parts I and III are concerned. In these two sections I have attempted to present much of the amazing progress of the last dozen years which saw the evolution of microbial genetics into a basic field for all biological sciences. However, I have felt that even in these days of justified emphasis on molecular aspects, the discussion of such topics as "Representative Mutant Types" and "Population Changes" should not be eliminated from a comprehensive text on bacterial genetics. Accordingly, I have placed these discussions into a separate section, Part II of this book; this section contains, I believe, much material of continued interest and importance to the bacteriologist, particularly to the medical bacteriologist and the bacterial physiologist.

Those who wish primarily to study or teach such problems as the nature of genetic information, mutation, transfer and recombination of genetic information, "gene action," and the molecular basis of these events are encouraged to proceed directly from the end of Part I to the beginning of Part III, possibly discussing only portions of Part II at the end; others may wish to follow the sequence which I have chosen. The choice will depend on the time available and on the principal areas of interest, but alterations of sequence, or even an elimination of certain chapters, should be feasible since I have attempted to write the book in a manner permitting such rearrangements.

As in the first edition, I have made no attempt to present an exhaustive list of references. Rather, I have relied mainly on two criteria for inclusion of a given reference: either (a) it is the first report of the problem under discussion, or (b) it contains a large list of references to earlier studies. As a consequence of this procedure I may have omitted or overlooked quite a number of useful references without any intention of slighting their value. Many additional references can be found in two admirable books which were published in the last two years and which complement my own efforts in many respects. They are W. Hayes' *The Genetics of Bacteria and Their*

Viruses (John Wiley and Sons, Inc., N. Y., 1964) and G. Stent's *Molecular Biology of Bacterial Viruses* (Freeman and Co., 1963). The interested reader should consult these books not only for additional references but also for additional details. Such details are beyond the scope of my book, which, like its first edition, is designed to make the basic and sometimes rather complex facts and publications palatable and comprehensible to the uninitiated.

A number of colleagues and friends have made valuable contributions to this second edition and I would like to record my thanks to them here. Many colleagues and their publishers gave me permission to reproduce illustrations and tables from published material; some, like E. Adelberg, even permitted me to prepare some unedited figures based on unpublished sketches (see Chapter 15) or, like T. Jukes, permitted me to use previously unpublished material (Table 23). Drs. Vernon Bryson, Edward Garber, and Ross W. I. Kessel have read the entire manuscript; Drs. Edward Adelberg, Robert Austrian, Donald Bacon, Ekkehard Bautz, Rollin Hotchkiss, Otto Landman, Sol Spiegelman, Henry Vogel and Norton Zinder read certain chapters of the manuscript. I am deeply indebted to all of them for their suggestions and advice, but any remaining errors should not, and cannot, be blamed on them. Mrs. M. Auyash and Mrs. M. Schmidt were of enormous help in preparing the typed manuscript, Miss J. Grellner gave invaluable aid in proof-reading, and the staff of W. B. Saunders Company was most cooperative and efficient during the preparation of the printed text.

Much of the book was written under unusually stimulating and pleasant environmental conditions, during a sabbatical year spent in Jerusalem and Paris. My host in Jerusalem was Dr. A. L. Olitzki, Chairman, Department of Bacteriology, Hebrew University–Hadassah Medical School, my host in Paris was Dr. F. Jacob, Institut Pasteur. I am extremely grateful to both of them for their hospitality and interest. I also wish to record, with appreciation, that my stay with them was made possible through a Special Fellowship (ESP-17,699) of the U. S. Public Health Service, National Institutes of Health.

WERNER BRAUN

New Brunswick, N. J.

PREFACE TO THE FIRST EDITION

The history of science is characterized by sudden spurts of progress which frequently occur following the merger of once separated disciplines. The field of bacterial genetics represents one of the most recent examples of such scientific cross-fertilization from which a subject with real hybrid vigor has evolved. The progress in this field during the last ten years has contributed not only significant information for geneticists, but what is perhaps even more important, it has resulted in the development of a branch of science that may take its place alongside biochemistry as necessary for understanding the nature and activity of microorganisms. Thus it has been recognized that a majority of problems in bacteriology and its allied fields, such as medicine, public health, bacterial metabolism and industrial fermentation, require an understanding of the nature and control of variation. This recognition of the growing importance of bacterial genetics is reflected in the remarkable increase of bacteriological publications that either deal with genetic problems or utilize the techniques developed by bacterial geneticists. In addition several universities have added formal courses on the subject to their curriculum.

Yet, despite the fact that bacterial genetics is gaining such importance in basic and applied research, it also has become evident that many students and professional workers without specialized training in genetics have had difficulties in understanding and following pertinent progress in this field. Apparently, there are two primary reasons for these difficulties: (1) the geneticists who work with bacteria have transferred many of their special terms into the field of bacterial genetics, and much of this language, as well as many of the underlying principles, are foreign to students of bacteriology; (2) the places of publication of fundamental data have been widely scattered, many of the important papers having appeared in journals that are read by very few bacteriologists.

This book has been written in an attempt to aid in overcoming these difficulties. It tries to present the more important findings and principles of bacterial genetics to those primarily trained, or being trained, in bacteriology, and it tries to provide a basis for better evaluation of the relationship between bacterial genetics and such diverse problems as pathogenesis, general laboratory techniques, bacterial physiology, epidemiology, therapy, and taxonomy. Beginning with a review of those general principles of genetics which are necessary for the understanding of bacterial genetics, the text endeavors to furnish a general account of the present status of bacterial genetics in a manner which, it is hoped, is elementary enough for the beginning student and sufficiently comprehensive to be of value for the research worker. But even though this book was written with the needs of bacteriologists in mind, it is hoped also that its contents will prove equally useful to students and research workers in the general field of genetics. The latter may find here not only a compilation of progress in an allied field but also information that should be of value to basic genetic problems.

In presenting this outline of bacterial genetics no attempt has been made to cover all the details of this rapidly expanding field and the space allotted to the various problems has been determined to a large extent by the apparent importance of the particular problem for general bacteriological questions. Thus the relatively extensive discussion of population changes should not be blamed on the author's preoccupation with such problems but on his conviction that these problems must be thoroughly understood and recognized by anyone connected with studies on bacteria. Throughout the book only representative examples of published data are cited and consequently many equally valuable contributions to the subject had to be omitted both in the text and in the literature references. In most instances, an effort has been made to cite those literature references which in turn will guide the reader to older publications.

I am greatly indebted to many colleagues and friends for their assistance in the preparation of this book. Many of them have contributed illustrations, including some previously unpublished material. The names of these contributors are indicated in the figure legends. I wish to express my collective thanks to them as well as to the various publishers who gave permission for reproducing previously published figures and tables. I am particularly indebted to Drs. Emily Kelly, Edward Garber, Vernon Bryson and Mr. Leonard Mika, who read the manuscript in its entirety, and to Drs. Joshua Lederberg, Rollin Hotchkiss and Robert Austrian, who read certain chapters of the manuscript. All of them contributed valuable suggestions and editorial advice but, of course, they are in no way responsible for any remaining errors or omissions. The artistic skill of Mr. James Decker, who prepared all of the original drawings, and the diligence of Mr. Austin Hoffman, who typed the entire manuscript, were of invaluable help in the preparation of the book. I also wish to express my sincere appreciation to the staff of W. B. Saunders Co.; their interest and efficiency were of great help at all times. Finally, it is a real pleasure to acknowledge the interest of Dr. William Burrows without whose encouragement this book probably would still be an idea in the author's mind.

WERNER BRAUN

Thurmont, Md.

CONTENTS

PART I

PART
I

[1]

INTRODUCTION AND ORIENTATION

Microbial genetics, including its major subdivision—bacterial genetics, is a relatively young field. But despite this youthfulness, it has achieved unusual distinction through its own contributions, through its unique influence on the development of other fields of scientific endeavor, and through its potential influence on man's future ability to manipulate some of the biological processes. Since the early 1940's, bacterial genetics has elucidated many of the once puzzling and controversial aspects of bacterial variations, made revolutionary contributions to genetics in general, nurtured the field of biochemistry, and helped substantially to give birth to the field of molecular biology. Two principal reasons may be held responsible for this success. First, it has become evident that, except for minor differences, the basic principles of genetics—the science of heredity—apply equally to all animals and plants, regardless of whether they are multicellular or unicellular. All available evidence indicates that the determinants of hereditary characteristics—their nature, sites, transmission and stability—and the manner in which they control the processes leading to the actual development of the detectable characteristics, are similar in bacteria and in higher organisms, though sometimes less complex in bacteria. Second, bacteria have largely replaced such prior favorites as the fruit-fly, mice and corn in research on heredity because of the rapidity with which bacteria multiply, their enormous population size, and the relative simplicity of their cultivation. Furthermore, bacteria permit us to study biological phenomena on a cellular basis without the complex interactions and interdependencies typical of higher organisms. It is noteworthy that this lesser complexity (which as we shall see is only relative, since intracellular and intercellular events are quite complex even among bacteria) has made it possible, in recent years, to utilize the techniques and knowledge developed in studies with microorganisms, for the analysis of the problems of multicellular organisms.

Thus, within a period of 10 years the tables have been turned. Once bacterial genetics was presented most easily as a field that drew on and grew from the known principles of genetics of higher organisms; now the more crucial data, particularly in regard to the chemical basis of heredity, have emerged from the study of microorganisms. While classic genetics, including the early studies in bacterial genetics, was essentially statistical in its approach, modern genetics, thanks greatly to experimentation with microorganisms, is based largely on chemical and physical considerations and data. In fact, genetics has become the science of biological communication mechanisms, which attempts to unravel the molecular basis for the way in which *information*, a modern term for the determinants of hereditary characteristics, is passed from cell to daughter cell, that is, from one generation to another. In addition, genetics attempts to analyze the mechanisms by which such information controls (on an *intra*cellular level in microorganisms, and on both *intra-* and *inter*cellular levels in multicellular organisms) the development of the characteristics that typify a single cell or a multicellular organism. Genetics also concerns itself with an analysis of factors that control competitive events among members of populations in which some of the members, though closely related to the others, contain slightly different sets of information and thus different survival values.

In this book we shall discuss all of these areas as they apply to bacteria and to some other microorganisms. But since in modern bacterial genetics so many concepts have been explored with the aid of techniques derived from the study of other phenomena, it will be necessary for us to begin our discussions with a brief, general survey of our entire subject. Following this initial orientation, we shall add more specific details in later chapters.

THE BEGINNINGS OF GENETICS AND THE CONCEPTS OF GENOTYPE AND PHENOTYPE

The old saying "like begets like" expresses the well-known fact that the offspring or *progeny* usually mirrors the general characteristics of the parents. This applies not only to higher organisms in which sexual processes are the rule rather than the exception, but also to organisms, like bacteria, in which the asexual mode of reproduction is the most frequent and in which sexual processes, when they occur, are generally of a more primitive nature.

The manner in which hereditary traits are transmitted from generation to generation was the subject of intense experimental research with higher organisms during the first half of the present century, receiving their initial impetus through the ingenious experiments on peas conducted by the Austrian monk, Gregor Mendel, in the 1860's. Mendel's studies, initially unnoticed, were independently rediscovered and extended by DeVries, Correns and Tschermak in 1900, and since then research has continued, first with higher animals and plants, and later more extensively with bacteria and viruses, in laboratories throughout the world. These investigations on the principles and material basis of heredity and variation have demonstrated that what is transmitted from parent to offspring (i.e., from generation to generation) is a set of determinants (information), of a now quite well understood chemical nature, that control biosynthetic cellular processes, and with it the reaction range of an individual or of a cell. The sum total of these heritable determinants is called the *genotype.*

Everyday experience shows us that despite similarity in genotype, as, for example, in identical twins or a group of purebred plants maintained under different environmental conditions, considerable differences may exist in appearance, i.e., the manner in which the inherited traits express themselves under the influence of the environment. What is inherited therefore is an ability to react in a specific way to specific environmental conditions. The sum total of the realized characteristics, in other words, the appearance of morphological characteristics as well as the manifestation of physiological processes in individuals, is called the *phenotype.* Phenotypic differences between organisms of similar genotype are referred to as *modifications.* Thus the interaction between hereditary determinants and environmental influences may cause divergent phenotypes despite the presence of identical genotypes; however, the genotype controls the potential range of such phenotypic differences. To choose a simple illustration let us consider the skin pigmentation of whites and Negroes. This difference in pigmentation is controlled by hereditary determinants (*genotypic differences*) yet the actual skin color will greatly depend on the extent of the individual's exposure to sunlight (*phenotypic differences*). With prolonged exposure to sunlight, the skin of whites may become as dark as that of Negroes who have not been similarly exposed; yet after equally intense exposure the latter would manifest a far darker skin pigmentation than that ever possible for a white person (Fig. 1).

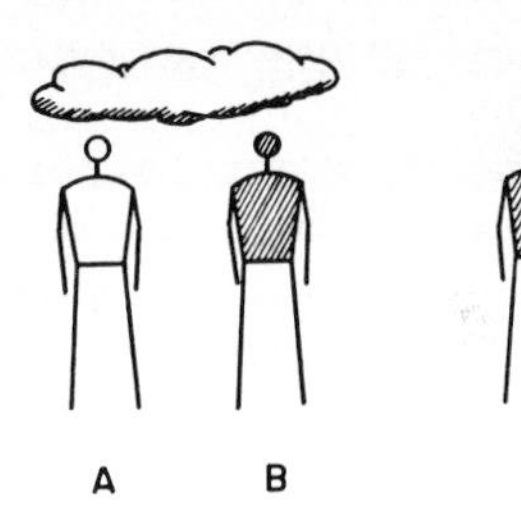

FIGURE 1. Sketch illustrating the difference between phenotype and gentotype. (See text for a description of this example.)

The foregoing example illustrates not only the potential plasticity existing in each organism or cell, but it also demonstrates that under certain environmental conditions the phenotypic expression of one genotype (the sum of inherited determinants) may be identical to that of an entirely different genotype. Such a phenomenon has been termed *phenocopy.*

Even though environmental effects are capable of modifying the phenotype, as a rule such *modifications* persist only in the presence of the specific environmental condition and will not be transmitted to and inherited by the offspring. Cutting off the tails of mice for many generations does not reduce the length of tails in the progeny; neither does the exposure of flagellated bacteria to phenol, interfering with the development of flagella, cause the disappearance of flagella in the progeny when the latter are grown in phenol-free media. These and many other experimental studies have led to the conclusion that, except for rare and unique phenomena such as the manifestation of new characteristics in certain phage-infected bacteria (p. 169), acquired characteristics are not inherited. This does not mean that the genotype remains entirely unaffected by the environment. As will be discussed subsequently, changes in the genotype occur occasionally in all organisms, and certain environmental agents are capable of enhancing the rate of such changes. In addition, the environment plays a most important role in promoting the selective survival of individuals with hereditary determinants that control characteristics best adapted to the existing environmental conditions.

It is now well established that practically all characteristics, both morphologic and physiologic, are under the direct or indirect control of the hereditary information residing in the nucleic acids. In general, it is not the trait itself which is inherited, rather it is the potential to develop the particular trait under proper environmental conditions that is transmitted from generation to generation. Thus learning is not inherited, but the ability to learn is; cancer is not inherited but the tendency to develop certain types of cancer appears to be a hereditary trait. In the final analysis all hereditary characteristics are probably the end products of biochemical processes. This applies equally to physiological characteristics, morphological characteristics, and even to the ability to learn which depends on the development of the brain cells, a process involving an as yet unknown series of complex biosynthetic interactions. Therefore, the hereditary determinants, now identified as components of nucleic acid, may be said to control in a specific manner biosynthetic reactions and the biochemical activities of an organism. Later we shall discuss in more detail the current knowledge regarding the manner in which hereditary information can control the specificity and rates of various biochemical processes that lead to the discernible characteristics and functions of organisms. But first, we must orient ourselves in regard to the chemical nature of the material that can pass on specific information from cell to cell, or from generation to generation.

ON THE CHEMICAL NATURE OF INFORMATION

In order to function as an informative family of molecules, the chemical substances that make up hereditary determinants must have at least the following attributes: they must be capable of spelling out specific messages, just as the letters of an alphabet make meaningful words; they must be relatively stable; and they must be able to replicate themselves in order to be passed on from one cell to another without being lost in the parental cell. In addition, they may be expected to control in a specific manner the formation of other, chemically different, molecules that participate in biosynthetic and metabolic events, and contribute to structural cellular components. So far, we know of only one group of chemical substances that meets these requirements—the nucleic acids.

There are two major types of nucleic acid, *deoxyribonucleic acid* or

DNA, and *ribonucleic acid* or *RNA*. Both are polymers of nucleotides, each nucleotide containing a pyrimidine or purine base, a phosphate and a pentose sugar. In the case of DNA, the sugar moiety is deoxyribose; in the case of RNA, it is D-ribose. In the case of DNA, the most commonly occurring pyrimidine bases are *cytosine* (C) and *thymine* (T); in the case of RNA, they are cytosine and *uracil* (U). In both DNA and RNA the most commonly occurring purine bases are *adenine* (A) and *guanine* (G). Thus, in both DNA and RNA, we have four principal nitrogenous bases which, as component of nucleotides, form the fundamental elements of long polymers. Nowadays, we know quite a bit about the way in which these four basic elements can lead to specific information by virtue of the sequence in which they occur. We also know, at least in DNA, about mechanisms that permit the replication of such sequences, and we have good reason to believe that somewhat similar mechanisms play a role in RNA replication.

To familiarize ourselves with the general principle of specificity and replicability of nucleic acids, particularly of deoxyribonucleic acid, let us take for granted, for the moment, that each message unit, code word, or *codon* in the nucleic acid "language" is represented by not one, but by three letters (i.e., not by one nucleotide but by three neighboring nucleotides). Thus, the basic "alphabet" of DNA consists of codons such as:

–ATA*–ATG–GTA–TTT–CTG–

In the case of RNA we merely have to substitute U for T. Both DNA and RNA are long chains of these basic units and the specific informative qualities of the two types of nucleic acid depend on the type and sequence of the nucleotides making up the code. For example,

(1) —A–T–T—G–T–C—A–A–T—T–T–G— spells out a different message

from:

(2) —A–T–T—G–A–C—A–A–T—T–T–G—

or from:

(3) —T–T–T—G–T–C—A–A–T—T–T–G—

To translate this into more familiar terms, we could equate as follows:

A–T–T = *B*

G–T–C = *A*

A–A–T = *N*

T–T–G = *D*

G–A–C = *O*

T–T–T = *L*

*It is customary to list only the abbreviation for the base, even though the basic unit in nucleic acids is the nucleotide, i.e., base + phosphate + sugar. However, since the last two moieties are identical for all nucleotides, as far as we know now, except for the occurrence of deoxyribose in DNA and of ribose in RNA, it suffices to spell out the specificity-controlling elements by listing the sequence of the different bases.

Message (1) now makes sense to human eyes and ears as the message *BAND*, message (2) conveys an entirely different meaning, namely *BOND*, and message (3) has a still different meaning, namely *LAND*. The total inherent or genetic information of each cell appears to consist of a large number of such pieces of information.

Thus we can see that the nucleic acids have two of the attributes we listed as prerequisites for informative chemical structures: (1) they can, with the aid of a few basic elements, spell out different messages, and (2) as shown in the last example (*BAND, BOND, LAND*), these messages are translatable into another language consisting of different letters (i.e., A–T–T = *B*, etc.). We know now that this is one of the important qualities of the "nucleic acid language": although it is made up of four basic elements, it is translatable into the "protein language," which is composed of at least 20 basic elements – the amino acids. As an example, we may equate the nucleotide sequence A–T–T with amino acid 1, G–T–C with amino acid 2, T–T–G with amino acid 3, etc.

Since we know that specific proteins not only form many of the cell's structural elements but, more importantly, control as enzymes most of the biochemical events in living cells, we have in the "nucleic acid" language a basic information agency controlling the specific events and structures of living organisms. In most living entities this information seems to be channeled as follows:

$$\text{DNA} \rightarrow \text{RNA} \rightarrow \text{protein.}$$

This sequence of events, with DNA acting as the basic site of information, is regarded as the basic dogma of modern biology. In some instances, however, particularly in the RNA viruses, RNA appears to be the basic information agency and the sequence becomes:

$$\text{RNA} \rightarrow \text{protein.}$$

TRANSFER OF INFORMATION

We previously stated that chemical substances that act as determinants of hereditary traits must have at least one other vital attribute: they must be capable of replication. Do the nucleic acids meet this requirement? The answer for DNA is in the positive (RNA also can replicate itself in certain exceptional instances, such as the RNA viruses and bacteriophages). The proof that DNA may replicate a structure like itself has come in recent years from studies with radioactively labeled components of DNA, which we shall review later. But even before this, in 1953, Watson and Crick proposed a molecular structure for DNA that allows for the replication of a specific sequence of nucleotides. Their proposal was that the DNA molecule consists not of *one* chain of deoxyribonucleotides, but of *two* complementary chains which are held together, much like the rungs joining the two sides of a ladder, by hydrogen bonds between the bases of each nucleotide (see pp. 47-49 for details). They proposed that A, as a rule, pairs through hydrogen bonds with T, and C hydrogen-bonds specifically with G.* Thus we have a paired double-chain – actually (since these chains

*Mnemonic note: A and T make the word "at," C and G look somewhat alike.

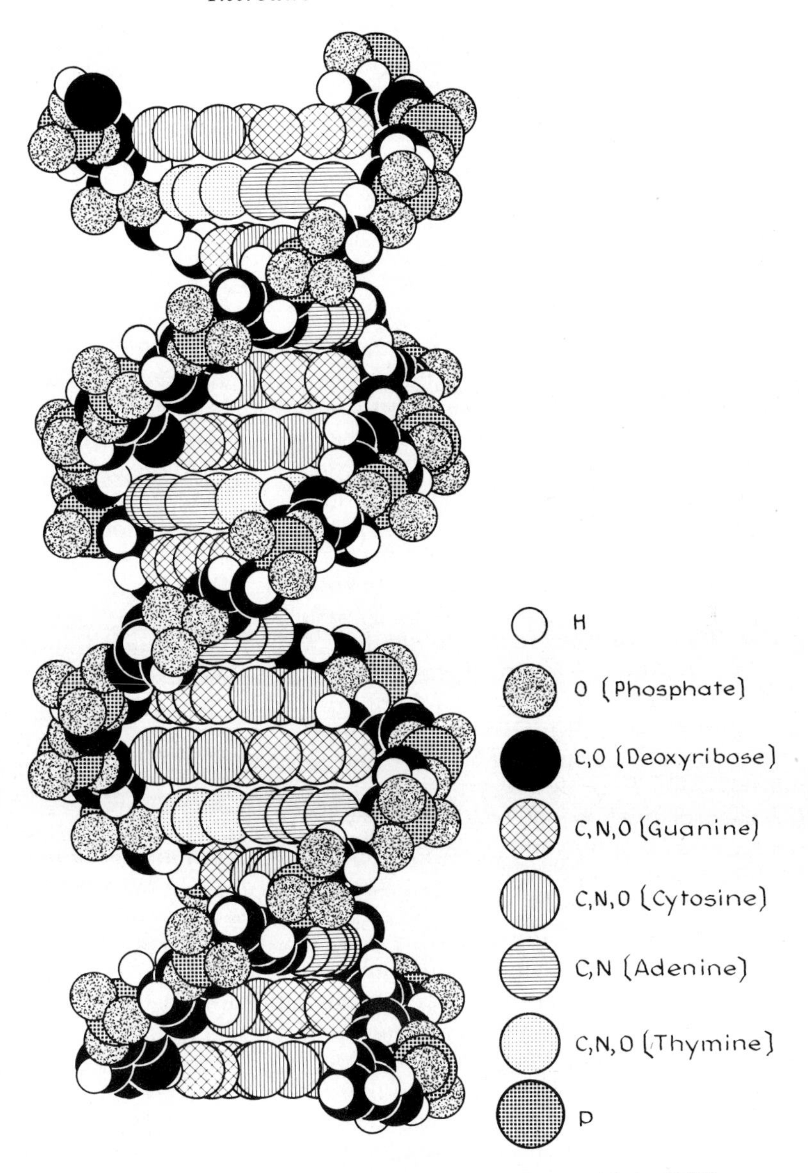

FIGURE 2. Model of the DNA double helix. (From Baldwin, 1964.)

are spirally wound around each other) a double-helix (Fig. 2)—which when stretched out may, for example, look as follows:

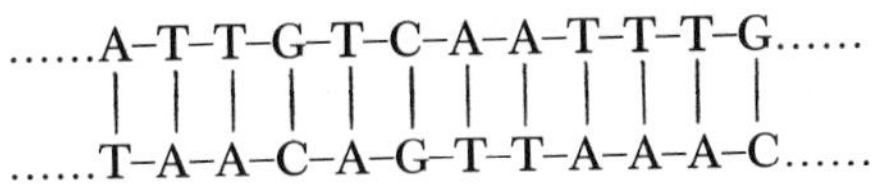

Each vertical line represents hydrogen bonds. It is believed that at the time of replication the hydrogen bonds break, resulting in two separate poly-deoxynucleotide chains, each of which will then, with the aid of appropriate enzymes, build up a complementary chain, hydrogen-bonding the corresponding base (+ sugar + phosphate). Accordingly, we may write:

←———————————————
(assumed direction of process of replication)

......–A–T–T–G–T
......–**T–A–A–C–A** C–A–A–T–T–T–G–......

......–**A–T–T–G–T**
......–T–A–A–C–A G–T–T–A–A–A–C–......

The boldface bases represent the newly polymerized nucleotides. Occasionally an error may occur in the pairing of the old nucleotide with the complementary new nucleotide, thus upsetting the old sequence and its specific message. Such rare events provide occasional opportunities for the creation of new information that may be of value to the organism if it leads to traits which are better suited to the organism's existing environment. At the same time, the fact that such errors in replication are so rare fulfills the additional attribute we postulated for informative molecules which are part of the hereditary determinants, namely, their relative stability.

Long before the role of DNA in heredity was substantiated on the basis of its unique structure and properties, it was quite decisively identified as a fundamental cellular material in heredity through a series of direct and indirect observations. Thus, in the early years of genetic studies with higher organisms, during the first two decades of this century, it was already established that there is a perfect correlation between the non-arbitrary distribution of nuclear elements among the progeny of cells (specifically of sex cells or *gametes*) and the distribution of determinants of hereditary traits. Since these nuclear elements were uniquely rich in DNA, DNA was regarded as the hereditary substance, occurring as a rule in association with proteins, which were regarded as structural components of the morphologically distinguishable *chromosomes* – the carriers of the hereditary traits. A typical cell of higher organisms contains several distinct chromosomes (the actual number depends on the species) and as a result each chromosome occurs paired, or *diploid*, in somatic cells and singly, or *haploid*, in the gametes (egg, sperm). Bacteria are usually haploid.

In both higher organisms and bacteria, the entire set of informational chromosomal material is referred to as the *genome*. In the pre-"molecular biology" era of genetics it was postulated that hypothetical subunits, the *genes*, were the determinants of individual traits. However, with the aid of bacterial genetics, these units, once brilliantly postulated wholly on the basis of indirect evidence, have been resolved through direct experimental evidence into a series of chemically definable subunits, i.e., a series of specific nucleotides in appropriate sequence. Thus, substantial direct evidence for the involvement of DNA in heredity has come from studies with bacteria in which it was shown possible, at least in some species, to transfer specific bits of information from one cell to another with the aid of highly purified DNA extracted from a donor cell. In this so-called *transformation* (see p. 239) the new bit of information becomes a heritable part of the recipient cell, and this remarkable event is specifically abolished following the exposure of the transforming extract to the enzyme that specifically depolymerizes DNA. It has also been demonstrated that radioactive disintegration of specific components of DNA results in the destruction of information. In addition, studies with certain bacterial viruses, or bacteriophages, which replicate only with the aid of a bacterial host cell, have shown that what the informative phage injects into its host cell, to cause production of more phage like itself, is largely DNA.

Throughout the chapters to follow we shall hear about many other observations that substantiate the basic role of DNA in (a) the transmission of information from cell to cell, or from generation to generation, and (b) the specific control of intra- and intercellular biochemical events. This dominant position of DNA in biological events does not necessarily mean that apart from DNA and its close relative RNA, there might not be other molecules with informative qualities that can be replicated; however, at the present we are unaware of such substances. Also, it remains possible that in order to function, DNA may have to be complexed with other substances, such as carbohydrates other than ribose or its deoxy- derivative. But the specificity of the message that is transcribed into complementary molecules within the cell and passed on to other cells during reproduction must be dependent, as far as we can see today, on the uniqueness of the sequence of nucleotides in DNA and the relatively error-free replication of such sequences.

MECHANISMS RESULTING IN ALTERED INFORMATION

The information carried by DNA, however, does not represent an absolutely stable and unalterable message. If the information passed on from generation to generation (i.e., from cell to cell in the case of bacteria) were unalterable, the reaction range of closely related organisms would be fixed, and any sudden environmental change that would be detrimental to such organisms with a fixed genotype also would be the end of the species. For example, an antibiotic would be able to wipe out an entire species of bacteria if the information making this species susceptible to the antibiotic was not subject to sudden undirected alterations in a few individuals, permitting them to persist even in the presence of the usually fatal drug. A lack of *complete* stability of the information passed on from generation to generation, therefore, is beneficial to the survival of the species, since the occasional occurrence of a new genotype can provide plasticity in response to new environmental conditions by creating a new reaction range for at least some individuals of the species.

We shall later see that changes in the genotype, referred to as *mutations*, occur occasionally in perhaps one out of 10 million related individuals. We shall also see that such mutations involve rare alterations in single determinants, or only bits of the total information. As a rule, mass alterations of information, affecting many different traits, do not occur as the result of rare errors in the replication of DNA. However, other mechanisms have evolved which do permit the occurrence of sometimes rather drastically altered information in the progeny. These mechanisms involve the pooling and usually an immediate reshuffling (*recombination* is the geneticist's term) of information possessed by closely related, but genotypically different, organisms. The prerequisite for such reshuffling is the existence of sexual mechanisms of reproduction in which information from a donor (male) and a recipient (female) can be recombined in such a manner that bits of one set of information replace corresponding bits of another set of information. For example, in the case of bacteria that can participate in recombinational events, we may find:

Donor : a b c d e f g h
Recipient : A B C D E F G H } *Progeny (Recombinant)*: ABcdeFGH

While such mechanisms of recombination have evolved farthest in higher organisms, in which the contribution of information from both parents can be of almost equal magnitude, the sex-like mechanisms discovered in bacteria involve, as a rule, unequal contributions by the two parents.

Four types of processes of genetic transfers from a donor to a recipient are known to occur among bacteria. They have been observed so far only in certain bacterial species (see pp. 239 to 357), and not all of them occur in the same species. We shall discuss each type of genetic transfer in detail later, but it will be helpful to sketch here the principal features of each of these processes (Fig. 3).

(1) In so-called *transformation,* chemically extracted ("naked") DNA, or naturally released extracellular DNA, can transfer information affecting one trait, or occasionally two traits, from one bacterium to another related bacterium.

(2) In the process of *transduction*, informative DNA (again only bits that affect one, and sometimes two, traits) is transferred from one bacterium to a related one with the aid of bacteriophage. In this process the protein coat of the phage, which assists in the injection of the phage's internal DNA into a susceptible bacterial host cell, packages and transfers bacterial DNA instead of (or in addition to) phage DNA. The bacterial DNA inside the phage originates from the phage's prior bacterial victim, and may become incorporated in the information of the bacteria into which the phage has injected the informative bacterial DNA.

(3) In *conjugation*, the donor bacterium can contribute a very substantial part, or even all, of its information (in the form of a just replicated set) to the related recipient; the process of transfer of such information requires direct contact between the cells and involves the migration from one cell to the other of a chromosome-like DNA entity, on which information is arranged in a linear fashion (informative linear sequences of nucleotides). If the information in the donor's DNA differs from that available in the recipient's DNA, the new information does not become available *in toto* to the progeny following transfer of the informative polynucleotide

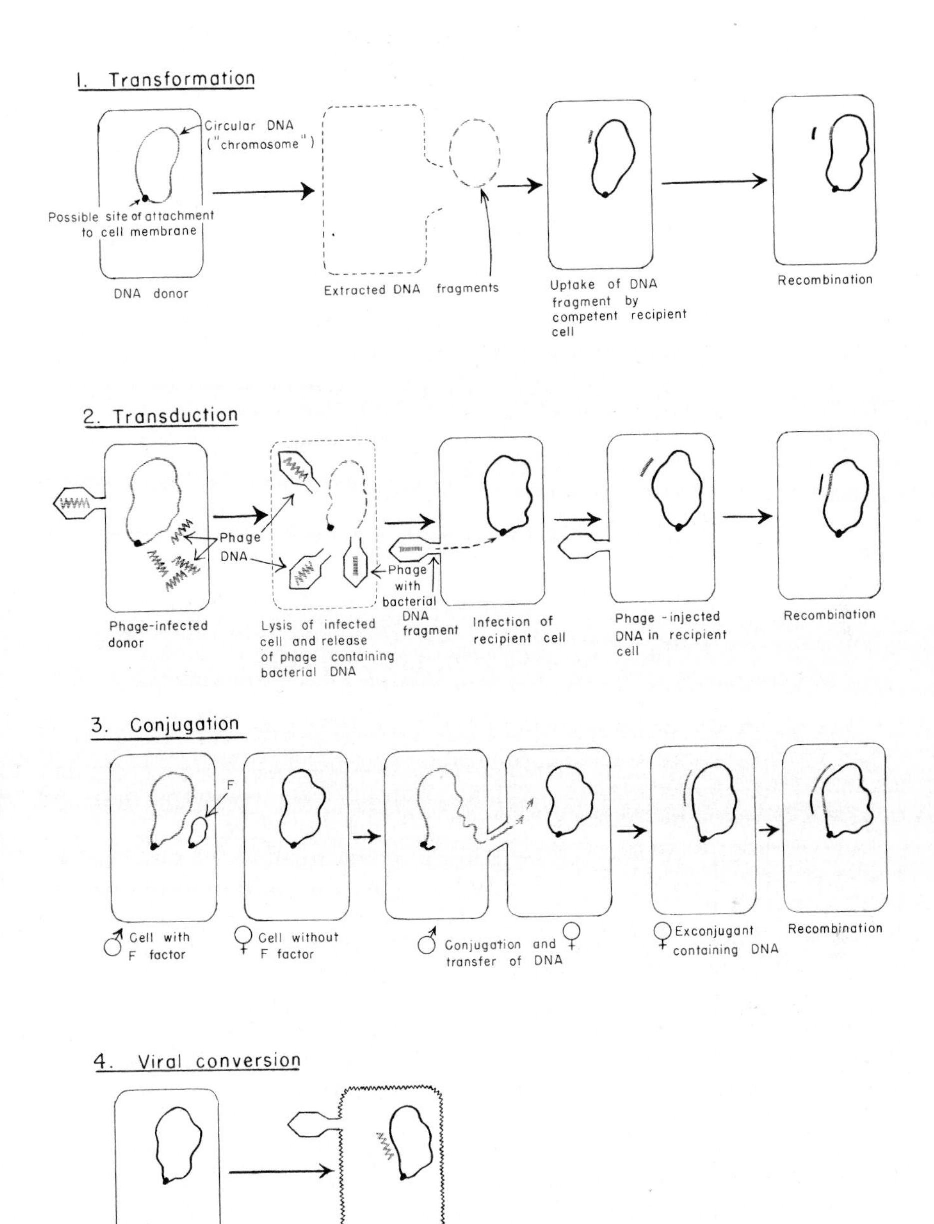

FIGURE 3. Diagrammatic representation of four different types of transfer of genetic information in bacteria.

chain. Rather, an exchange (recombination) may occur between the new and the old information of the recipient, as indicated on page 12.

(4) The fourth type of process resulting in altered information involves the transfer of cellular entities that have been labeled *episomes*. (We shall refer to some of these, later on, as "nonchromosomal replicons.") These entities, DNA in nature, can add, in a somewhat complex fashion to be discussed later, new information to that pre-existing in the cell. One example of such alteration of existent information by the addition of episomes is the phenomenon of *viral conversion*. In viral conversion, the presence of the genotype (information) of the phage, or virus, in the cell can result in a new bacterial phenotype. In other words, certain inherent traits of the bacterium, such as the composition of its cell wall, may be altered as the result of phage infection and the subsequent presence of additional information associated with phage DNA. This added information will not participate in recombination (i.e., the new information will not *replace* some pre-existing information). Rather, changes due to the episomal phage DNA represent *added* bits of information that persist only as long as the added phage DNA coexists with the bacterial DNA within a given cell.

CELLULAR SITES OF INFORMATION

The major site of informative DNA in the cell of higher organisms is in the nucleus, where at least at time of nuclear division, one can recognize organized rod-shaped, fairly complex, intranuclear structures that are rich in DNA-protein. These structures are the *chromosomes*. Similarly, complex structural elements do not appear to exist within the nucleus-like region of bacterial cells. Rather, a simpler, very long, circular and fibrous DNA structure, presumably equivalent to a component of the more complex chromosomes of higher organisms, appears to be the major carrier of information in bacteria. Although it is thus likely that the elements referred to as chromosomes in cells of higher organisms and in bacteria are not identical in their chemical and morphological complexity, they are identical in their function as carriers of informative nucleotide sequences. The results of experiments concerned with the migration of information from one cell to another in bacterial conjugation also force us to conclude that in bacteria, as in higher organisms, the informative determinants, i.e., the specific polynucleotide sequences, are arranged in linear fashion. Although chromosomal sites are regarded as the major sites for storage of informative DNA, episomal prophages (p. 265) represent an example of carriers of information that may exist either in direct association with chromosomal elements or as free entities in the extrachromosomal cytoplasm. Apart from this infectious, phenotype-altering unit, other organized, self-replicating cytoplasmic determinants, such as the plastids and possibly also the mitochondria of higher plants, seem to be lacking in bacteria or, at least, have not yet been recognized.

EXPERIMENTAL AND DEDUCTIVE APPROACHES IN GENETICS

The preceding introductory remarks have already indicated that modern genetics, and particularly its important subdivision, bacterial genetics, has become to a considerable extent an inquiry into the molecular basis of the specificity of the information-carrying DNA, its mode of replication and transfer from cell to cell, and its ability to control the specificity, activation and rate of the many intra- and intercellular biochemical processes. Also, modern genetics has concerned itself with the way in which certain portions of the DNA molecule may lose or change parts of their specific informative qualities, or interchange bits of information with DNA molecules of other, closely related cells during sexual processes.

But long before investigations on the molecular level had become possible, many end-results of alterations in chromosomal DNA had been analyzed without much knowledge of the underlying molecular events. For example, the occasional occurrence of undirected changes in specific hereditary traits was recognized and studied long before evidence accumulated that such changes could be due to an occasional error in the replication of a given nucleotide sequence in the DNA polymer. Also, many sequential biosynthetic steps controlling the development of specific heritable traits were subjected to analysis long before there was even a glimmer of understanding regarding the molecular basis for control mechanisms in cellular processes. Thus, we shall find in the chapters to follow a considerable amount of information on phenomena of variation and heredity based principally on the study of how such processes express themselves; a direct analysis of some of the causative mechanisms has only become feasible in recent years. Yet it is characteristic of the intellectual power and appeal of genetics that it has been possible to deduce much regarding the nature of causative factors even during periods of scientific endeavor when most observations centered on the analysis of end-results of changes in hereditary determinants. Consequently, we shall find that in this book many topics are discussed both from the standpoint of earlier, essentially statistic and deductive, observations as well as from the more recent standpoint of assigning these events a specific molecular basis. One might compare modern and classic genetics with modern nuclear physics and classic physics. In this case too, it was possible to state, for example, much about the nature of radiation before the intra-atomic details were known.

The powerful tool of deduction from detectable phenomena to the probable nature of their causes—a methodology that has been of great usefulness for the development of genetics, including bacterial genetics—also has produced a certain amount of misunderstanding, particularly among those who are less prone to deduction and speculation. It, therefore, may be helpful to point out that geneticists, perhaps uniquely so among experimental biologists, accept the usefulness of speculative deduction to such an extent that they frequently state as a positive fact something that represents no more than the most likely, but not necessarily sole, interpretation of available data. Perhaps more so than in most experimental sciences, the geneticist's "*is*" often represents only a "*may be*." This *modus operandi* has proved extremely useful because it has provided working hypotheses that permitted the experimental testing of ideas. Whenever any of these hypotheses has turned out to be correct—and this has not happened frequently enough to cause confusion—the typical geneticist, as well as his successors and allies, the biochemists and biophysicists, has immediately discarded the old concept for a new one. Thus, what is stated in the pages to follow must be regarded as current concepts, most of which, it is hoped, will turn out to be permanent facts.

[2]

THE EVOLUTION OF BACTERIAL GENETICS

The start of bacterial genetics as a separate and respected discipline is generally ascribed to the early 1940's. It was then that a series of studies indicating the universal applicability of genetic principles to all living organisms, including bacteria and viruses, attracted the attention of biologists as a group. As we shall see in subsequent chapters, the investigations of these first few years of organized bacterial genetics dealt principally with experimental evidence for similarities in the nature, transmission and function of hereditary determinants in both bacteria and higher organisms. Prior to this time, bacteriology and genetics had gone very much their own way. Bacteriologists, though cognizant of bacterial variability since the days of Pasteur, chose to interpret such variability in terms that more often than not were unrelated to established genetic principles. Geneticists, on the other hand, either were completely disinterested in bacteriology (which was at that time regarded by many as an art rather than a science) or doubted the applicability of genetic principles to forms as primitive as the asexually-reproducing, unicellular bacteria.

CLASSIC GENETIC PRINCIPLES

To appreciate the gulf that once existed between genetics and bacteriology, let us summarize some of the general genetic principles that had been recognized in studies with higher organisms during the first few decades of this century, and then let us compare these with the earlier viewpoints of bacteriologists. Prior to the advent of bacterial genetics, geneticists working with higher plants and animals had established the following:*

a. Hereditary characteristics, including the appearance, structure and physiology of an organism, are under the primary control of self-

*For further information, see Herskowitz, J. H., *Genetics*, Little, Brown and Co., Boston, 1962; Dodson, E. O., *Genetics, the Modern Science of Heredity*, W. B. Saunders Co., Philadelphia, 1956; Srb, A. M. and Owen, R. D., *General Genetics*, W. H. Freeman, San Francisco, 1958.

duplicating nuclear elements which in sexual as well as in asexual propagation are transmitted from generation to generation.

b. While these nuclear elements, genes, determine the reaction range of an organism, the final expression (phenotype) of a given characteristic can be modified by existing environmental conditions.

c. Environmentally induced modifications of gene-controlled characteristics are maintained only as long as the specific modifying environmental conditions persist; acquired characteristics are not inherited. In a few exceptional instances, certain environmental conditions may cause the appearance of new heritable characteristics that are controlled by cytoplasmic factors and are maintained even after a change of environment; yet even this apparently rare phenomenon is under gene-control since the range of such potential transformations is determined by specific genes.

d. Genes act by controlling the specificity and rate of biosynthetic processes.

e. One gene may affect several characteristics, but several genes may also interact to affect one particular characteristic.

f. Genes are not absolutely stable and may occasionally change (mutate) spontaneously, causing a change in the characteristic(s) which they control. The rate of mutation is constant for a given gene but may differ between genes. Certain environmental agents are capable of increasing the spontaneous mutation rate.

g. Many mutational changes are associated with structural changes in the gene-carriers, the chromosomes.

h. Although genes are hypothetical units, there is a material basis for heredity. In the transmission of hereditary determinants a direct correlation exists between the distribution of the chromosomes, as evidenced by cytologic observations, and the distribution of the genes associated with the chromosomes, as demonstrated by breeding experiments.

i. In sexually reproducing organisms certain laws exist for the mode of distribution of chromosomes and their genes among the progeny, producing phenomena known as segregation, linkage and recombination of genes and of the characteristics which they control.

j. The chief sources of variation among the characteristics of related organisms are (1) genic differences due to spontaneous and undirected mutation of individual genes, or due to new assortment of genes in the case of sexual reproduction, where parents of dissimilar genotypes contribute different genes to the offspring, or (2) environmentally induced differences causing, as a rule, only temporary changes of the phenotype.

k. Within a population of genetically different members, the opportunity for survival and propagation under given environmental conditions is not the same for each individual. Different genotypes have different selective values. The influence of the environment, as a *selective* force, leads to the survival of the fittest, a principle of natural selection that was first pronounced by Charles Darwin more than a century ago. Selection superimposed upon genic differences among related individuals thus plays a most important role in population changes and evolutionary processes. The individual members of a population do not undergo stable changes in response to the environment, but the population can undergo changes because environmental conditions cause the selective survival of the fittest, genetically different, members of a population. Undirected, spontaneous mutants and their selection thus can contribute to gradual population changes, which may give the over-all appearance of having been directed.

EARLY CONCEPTS OF BACTERIAL VARIATION

In contrast to the recognition by modern geneticists that changes in hereditary characteristics are essentially undirected by environmental conditions, as expressed in *c*, *f*, *j* and *k* in the previous section, the ideas of direct adaptation and inheritance of acquired characteristics were predominant in the older bacteriological literature. Bacteriology thus won the dubious distinction of being known as the last stronghold of Lamarckism. (The French biologist Lamarck, 1744–1829, was an early and prominent proponent of the now discredited idea of inheritance of acquired characteristics and his theory of biological evolution was based on such ideas.) Yet this retention of Lamarckian ideas among bacteriologists is not too surprising if we remember that in studies with bacteria we usually deal with very large populations of organisms that can propagate *asexually* at rapid rates. This can and did prevent the identification of changes in individual organisms. In practically all older studies, changes in heritable characteristics which may have occurred in single cells remained undetected until such altered cells had given rise to many progeny. What generally has been observed among bacteria, therefore, is a change in populations rather than a change in individual cells.

Prior to the development of a recognized discipline of bacterial genetics, such population changes were interpreted primarily in four different ways. Many believed that they represented direct adaptation to environmental influences, involving changes caused by the environment in all or a few cells of a population (Fig. 4*A*). Others have proposed a major role of *Dauermodifikationen* (lasting modifications); these are environmentally induced adaptive changes which persist, without affecting any inherent factors, for many generations after the removal of the inductive environment (Fig. 4*C*). Still others have interpreted bacterial changes as orderly life-cycles in which the expression of each stage is dependent on the environmental conditions (Fig. 4*B*). Only a minority group of early investigators recognized bacterial variation as a phenomenon that can involve the occurrence of spontaneous and undirected changes (mutation) in one or a few cells which are subsequently selected under appropriate environmental conditions (Fig. 4*D*). The last interpretation, bringing the basic mechanism of changes among bacteria in line with those known in higher organisms, gained overwhelming acceptance when techniques were devised which permitted (1) a distinction between changes affecting either single cells or all cells within a bacterial population and (2) the differentiation between absence or presence of changes induced by the environment.

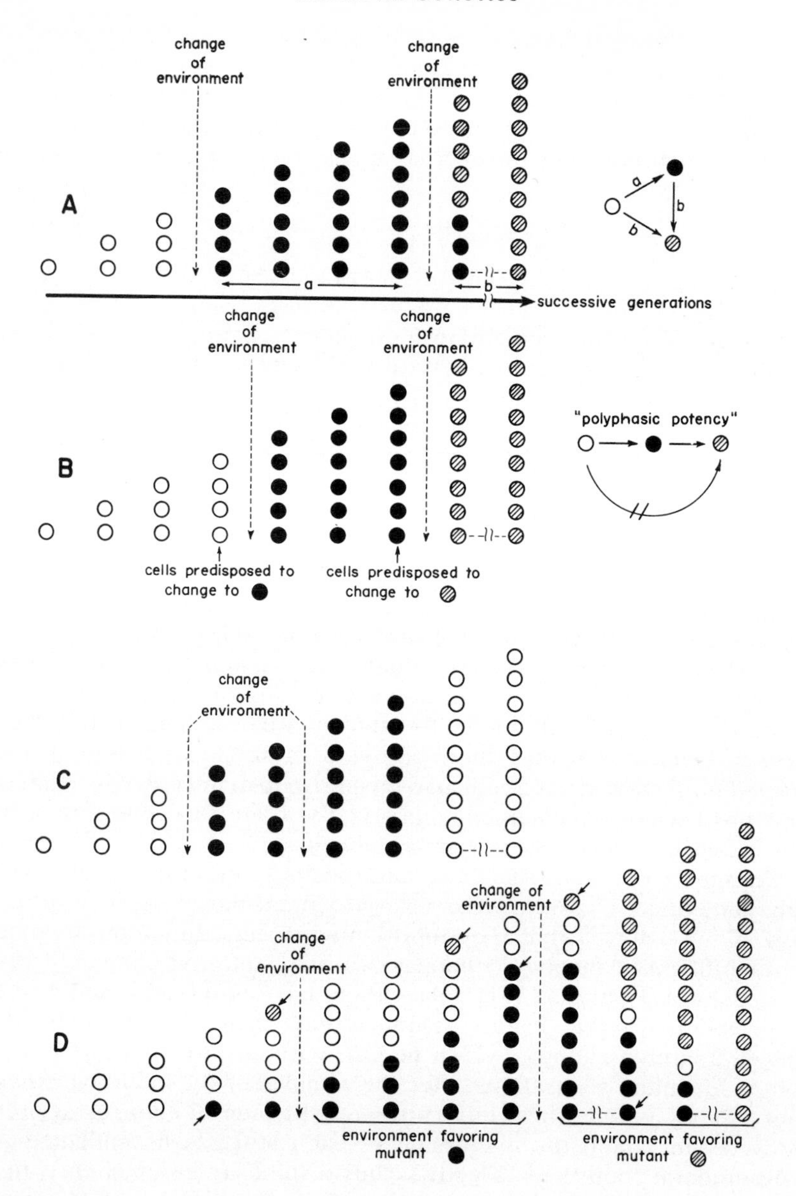

FIGURE 4. Diagrams illustrating various concepts that have been proposed to explain the mechanism of variation within bacterial populations. A, *Adaptation,* involving a directed change of bacteria under the influence of the environment (environmental conditions indicated as *a* and *b*); B, *life cycle,* involving an orderly succession of "culture phases," the expression of each stage depending on the environmental conditions; C, *Dauermodifikationen,* involving direct adaptations that will persist for prolonged periods following the removal of the environmental condition that induced the change; D, *mutation and selection,* involving the spontaneous occurrence, independent of existing environmental conditions, of a few genetically different cells and their subsequent selection under appropriate environmental conditions. Arrows designate new mutants. The increase in population size is indicated, schematically only, by an increasing number of circles.

The early 1940's saw the rapid development and application of such techniques. Yet although the beginnings of an organized research field of bacterial genetics may be traced back to those years, (cf., Luria, 1947) the older literature contained a large amount of valuable experimental material on the manifestations of bacterial variation, including data that subsequently could be aligned successfully with the newer interpretations regarding the underlying mechanisms of bacterial variation (cf. Braun, 1947).

Following are references to some representative early investigators of bacterial variation, classified according to the concepts which they advanced in the interpretation of their results.

ADAPTATION

The views of Seppilli (1939) and Manwaring (1934) are representative of those who endowed bacteria with a hypothetical inherent potential of sufficient flexibility to permit direct adaptation to a multitude of environmental conditions. These workers entirely rejected the applicability of the mutation concept to bacteria. In the absence of any critical evidence to the contrary, many bacteriologists used to share such views. Terms such as "adapted" and "acquired" became common in the numerous descriptive studies on bacterial variation which followed the Koch-Cohn era (1881) of extreme monomorphism. Even in the literature of the 1940's and 1950's one could still find a few proponents of the idea that direct adaptations may play a *major*, though not exclusive, role in bacterial variation (for example, Hinshelwood, 1947). Such ideas were advanced with a considerable degree of conviction and emotion, resulting in many highly charged discussions between proponents of neo-Darwinian ideas (see p. 18) and proponents of Lamarckism. Now that experimental evidence and newer knowledge have decided the issue, it is extremely difficult to convey the intensity of some of the controversies that raged during the 1940's.

LIFE-CYCLES

A concept that enjoyed considerable popularity, especially in the 1930's was the "cyclogenic" or ontogenic theory advanced by Enderlein (1925), Mellon (1926, 1942), Hadley (1927, 1937) and others. This concept attributed to bacteria the ability to go through orderly life-cycles similar to the well-known cyclic stages of parasitic protozoa. The aforementioned workers were primarily concerned with studies on pathogenic bacteria and with changes involving antigenic, morphologic and virulence characteristics. To these variational phenomena they applied the term *dissociation*, first used by de Kruif (1921) to denote the appearance, in a pure culture, of relatively stable but reversible types which differ usually in several characteristics from those of the parent types. The origin of the term "dissociation," as well as of ontogenic concepts, can actually be traced back to the bacteriological work of the 1870's, when the apparent fragmentation (i.e., "dissociation") of long filamentous cell structures into short bodies, and subsequent reversal of this change under proper conditions, was first observed. The later investigators extended the idea of dissociation and its ontogenic interpretation beyond this simple cellular change and applied it to the majority of variational phenomena observed in bacteria, which in the 1920's and 1930's centered principally around variability in antigenicity, virulence and morphology of pathogenic bacteria. In general, the cyclogenic or ontogenic theory stressed the polyphasic potencies of the bacterial cell and maintained that the "chief culture phases" (e.g., antigenically smooth, mucoid, or rough) are stages in an orderly predetermined life-cycle in which the expression of each stage is dependent on the environmental conditions. Hadley has stated that "each culture phase represents a stage in the development of the bacterial individual whose span of life extends from the gonidium (or similar reproductive entity) to the reproductively mature rough-phase culture. On these grounds, the bacterial individuum should not be conceived of as a single cell, but as the entire range of successive culture development from gonidium to mature form." These ideas have failed to survive under the impact of critical evidence (see Braun, 1947, for a review of such evidence).

MUTATION AND SELECTION

Prior to the days of systematic research in bacterial genetics a number of bacteriologists suggested that many variational aspects observed among bacteria might be due to mutation and selection. Such suggestions were based on analogy with genetic information obtained in studies with plants and animals, rather than on critical experimental evidence. As early as 1901, soon after DeVries advanced the mutation theory for higher organisms, Beijerinck (1901, 1912) suggested that phenomena of the kind which were later termed "dissociation" may be due to mutations. Other early supporters of the mutation and selection concept in bacteriology were Neisser (1906), Massini (1907), Cole and Wright (1916), and, with certain reservations, Eisenberg (1914) and van Loghem (1929). In addition, Lewis (1934), Lindegren (1935), Reed, (1937), Reimann (1937), Nyberg (1938), Seiffert (1936), Deskowitz (1937), and Parr and Robbins (1941) were prominent among the supporters of the mutation concept whose publications preceded those which will be discussed in the following chapters.

SEX-LIKE PROCESSES IN BACTERIA

The existence of at least one case of transfer of genetic information between related bacterial cells (other than mother and daughter cells) was suggested as early as 1928 when Griffith first described the transformation of pneumococcal types. But the true nature of this process, specifically the involvement of DNA, was not recognized until 1944 (see p. 243). Following this, in 1947, Tatum and Lederberg presented their evidence for the occurrence of recombination in *E. coli* (see p. 291). But even before that time, as early as 1925, a number of investigators reported observations that suggested to them the occurrence of recombination. Their evidence, however, was quite controversial, and it was not until the late 1940's and early 1950's that the existence of sex-like phenomena in bacteria was documented by critical experimental evidence. These events, in turn, contributed greatly to the subsequent development of the experimentation concerned with molecular aspects of genetics that dominates the bacterial genetics of today.

[3]

THE CYTOLOGICAL BASIS OF BACTERIAL GENETICS

The ultimate goal of all inquiries into mechanisms of heredity and variation is an understanding of the structure, synthesis, function and interaction of the molecules associated with these events, and a recognition of the morphological elements of the cell with which these molecules are associated. In the case of higher organisms, the recognition of pertinent morphological elements advanced far more rapidly than the recognition of molecular aspects. Long before the advent of molecular biology, cytological studies on higher plants and animals had furnished geneticists with a material basis for genetic phenomena which complemented, and in many respects extended, the information derived from breeding and mutation studies. The situation is quite different with bacteria. We now know more about molecular aspects of information transfer and control in bacteria than we know about the nature and behavior of the cellular structural elements with which these molecules may be associated. For example, in higher forms the morphology of the intranuclear chromosomes and their visible behavior during nuclear division (*mitosis*), particularly their special behavior during the so-called reduction division (*meiosis*) preceding the maturation of germ cells (gametes), furnished important evidence for the role of these visible elements in the transmission of hereditary determinants.

Experimental evidence has demonstrated that in bacteria, just as in higher organisms, the informational molecular units, confined to a specific region of the cell, are not distributed at random, but are arranged in a linear fashion and can be so transferred from one cell to another during conjugation. This suggests the existence of structural elements similar to the chromosomes. However, true chromosomes have not been detected in bacteria, despite the transient belief of some who attempted to interpret the variable morphology of nucleoid regions of certain bacteria as different stages in the division of chromosomal elements. The difficulties encountered in cytological studies of bacteria are principally due to their size, which places many of the pertinent structures at the lower limit of resolution, and also to what appears to be a lesser degree of organization of the structural elements with which informational molecules are associated. Despite such difficulties, some facts pertinent to genetic problems have emerged and their review is appropriate at this point (see also Luria, 1960; Murray, 1960; Salton, 1960; and Robinow, 1960a, 1962).

GENERAL ORGANIZATION OF THE BACTERIAL CELL

An idealized bacterial cell consists of dense *protoplasm*, with one or more areas of lesser density which are akin to *nuclei* and are now generally referred to as *nucleoids* or *nucleoplasm* (Fig. 5). The protoplasmic mass is surrounded by a *plasma membrane* or cytoplasmic membrane, which, as a rule, is, in turn, surrounded by a rigid *cell wall* (Fig. 6). Many bacteria, in addition, excrete materials such as polysaccharides or polypeptides that may remain attached to the cell wall and thus form an outer *capsule.*

PROTOPLASM AND ITS INCLUSIONS

The protoplasm of bacteria, which is rich in RNA, shows in electron micrographs principally as a multitude of granules; these are the RNA +

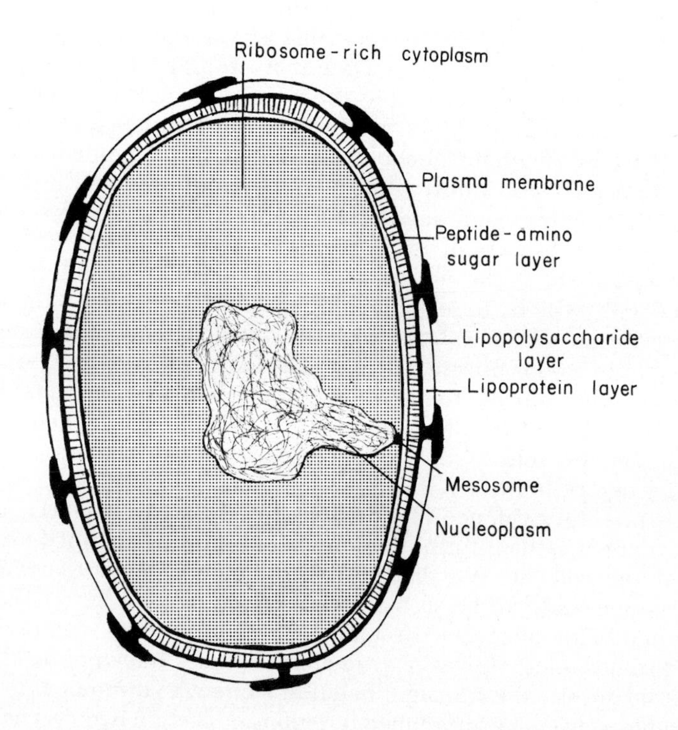

FIGURE 5. Diagrammatic sketch of the major components of an idealized bacterium. The cell wall structure is that of a smooth gram-negative organism and is shown as suggested by Wardlaw (1964). Only a very few sites of penetration of the lipopolysaccharide layer through the lipoprotein layer are indicated in this sketch, whereas there are assumed to be a multitude of such sites of penetration.

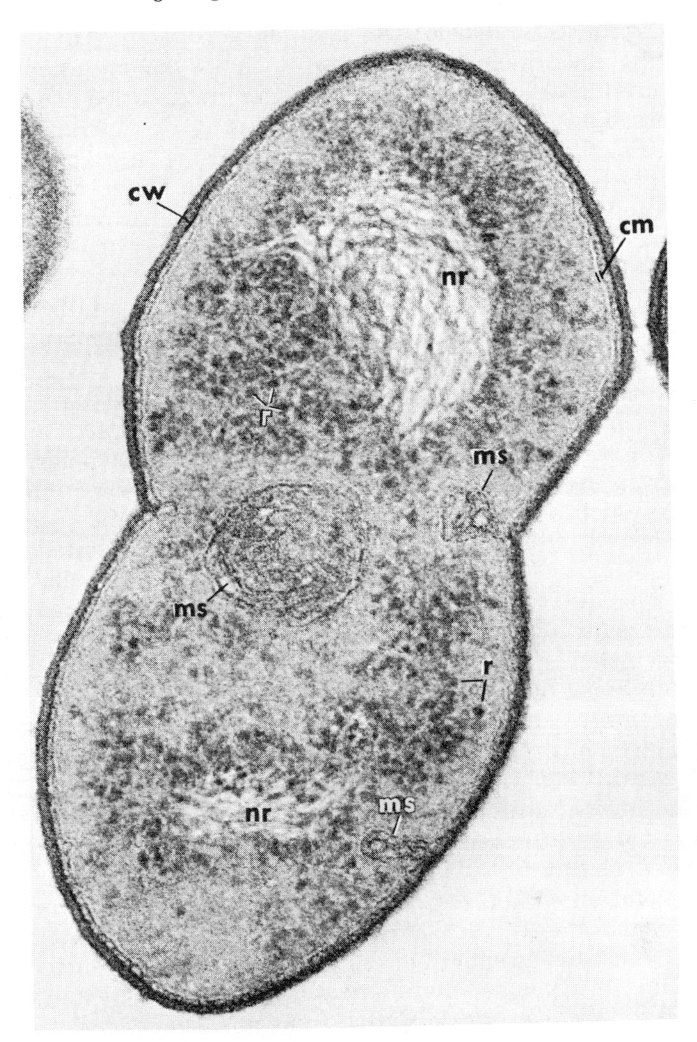

FIGURE 6. Electron micrograph of a dividing cell of *Diplococcus pneumoniae*. The nucleoid regions (*nr*) show a network of DNA fibrils and are surrounded by masses of ribosomes (*r*). Three mesosomes (*ms*) are visible; two of them are connected with the cell membrane (*cm*), which lies next to the cell wall (*cw*). (Magnification: × 250,000.) (Photo by A. Tomasz and J. Jamieson, from Pallade, 1964.)

protein-containing microsomes or *ribosomes*, now clearly implicated as the sites of protein synthesis (see p. 331). Cells contain ribosomes of different sizes, which may be a reflection of the particles' gradual growth into full-sized ribosomes. Most ribosomes are about 180 Å in diameter, have a molecular weight of approximately 3×10^6 and when separated in the ultracentrifuge, show a sedimentation coefficient of 80 S (1 S = 1 Svedberg unit = 10^{-13} cm/sec/unit field).* In addition to ribosomes, the protoplasm may contain membranous organelles, such as the mesosomes, which appear to originate from the membrane by an invagination and "pinching-off" process (Fitz-James, 1960). Typical mitochondria comparable to the distinct intracellular organelles of higher organisms, in which they are the major site of cytochrome enzymes and of enzymes concerned with fatty acid oxidation, oxidative phosphorylation and the citric acid cycle, do not seem to occur in bacteria. In bacteria these enzymes appear to be associated with the plasma membrane and with the mesosomes. There is some evidence suggesting that, like mesosomes, mitochondria of higher organisms evolved by a gradual invagination of the plasma membrane.

PLASMA MEMBRANE

The plasma membrane, rich in lipoprotein and RNA, represents a barrier with selective permeability separating the protoplasm and its contents from the exterior. As a rule, a cell wall, and sometimes surface appendages such as flagella and fimbriae, surrounds the plasma membrane. In some bacteria, however, namely the so-called pleuropneumonia-like group of organisms (PPLO) and also in L-forms, which occur in a number of bacterial species (see p. 148), such outer coverings are either absent or greatly reduced and the delicate plasma membrane in these fragile organisms is the structure exposed to the outside world. In recent years a number of agents (see p. 147) have been discovered that are able to strip the entire cell wall, or components thereof, from the inner portion of the cell, which is represented by the membrane-covered cytoplasm and its inclusions. If cell wall components are totally absent, the remaining membrane-covered structure is referred to as *protoplast*; if parts of the cell wall remain attached to the membrane, the structure is called a *spheroplast*. The term "spheroplast" has its origin in the fact that these cell wall-deficient structures lack the rigidity-producing components of the wall, consequently such structures, when placed into a hypertonic environment, assume a *spherical* shape. Survival of wall-deficient bacteria in an isotonic or hypotonic environment is not possible since hypertonicity is required to take over the corsetting functions usually performed by the cell wall.

CELL WALL

In both gram-positive and gram-negative bacteria, the rigid portion of the cell wall is composed of polypeptides (polymers of α-ϵ-diaminopimelic acid [DAP], D-alanine, glutamic acid, glycine and lysine) in association with acetylglucosamine, acetylmuramic acid, sugars, galactosamine and teichoic acid. These peptide-amino sugar complexes (also referred to as mucopeptides), together with a small amount of lipid, represent the recognized components of gram-positive walls. The more complex walls of gram-negative bacteria contain, in addition, layers of lipoprotein and lipopolysaccharide, which probably are superimposed on the rigidity-

*For the sake of comparison: soluble proteins are sedimented in the 4 *S* to 6 *S* fractions and DNA in the 8 *S* fraction.

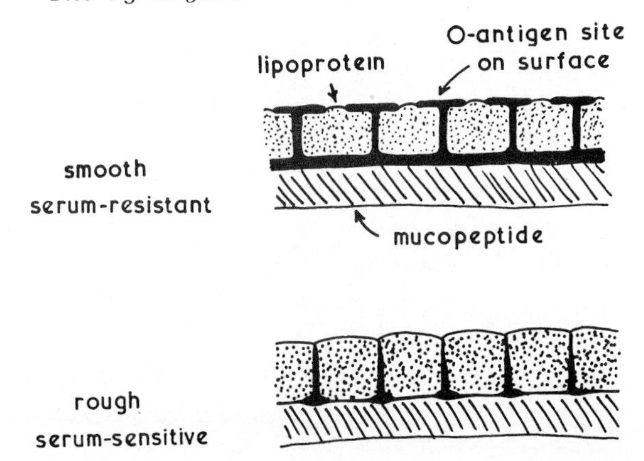

FIGURE 7. Suggested structural arrangement of cell wall components (in cross section) of *E. coli*. (From Wardlaw, 1964.)

producing mucopeptide layer or may be interspersed with it. If they are superimposed, they must contain holes or gaps, since studies on phage adsorption, and wall-destroying agents have demonstrated that the deeper wall layer can be attacked, even in the presence of a presumably undamaged lipoprotein coat (see Fig. 5). A possible mode of organization, as suggested by Wardlaw (1964), is shown in Figure 7.

NUCLEOIDS AND THE CHROMOSOME-LIKE STRUCTURES THEY CONTAIN

All bacteria contain either one or several Feulgen-positive (DNA-rich) intracytoplasmic regions that are vesicular in appearance and that show up in electron micrographs as areas of lesser density. These regions, devoid of the typical nuclear membrane of higher organisms, have been referred to either as nuclei, nucleoids, nucleoplasm, nuclear vacuoles, or chromatin bodies. Owing to the absence of easily detectable and distinctive internal organization, these cellular regions have been regarded as structures that might be comparable to the interphase chromosomes of higher organisms. Actually, bacteria do not appear to have typical chromosomes in the sense of the complex nucleoprotein structures of higher organisms. Rather, as indicated by recently employed, newer techniques, the bacterial nucleoid contains long fibrillar DNA-rich elements, about 1400 μ in length and 30 Å in diameter.

Figure 8 shows such fibrous DNA as it appears in an electron micrograph of a ruptured bacterium; Figures 9 and 10 show similar fibers within the nucleoids of whole bacterial cells. No free ends are visible (see Fig. 8); this is in accordance with the view that the bacterial DNA (about 10^{-14} gm/cell for *E. coli*) is organized as an unbranched circular (in the sense of "no open ends") structure. This conclusion is also supported by data from genetic transfers (see Chapter 15) and by the remarkable autoradiographs of isolated bacterial "chromosomes" obtained by Cairns (1963) (Fig. 11).

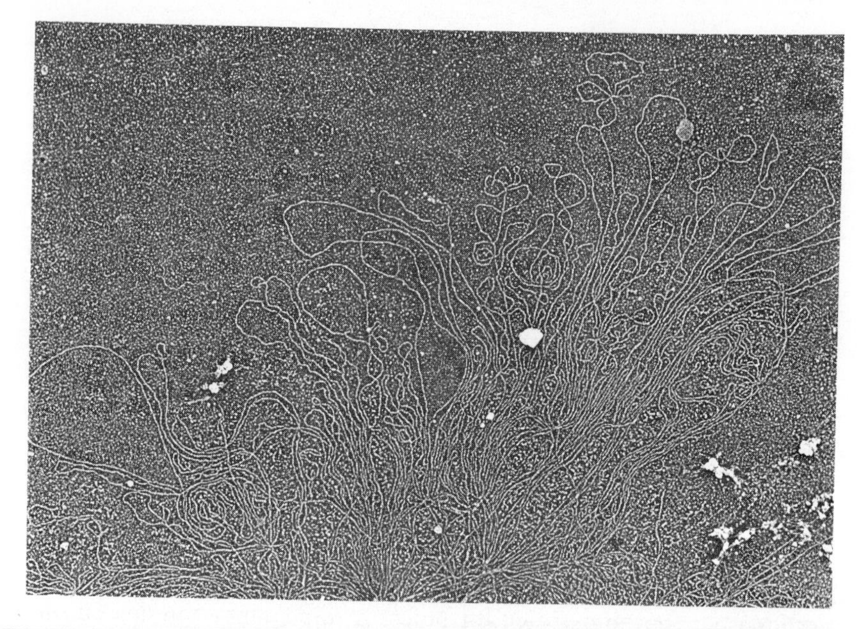

FIGURE 8. Electron micrograph of DNA released from a *Micrococcus lysodeikticus* protoplast by lysis in a spreading, monomolecular film of protein at a water-air interface. (Magnification: approximately × 31,000.) (From Kleinschmidt *et al.*, 1961.)

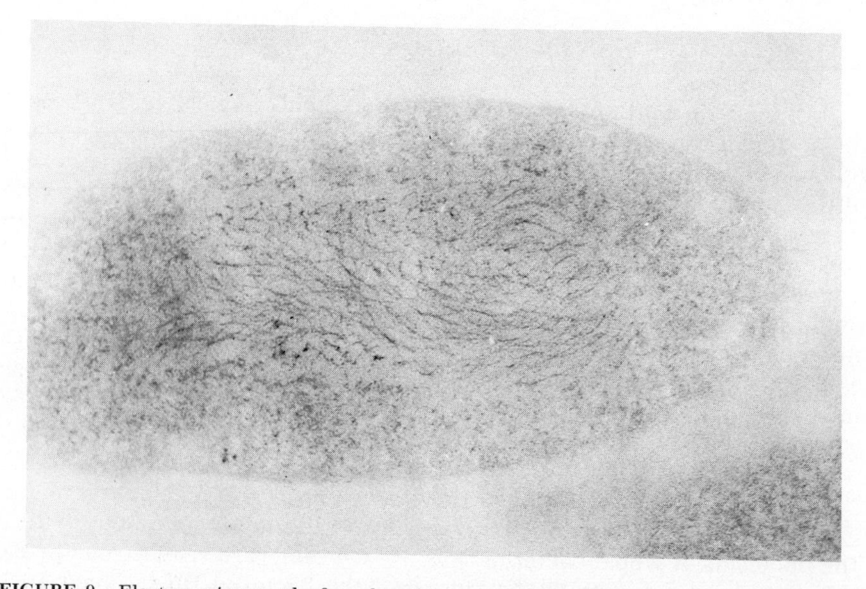

FIGURE 9. Electron micrograph of an ultra-thin section of *Escherichia coli* fixed in an isotonic solution of 1 per cent OsO_4 and $K_2Cr_2O_7$ at pH 7.2, subsequently treated with an aqueous solution of uranyl acetate, and embedded in Vestropal. Section thickness is approximately one-eighth of the diameter of the nucleoid. The fibrous pattern in the nucleoid is formed by the side-to-side aggregation of individual DNA helices which occurs in the course of preparation of the specimen for electron micrography. (Courtesy of W. Fuhs.)

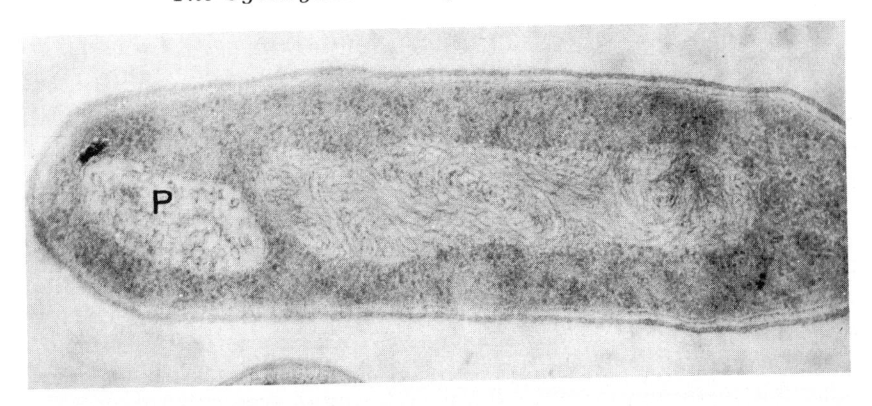

FIGURE 10. Electron micrograph of an ultra-thin section of *Bacillus subtilis*, prepared as explained in Figure 9. (Courtesy of W. Fuhs.)

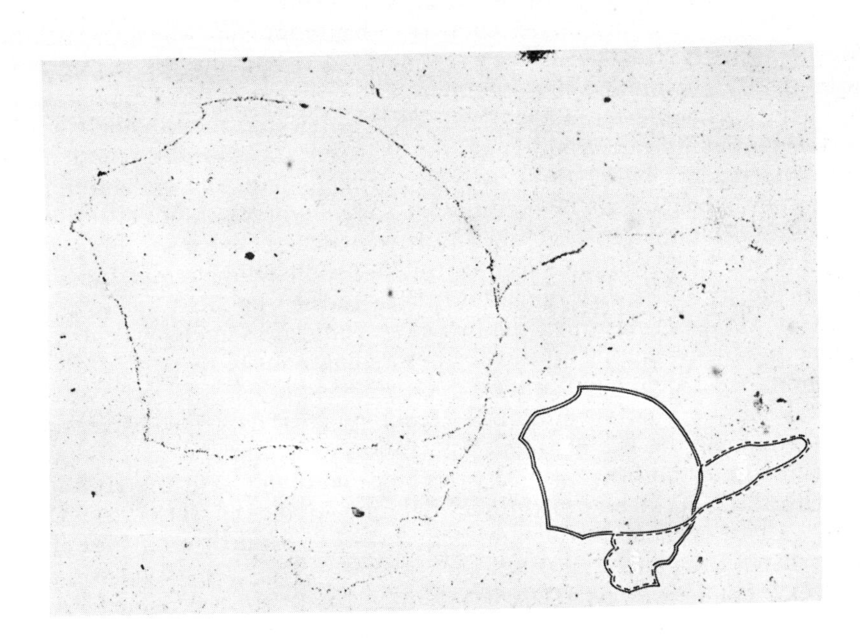

FIGURE 11. Autoradiograph of the chromosome of *E. coli* Hfr K-12, labeled with tritiated thymidine for two generations and extracted with lysozyme in a dialysis chamber. Exposure time was two months. The inset is an interpretive diagram of the replication process, which should be compared with the last double loop of Figure 20. (From Cairns, 1963.)

Cairns pulse-labeled cells of a thymine-requiring *E. coli* strain with tritium-labeled thymidine, ended the pulse by dilution with cold thymidine, lysed the cells by dialysis against 1 per cent Duponol (sodium dodecyl sulfate) and collected the DNA on a Millipore filter membrane; the exposure time for subsequent autoradiography was about two months. Circular DNA structures also have been identified in bacteriophages (Kleinschmidt *et al.*, 1963).

It is at present unknown whether each nucleoid contains one giant circular DNA molecule, or a series of linearly arranged DNA molecules, interconnected and organized into one giant linear and circular structure, or possibly even, in some cases, a series of such structures (see also p. 37). In recent years, it has become increasingly obvious that chromosomes of higher organisms are far more complex, far more evolved structures than the relatively simple DNA fibers of bacteria. [In fact, speculations of Jacob and Brenner have suggested that the chromosomes of higher organisms may have evolved as organized structural assemblies of a multitude of bacterial DNA loops or "replicons" (see p. 124).] Despite the probable difference in the organization of nuclei and intranuclear DNA structures in bacteria and in higher organisms, it has remained customary to refer to "bacterial nuclei," and to the DNA structures they contain as "bacterial chromosomes." For the sake of simplicity we shall adhere to this convention in this book, but it should be remembered that in reality there is probably a great deal of structural difference between "nuclei" and "chromosomes" of bacteria and those of higher organisms.

Historically, an organized nucleus in bacterial cells was described by Meyer as early as 1897 and was recognized repeatedly thereafter, (see Knaysi, 1951; Robinow, 1945). Remarkable progress in the demonstration of nuclei was achieved following the recognition that the ribonucleic acid of the basophilic bacterial cytoplasm obscured the staining reactions of the nucleus. Following the removal of ribonucleic acid by either mild hydrolysis, ribonuclease or preliminary partial starvation of cells, the nucleus can be stained by a number of dyes known to have a specific affinity for nuclei of higher organisms or by means of the Feulgen reaction which is specific for aldehydes, including those formed by DNA following hydrolysis. The DNA nature of the bodies recognized as nuclei was also confirmed by ultraviolet absorption, by autoradiographs of bacteria grown on tritium-labeled thymidine and by the modifying effects of DNAase treatment. Robinow (1942) popularized a technique first described by Pickarski (1937), namely the use of Giemsa's solution for staining nuclei following fixation with osmium tetraoxide vapor and treatment with 1 N HCl at 60° C. With the help of this technique, Robinow (1942), Bisset (1951), Delaporte (1950), and others demonstrated deeply stained, often vesicular, bodies within the bacterial cell (Fig. 12). These bodies, consisting primarily of deoxyribonucleoprotein (DNA-protein), are extremely variable in shape and have been described as usually rod-shaped in actively growing cells of Eubacteriales, and as spherical in most cocci, acid-fast and diphtheroid bacteria. The "double rod" or paired appearance of many nuclei has been regarded as reflecting the distribution of chromatinic and DNA-rich material during nuclear division. A nuclear body also has been demon-

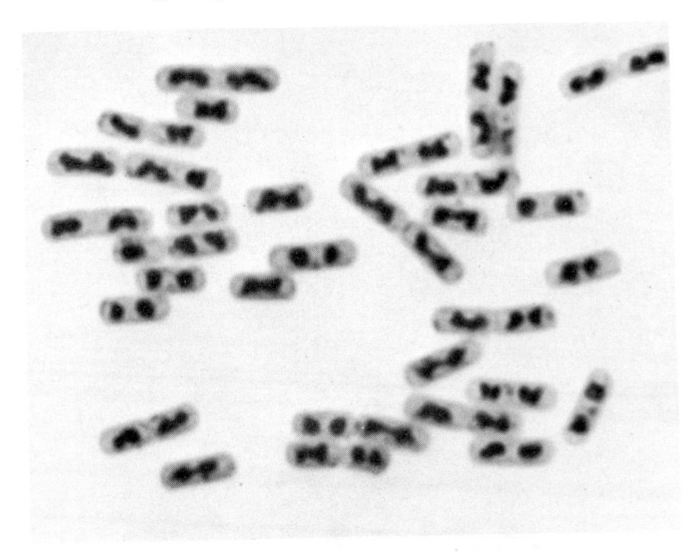

FIGURE 12. Nucleus-like structures in *Bacillus cereus* cells. Fixed with osmium vapor and stained by acid-Giemsa. Photographed mounted in water. (Magnification: × 3000.) (Courtesy of C. Robinow.)

strated in spores, and its content of DNA has been determined quantitatively with the aid of P^{32} in *Bacillus cereus* and *B. subtilis* as approximately one-half that of the vegetative cell (the latter observations reflect the fact that vegetative bacteria may possess more than one nucleus) (Fig. 13).

The number of nuclei per vegetative cell may vary. Thus, cocci are usually uninuclear, whereas cells of rodlike bacteria are frequently multinuclear. The latter may contain two nuclei or multiples of two, particularly during stages of active growth (see Fig. 12). The multinuclear condition is caused by a lack of synchronization between the rate of growth and the rate of cell division. The rate of nuclear division appears to be proportional to the rate of growth. Therefore, in young, actively growing cultures, multinuclear cells are apt to predominate because the nucleus may divide several times before the cell divides. In older cultures the majority of cells may become uninuclear. Many inhibitory conditions, such as exposure to ultraviolet radiation or penicillin, also cause the formation of multinuclear cells, since such conditions can interfere with cell division without immediate effects upon nuclear division. Thus filamentous cells containing many nuclei are formed under these adverse conditions (Figs. 14 and 15).

The existence of more than one nucleus in many bacterial cells is an important factor from a genetic point of view, since, for example, in the presence of an unaltered bit of information in *one* nucleus, the altered information in the *second* nucleus may not express itself. To appreciate such interactions among several nuclei of a cell, we must pause now to review some of these phenomena which were first elucidated in studies with higher organisms.

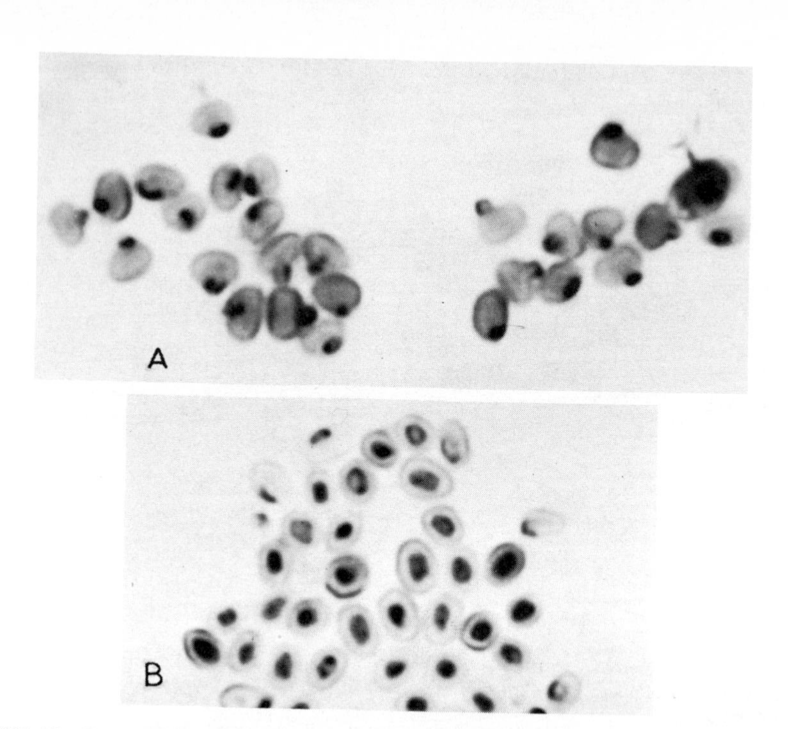

FIGURE 13. Spores of *B. megatherium*. A, Resting spores of *B. megatherium* from a 4-day culture on potato extract agar. The nucleoids are at the periphery. B, Spores from the same culture as those in A, fixed after 10 minutes on heart infusion agar at 37° C. In most of the spores the nucleoid is now in the interior of the cell and appears to be ring-shaped in optical section. Both preparations were fixed with osmium vapor, hydrolyzed with 1 N HCl at 60° C and stained with DeLamater's SO_2-thionine. Photographed mounted in water. (Magnification: × 3600.) (Courtesy of C. Robinow.)

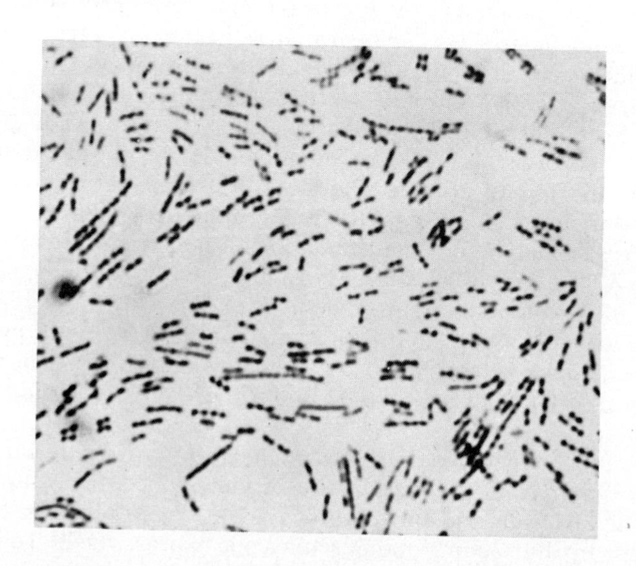

FIGURE 14. Cells of *E. coli*, B/r (radiation-resistant) streaked on nutrient agar following 25 ergs/mm UV irradiation and incubated for 3 hours at 37° C. Stained by the method of De-Lamater (1951). (Magnification: × 1250.) (Courtesy of V. Bryson.)

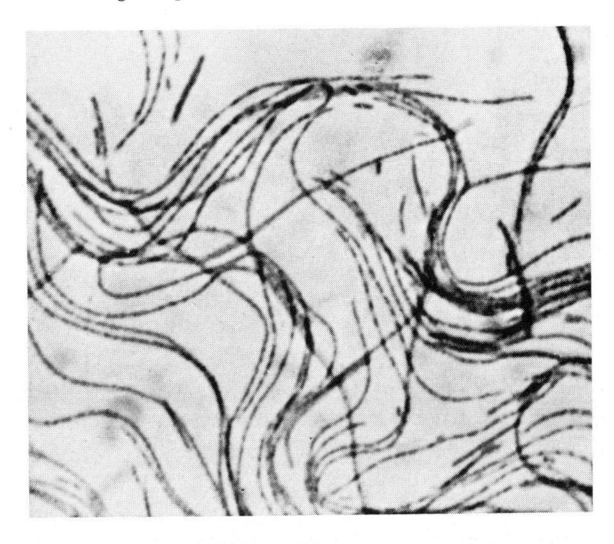

FIGURE 15. Cells of *E. coli,* B (radiation-sensitive) treated as described in Figure 14. (Magnification: × 1250.) (Courtesy of V. Bryson.)

PLOIDY, MULTINUCLEAR CONDITIONS AND THE PROBLEM OF DOMINANCE AND RECESSIVENESS

In higher animals and plants, which usually contain one nucleus per cell, the genetic information carried in this nucleus may be present in one, usually two and occasionally in more than two, sets. To understand why there may be more than one set of information per cell, let us equate one set of total nuclear information with the symbol *S*. If, in a *uninuclear* cell line, this set of information had to be divided among mother and daughter cells, each one would only receive ½ *S*, an impossible situation. Therefore, *S* must double prior to nuclear division and cell division. This is what happens in simple nuclear division or *mitosis* of higher organisms. Actually, each cell other than the sex cells or gametes of higher organisms carries, as a rule, a double set of information in each nucleus (2 *S*), so that just prior to mitosis we have 4 *S*, yielding after division two cells, each containing the typical 2 *S*. Cells having 2 *S* per nucleus are called *diploid*, those having only 1 *S* are *haploid*, and cells having multiple sets (e.g., 3 *S*, 4 *S*, 6 *S*) are called *polyploid* (Fig. 16).

Bacteria, as a rule, are considered to be haploid. Gametes (sex cells) of the higher organisms, in contrast to the somatic cells of multicellular organisms, also are haploid. Why this is a necessity becomes clear when we ask ourselves what would happen if gametes participating in sexual processes were diploid. 2 *S* would be combined with 2 *S* and we would have

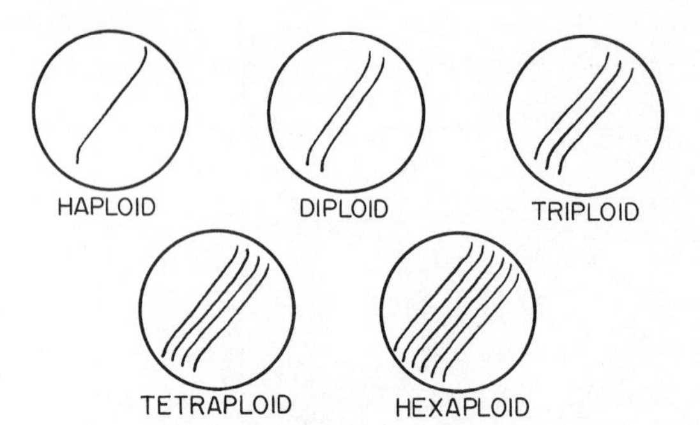

FIGURE 16. Diagram of nuclei containing one set of chromosomal material (haploid), two sets (diploid), etc.

twice the usual number of *S*'s in the nucleus of the resulting zygote, namely 4 *S*. If the progeny of such a cell, in turn, were to participate in sexual reproduction, we would get zygotes containing 8 *S*, etc., again an impossible situation. What actually happens is that prior to the maturation of the gametes in higher organisms, the normal complement of 2 *S* per nucleus is reduced, in a nuclear reduction division or *meiosis*, to *S*. In fertilization the 2 *S* complement per nucleus, and with it per cell, is reestablished. Thus, the typical nuclear state in higher organisms is 2 *S*, i.e., diploid (Fig. 17). In some bacteria a situation akin to the 2 *S* state occurs briefly after conjugation between 1 *S* partners, but is, as a rule, quite rapidly reduced to 1 *S* during the next cell division. Thus, as indicated in Figure 17, the typical nuclear state in bacteria is 1 *S* per nucleus.

Now, what happens in a uninuclear cell when 2 *S* are present in each nucleus and the information contained in *one* of these sets is not entirely identical with that contained in the other set? For example, let us write the message in such a nucleus as follows:

A B C D E F g H I J K
A b C D E F G H I J K

Each letter stands for a piece of information (nucleotide sequence) controlling a hereditary characteristic. In such a cell the *recessive* bit of information "b" does not express itself in the presence of the *dominant* message "B," and the dominant message "G" overshadows, so to speak, the presence in the genotype of the recessive message "g." Recessive messages such as "b" and "g" would only express themselves in cells of the genotype:

A b C D E F g H I J K
A b C D E F g H I J K

The recessive determinants of hereditary traits are identical here in both chromosomes. Thus, a cell with the genotype Bb has the phenotype "B"; a cell with the genotype bb has the phenotype "b." (In classic genetics, genes located at corresponding sites of homologous chromosomes, but producing somewhat different effects were referred to as *alleles*; in other words, it became customary to speak of dominant and recessive alleles.)

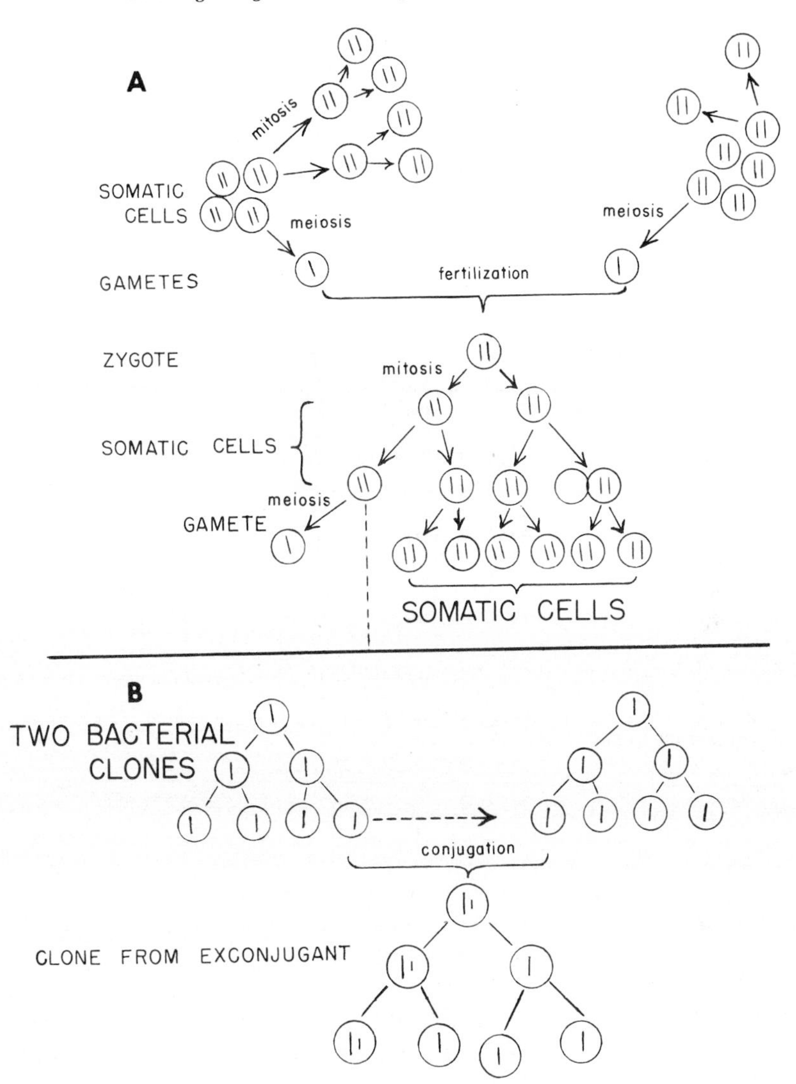

FIGURE 17. Diagrammatic representation of the typical nuclear state in higher organisms (**A**) and the nucleoid state in bacteria (**B**). Each circle represents a nucleus or nucleoid, respectively, and each long line therein represents one total set of information.

Interrelationships between allelic determinants also play a significant role when unlike determinants, instead of being contained in two chromosomes of the same nucleus, are located in different nuclei of multinucleate haploid cells, a condition that frequently occurs in bacteria. If cells contain several nuclei that differ from each other in their information, i.e., in their respective complements of determinants, they are called *heterokaryotic* and the condition is described as *heterokaryosis* (Fig. 18). A recessive

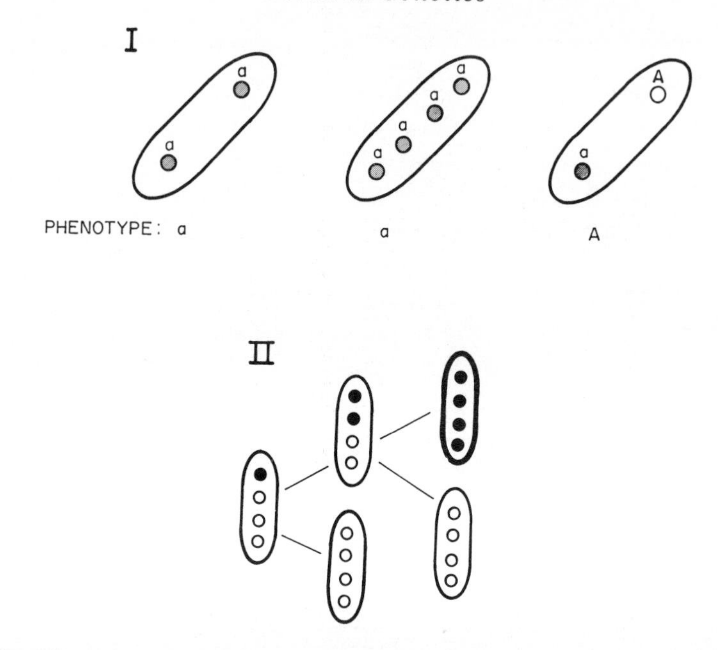

FIGURE 18. I, Diagram of multinucleate cells. Nuclei with identical genotype are indicated by equal shading. Cell at right is heterokaryotic. II, Diagram illustrating the delay in phenotypic expression of a recessive mutation that occurs in only one of the nuclei (black nucleus in this diagram) of a multinucleate cell.

determinant (a "recessive gene" in classic genetics) existing (or arising by mutation) in only one of the nuclei of a *heterokaryotic* cell will fail to express its effect, just as a recessive determinant will fail to manifest its influence in a uninucleate diploid cell in the presence of its dominant normal allele. Yet by subsequent nuclear and cell divisions a homokaryotic cell will result in which the recessive determinant can exert its influence (see Fig. 18). Dominant determinants, of course, are capable of exerting their influence even when present in a single set, both in heterokaryotic as well as in diploid cells.

THE REPLICATION OF INTRANUCLEAR ELEMENTS

We have already referred to the fact that electron microscopy of sections of bacterial nucleoids has revealed that the nucleoids contain fibrillar elements (see Figs. 9 and 10). The recognition of these fibers has become the basis for some speculations regarding the actual organization and possible modes of replication of intranuclear material of bacteria. Kellenberger (1960) has proposed that the fibers, which appear to consist of DNA plus polyamines, are not just simple DNA molecules, but a series of DNA pieces that are linked lengthwise by protein "linkers" in the fashion indicated in Figure 19. He suggests that replication of such a structure may occur by a doubling of the cylinder (Fig. 19), with an eventual joining of the open ends. Robinow has proposed that there are filamentous subunits, each consisting of a bundle of fibers, that replicate by laying down a copy of each fiber. He suggests that the new fibers then move in a forward direction from the old fibers, thus giving the entire structure the appearance of longitudinal growth from one end, a phenomenon which seems to be detectable in microscopic studies of dividing nuclei. Cairns (1963), in his autoradiographs of tritium-labeled *E. coli* DNA, observed evidence for a sequential lengthwise doubling of the DNA fiber (see Fig. 11), which caused him to suggest the type of duplication process indicated in Figure 20. As we shall see later, there is some good experimental evidence supporting the validity of Cairns' model (p. 253).

The suggestion has been made (Jacob *et al.*, 1963) that the orderly, equal distribution of replicated DNA, which is controlled by a complex mitotic apparatus in higher organisms, may proceed in bacteria as indicated in Figure 21. The DNA (two circular structures are shown in Figure 21, one chromosomal and the other controlling sexual reproduction in *E. coli*) is attached to the cell membrane at one spot in the equatorial plane of the cell. The attachment may not be direct, but may be via a mesosome

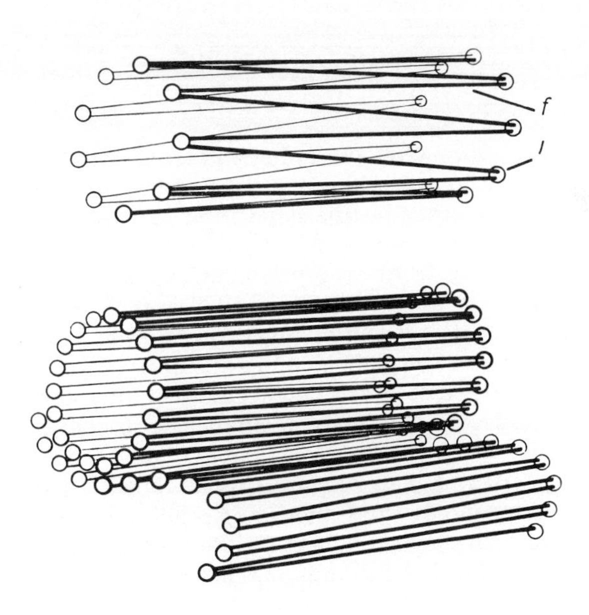

FIGURE 19. Schematic drawings of the possible structure of a bacterial nucleoid and of its replication. DNA fibrils (*f*) are assumed to be joined to each other by small protein "linkers" (*l*). The linkages are assumed to be continuous, resulting in a genetically circular linkage group. (From Kellenberger, 1960.)

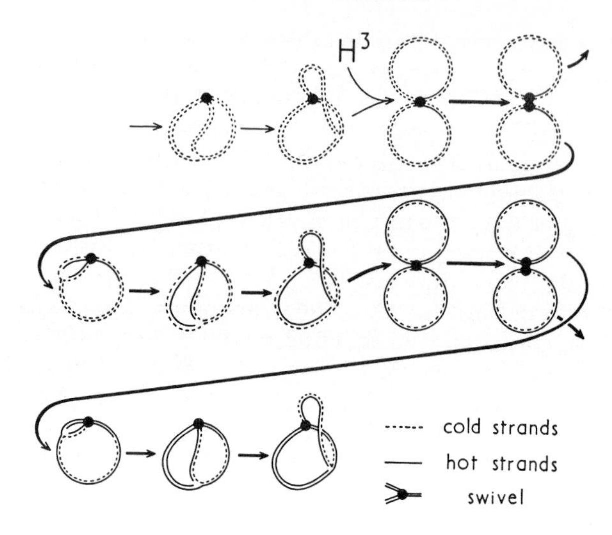

FIGURE 20. Diagrammatic representation of two rounds of replication of a circular chromosome following the introduction of a labeled precursor at some arbitrary point in the cycle. The assumption has been made that duplication always starts at the same point and advances in the same direction, an assumption that is supported by data cited in Chapter 13. The existence of a swivel, permitting free rotation of the non-duplicated part in relation to the rest of the chromosome, is assumed in order to allow the presumably necessary unwinding of the parental double helix. (From Cairns, J., 1963.)

(Ryter and Jacob, 1963) (Fig. 22). Following lengthwise replication of the circular DNA (see Figs. 20 and 21), the resulting doublet structures are separated from each other by the deposition of membrane material between them. As the membrane grows, the two equivalent DNA halves are progressively separated from each other and come to lie within cellular regions that may subsequently be separated from each other by septum formation, followed by separation of the resulting daughter bacteria.

Although the exact morphological details of organization and replication of intranuclear structures have remained unknown, it has been possible to conclude, on the basis of studies with radioactively labeled nuclear materials, that the general mode of replication of bacterial DNA is "*semiconservative.*" Let us explain this statement. Theoretically, one could expect either one of three modes of replication (Fig. 23): (a) *conservative*, in which all the old nuclear material remains (or is "conserved") in the maternal nucleus, the daughter nucleus consisting of only newly formed material; (b) *semiconservative*, in which one-half old material and one-half newly synthesized material appear both in mother- and daughter-nuclei; and (c) *dispersive*, in which old and new materials are randomly distributed among mother- and daughter-nuclei. We shall later review in more detail the actual experimental evidence for the semicon-

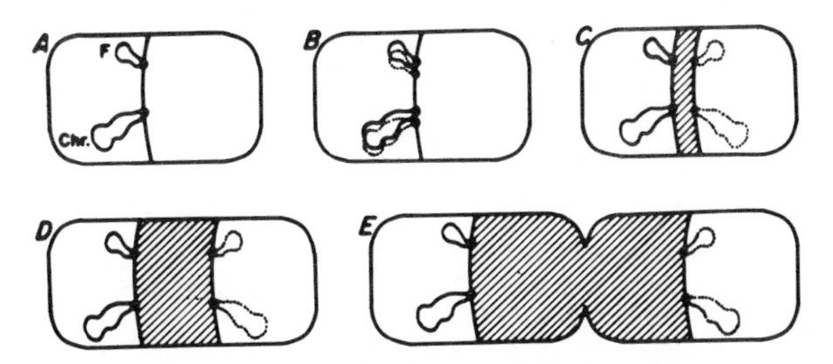

FIGURE 21. A model of the organization of DNA in a cell of *E. coli* and its mode of distribution to daughter cells. The bacterium (F^+) carries two independent self-replicating units: the chromosomal replicon and the *F* replicon. The two replicons are assumed to be attached, possibly via a mesosome, to the cell membrane along the equatorial perimeter of the bacterium. Following replication, elements of the bacterial membrane are assumed to grow between the attachment sites of the daughter replicons, pushing them progressively apart and into the future daughter cells. (From Jacob *et al.*, 1963.)

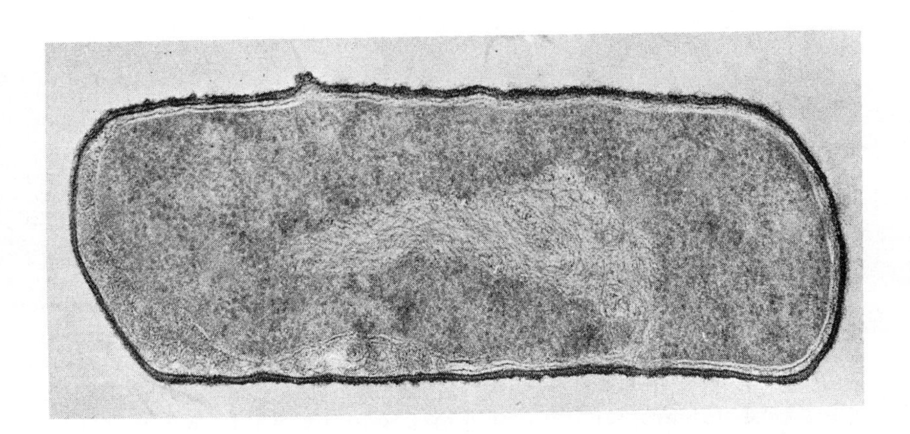

FIGURE 22. Electron micrograph of an ultra-thin section of *B. subtilis*, fixed after 30 minutes in a hypertonic medium. Note the apparent attachment of the nucleoid (via a mesosome?) to the cell membrane. (Magnification: × 81,000.) (From Ryter and Jacob, 1963.)

servative mode of replication of nuclear material, and we shall then see how well this fits into the molecular aspects of replication of the basic substance concerned with genetic information – the DNA.

REPRODUCTIVE MECHANISMS OF THE BACTERIAL CELL

In discussing the bacterial nucleus and in Chapter 1, we have already referred to several reproductive mechanisms in bacteria: (1) vegetative,

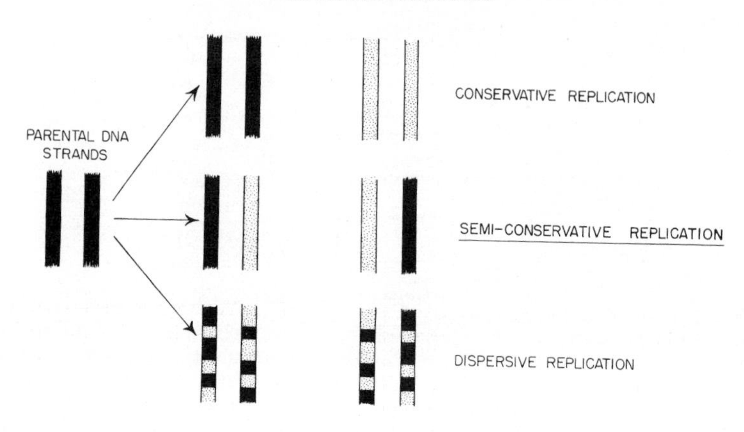

FIGURE 23. Diagram illustrating three possible modes of replication of DNA. Parental DNA is indicated in black; the newly synthesized DNA is indicated by the dotted area.

asexual reproduction by simple cell division following nuclear division, the latter being preceded by the replication of nuclear DNA; (2) spore formation, now also believed to be essentially vegetative in nature (cf. Robinow, 1960b); and (3) sexual and sex-like reproduction involving the transfer of nuclear, and sometimes extranuclear, material from one cell to another either after direct cellular contact (conjugation), via phage (transduction), or through naked, extracellular DNA (transformation).

At one time, the existence of still other, more complex modes of reproduction, involving "large amorphous bodies" and filtrable chromatin-rich granules, was postulated in the case of so-called "L-forms." We now know that these odd cellular structures, capable of vegetative reproduction under specific environmental conditions, actually are the result of a loss of the capacity to form cell walls. We shall, therefore, discuss these altered cellular structures in Chapter 8, when we deal with mutants affecting cellular morphology. However, reference should be made here to one particular phenomenon of bacterial reproduction that is of potential importance to genetic experimentation. It concerns apparently differential modes of cellular division during the asexual reproduction of so-called "smooth" and "rough" types of Eubacteriales (see also p. 154). Bisset (1950) has presented evidence indicating that smooth type bacteria are usually unicellular, having a tendency to separate completely at time of cell division. In contrast, rough type cells are described as usually multicellular, usually four-celled elements, in which a cell wall and membranous septa separate the individual cells which have a tendency to remain attached at the point of division. This differential mode of division, aside from being responsible for the different types of colonies formed by smooth and rough bacteria (see Fig. 69), could be of critical importance in any genetic study designed to test the behavior of the progeny of a single cell, a *clone* in the language of the geneticist. In the case of multicellular rough elements, it would be impossible to isolate a clone merely by picking a single colony, since such a colony would be likely to have developed from several sister cells. Similar considerations apply to the isolation of clones from species where cells do not tend to occur singly; for example, in the case of staphylococci or streptococci.

BACTERIAL CYTOGENETICS

As we have seen, cytological studies have indicated that bacteria, though probably somewhat less complex than higher organisms in regard to certain intracellular morphological structures, possess at least recognizable DNA-rich structures which are distributed from mother to daughter cells. A continuity of nuclear ("nucleoid") material and of the information associated with it is thus assured, and the conclusion may be drawn that the material basis for hereditary determinants in bacteria is comparable to that established earlier for higher organisms. However, systematic efforts to correlate cytologic structures with genetic processes in bacteria, i.e., the development of a field of bacterial cytogenetics, has not progressed quite as rapidly as was once anticipated. There are certain notable exceptions to this statement (see pp. 86 and 109), but in general the small size of bacteria has prevented thorough cytogenetic studies. On the other hand, many of the favorable attributes of these small organisms have made it possible to exploit them for studies on the chemical basis of genetic phenomena, which had been impossible or difficult with higher organisms. We thus have arrived, during recent years, at the curious point where we have a good deal more insight into the molecular basis of heredity in bacteria than we have into the morphological cellular structures with which the storage and transfer of bacterial information is associated.

[4]

SOME MOLECULAR ASPECTS OF BACTERIAL GENETICS

In Chapter 1 we discussed briefly why nucleic acids have been singled out as the molecules concerned with the cell-to-cell transfer of information and as the informed regulators of intracellular processes. We have already referred to some of the unique molecular properties of nucleic acids, but we must now take a closer look at them. In doing so, we shall restrict ourselves in this chapter to those aspects of nucleic acid chemistry that are of principal importance to the transfer of information from one cell to another; in other words, we shall concern ourselves now with the *structure of nucleic acids and their replication*. In a later chapter (p. 345), when we discuss intracellular control mechanism, we shall deal more extensively with the question of how the specificity of nucleic acid molecules is translated into the formation and function of specific proteins.

As far as we know, it is DNA that provides and transmits all basic information in bacteria; RNA merely serves as an intracellular transmitter or messenger of such information from the nucleus to the sites of protein formation. We, therefore, shall focus most of our attention in this chapter on DNA chemistry. However, we shall also deal with some aspects of RNA chemistry for two reasons: (1) *structurally* RNA shows a resemblance to DNA, and (2) *functionally* RNA also can occupy a principal role as transmitter of information, as exemplified in the case of certain plant and animal viruses.

COMPONENTS OF DNA AND RNA

Both DNA and RNA are polymers of nucleotides. Therefore, DNA can be regarded as a polydeoxyribonucleotide and RNA as a polyribonucleotide (for general references see Steiner and Beers, 1961; Burton, 1962). Each nucleotide is a complex consisting of three components: a nitrogenous base, a pentose sugar, and phosphoric acid (Fig. 24). The sugar is D-ribose in the case of ribonucleotides, and it is 2-deoxyribose in the case of deoxyribonucleotides (the pentose carbons are designated as C′1 through

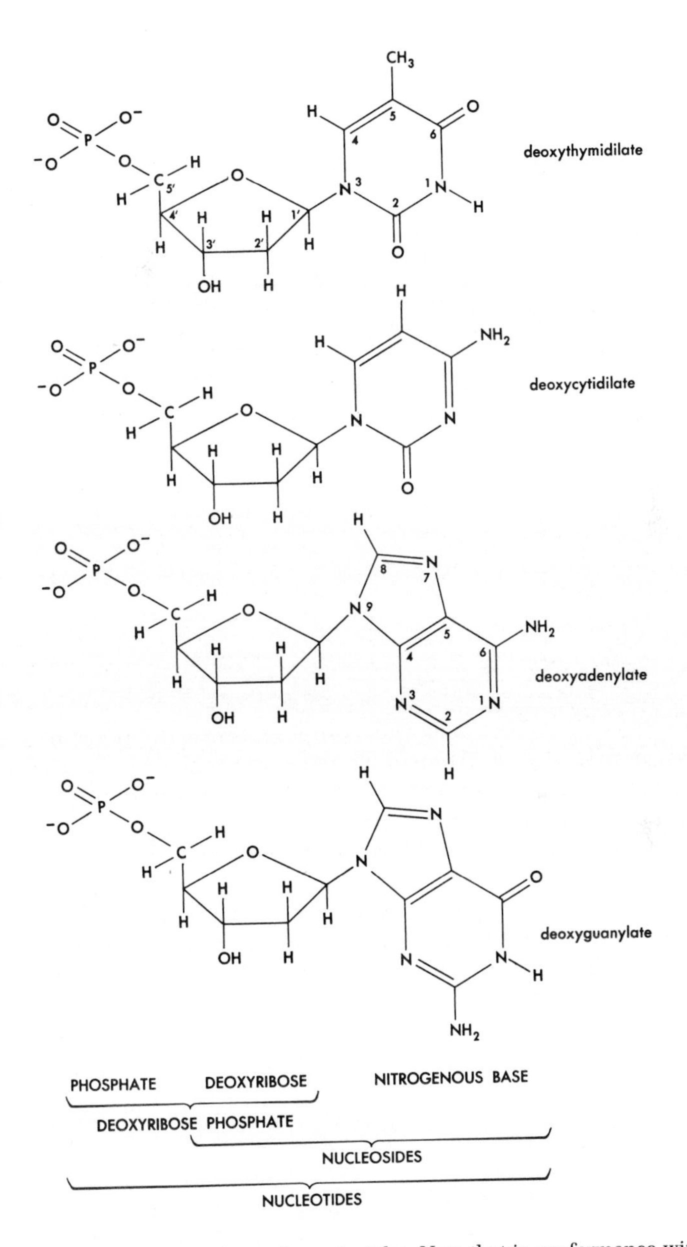

FIGURE 24. The four common deoxyribonucleotides. Note that in conformance with the conventional symbolism of organic chemistry the carbon atoms in the ring structures are not shown, but are implied by a bond angle. (From Stahl, 1964.)

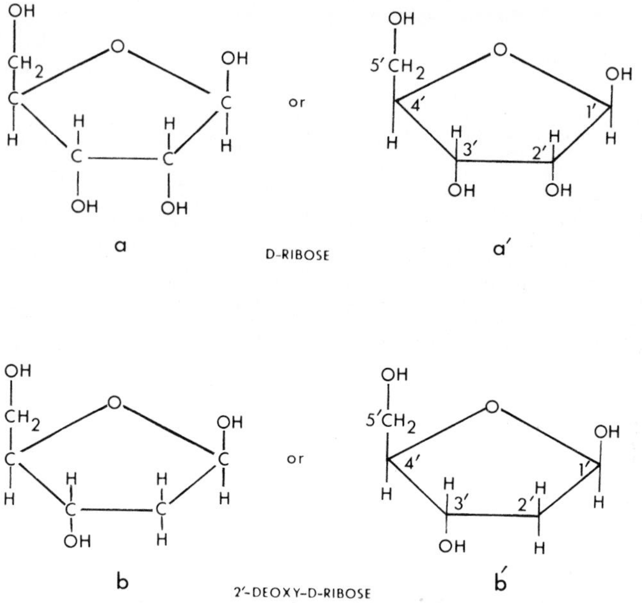

D-RIBOSE

2′-DEOXY-D-RIBOSE

FIGURE 25. Pentose sugars found in nucleic acids. a and b show the carbons in the ring; a′ and b′ use the convention of only indicating the carbons by the bond angle.

C′5; see Figure 25). The nucleotide complex minus the phosphate is called a *nucleoside* (Fig. 24). A glycosidic bond unites the sugar with the base at the C′1 position. The bases are either purines or pyrimidines; their basic ring structures are shown in Figure 26.

The *pyrimidines* commonly found in DNA are:

thymine (2,6-dihydroxy-5-methyl-pyrimidine) [T],
cytosine (2-hydroxy-6-amino-pyrimidine) [C]

and more rarely 5-methyl-cytosine (replaces cytosine partially in DNA from plants, calf thymus, bovine sperm and spleen) and 5-hydroxymethyl-cytosine (replaces cytosine in some T-phages).

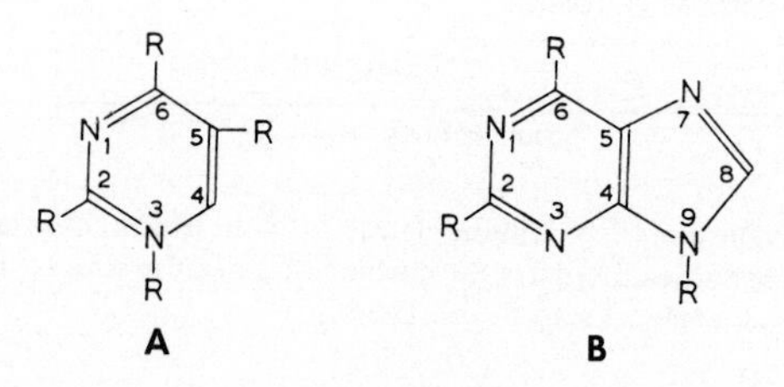

FIGURE 26. Base structure of (A) pyrimidines and (B) purines. (From Steiner and Beers, 1961.)

The *purines* most frequently found in DNA are:

adenine (6-amino-purine) [A]

and guanine (2-amino-6-hydroxy-purine) [G].

In RNA, the commonly occurring purines and pyrimidines are identical with those from DNA, except that uracil (2,6-dihydroxypyrimidine) occurs in place of thymine.

In addition to these commonly isolated bases, whose structural formulae are shown in Figure 27, trace quantities of derivatives of these bases (for example, 5-hydroxymethyl-uracil, 6-methyl-amino-purine and 2-methyl-adenine) have been reported in nucleic acid digests from various sources.

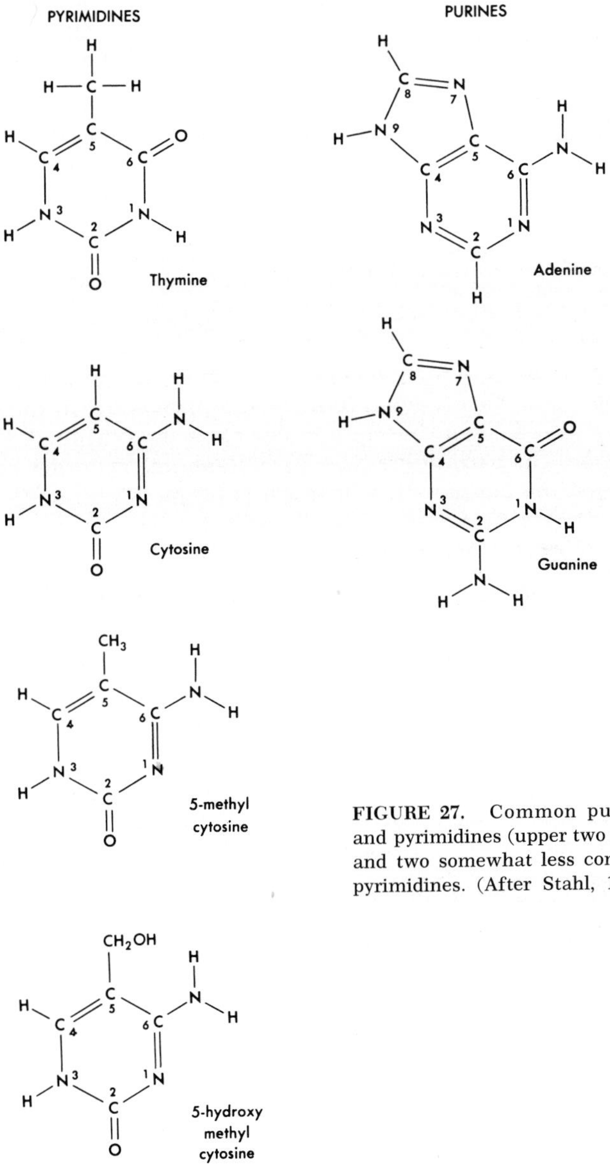

PYRIMIDINES

PURINES

Thymine

Adenine

Cytosine

Guanine

5-methyl cytosine

5-hydroxy methyl cytosine

FIGURE 27. Common purines and pyrimidines (upper two rows) and two somewhat less common pyrimidines. (After Stahl, 1964.)

TABLE 1. *Base ratios of some DNAs**

ORGANISM	A/T	G/C	$\frac{A+T}{G+C}$	$\frac{\text{6-AMINO}}{\text{6-KETO}}$
Tobacco mosaic virus				
Phage *T2*	1.00	1.09	1.87	0.97
Phage $\varphi X174$ (single-stranded DNA)	0.75	1.31	1.35	0.76
E. coli	1.09	0.99	1.00	1.05
Serratia marcescens	1.03	0.85	0.69	1.15
Pneumococcus	0.945	1.14	1.59	0.92
Yeast	0.964	1.08	1.80	0.95
Sea urchin	1.02	1.01	1.85	1.01
Salmon sperm	1.02	1.01	1.43	1.00
Ox liver	0.99	1.00	1.37	1.00
Calf thymus	0.985	1.15	1.28	0.938
Man—sperm	0.98	1.03	1.67	0.976
Man—thymus	1.05	1.00	1.54	1.03
Man—liver	1.00	1.00	1.54	1.00

*From Sager, R., and Ryan, F.: Cell Heredity. New York, J. Wiley and Sons, Inc., 1961.

Certain quantitative relationships among the bases of DNA were recognized quite some time before Watson and Crick (1953) furnished a plausible, and now generally accepted, model for the linkages and spatial organization of the bases, deoxypentose and phosphate, in the DNA molecule. Thus, it was known that on a molar basis the purine (A + G) content always equaled the pyrimidine (C + T) content, and that there was also an equivalence of the bases with a *keto* group in the 6-position (G + T) to the bases with an *amino* group in the 6-position (A + C) (cf., Chargaff and Davidson, 1955). In other words, it was known that:

$$\text{adenine} + \text{guanine} = \text{cytosine} + \text{thymine}$$
$$\text{adenine} + \text{cytosine} = \text{guanine} + \text{thymine}$$

and it followed that:

$$\text{adenine} = \text{thymine}$$
$$\text{guanine} = \text{cytosine}$$

Table 1 lists a few actual examples of base ratios in DNA from different sources. It can be seen that, depending on the species, A + T may differ considerably from G + C. This reflects the fact that A may differ from G, and T from C. For a *given* species, however, the ratio of $\frac{A+T}{G+C}$ (also written AT/GC)† is identical in each cell.

Another important set of facts about DNA was discovered in the early 1950's prior to the advent of the Watson-Crick model. It was established, with the aid of enzymatic studies, that phosphodiester linkages connect the nucleotides, which contain the just discussed bases, and it was demonstrated that these linkages must be of the 3′-5′ type (Fig. 28).

†Also frequently presented as G-C ratio or as percentage of GC.

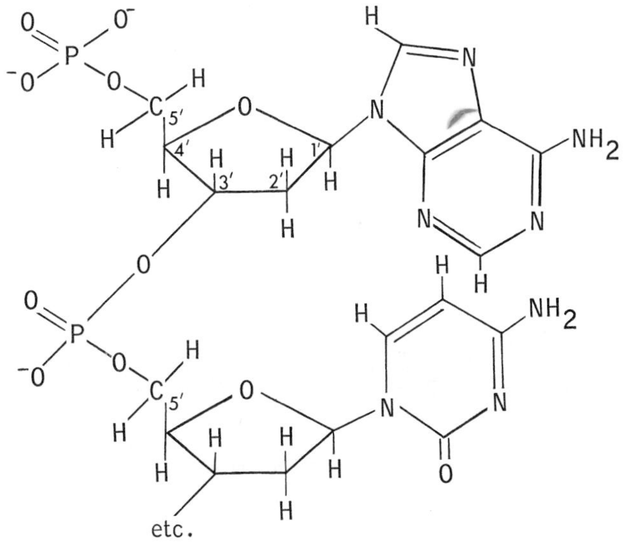

FIGURE 28. The 3′-5′ linkage of nucleotides.

ARRANGEMENT OF NUCLEOTIDES IN DNA

These just reviewed relationships among the bases, and the data furnished by crystallographers (Wilkins *et al.*, 1953; Franklin and Gosling, 1953), led Watson and Crick (1953) to the now generally familiar formulation of the double helix structure shown in Figures 2 and 29. In this structure, two long strands of polydeoxyribonucleotides are wound in spiral fashion around each other, and hydrogen bonds connect the purine and pyrimidine bases of one strand with the pyrimidine and purine bases of the other strand. The hydrogen bonding is not arbitrary, but always connects A with T, and C with G, thereby accounting for the relationships among bases cited on page 46, and resulting in two polydeoxyribonucleotide strands that are *complementary* to, but not identical with, each other. The two strands are "antiparallel," which means that in one strand the phosphodiester linkages connecting the deoxynucleotides are 3′-5′, and in the complementary strand they are 5′-3′; turning the molecule around by 180° does not change its appearance (Fig. 30). The nature of the hydrogen bonding between A and T is not the same as that between G and C, because, as shown in Figure 31, the A-T pairing involves two hydrogen bonds, and the G-C pairing, three hydrogen bonds. As we shall see shortly, this difference in bonding strength can account for differences in the stability of G-C and A-T pairs which one observes when one attempts to split apart the two strands of the double helix.

At this point it is important to recall that even though the pairing *between* complementary nucleotides of the two chains of the DNA double helix is a fixed relationship (identical, as far as we know, in all species), the order of nucleotides *within* each polynucleotide chain differs among

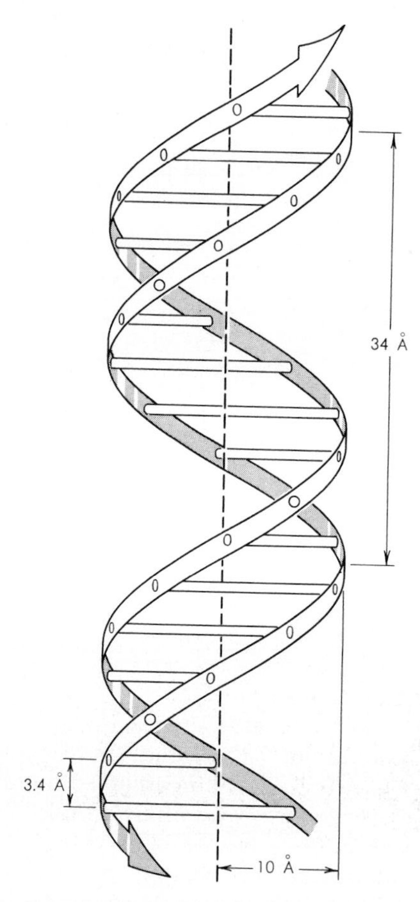

FIGURE 29. Schematic representation of a DNA molecule. (From Stahl, 1964; after Watson and Crick, 1953.)

strains, species and genera. In fact, as outlined in Chapter 1, it is this difference in nucleotide content and sequence that accounts for strain and species differences in information. However, until now it has been much more difficult to analyze the sequence of deoxynucleotides within each DNA chain, compared to the relative ease with which the relationships between the two members of a hydrogen-bonded pair of nucleotides in the complementary chains of the DNA double helix were detected and confirmed. Nevertheless, it has become possible to demonstrate that two unrelated bacterial species with similar base composition of their DNA (*Pseudomonas aeruginosa* and *Alcaligenes faecalis*) can have very different distributions of known base sequences, whereas related organisms (*E. coli* and *Salmonella typhimurium*) show striking similarities (Burton, 1962). This demonstration supports the genetic significance of base sequences,* and was made possible by treating DNA with diphenylamine in formic acid. Such treatment releases purine-free blocks of linked pyrim-

*More correctly: sequences of nucleotides containing specific bases.

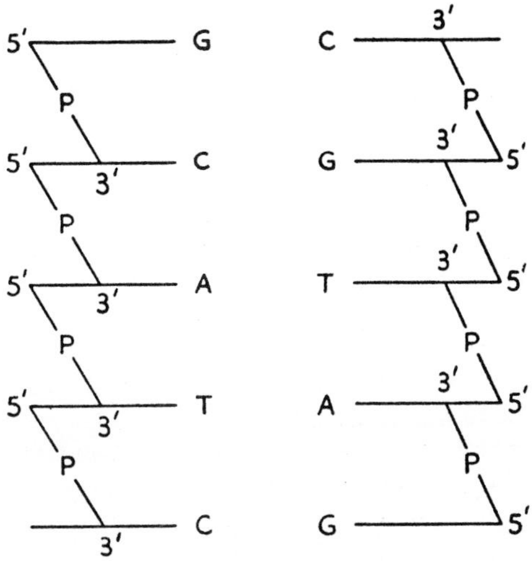

FIGURE 30. Diagram showing the reverse direction of the two DNA strands. (From Burton, 1962.)

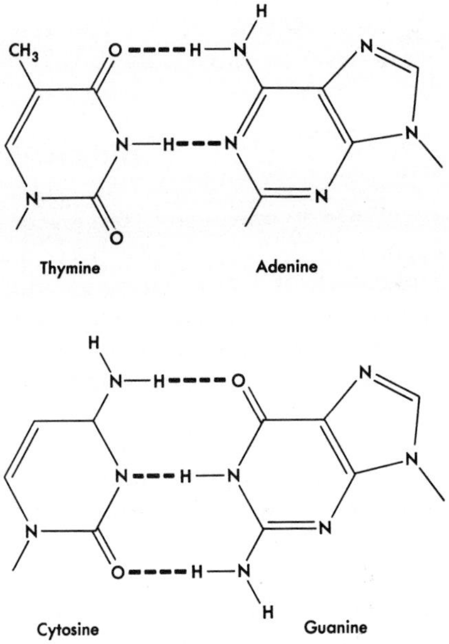

FIGURE 31. The normal type of hydrogen bonding between bases as it occurs in DNA. (From Stahl, 1964.)

idine nucleotide sequences, which can then be determined quantitatively following their separation by chromatography.

SIZE OF THE DNA MOLECULE

Physical and chemical evidence shows that DNA molecules, isolated from cells by chemical means, usually contain approximately 10,000 paired deoxynucleotide units each, and have a molecular weight of 6 to 10 million. Many such DNA molecules, usually heterogenous in size, can be isolated from a given cell, unless special care is taken to avoid DNA fragmentation. This shows that in the isolation procedures most commonly employed in the past, DNA tends to undergo random fragmentation. It has been demonstrated that shearing forces as small as those produced by pipetting suffice to degrade highly polymerized DNA. It has therefore been suggested by some (see Levinthal and Davison, 1961) that DNA exists *in vivo* as a very much larger molecule than those recovered after extraction, or that, possibly, DNA molecules are hooked together by non-DNA linkers *in vivo* (see Fig. 19). We shall see later that the genetic evidence from conjugation studies with *E. coli* is compatible with the idea that the DNA exists *in vivo* as one long molecule. This is further supported by the recent finding that under appropriate conditions the DNA of phage T_2 can be recovered as a single particle having a molecular weight of about 130 million (Rubenstein *et al.*, 1961; Davison *et al.*, 1961). On this basis, since *E. coli* cells contain approximately 6×10^9 MW of DNA, and the pieces obtained after extraction have a MW of about 7×10^6, one would have to postulate that *E. coli* DNA (if it should exist as one long molecule *in vivo*) breaks into about 1000 pieces upon extraction. As shown in Figure 11, long (1400 μ) DNA molecules can be isolated from *E. coli* following gentle lysis by dialysis against Duponol (Cairns, 1963).

REPLICATION OF DNA

Watson and Crick proposed that the unique relationships in base pairing (A-T; G-C) between complementary strands can account for the replication of DNA. Thus, as illustrated in Figure 32, a splitting of the double helix by the temporary disappearance of the hydrogen bonds between complementary bases would provide for the formation of a new complementary polynucleotide chain along each old chain; A would attract T (or vice versa) and G would attract C (or vice versa). In this manner each one of the old strands would form a new double helix with a newly synthesized complementary strand, the new strand of one new double helix being identical with the old strand of the other new double helix (Fig. 33). We can recognize this as the so-called "semiconservative" mode of replication, to which we already referred on page 38.

Some doubts were expressed initially regarding the possibility that a long double helix might unravel to permit such replication without the formation of too many twists. However, Levinthal and Crane have proposed a plausible scheme that portrays part of the replicating circular DNA molecule as a Y in which the vertical base represents the parent DNA helix and the two side arms represent the daughter helices, which, rotating on their own axis, are formed as the parent molecule untwists (Fig. 34). As replication proceeds, the vertical base of the DNA fragment shown in Figure 34 will become shorter as the arms of the Y, representing the daughter helices, lengthen. Since the two DNA strands have opposite polarities (Fig. 30), and since, according to the schemes just cited and the Cairns

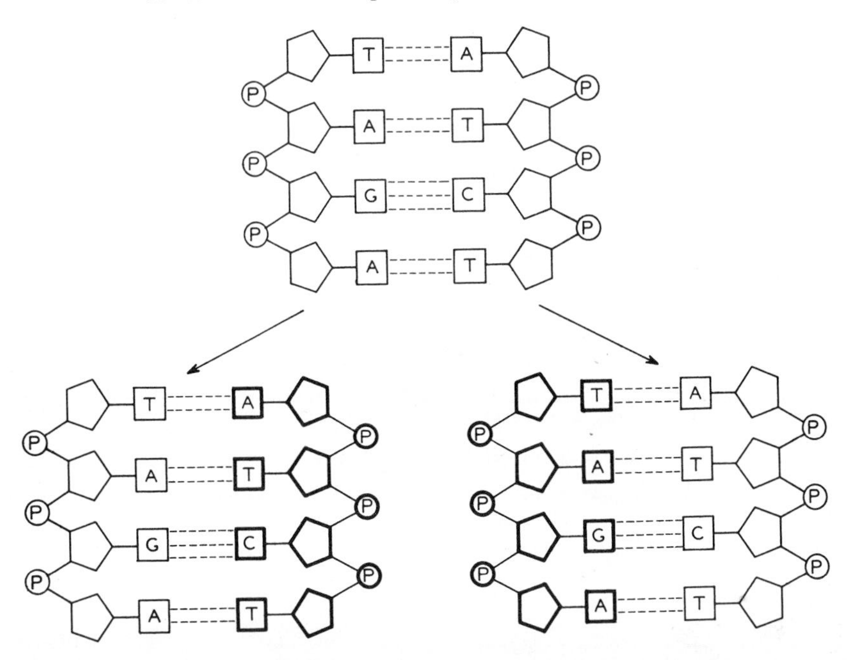

FIGURE 32. Proposed mode of replication of DNA. The bold-lined polynucleotide chains of the two daughter molecules represent newly synthesized strands. (From Josse *et al.*, 1961.)

data, synthesis proceeds simultaneously along both strands, two enzymes (or one enzyme with two different active sites) would be required to catalyze the two types of reactions indicated in Figure 35. One reaction would involve a 3′-OH end group of a DNA chain and the 5′-PPP group of a deoxyribonucleoside triphosphate, the probable building stone; the other, the 5′-PPP end of a DNA chain and the 3′-OH group of a deoxyribonucleoside (Baldwin, 1964). As we shall see subsequently, only the former synthetic reaction has been observed so far during the synthesis of DNA *in vitro* (p. 57).

The model just described (Figs. 32 to 35) is currently regarded as the most likely one and also is most acceptable from the standpoint of structure and energy. However, its validity is not yet completely assured. Alternate mechanisms of DNA replication have been proposed, including the possibility that a new double-stranded polymer may be built up next to the old double-stranded polymer without an untwisting of the latter.

Whatever the ultimate answer regarding the details of the mechanism of DNA replication might be, one thing appears to be clear: the mode of replication of individual DNA molecules is semiconservative, each daughter helix being composed of one paternal strand and one newly synthesized strand. Evidence for this has come from experiments by Meselson and Stahl with N^{14}- and N^{15}-containing DNA molecules, and from the studies by Kornberg and his associates on DNA synthesis *in vitro*.

3991

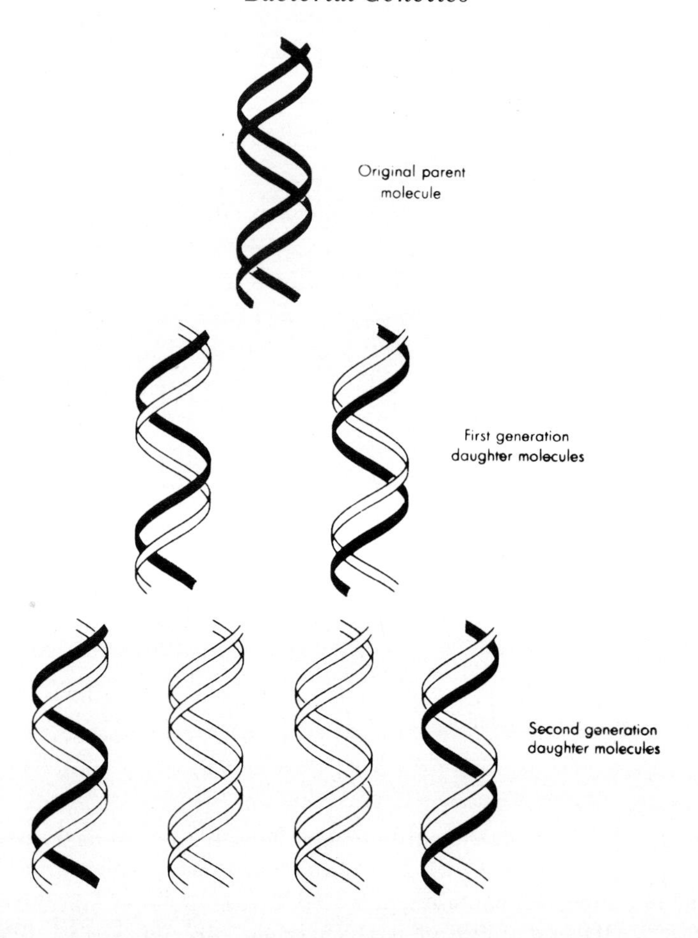

FIGURE 33. A model of the semi-conservative replication of DNA. The parental DNA strands are shown in black; the newly formed complementary strands are shown in outline. (From Meselson and Stahl, 1958.)

THE MESELSON-STAHL EXPERIMENT

In 1957 Meselson, Stahl and Vinograd developed a method which permits the separation of isotopically labeled DNA molecules, containing N^{15}, from less dense, ordinary DNA containing N^{14}. This method utilizes centrifugation of DNA in a *density gradient* which is produced when approximately 7 M cesium chloride in water is centrifuged at very high speed for several hours (Fig. 36). In such a CsCl density gradient, the DNA will "band" (or reach a sedimentation equilibrium) at exactly that density which corresponds to its own. The ability of DNA to absorb ultraviolet rays (UV) can then be utilized to locate the precise level at which the DNA banded. Since this level is dependent on the density, a DNA in which the

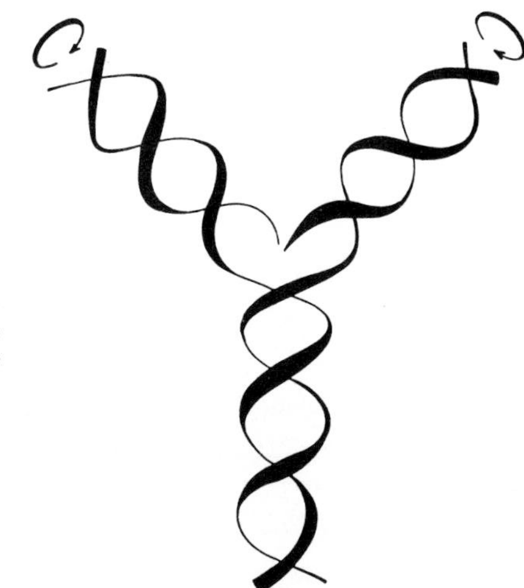

FIGURE 34. One possible method of unwinding that could be operative during DNA replication. (From Steiner and Beers, 1961; after Levinthal and Crane, 1956.)

ordinary nitrogen (N^{14}) of the bases has been replaced by heavy nitrogen (N^{15}) will band at a lower level than ordinary DNA. Thus, two distinct UV-absorbing bands will be found in a CsCl density gradient containing both N^{14} DNA and N^{15} DNA.

This phenomenon was used by Meselson and Stahl (1958) to distinguish between old and newly formed DNA, and to assay their distribution during successive generations of bacterial growth as follows: *E. coli* cells were grown for several generations in a medium containing $N^{15}H_4Cl$ as the sole source of nitrogen so that all of the N^{14} of the cells was replaced by N^{15}. These cells were then transferred to an ordinary N^{14}-containing medium and removed from it after various periods of time for an analysis of the behavior of their DNA following ultracentrifugation in a CsCl

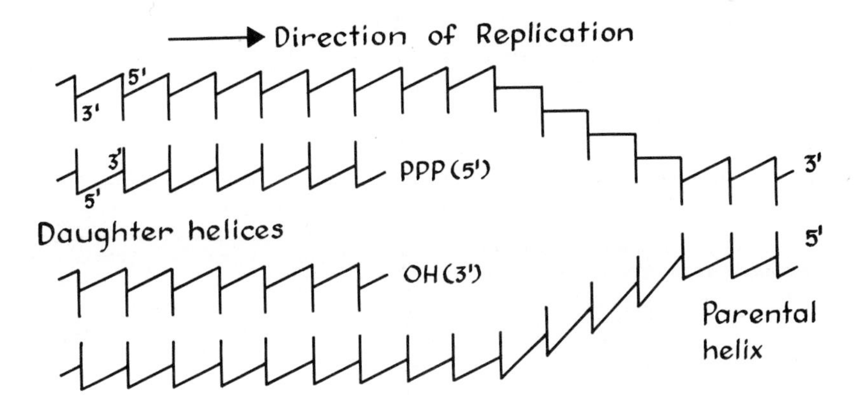

FIGURE 35. A model for DNA replication (assuming the existence of 5′-PPP ends on DNA chains). (From Baldwin, 1964.)

NAZARETH COLLEGE
LIBRARY

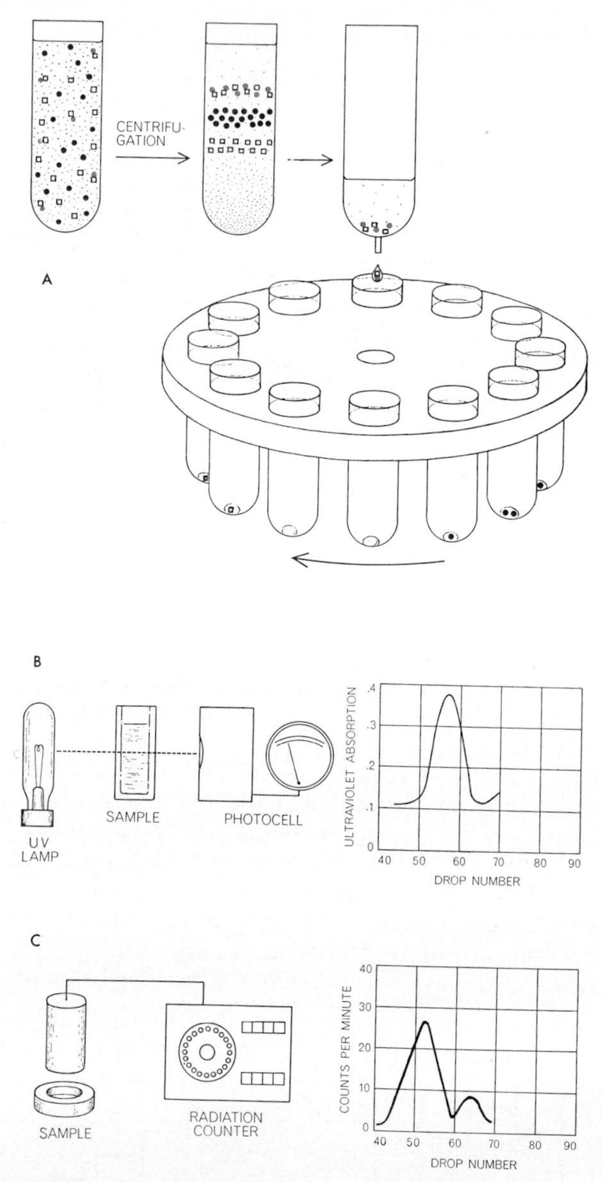

FIGURE 36. An outline of the cesium chloride density gradient procedure. A mixture of heavy (squares), hybrid (black dots) and light (gray dots) DNA is centrifuged in a concentrated solution of cesium chloride (tiny dots). After several hours of spinning in the ultracentrifuge, the CsCl forms a density gradient, with the highest salt concentration at the outer (bottom) end of the tube and the lowest salt concentration at the inner (top) end of the tube. During this process each species of DNA forms a band at the level corresponding to its own density. After removal of the tubes from the centrifuge, a hole is punched through the bottom of the plastic centrifuge tube and the contents of the tube are collected, drop by drop, in a fraction collector (A). The drops, representing different layers of the density gradient, are then analyzed for DNA content by measuring the absorption of ultraviolet light in a spectrophotometer (B), and their content of radioactivity is measured in a radiation counter (C). The example in the lower right-hand corner shows heavy single-stranded DNA in one band and lighter double-stranded DNA in another band. (From Sinsheimer, 1962; reproduced with the permission of the *Scientific American*, Inc.)

density gradient. As shown in Figure 37, at the time of transfer of $N^{15}H_4Cl$-grown cells to the $N^{14}H_4Cl$ medium only one band was found, namely a band typical of N^{15} DNA. After one doubling in the presence of N^{14}, again only one band appeared, but if we check its position against the reference bands of N^{14} and N^{15}, shown in the bottom frame of Figure 37, we see that this band occupies a position that is exactly intermediate between N^{14} and N^{15}. This indicated that all cells now contained hybrid molecules, half of each representing the old N^{15} DNA and half representing the newly synthesized N^{14} DNA. After a second doubling in the presence of N^{14}, two bands with equal DNA concentration were found; one represented the N^{15}-N^{14} hybrid band and the other was typical of N^{14} DNA. In succeeding generations, the intensity of the latter band increased, while that of the hybrid band decreased.

These results are in full accord with the scheme of semiconservative replication shown in Figure 33. If we follow this scheme, it will be easy to see that during the first doubling, single strands of N^{15} DNA should have remained intact and served as templates for new complementary strands that are built up from N^{14} bases. Thus, in the first daughter generation, all DNA molecules should have been hybrids, as indeed they proved to be, consisting of one old N^{15} strand and a new N^{14} strand. In the next generation half of all the DNA molecules contained *only* N^{14}, since they represent double strands produced from the N^{14} DNA strands of the parents and hydrogen-bonded to a newly synthesized N^{14}-containing chain of nucleotides; the other half of the DNA molecules consisted of hybrid N^{14}-N^{15} DNA in which each persisting N^{15} DNA strand hydrogen-bonded with a newly synthesized chain of N^{14}-containing nucleotides.

Meselson and Stahl furnished further evidence for the conclusion that the first generation hybrid molecules were indeed made up of the intact N^{15} strand hydrogen-bonded to a N^{14} strand. As we shall see shortly, certain conditions, including heating, have proved capable of breaking the hydrogen bonds, thereby "single-stranding" the original double-stranded helix. When such heating was applied to the N^{14}-N^{15} hybrid DNA of the first daughter generation, the molecules became separable into two subunits of different density.

While the foregoing data are best explained on the basis of semiconservative replication of double-stranded DNA, alternate mechanisms including, for example, replications involving two double-stranded helices that can not be separated by CsCl, cannot be ruled out (Cavalieri, 1961), since such events also would fit the observations of Meselson and Stahl.

The type of experiment just described for *E. coli* also was carried out with *Chlamydomonas*, as well as with other plant and animal cells, and yielded identical results. It is, however, worthy of note that in studies carried out by Kozinski (1961) with phage, evidence was obtained indicating that, while the usually isolated pieces (subpieces) of DNA reveal replication in a semiconservative fashion, the larger, and presumably continuous, DNA unit may replicate in a dispersive manner (see Fig. 23).

DNA SYNTHESIS *IN VITRO*

Chemical data on the enzymatic synthesis of DNA *in vitro*, collected since 1956 principally by Kornberg and his associates (see Kornberg, 1960,

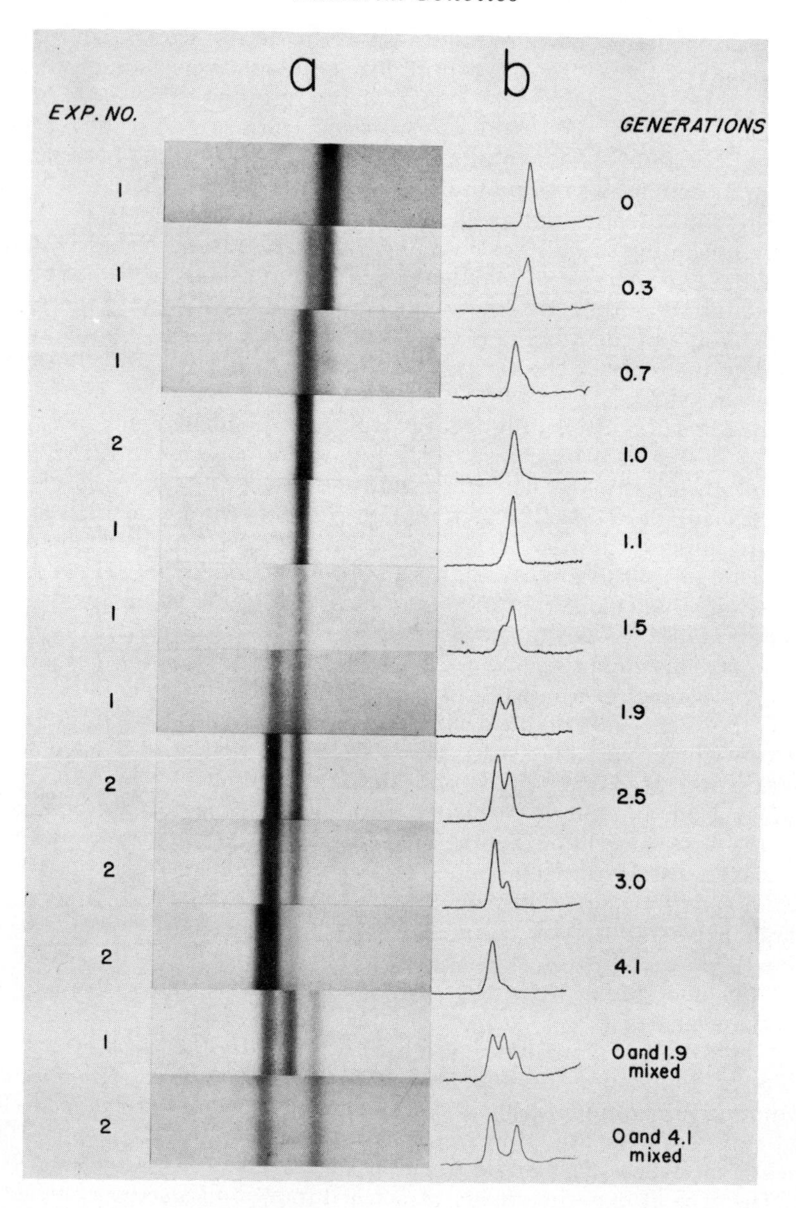

FIGURE 37. Ultraviolet absorption photographs showing DNA bands resulting from density gradient centrifugation of lysates of bacteria sampled at various times following the addition of an excess of N^{14} substrates to a growing culture of N^{15}-labeled cells. The density of the CsCl solution increases to the right and regions of equal density occupy the same horizontal position on each photograph. Next to the photographs are densitometer tracings which are proportional to the DNA concentrations. The degree of labeling of a species of DNA corresponds to the relative position of its band between the bands of fully labeled and unlabeled DNA in the lowermost frame, which serves as a density reference. (From Meselson and Stahl, 1958.)

1961, 1962), have proved to be in general agreement with the mechanical model of DNA replication proposed by Watson and Crick. Kornberg, working with *E. coli*, isolated polynucleotide pyrophosphorylase (now called deoxyribonucleotide polymerase), which is capable of catalyzing the polymerization of deoxyribonucleoside *tri*phosphates in the presence of Mg^{++} and a DNA "primer" (Fig. 38). This enzyme is not unique for *E. coli*, but was subsequently isolated from other sources. When natural DNA serves as the primer, all four of the deoxynucleotides (A, T, G, C) are required for the reaction, and it has turned out that the most effective, probably the only, priming is provided by "single-stranded" DNA (see pp. 58 to 63). But what is most important is the proof that the newly synthesized DNA has a base composition identical with that of the DNA primer and, according to studies on specific dinucleotide frequencies, its base sequence is identical to that of the primer (Table 2). These studies have shown that enzymatic DNA replication involves base pairing of A to T, and of G to C, and that two strands of opposite direction (5′-3′, 3′-5′) are produced as had been predicted by the Watson-Crick model (see Fig. 32). However, as mentioned briefly before, the enzyme active *in vitro* is known to control only reactions between the 3′-OH end group of the growing DNA chain and the 5′-PPP group of a deoxyribonucleoside triphosphate and thus does not suffice to explain the *in vivo* synthesis of antiparallel chains (see p. 49). Nevertheless, it is now generally assumed that enzymatic DNA synthesis *in vivo* may occur in a fashion that is not too different from that demonstrated *in vitro*.

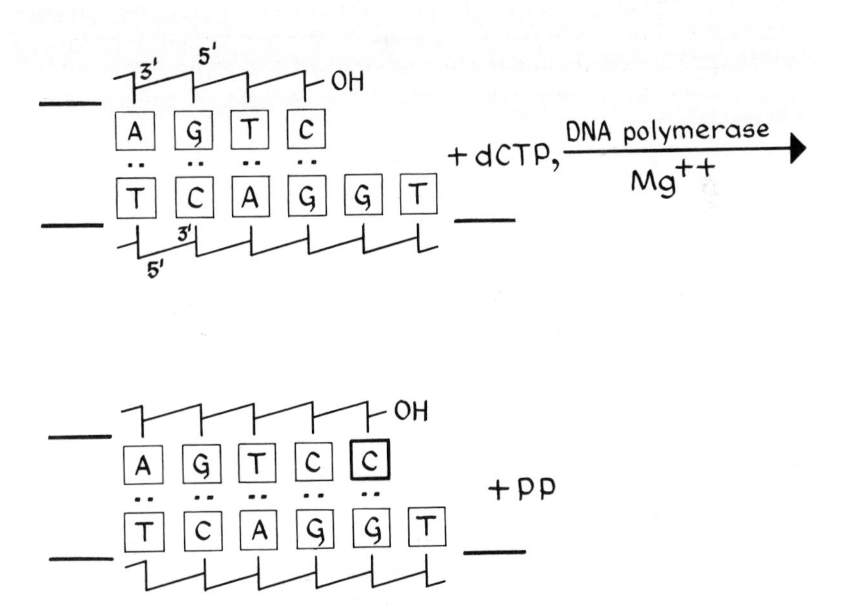

FIGURE 38. DNA synthesis *in vitro* involving the addition of a nucleotide at the 3′-OH end of a DNA strand and governed by base pairing of the added nucleotide to the complementary nucleotide of the other strand. (From Baldwin, 1964.)

TABLE 2. *Chemical composition of enzymatically synthesized DNA, synthesized with different primers**

DNA	A	T	G	C	$\frac{A+G}{T+C}$	$\frac{A+T}{G+C}$
Mycobacterium phlei						
Primer	0.65	0.66	1.35	1.34	1.01	0.49
Product	0.66	0.65	1.34	1.37	0.99	0.48
Escherichia coli						
Primer	1.00	0.97	0.98	1.05	0.98	0.97
Product	1.04	1.00	0.97	0.98	1.01	1.02
Calf thymus						
Primer	1.14	1.05	0.90	0.85	1.05	1.25
Product	1.12	1.08	0.85	0.85	1.02	1.29
Bacteriophage T2						
Primer	1.31	1.32	0.67	0.70	0.98	1.92
Product	1.33	1.29	0.69	0.70	1.02	1.90
A-T copolymer	1.99	1.93	<0.05	<0.05	1.03	>40

*From Kornberg. *In* Allen, J. M. (Ed.): Control of Cellular Activity. New York, McGraw-Hill Book Company, 1962.

It has also been possible to synthesize *artificial polydeoxyribonucleotides* with the aid of the polymerase enzyme and without a primer. These artificial polynucleotides are produced when, for example, deoxyadenosine triphosphate and deoxythymidine triphosphate are exposed to polymerase for a prolonged period of time in the absence of DNA primer. The resulting double-stranded structure, with a molecular weight of several million, looks like this:

```
...–A–T–A–T–A–...
    ‖  ‖  ‖  ‖  ‖
...–T–A–T–A–T–...
```

This is referred to as a dAT (d stands for deoxy-) *copolymer*. Such synthetic copolymers have been very useful for chemical studies on information transfer (see p. 337).

DENATURATION AND RENATURATION OF DNA

The validity of the Watson-Crick structure of DNA is also supported by *in vitro* studies on the transition of DNA from an ordered, rigid, double helix structure to a flexible, single-stranded structure which results when agents capable of splitting hydrogen bonds are applied to native DNA (Marmur and Doty, 1959; Marmur *et al.*, 1963). This transition is usually referred to as *denaturation* and the reverse process (i.e., the restitution of hydrogen bonding and formation of a double helix from complementary single strands) as *renaturation*. Denaturation can be achieved through

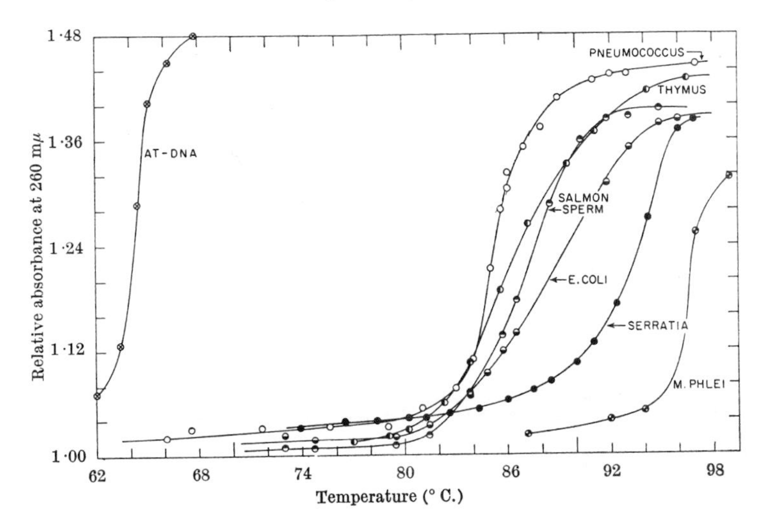

FIGURE 39. Relationship between temperature and changes in absorbance, at 260 mμ, of deoxyribonucleic acid solutions from different sources. All DNA preparations were dissolved in 0.15 M sodium chloride and 0.015 M sodium citrate. (From Marmur, J., and Doty, P., 1959, Nature, *183*:1427.)

variations in pH or ionic strength, and by exposure to urea and to heat. In the case of heat, the transition from the double-stranded to the single-stranded state, measurable by changes in optical density at 260 mμ, occurs within a very narrow temperature range (Fig. 39), which usually lies between 80° and 100° C; such denaturation is referred to as the "melting-out" of DNA. The actual temperature at which a given DNA melts was shown by Marmur and Doty (1962) to depend on its G-C content. We previously referred to the fact that the hydrogen bonding between G and C is stronger than that between A and T (p. 47). Therefore, the higher the content of G-C, the higher the temperature required for melting. Determination of the melting temperature (T_m) thus is a simple method for the assessment of the G + C content of a given DNA preparation (Fig. 40). We already have referred to the fact that this G + C content can be typically different for the DNA of different species (see Table 1).

Centrifugation in a CsCl density gradient provides another method for determination of a DNA's base content (Schildkraut *et al.*, 1962), since the buoyant density of DNA in solution also increases with increasing content of G-C pairs (Fig. 41 and Table 3).

The spread of the melting temperature range and the width of the band in a CsCl density gradient will reflect the heterogeneity of a given DNA preparation in regard to G-C content. For DNA preparations of all the bacterial species so far tested, both the range of T_m and the width of the sedimentation band have been found to be very narrow, indicating that all molecules in a given bacterial DNA preparation have similar G-C content.

The transition of double-stranded DNA to the single-stranded state can be demonstrated by electron microscopy and can be measured in

Text continued on page 63

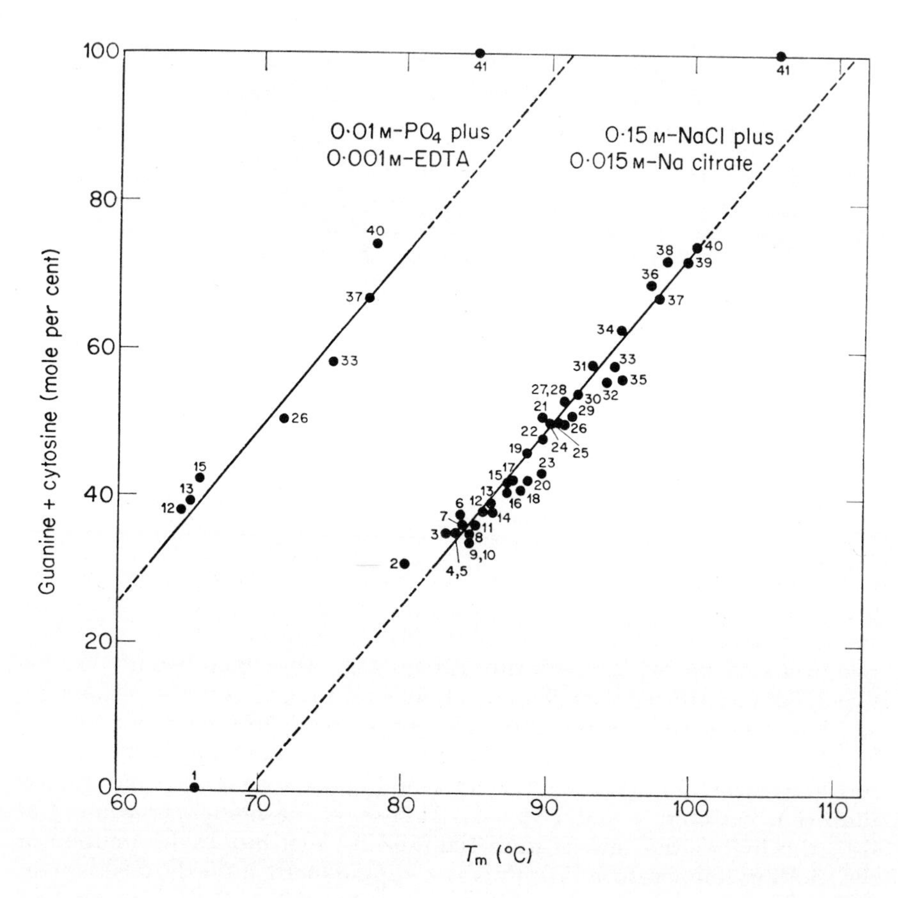

FIGURE 40. Dependence of the denaturation temperature, T_m, on the guanine plus cytosine (G-C) content of various samples of DNA. The DNA samples were dissolved in either of the two solvents shown in the figure. The T_m represents the midpoint of the hyperchromic increase of individual DNA absorbence-temperature profiles plotted as a function of the G-C content. The numbers next to each T_m value in the figure refer to the DNA extracted from the following organisms: 1, poly d-AT; 2, *Cl. perfringens;* 3, *Past. tularensis;* 4, *M. pyogenes* var. *aureus;* 5, *B. cereus;* 6, *Pr. vulgaris;* 7, *B. thuringiensis;* 8, T_2r^+; 9, T_4r^+; 10, T_6r^+; 11, *S. cerevisiae;* 12, *B. megaterium;* 13, *D. pneumoniae;* 14, *H. influenzae;* 15, calf thymus; 16, *N. catarrhalis;* 17, chicken liver; 18, salmon sperm; 19, wheat germ; 20, *B.-subtilis;* 21, *B. licheniformis;* 22, T_7; 23, *V. cholerae;* 24, T_3; 25, *N. flavescens;* 26, *E. coli;* 27, *Salm. typhosa;* 28, *Sh. dysenteriae;* 29, *N. meningitidis;* 30, *Salm. typhimurium;* 31, *B. abortus;* 32, *A. aerogenes;* 33, *S. marcescens;* 34, *Ps. fluorescens;* 35, *Azot. vinelandii;* 36, *Myco. phlei;* 37, *Ps. aeruginosa;* 38, *Sar. lutea;* 39, *M. lysodeikticus;* 40, *Strep. viridochromogenes;* 41, poly d-GC. (From Marmur and Doty, 1962.)

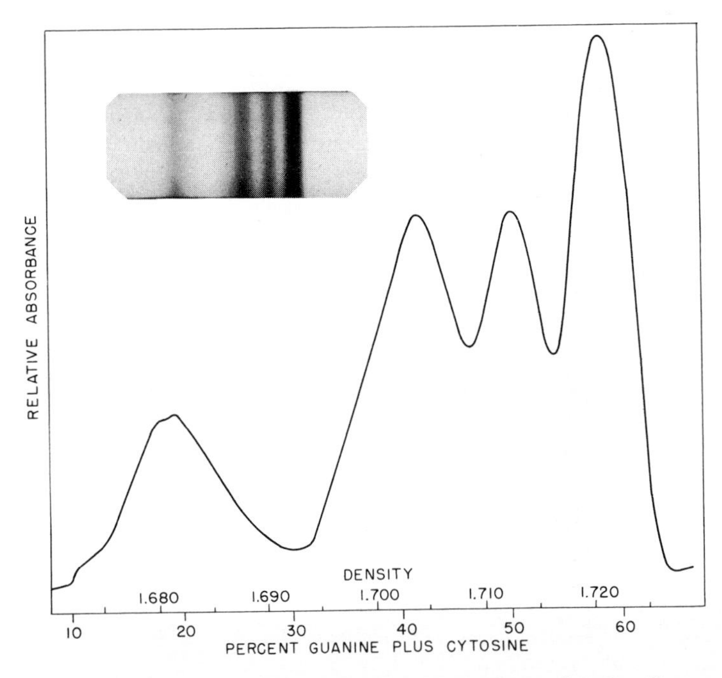

FIGURE 41. Separation of (from left to right) polydeoxyadenine-thymine, *D. pneumoniae*, *E. coli*, and *Serratia marcescens* deoxyribonucleic acids by density gradient centrifugation. The photograph was taken after centrifugation at 44,770 rpm for 30 hours. The tracing was taken with a microdensitometer in the region of the four bands. Note that the G-C scale does not apply to the poly d-AT sample. (From Doty *et al.*, 1959.)

TABLE 3. *Base composition and density of several bacterial DNAs**

SPECIES	DENSITY ($g\ cm^{-3}$)	%GC	SPECIES	DENSITY ($g\ cm^{-3}$)	%GC
Aerobacter aerogenes	1.716	57	*N. flavescens*	1.706	47
Bacillus cereus	1.696	37	*N. meningitidis*	1.703	50
B. megaterium	1.697	38	*N. perflava*	1.707	48
B. stearothermophilus	1.705	46	*N. sicca*	1.710	51
B. subtilis	1.703	44	*Pasteurella tularensis*	1.695	36
B. thuringiensis	1.695	36	*Proteus morgani*	1.710	51
Brucella abortus	1.715	56	*Pr. vulgaris*	1.698	39
Clostridium perfringens	1.691	32	*Pseudomonas aeruginosa*	1.727	68
Diplococcus pneumoniae	1.701	42	*Ps. fluorescens*	1.721	62
Erwinia carotovora	1.709	50	*Salmonella typhimurium*	1.712	53
Escherichia coli, B	1.710	51	*Salm. typhosa*	1.711	52
E. coli, B/r	1.710	51	*Sarcina lutea*	1.731	72
E. coli, K-12	1.710	51	*Serratia marcescens*	1.718	59
E. coli, TAU^-	1.710	51	*Shigella dysenteriae*	1.710	51
Hemophilus influenzae	1.698	39	*Streptococcus faecalis* (group D)	1.697	38
Micrococcus lysodeikticus	1.731	72	*Streptomyces viridochromogenes*	1.729	70
M. pyogenes var. *aureus*	1.693	34			
Mycobacterium phlei	1.732	73			
Neisseria catarrhalis	1.701	42			

*From Schildkraut, C. L., Marmur, J., and Doty, P.: J. Mol. Biol., *4*:430, 1962.

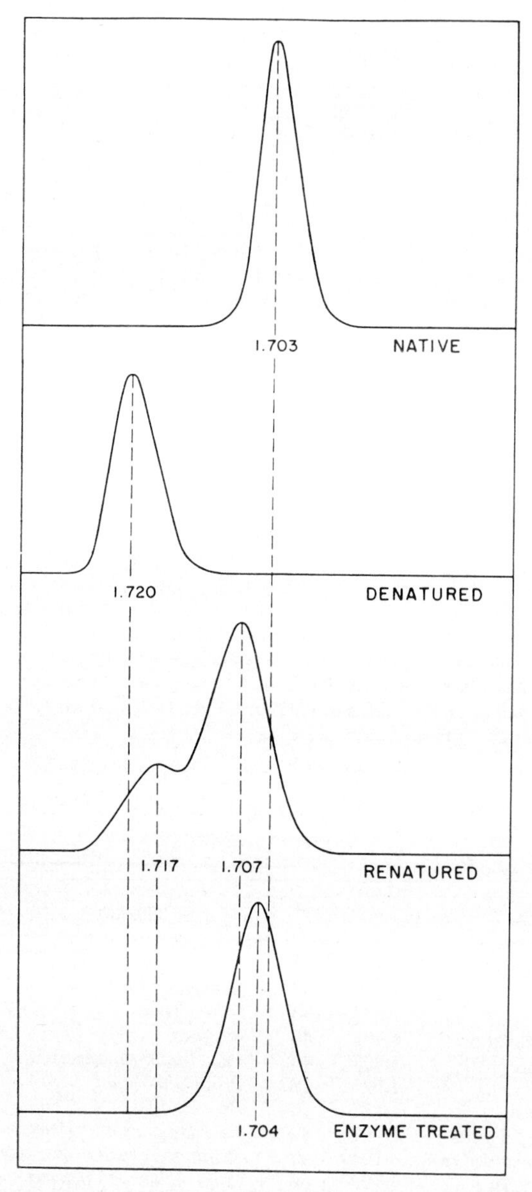

FIGURE 42. Density, as determined by centrifugation in a CsCl gradient, of native, denatured and renatured (± enzyme-treated) DNA of *B. subtilis*. Denatured = heated for 10 minutes at 10 μg per ml at 100° C in 0.285 M NaCl plus 0.0285 M Na citrate and then cooled quickly. Renatured = slowly cooled following denaturation; about 80 per cent of the DNA renatures. Enzyme treated = treatment with the *E. coli* phospodiesterase of Lehman (1960) which causes a disappearance of the denatured band and a decrease in the buoyant density of the renatured band. (From Marmur *et al.*, 1962.)

various ways, including changes in viscosity, optical rotation, density in a CsCl gradient (Fig. 42), and alterations in the preparation's *hypochromism*. The hypochromism phenomenon takes place because the ultraviolet absorption of a DNA polymer is considerably less than that expected from a summation of the UV absorptions of the DNA's constituent bases. As a result, either horizontal (H-bonds) or extensive vertical (nucleotide) disruption of the polymer increases optical density in the UV range, and this can be used for the rapid determination of transitions from the double-stranded (helix) to the single-stranded (coil) state.

When a heated, melted DNA preparation is cooled slowly, instead of rapidly, a good deal of renaturation (i.e., restitution of hydrogen bonding between complementary bases of the separated nucleotide chains) takes place (see Fig. 42). The occurrence of such renaturation is dependent on the complementarity of the separated strands. Consequently, it is possible to determine whether or not DNA's from two different species are similar in base-content and -sequence by looking for the extent of renaturation (indicated by density changes) following the heating and slow cooling of a mixture of the two DNA preparations in which one is labeled with N^{15} (Schildraut *et al.*, 1961).* Such "matching" of DNA from different sources may develop into an important tool in bacterial taxonomy, because similarity in DNA structure can be regarded as a criterion of natural relationships.

RNA AS SOURCE OF INFORMATION

All available evidence indicates that in the case of some plant and animal viruses, and also in the case of certain bacteriophages known as f2, RNA, rather than DNA, can function as the basic transmitter of information (Loeb and Zinder, 1961; Cooper and Zinder, 1962). A lack of involvement of DNA in the replication of such informative RNA is suggested by the finding that in the case of these viruses, RNA replication, and with it the production of more RNA virus, can occur in the absence of DNA synthesis. An RNA-dependent RNA polymerase has been demonstrated in both RNA virus and RNA phage infections (see August *et al.*, 1963; Spiegelman and Doi, 1963). The possibility remains that in bacteria, as well as in higher plants and animals, in which RNA usually serves only as the intermediary between DNA information and protein synthesis (see Chapter 16), some possibly autonomous extranuclear determinants might also be RNA in nature and behave somewhat like the RNA viruses just mentioned (i.e., serve as direct templates for the formation of new informational RNA). We, therefore, must include some remarks about RNA structure and replication in our present discussion on the chemical nature of cell-to-cell transmitters of information.

*We shall see later that the occurrence of denaturation and renaturation can also be measured biologically, because the activity of transforming DNA is impaired by melting and is repaired by renaturation (p. 263).

STRUCTURE OF RNA

It has only recently been recognized that there are several different types of RNA, namely (1) *messenger RNA,* (2) *amino-acid-transfer RNA* or *soluble RNA*, and (3) *ribosomal RNA*. Prior to this recognition, RNA chemistry was quite confused because, for example, it was difficult to understand why, even though RNA was recognized as the intracellular transmitter of information from DNA to protein, base ratios in the cell's total RNA failed to match the distinctive base ratio of the same cell's DNA. This puzzling discrepancy was resolved when it was shown that the actual RNA (the messenger RNA) involved in the transfer of information from DNA to sites of protein synthesis did have base ratios identical with the cell's DNA. In contrast, the other two types of RNA (amino-acid-transfer RNA and ribosomal RNA) showed quite different over-all base ratios.* These differences are not surprising when recognition is made of the entirely different functions of the three RNA's, which we shall discuss in more detail in Chapter 16. It will suffice to state here that the amino-acid-transfer RNA serves to bring the "activated amino acids" to the messenger RNA template where they are assembled into specific polypeptides according to the specific polynucleotide sequence of the messenger RNA (see Fig. 138); the ribosomal RNA, on the other hand, may serve structural functions.

The structure of the three RNA's also may be different. Messenger RNA, which mirrors DNA in composition and nucleotide sequence, may resemble single-stranded DNA structurally; it can form hybrid helices with DNA. The other two RNA's have complex structures that are as yet not fully understood. Transfer RNA appears to consist of double-stranded helical regions and of non-paired, non-complementary nucleotide sequences. It has been suggested that such a structure may be produced by a folding back of the RNA polynucleotide chain upon itself (see Chapter 16 for further details).

RNA SYNTHESIS

The heterogeneity of composition and function of the total cellular RNA is also reflected in the relative complexity of the enzymes involved in RNA synthesis. In 1955, Grunberg-Manago and Ochoa isolated an enzyme, polynucleotide phosphorylase, which in the presence of Mg^{++} catalyzes the polymerization of nucleoside *di*phosphates into polynucleotides, liberating inorganic orthophosphate (see Ochoa and Heppel, 1957). The linkages are of the 3′-5′ type, as in DNA, but a primer is not required, even though it accelerates the rate of synthesis. The first polyribonucleotide phosphorylase was isolated from *Azotobacter vinelandii*, but similar enzymes were subsequently isolated from a large number of bacterial and mammalian sources. Grunberg-Manago isolated a polyribonucleotide phosphorylase from yeast that lacked the requirement for Mg^{++}. It has been possible to use these enzymes for the synthesis of polynucleotides containing only one base (for example, poly-A) and also for the synthesis

* $\frac{\text{adenylic + uridylic}}{\text{guanylic + cytidylic}}$ being near 1 in the former and approximately 0.8 in the latter.

of co-polymers such as poly-AU. As we shall discuss in Chapter 16, these synthetic polymers have been vital for the experimental analysis of the "genetic code," i.e., the demonstration that the incorporation of specific amino acids into polypeptides is controlled by a triplet code, spelled out by specific nucleotide combinations.

In addition to the polyribonucleotide phosphorylase, which may actually represent a mixture of different enzymes, an enzyme, RNA polymerase, has been isolated that requires all four nucleoside *tri*phosphates and a DNA primer (Hurwitz and August, 1963). This DNA-dependent RNA synthesis probably involves the formation of messenger RNA, since it has been demonstrated that the resulting nucleotide sequence complements that of the deoxynucleotides in the DNA primer. However, evidence for the production of transfer RNA by the DNA-dependent RNA polymerase also has been obtained (Hurwitz *et al.*, 1963). DNA-dependent polymerases have been found in a wide variety of bacteria, animals and plants. A number of RNA-dependent polymerases, requiring triphosphates as substrate, also have been isolated (see Spiegelman and Doi, 1963) and, finally, a specific enzyme involved in the synthesis of amino acid acceptor RNA has been recognized. The exact functions of these various enzymes *in vivo* have not yet been fully elucidated. This is not surprising because, as we have stated earlier, the requirement for separating the cell's total RNA into various types of RNA involved either as intermediary, or more rarely as initiator, in the control of specificity has been recognized only quite recently.

[5]

MUTATION

Now that we know something about the chemical basis of the transmission of information from cell to cell, it should not surprise us to learn that occasionally errors can occur in the intricate process of DNA replication. If we were to view this problem from a purely theoretical standpoint, we could expect that in the course of DNA synthesis the wrong base may pair occasionally with what is supposed to be its complementary base in the old strand. A new nucleotide sequence would thus be formed in this particular region, which may then cause the incorporation of a different amino acid into the protein it controls; this could result either in new information or a lack of information. As we shall see, this theoretical expectation has been confirmed by recent experimental data. However, even before the present recognition of the molecular events associated with changes in hereditary determinants, it was recognized, principally in studies with higher plants and animals, that the stability of hereditary determinants was far from absolute. It was known (1) that sudden changes could occur in the nuclear determinant of hereditary characteristics; (2) that such changes were undirected, i.e., they took place independent of environmental conditions; (3) that the rate at which such changes occurred was relatively constant for a given determinant, but differed among determinants; and (4) that such changes were transmitted to the progeny.

Despite the early recognition of bacterial variability, there was, as we discussed in Chapter 2, a long lag between such recognition and the acceptance of the applicability of the mutation concept to bacteria. As a result, the experimental approach to bacterial genetics in the 1940's and 1950's was concerned largely with the problem of bacterial mutability, its origin, cause and manifestation and the effect of mutation on changes in bacterial populations. The actual experiments were based mostly on statistical considerations and observations, rather than on a direct elucidation of molecular events, which were then only poorly understood. In this and the following chapter we shall follow historical precedent and first discuss the studies which have dealt with the detectable results of spontaneous changes in the bacterial genotype, and after that we shall concern ourselves with some of the probable underlying molecular events.

A great variety of studies of the 1940's and 1950's demonstrated that hereditary changes in bacterial cells can be caused by *mutations*. As in higher organisms, mutations can be defined as spontaneous, undirected changes that may occur in the determinants of hereditary characteristics, or in more modern terms – affect part of the organism's information.*

A mutation is a rare event which usually occurs at a rate of between 1×10^{-4} and 1×10^{-10} per bacterium per unit time or per generation. This means that, depending on the *mutation rate*, one bacterial cell in 10,000 or one cell in 10 billions is apt to be a mutant. A mutant cell is a cell carrying altered information and as such will give rise to mutant clones. Naturally, only a few of the spontaneously occurring mutations are usually detected; unless the environment is suitable for the establishment of the mutant in the population in which is has occurred, the mutant cell will have little survival value and remain undetected. Even under standard environmental conditions, mutation rates differ for different characteristics and they may also differ for similar characteristics between different strains. However, mutation rates are relatively constant for any given determinant (nucleotide sequence) in a given strain. For example, the mutation rate from streptomycin sensitivity to streptomycin resistance in strain B of *E. coli* has been found to be 1×10^{-10} in numerous tests conducted at different times. Certain environmental agents are capable of increasing spontaneous mutation rates significantly and such agents are called mutagens (see Chapter 6).

Mutations are entirely undirected in the sense that mutants occur independently of the environment to which they may be better adapted. Thus, mutations to bacteriophage or streptomycin resistance can occur in bacterial populations growing in the absence of phage or streptomycin. However, in order to detect such mutants it usually becomes necessary to submit the populations to the influence of phage or streptomycin. Under such conditions the susceptible parent cells fail to grow whereas the resistant mutants become detectable through their ability to grow in the selective environment. Screening procedures employing selective environments have been extremely valuable in the demonstration of the occurrence of spontaneous undirected mutations among bacteria.

EVIDENCE FOR THE OCCURRENCE OF MUTATIONS IN BACTERIA

Although intensive studies of higher organisms had familiarized geneticists with mutations over a period of almost 50 years, a clear experimental demonstration of the occurrence of spontaneous, undirected mutations in bacteria was lacking until Luria and Delbrück (1943) reported their "fluctuation test." Since their test is based on statistical considerations and is somewhat indirect in nature, we shall first review a simpler and more direct experimental proof which was contributed by Newcombe in 1949.

*Originally this definition was restricted to changes in nuclear determinants; however, it is no longer necessary to restrict it to this level, since determinants associated with DNA-containing elements that spend at least part of their existence in an extranuclear environment (e.g., some episomes) also may undergo spontaneous changes that operationally can be akin to changes in nuclear determinants.

NEWCOMBE'S SPREADING EXPERIMENT

Newcombe (1949) designed an experiment with the phage-susceptible B/r strain of *E. coli* which would permit a differentiation between the possibility that phage-resistant variants arise due to the exposure to the specific phage-containing environment ("direct adaptation" hypothesis) and the possibility that phage-resistant variants arise spontaneously during normal growth in the absence of phage (spontaneous mutation hypothesis). Under the latter hypothesis the addition of phage would merely select the resistant cells already present. He plated phage-susceptible cells on agar and incubated the plates for several hours during which time a limited population increase, i.e., growth into microcolonies, took place. On alternate plates, the cells were then redistributed over the agar surface by spreading with 0.1 ml of saline. The remaining plates were left undisturbed. All plates were then sprayed with phage T_1, reincubated, and the number of colonies that developed from the surviving resistant cells were counted. If the resistant variants developed due to contact with the phage ("direct adaptation" hypothesis) it should make no difference whether or not plates were spread prior to spraying with phage; all bacteria present at the end of the initial growth period would be assumed to be phage-susceptible and spreading would only result in the redistribution of members of a homogeneous population. Therefore, according to the "direct adaptation" hypothesis no significant differences in final colony counts (colonies developing from phage-resistant cells) would be expected between spread and unspread plates. In contrast, if phage-resistant variants arise spontaneously in the absence of phage (mutation hypothesis) both resistant and susceptible cells should be present after the initial growth period, provided a sufficient population size had been reached at

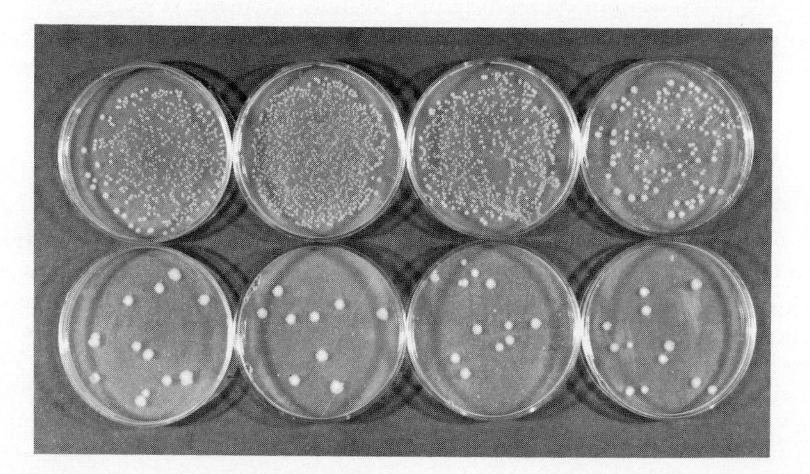

FIGURE 43. Newcombe's spreading experiment: 5.7×10^6 bacteria were plated and incubated for six hours; the plates in the upper part of the picture were then respread with 0.1 ml sterile saline, and all were sprayed with phage T_1. The population increase prior to respreading and phage exposure was in the vicinity of 5000-fold. (Courtesy of H. B. Newcombe.)

TABLE 4. *Resistant colonies developing after spraying agar plate cultures of* E. coli *with phage T_1, showing the effect of redistribution by spreading prior to spraying.*†

INCUB. (HR.)	3		4		5		6	
Bact. plated	5.1 x 10^4		5.1 x 10^4		5.1 x 10^4		5.1 x 10^4	
End No. bact.*	1.7 x 10^6		2.3 x 10^7		2.6 x 10^8		2.8 x 10^9	
Factor increase	33		480		5,100		54,900	
Resist. colonies	unsp.	sp.	unsp.	sp.	unsp.	sp.	unsp.	sp.
replicate test 1	0	0	0	0	5	194	46	2,254
2	0	0	3	0	3	14	25	1,434
3	0	1	0	6	4	16	45	3,294
4	0	0	2	0	8	13	49	3,719
5	0	0	1	0	2	4	26	1,538
6	0	1	2	2	6	112	49	399
Total	0	2	8	8	28	353	240	12,638

*Estimated by washing and assay; averages of three independent determinations. unsp. = unspread; sp. = spread.

†From Newcombe, H. B., Nature, *164*:50, 1949.

the time of phage-spraying. Depending on whether such mutations occurred during the last or previous generations a micro-colony may contain from one to several mutant cells since one mutant cell appearing in prior generations could have given rise to mutant clones or mutant clusters within single colonies. Spreading would break up such mutant clusters and each individual mutant cell would then give rise to a resistant colony. However, on unspread plates each cluster within each individual micro-colony would give rise to only one single resistant colony. Thus, if the resistant cells arose by spontaneous mutation, prior to contact with phage, more resistant colonies should be found on spread plates than on unspread plates. This is exactly what was observed (see Figure 43 and Table 4). This experiment thus confirms that phage-resistant variants arise by a spontaneous change (mutation) prior to exposure to phage. The phage acts merely as a selective agent permitting the detection of the few phage-resistant mutants present in the population.

Similar results were obtained when the spreading test was used in a study with streptomycin-resistant variants (Bornschein *et al.*, 1951).

THE FLUCTUATION TEST

Luria and Delbrück (1943) submitted experimental evidence for the spontaneous occurrence of bacterial variants several years prior to the publication of Newcombe's spreading experiment. Their evidence was based on the results of the fluctuation test (Fig. 44) which is performed as follows: a series of tubes, usually containing 0.2 or 0.5 ml of liquid medium, is inoculated with a small number of phage-sensitive cells. These cultures are incubated, without phage, until a certain population size is reached. The number of phage-resistant mutants in each tube is then determined following exposure of the cultures to phage, usually by pouring the contents of each tube into an agar plate containing phage. The results ob-

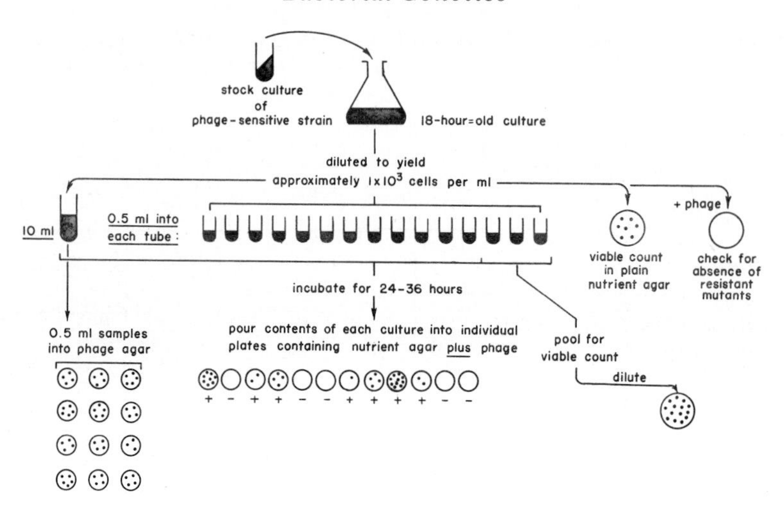

FIGURE 44. Diagram of the fluctuation test. In this example a test for phage-resistant mutants of *E. coli* is illustrated.

tained from such a *series of similar cultures* can then be compared with the results of a series of samples taken from *one culture* started with a similar concentration of cells per ml and permitted to attain a similar population size per ml. The principle of the test is this: if resistant variants arise because of contact with the phage (adaptation) it should not make any difference whether populations exposed to phage came from a series of similar cultures or from one culture. At the time of exposure to phage, all cells would presumably be sensitive and the number of resistant bacteria obtained from a series of similar samples should show only the fluctuation due to sampling error (Poisson distribution) regardless of whether they came from a series of parallel cultures or from replicate sampling of a single culture. On the other hand, if resistant bacteria arise spontaneously prior to the exposure to phage, a series of similar cultures will yield results different from those obtained with a series of samples from one culture. The reason is again the clonal distribution of mutants discussed above in connection with Newcombe's experiment. Parallel cultures may differ not only in the number of mutations which have occurred in each culture but in the time at which these took place during the culture's growth. Thus, if one mutation occurred just prior to exposure to the phage, a culture would display only one resistant cell; however, if a similar mutation occurred several generations earlier it would have given rise to a number of resistant descendants (clone). Hence, even if equal numbers of mutations occurred in parallel cultures, the number of phage-resistant cells at the time of exposure to phage would be expected to differ considerably among these cultures. Numerous tests have confirmed that this is the case; the fluctuation in the number of phage-resistant variants obtained in tests on a series of parallel cultures is significantly greater than that obtained in tests on a series of samples from one culture (Table 5 and Fig. 44). These results clearly support the hypothesis of spontaneous mu-

TABLE 5. *Number of bacteria* (E. coli) *resistant to a concentration of 5 units of streptomycin per ml of agar medium in samples taken from a series of independent cultures and similar samples taken from a single culture which assayed 1.3 × 10^8 bacteria per ml.**

SAMPLES FROM INDEPENDENT CULTURES				SAMPLES FROM SINGLE CULTURE			
Culture no.	No. of resistant bacteria	Culture no.	No. of resistant bacteria	Sample no.	No. of resistant bacteria	Sample no.	No. of resistant bacteria
1	67	11	56	1	142	11	110
2	159	12	91	2	155	12	125
3	135	13	123	3	132	13	135
4	291	14	97	4	123	14	121
5	75	15	48	5	140	15	112
6	117	16	52	6	146		
7	73	17	54	7	141		
8	129	18	89	8	137		
9	86	19	111	9	128		
10	101	20	164	10	121		
Average			105.9	Average			131.2
Variance			2913.9	Variance			151.1
Chi-square			550.3	Chi-square			17.3
P much less than			0.001	P			0.26

*From Demerec, M., J. Bact., 56:63, 1948.

tation. Similar results were obtained when the origin of resistance to various antibiotics, resistance to radiation, changes in fermentative abilities, changes in antigenic characteristics, or changes in growth requirements were tested with the help of the fluctuation test.*

INDIRECT SELECTION TESTS

One of the important features of the techniques just described is the use of selective conditions (e.g., phage, antibiotic) which prevent the multiplication of the parent cells, but allow the growth of the mutants, thus permitting the detection of a few mutants among the many parent cells. Since most mutants arise at the rate of 1 in 10^8 or even 1 in 10^{10} cells, this elimination of the parent cells is usually required for the detection of mutants. Yet the most direct method of demonstrating the undirected, spontaneous origin of bacterial mutants would consist of the isolation of mutants in the absence of the environmental conditions that favor their establishment. This ideal situation has been achieved (1) in tests employing the replica plating technique, and (2) by "sib selection" in liquid media.

J. and E. M. Lederberg (1952) described a very simple method that permits the transfer or *replica plating* of bacterial growth from one initial plate to corresponding sites on a series of other plates. This transfer is accomplished with the help of velveteen which is placed, nap up, on a

*See Table 6 for some representative references.

cylindrical wood or metal support having a diameter slightly less than that of a Petri plate. A rubber band or metal flange is used to hold the fabric firmly in place. The colonial growth which has developed on the initial agar plate is then transferred to the velveteen by inverting this plate onto the fabric. The imprinted fabric now can serve as the master pattern for the inoculation of other plates, each thread in the pile fabric acting as an inoculating needle when sterile agar plates are inverted on the velveteen. Replica-inocula can be made from one imprinted velveteen sample onto numerous plates, containing different media if so desired. The resulting growth on all these plates will be at corresponding sites (Fig. 45) since

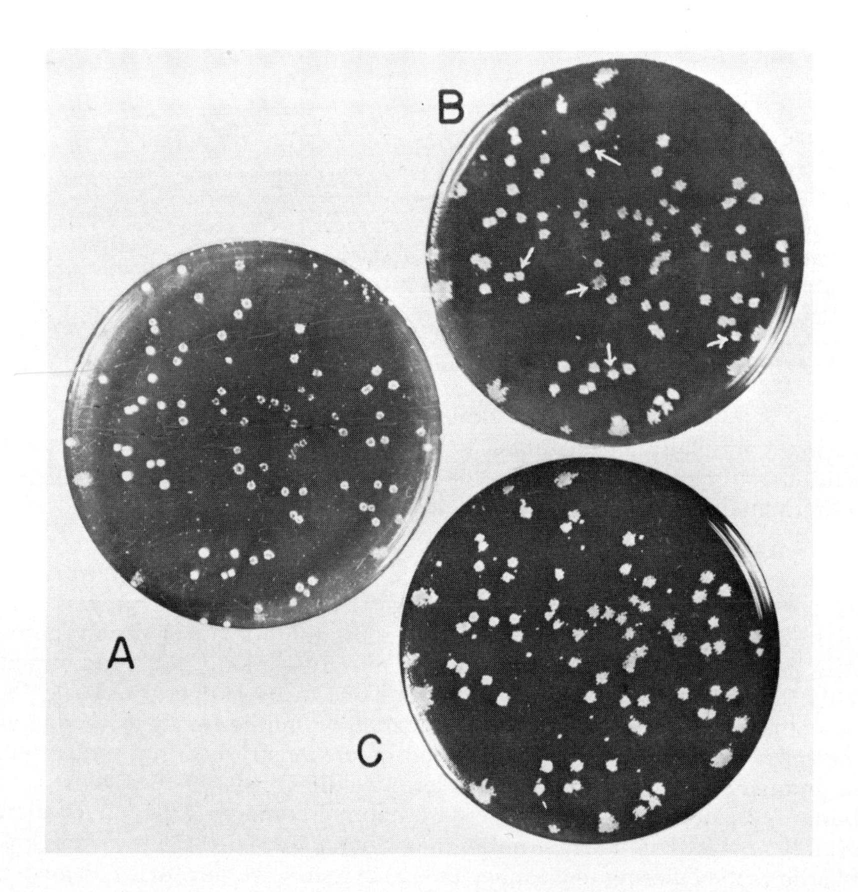

FIGURE 45. Replica plating. A, Initial plates; B and C, replicas. This picture also illustrates the use of replica plating for the isolation of auxotrophic colonies. A and B are plates with complete agar medium; C is a replica on minimal agar. The arrows designate the auxotrophic colonies which fail to grow on minimal medium. (Courtesy of J. and E. M. Lederberg.)

members of each clone that developed on the initial plate are distributed to the new plates without disturbance of their spatial relationships.* This has permitted a confirmation of previous observations regarding the clonal occurrence of bacterial variants which, as explained above, indicates that such variants arise spontaneously and independently of a specific environment. The growth from a phage-susceptible population which had developed on plain nutrient agar was imprinted on velveteen and serial replicas were then transferred to several plates containing nutrient agar *plus* phage. Colonies consisting of phage-resistant cells were found to develop on identical sites on each replica plate. This indicated that the resistant cells transferred to the phage plates were derived from small clones of resistant mutants already present at corresponding sites on the initial plain agar plate. Identical results were obtained in the case of streptomycin-resistant mutants.

The isolation of pure cultures of resistant mutants without exposure to any selective, or possibly inductive, agents was accomplished by replica plating in the following manner (Fig. 46). The growth from a phage-susceptible inoculum on plain agar was imprinted on velveteen which was then used for inoculating both plain and phage-containing nutrient agar plates. Subsequently, the area of growth on a plain plate corresponding to the site where a phage-resistant colony developed on "phage agar" was picked. Since it could be assumed that this area not only contained one or a few phage-resistant cells but was still highly "contaminated" with unchanged phage-susceptible cells, an enrichment procedure became necessary in order to obtain a pure culture of resistant cells. The isolate from the plain agar plate, therefore, was transferred to plain nutrient broth, incubated, and an aliquot from this broth culture was used for inoculating plain agar. The resulting growth, now containing a larger con-

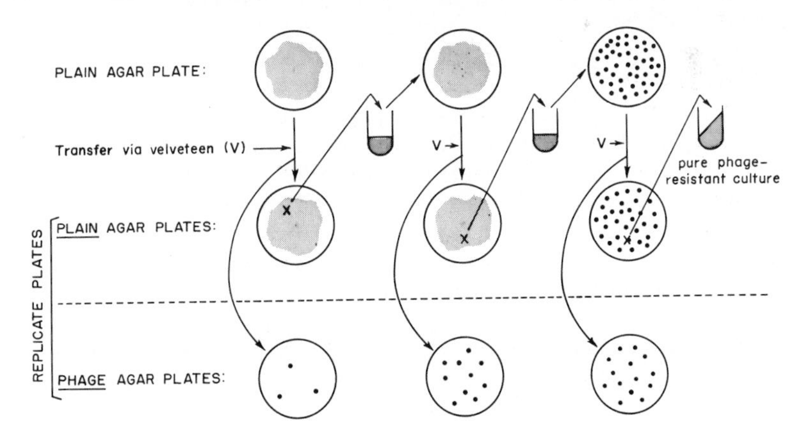

FIGURE 46. Diagram illustrating the technique of indirect selection of mutants by replica plating. See text for further details.

*The replica plating technique is useful for many purposes, including rapid detection of biochemical mutants (Fig. 45), classification of fermentation reactions, and determination of spectra of antibiotic sensitivity.

centration of phage-resistant cells, was then used for a repetition of the described replica platings. This procedure was repeated four times, and each time the location of the presumably phage-resistant cells on plain agar was determined by inspection of the site of growth on replicate plates containing agar *plus* phage. Following this process of indirect selection it was possible to obtain a pure culture consisting of stable, phage-resistant cells. Streptomycin-resistant populations were isolated by the same procedure. It is important to note that such variants were isolated without altering the media in which the bacteria grew; the indirectly selected resistant populations were not exposed either to phage or streptomycin at any time. These observations thus confirm the mutational origin of these variants, i.e., that they arose independently of the environment to which they are better adapted; they were "pre-adaptive" rather than "post-adaptive."

By so-called *sib-selection* in liquid media, Cavalli-Sforza and Lederberg (1956) succeeded in an even more impressive, and quantitatively more satisfactory, isolation of mutants in the absence of selective environmental conditions that would favor the growth of these mutants or conceivably induce their appearance. The indirect selection employed was based on the following consideration: assume that a population of 10^9 antibiotic-sensitive bacteria contains 10^3 antibiotic-resistant cells (or, in other words, a ratio of resistants to sensitives of $1/10^6$). A 0.1 ml sample of this population would contain 10^8 sensitive cells and 10^2 resistant cells. But how about a 0.0001 ml (10^{-4}) sample of the original population? It should contain 10^5 sensitives and "10^{-1} (=0.1)" resistants. Now, 10^{-1} resistant cells really means that it is probable that one of ten samples may contain one resistant cell. While nine out of ten samples would contain no resistant cells, the tenth sample would contain one resistant cell and the ratio of resistants to sensitives in *this* sample would be $1/10^5$. This means in this particular sample a ten-fold enrichment of the proportion of resistants to sensitives has taken place. If the sensitives can survive and multiply as efficiently as the resistants, it is now possible, by inoculation of a sample into fresh medium, to grow a population containing 10^9 sensitives and 10^4 resistants. The same dilution and enrichment procedure used before can now be applied. In one of ten tubes of a 10^{-5} sample of this population, one can expect to find one resistant cell among 10^4, again a ten-fold enrichment of the ratio of resistants to sensitives, compared to the previous cycle. By repeating the growth and dilution procedure through four more cycles, it should theoretically become possible to end up with a pure culture of resistant cells.

In practice, it becomes necessary to increase cell concentrations in each cycle somewhat so that instead of achieving one resistant per ten tubes, we obtain let us say, eight resistants in one out of ten samples and very much fewer or none in the other samples. By the plating of a subsample on selective medium, while the rest of the sample is stored in a refrigerator, it becomes possible to recognize the particular sample that should be used for further enrichment. Actual application of this procedure for the selection of streptomycin-resistant mutants, and also of chloramphenicol-resistant mutants, has shown that it is indeed possible to select spontaneously arising resistant mutants in accordance with the above predictions and in the absence of antibiotics in the environment (Fig. 47). The experiments showed close correlation between the actual extent of gradual enrichment in the proportion of resistant cells in each cycle and the mathematical predictions based on the considerations discussed above. Thus, this demonstration furnished convincing evidence, even for the most skeptical opponents of the mutation concept, that the fluctuations observed in the earlier analyses by Luria and Delbrück were not due to any obscure fluctuation of environmental conditions among parallel cultures, but did indeed reflect a random occurrence of spontaneous mutants.

The isolation of mutants in the absence of environmental conditions that favor their establishment was also accomplished in the case of streptomycin-resistant mutants of *Micrococcus pyogenes* (English and McCoy, 1951). It was observed that in the absence of streptomycin these mutants usually grew at a faster rate than the streptomycin-sensitive parent cells. Isolation of such fast-growing cells from cultures free of streptomycin and subsequent testing in streptomycin-containing media revealed that

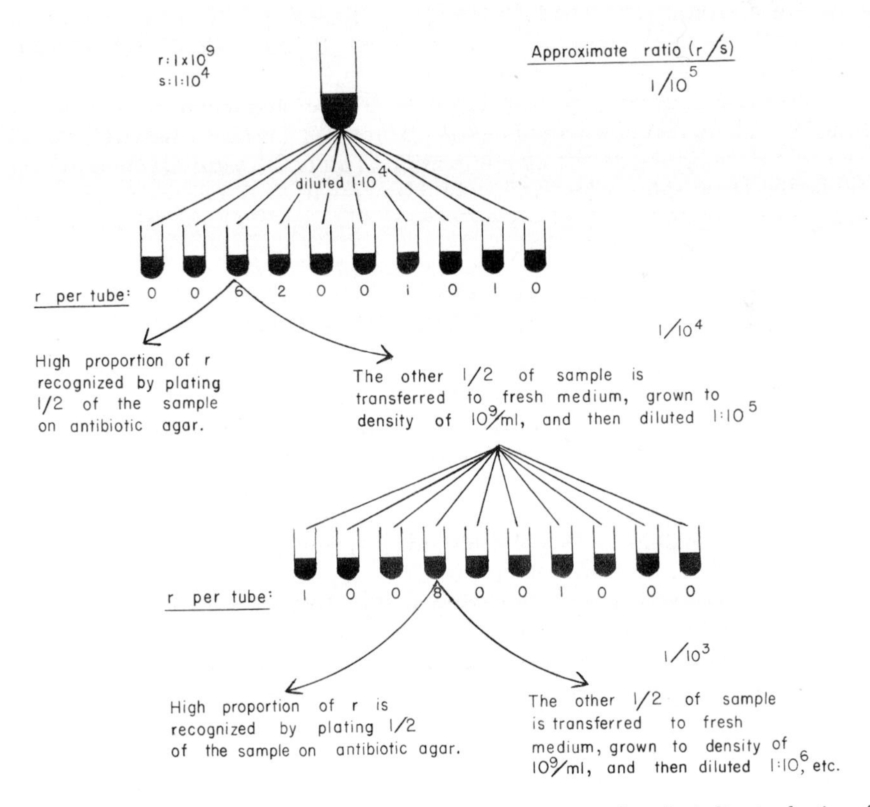

FIGURE 47. Outline of the dilution and sampling procedures used in the indirect selection of antibiotic-resistant mutants through sib selection.

every one of these isolates yielded streptomycin-resistant clones, thus again demonstrating that mutants can be isolated in the absence of the agent to which they proved resistant.

OTHER TESTS INDICATING THE "PRE-ADAPTIVE" NATURE OF BACTERIAL VARIANTS

Cavalli (1952) and Mitchison (1953) have used the *correlation between relatives* as an indicator of the undirected, spontaneous occurrence of mutants resistant to chloramphenicol or to streptomycin. They showed, with the aid of secondary characteristics (such as degree of resistance, rate of growth, or stability of resistance after prolonged cultivation), that the variation in these characteristics was much greater between resistant strains derived from different independent cultures than between separate isolates from the same cultures. This again reflected the clonal occurrence of bacterial variants.

Goldstein (1954) utilized the ability of penicillin to kill *multiplying* penicillin-sensitive cells, without harming *non-multiplying* cells, for an ingenious demonstration of the presence of spontaneous mutants in the absence of the environmental conditions to which they are better adapted. He argued that if streptomycin-dependent (*sd*) mutants arose in the absence of streptomycin within a streptomycin-sensitive *E. coli* population, they would not be able to multiply, and thus should be immune to the killing effects of penicillin; in contrast, the multiplying streptomycin-sensitive cells would be affected and an increase in the proportion of *sd* to streptomycin-sensitive cells would result. This was found to be the case. A 128-fold enrichment in the concentration of *sd* cells resulted following the exposure of streptomycin- and penicillin-sensitive *E. coli* populations to penicillin.

GENERALITY AND SIGNIFICANCE OF SPONTANEOUS MUTABILITY

In cases in which no effective selective agent capable of eliminating the parent cells in favor of the mutant cells is known, the mutational origin of variants is more difficult to demonstrate. This applies, for example, to many antigenic variants. Yet even in these cases indirect evidence indicative of mutational changes has been obtained. Thus, Zelle (1942) showed by repeated single cell isolations that 1 R cell occurred during 148 divisions of S cells obtained from an unstable *Salmonella typhimurium* strain. Stocker (1949) demonstrated the mutational origin of phase variants of *S. typhimurium* and estimated their mutation rates with the help of a technique that permitted visible differentiation of variants by plating them in media containing antiserum. In addition, it was shown that it is possible to utilize associated characteristics to create a selective environment for antigenic variants; thus, the mutational origin of R type cells in originally S type populations was demonstrated by utilizing the R type's greater resistance to D-alanine for the elimination of the parental S cells (see p. 180).

The various types of tests that we have just reviewed convinced most investigators that a major proportion of bacterial variants do owe their origin to spontaneous and undirected mutational changes, which for a given determinant occur only within a very small proportion of cells. The minority of dissenters who continued to favor direct adaptive mechanisms as a major mechanism in bacterial variation (e.g., Hinshelwood, 1947; Baskett and Hinshelwood, 1951) dwindled to practically zero in the 1950's. There is no doubt that certain adaptive mechanisms do occur (pp. 124 and 173), but the resulting changes in phenotype, produced under the influence of a specific environment, are usually not maintained following transfer to a different environment. There are certain hereditary determinants, such as the transiently extrachromosomal episomes, which are specifically susceptible to alterations by certain environmental agents (e.g., acridines), but again, in this case, such alterations are not specifically adaptive to the causative agent. The weight of available evidence thus has led to the general conclusion that a major proportion of lasting changes in hereditary bacterial characteristics is due to spontaneous mutations. However, it is very important to point out that the spontaneous origin of mutants, independent of specific environmental conditions, does not necessarily imply that the reactions of such mutants are identical in the absence and presence of a specific environment. For example, streptomycin-resistant mutants can display different metabolic reactions depending on whether they are growing in the absence or in the presence of streptomycin (Bragg and Polglase, 1962). Those reactions which they are capable of performing in the presence of streptomycin can be held responsible for their ability to grow under these normally inhibitory conditions. A mutation, therefore, may merely endow a cell and its progeny with the capacity to perform certain functions, or to display a certain phenotype, under appropriate environmental conditions.

All these demonstrations prove only that spontaneous changes in determinants of hereditary characteristics can occur independent of the environment to which the mutant is better adapted; they do not reveal anything about the intracellular location of the mutable determinants. Only with the aid of genetic transfers (e.g., transformation, transduction, conjugation) has it been possible to demonstrate that the cell's DNA-rich elements are involved in these mutational alterations. However, this does not mean that mutational changes are always restricted to chromosomal determinants. Carriers of information, such as the episomes which spend at least part of their existence independent of the chromosomal replicon (see p. 124), also are subject to spontaneous changes. Therefore, mutational events do not necessarily involve just chromosomal determinants. However, since the vast majority of determinants presently familiar to us *are* associated with chromosomal polynucleotides, it is fairly safe to associate most mutational events with changes in chromosomal equivalents, unless direct evidence is provided that other cellular elements are involved.

THE MUTON

Even prior to the time of molecular analyses of cellular elements involved in mutational events, it was already predictable by mere observa-

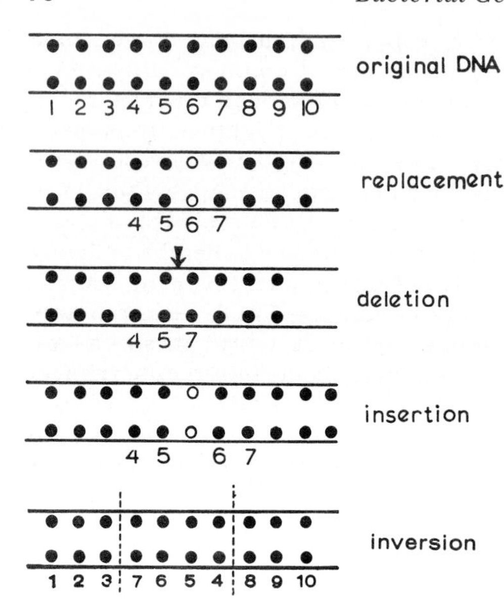

FIGURE 48. Different types of nucleotide changes in DNA. Each closed circle (●) represents a nucleotide; a hollow circle (○) indicates a nucleotide different from that in the original "wild type" DNA. (From Freese, 1963.)

tion of the end-results of mutational changes that separate and distinct entities (bits of information) of the total genome must be affected in individual mutational events. Thus, in an organism with the genotype A B C D E F . . . , a rare spontaneous mutational event may lead to A b C D E F . . . , another independent event to A B C d E F. . . , etc. This implied that independent determinants (or in other words, distinct and small parts of the total information) could mutate independently of one another. Benzer (1957) coined the word *muton* for this genetically distinct subregion of the total genome; it represents the smallest unit that, if changed, can cause a mutation.*

There is reason to suspect that not all mutational events involve mere substitutions of one or more nucleotides in a distinct DNA region. From data collected with higher organisms it may be expected that other types of changes, such as deletions, insertions and inversions, may also occur (Fig. 48). While such changes eventually would affect both DNA strands, as shown in Figure 48, even a change in only one strand could suffice to yield a mutant phenotype, since experimental evidence indicates that in the transcription of the DNA message to RNA, and its subsequent translation into protein, only one of the two DNA strands is being read (see p. 327). We shall discuss molecular events in mutation in more detail in the next chapter, which will deal with so-called *mutagenic agents* (i.e., agents capable of causing an enhancement of mutational events). Much of our knowledge regarding nucleotide alterations has been derived from studies with mutagens and it is therefore appropriate to discuss these problems further in this context.

*This unit, as defined, contrasts with the functional subunit of the genome, the *cistron* (p. 287), and the recombining subunit, which Benzer christened *recon* (p. 237).

BACK-MUTATIONS

Mutations not only may occur in one direction (for example, *ss* → *sr*, or $h^+ \rightarrow h^-$) but may also occur in the reverse direction (for example, *sr* → *ss*, or $h^- \rightarrow h^+$). Such reverse mutations, giving rise to so-called revertants, may or may not involve changes at identical sites of the polynucleotide chain. Quite frequently, the original, parental phenotype can be restored in the revertant by virtue of mutational alterations that involve a nucleotide region that is distant and distinct from the region that originally mutated. A mutation in this second region thus can create a *suppressor* effect, negating the phenotypic effect of the original mutation in the first region. In terms of nucleotide sequences, we may visualize the possibilities for reversions of a given mutant phenotype as follows:

	Region of control of specific enzyme	Suppressor region
Portion of parental genotype	...T T A C C T G T C T A A ...	A C T A T T G C T
Portion of mutant genotype	...T T A C *T* T G T C T A A ...	A C T A T T G C T

Revertants due to:

1. True back-mutation	...T T A C C T G T C T A A ...	A C T A T T G C T
2. Suppressor action	...T T A C *T* T G T C T A A ...	A C T *G* T T G C T

As we shall see later, only recombination tests between mutant and revertant can decide whether or not a back-mutation has affected identical sites of a given polynucleotide region (see p. 282), but sometimes satisfactory deductions can be made from observations on the phenotypic properties of the revertant. The following example will illustrate this: Böhme (1961) observed that streptomycin-dependent (*sd*) mutants of *Proteus mirabilis*, originally obtained from streptomycin-independent (*ss*) parents, can give rise to two types of *ss* mutants, namely (1) revertants that required no added growth factor ("prototrophs") and (2) revertants that would grow only in the presence of isoleucine and valine ("auxotrophs"). He interpreted this as an indication of a reverse mutation in the same functional region, in the case of the prototrophs, and an involvement of a suppressor mutation ($su\text{-}sd^- \rightarrow su\text{-}sd^+$), which in the $su\text{-}sd^+$ state* affects the function of the *sd*-controlling region *and* at the same time causes an added growth requirement:

$sd;\ su\text{-}sd^-$ (streptomycin-dependent) → $ss;\ su\text{-}sd^-$ (streptomycin-independent; prototroph)

$sd;\ su\text{-}sd^-$ (streptomycin-dependent) → $sd;\ su\text{-}sd^+$ (streptomycin-independent; auxotroph)

*Note that in employing the + symbol for the designation of the active suppressor we are deviating, for the sake of easier comprehension, from the customary genetic symbols which employ + to indicate the normal, wild allele and − to indicate the mutant allele.

By selection on minimal media on which the prototroph but not the auxotroph could grow, it became possible to isolate from *sd; su-sd*$^+$ the following type: *ss; su-sd*$^+$. These isolates behaved like prototrophs; i.e., there was no requirement for isoleucine and valine, presumably because the *sd* condition on which *su-sd*$^+$ acted (to cause independence from streptomycin and the growth factor requirement) was no longer present. It now was predictable that such *ss; su-sd*$^+$ types, though they could theoretically mutate from

$$ss;\ su\text{-}sd^+ \rightarrow sd;\ su\text{-}sd^+$$
$$(\text{or from } ss;\ su\text{-}sd^+ \rightarrow ss;\ su\text{-}sd^-)$$

should never yield *sd* phenotypes because the function of the sd region would be suppressed by *su-sd*$^+$. Only two simultaneous mutations, *ss* → *sd* and *su-sd*$^+$ → *su-sd*$^-$, would yield streptomycin-dependent cells; however, the likelihood of such simultaneous events can be calculated, on the basis of the individual mutation rates, to be less than 1×10^{-16}.* The experimental tests confirmed these predictions: following extensive screening on streptomycin-containing media, streptomycin-dependent mutants could not be isolated from the *ss; su-sd*$^+$ cells. Finally, recombination experiments utilizing transduction (p. 282) confirmed that some of the reverse mutations from streptomycin-dependence to -independence involved true reverse changes according to scheme (1) on page 79; others involved the action of a suppressor according to scheme (2) on page 79. Data like these support the conclusion that mere observation of a mutational event reestablishing the original phenotype does not suffice to prove that a true back-mutation (in the sense of involving the originally altered determinant) has occurred.

MUTATION RATES

Let us return now to a further discussion of mutational events as they become apparent from observations on a mutant's progeny. We find that for any given determinant the probability of a spontaneous change, e. g., the rate of mutation (usually expressed as the rate per bacterium per division) is quite low. We also find that the stability of each muton is fairly constant. This constancy in mutation rates, however, does not apply if we refer to a given characteristic rather than to its specific determinant. For example, not all changes from histidine-independence (h^+) to histidine-requirement (h^-) in *E. coli* have the same mutation rate. The reason is that phenotypically similar changes can be caused by mutations affecting any one of several different nucleotide pairs (mutons) making up one of the functional genetic regions (cistrons) which control histidine synthesis. For example, let us assume that the following sequence of nucleotide

*The probability of two simultaneous mutational events is the product of the probability of each single event.

pairs controls the formation of an enzyme critically involved in histidine synthesis:

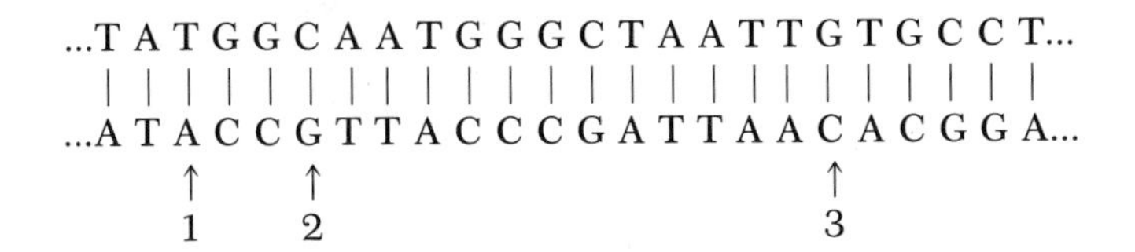

Any spontaneous alteration in nucleotide composition, for example at either site 1, 2, or 3, may alter the sense of the message and thus express itself as a mutation affecting the same characteristic (histidine synthesis in our present example). Since the likelihood of an error in DNA replication, or of an exchange of nucleotides in the absence of replication, may be different for sites 1, 2, and 3, we may obtain three different mutation rates for $h^+ \rightarrow h^-$ changes, depending on which nucleotide pair within the region controlling histidine synthesis has been affected. In some cases, entirely different genetic regions (distant blocks of separate nucleotide sequences in the DNA molecule) may affect one and the same detectable characteristic. In such cases, we may also observe different mutation rates for similar phenotypic changes.

Some examples of commonly encountered mutation rates are presented in Table 6.

METHODS FOR ESTIMATING MUTATION RATES

Several procedures have been developed for the estimation of mutation rates. Since mutants ordinarily arise under conditions in which both parents and mutant progeny can coexist, it is necessary to employ means that permit an estimation of the number of mutant clones arising within a population during a given period of time. Theoretically, in a population in which one mutation occurs per n parental bacteria, the number of mutant cells (i.e., the mutant frequency) will increase as follows:

Generation	*Parents*	*Mutants New Old*	*Total number of mutants*
1	n	1	1
2	2n	2+2	4
3	4n	4+4+4	12
4	8n	8+8+8+8	32

This means that in the absence of any selective forces interfering with the multiplication of mutant cells, the increase in the number of mutants in a population may, theoretically, be at a rate greater than logarithmic. This is due to the fact that, in addition to the progeny of mutants that oc-

TABLE 6. *Examples of mutation rates.*†

VARIATION INVOLVED	SPECIES	MUTATION RATE PER BACTERIUM PER GENERATION	REFERENCES
R ⟶ S (colonial morphology)*	*Salmonella aertrycke*	5 x 10^{-2}	Cold Spring Harbor Symposium, *11*:228, 1946
Flagellar antigenic phase;			J. Hyg., *47*:398, 1949
"group ⟶ specific*"	*Salmonella typhimurium*	3 x 10^{-4}	
"specific ⟶ group"*	*Salmonella typhimurium*	1 x 10^{-5}	
Pigmentation*	*Serratia marcescens*	1 x 10^{-4}	Cold Spring Harbor Symposium, *11*:25, 1946
Radiation resistance	*E. coli*	1 x 10^{-5}	Genetics, *32*:221, 1947
Threonine resistance	*Salmonella typhimurium*	4 x 10^{-6}	J. Bact., *62*:639, 1951
Resistance to isoniazid	*M. ranae*	3 x 10^{-6}	Amer. Rev. of Tuberc., *65*:768, 1952
Colonial morphology*	*Phytomonas stewartii*	1 x 10^{-6}	J. Agr. Res., *60*:217, 1940
Penicillin resistance	*Staph. aureus*	1 x 10^{-7}	Ann. Miss. Bot. Gard., *32*:131, 1945
Resistance to phage T_3	*E. coli*	1 x 10^{-7}	Genetics, *30*:119, 1945
Resistance to phage T_1	*E. coli*	3 x 10^{-8}	Genetics, *28*:491, 1943; *30*:119, 1945
Tryptophan independence	*Salmonella typhimurium*	5 x 10^{-8}	J. Bact., *56*:374, 1948
Histidine independence (h^- to h^+)	*E. coli*	3 x 10^{-8}	Genetics, *34*:72, 1949
Histidine dependence (h^+ to h^-)	*E. coli*	1 x 10^{-6}	Genetics, *36*:460, 1951
Utilization of itaconate as C source	*Pseudomonas fluorescens*	2 x 10^{-8}	J. Bact., *58*:171, 1949
Sulfathiazole resistance	*Staph. aureus*	1 x 10^{-9}	Genetics, *32*:249, 1947
Inability to use galactose (gal^+ to gal^-)	*E. coli*	1 x 10^{-10}	J. Bact., *85*:244, 1963
Streptomycin dependence	*E. coli*	1 x 10^{-10}	J. Bact., *57*:565, 1949
Streptomycin resistance (1000 μg)	*Ps. aeruginosa*	4 x 10^{-10}	Pediatrics, *4*:214, 1949
Streptomycin resistance (1000 μg)	*E. coli*	1 x 10^{-10}	J. Bact., *57*:565, 1949
Streptomycin resistance (1000 μg)	*Shigellae*	3 x 10^{-10}	Pediatrics, *4*:214, 1949
Streptomycin resistance (1000 μg)	*H. pertussis*	1 x 10^{-10}	Pediatrics, *4*:461, 1949
Streptomycin resistance (1000 μg)	*Salmonella typhosa*	1 x 10^{-10}	Pediatrics, *4*:214, 1949
Streptomycin resistance (25 μg)	*Salmonella typhosa*	5 x 10^{-6}	Pediatrics, *5*:78, 1950
Streptomycin resistance (25 μg)	*H. pertussis*	6 x 10^{-10}	Pediatrics, *5*:78, 1950

†All estimates, except those indicated by (*), are based on the fluctuation test

curred in prior generations, newly arising mutants are added in each generation. In order to distinguish *mutation rate* (which is the rate of occurrence of new *mutational events*) from *mutant frequency* (which is the *number of mutants* in the population) special techniques and considerations must be employed. The fluctuation test has proved most useful for this purpose, particularly when selective agents capable of eliminating the parent cells in favor of the mutants are employed (see Fig. 44).

Without going into the details of the statistical considerations which underlie the calculations of mutation rates, the general principle used can be stated quite simply (see Witkin, 1950, for more details). From a series of parallel cultures, started with a small number of cells, the number of cultures containing no mutants and the number of cultures containing mutants are determined following exposure to the selective agent. This is usually accomplished by pouring the contents of each of a series of parallel broth cultures into a plate with nutrient agar containing the selective agent (phage, streptomycin, etc.) and recording the number of plates in which colonies arise following incubation. The actual number of mutants in each culture, i.e., the number of colonies developing on a plate, can be neglected in this method, thus eliminating errors that may arise because of differences in the growth rates of the mutants which may have affected their rate of establishment in the parent population (selective effects). The sole criterion used for the calculation of the mutation rate is whether or not a mutation has *occurred* in a culture. Determination of the average number of cells per culture at time of screening (exposure to phage, etc.) and knowledge of the percentage of cultures containing no mutants suffice to estimate the mutation rate, a, per bacterium per division cycle, according to Luria and Delbrück's (1943) formula:

$$a = -(\ln 2)(\ln p)/N$$

where p is the fraction of cultures containing no mutants and N is the average number of bacteria per culture at the end of growth (see also Newcombe, 1948).

In the method just described, events following the appearance of mutants are disregarded, since no attention is paid to the number of mutants that established themselves in each of the parallel cultures. However, a method of estimating mutation rates by noting the average number of mutants per culture in a series of parallel cultures has also been developed, but it can be applied only if the growth rates of the mutant and parent strains are the same in the medium used. In this case the mutation rate is calculated according to the formula:

$$r = (aN/\ln 2)\ln(CaN/\ln 2)$$

where a is the mutation rate/bacterium/division cycle, r is the average number of mutants/sample, N is the average number of bacteria/sample at the end of growth, and C is the number of cultures.

Other methods are based on the number of mutant clones appearing during growth on solid medium (see also p. 87), the highest number of mutants occurring in any one of a series of cultures (see Witkin, 1950), a direct enumeration of randomly distributed mutant papillae (h^+) growing from the surface of parental (h^-) colonies (Ryan *et al.*, 1955), or direct estimations of mutant frequency under environmental conditions which inhibit the multiplication of mutant cells (Ogur *et al.*, 1959). Improved formulae for the calculation of mutation rates, taking into consideration the delay in phenotypic expression of mutations (see p. 107) as well as several of the complex features of population dynamics, have been evolved (Newcombe, 1948; Lea and Coulson, 1949; Armitage, 1952; Northrop and Kunitz, 1957). However, these formulae involve too many statistical considerations to be discussed here.*

In cases in which the parent population cannot be eliminated by selective agents it is possible to estimate the mutation rate in initially homogeneous cultures on the basis of the proportion of mutant cells present after a known number of generations have elapsed, *provided the growth rates of parent and mutant cells are identical* (Stocker, 1949). In the latter case the proportion of mutant cells in a culture, initially consisting of one type only and maintained in continuous logarithmic growth, will increase linearly with the number of generations at a rate proportional to the mutation rate. Under these conditions, the mutation rate $= \frac{\text{proportion of mutant cells}}{\text{number of generations}}$. Stocker used this method in a study of phase variation of *Salmonella typhimurium*, which we shall discuss in more detail later (p. 170).

FACTORS INTERFERING WITH A TRUE ESTIMATE OF MUTATION RATES

Mutation rates that have been determined by any of the available methods must be regarded as only approximately correct. A number of factors contribute to the difficulty of getting entirely accurate rates. Among them are (1) inhibitory effects produced by parental cells which may interfere with the multiplication of mutant cells; (2) a delay in the phenotypic expression (*phenomic lag*) of many, but by no means all, mutational changes due to the time required for the manifestation of changes in the affected biochemical reactions; (3) a delay in phenotypic expression of a recessive mutation occurring in one nucleus of a multinucleate cell, due to the time (divisions) required for the mutant nucleus to segregate from the non-mutated nuclei (Fig. 49); (4) a delayed increase in the number of descendants of a mutated cell as a result of the so-called *segregation lag*; (5) selective effects causing differences in the growth of mutant and parent cells (p. 198);† and (6) the temporary residual growth of parental cells under selective conditions which supposedly inhibit the growth of parental cells. We shall discuss some of these factors here; others, namely those which have been elucidated with the aid of mutagens, will be considered in the next chapter.

The masking of the true number of mutational events by the *inhibitory*

*The interested reader is referred to the original publications, and Lederberg's chapter in *Bacterial Physiology*, edited by Werkman and Wilson, Academic Press, Inc., New York, 1951.

†This factor plays no role in the method based upon absence or presence of mutants in a culture (p. 83), thus making it generally the method of choice.

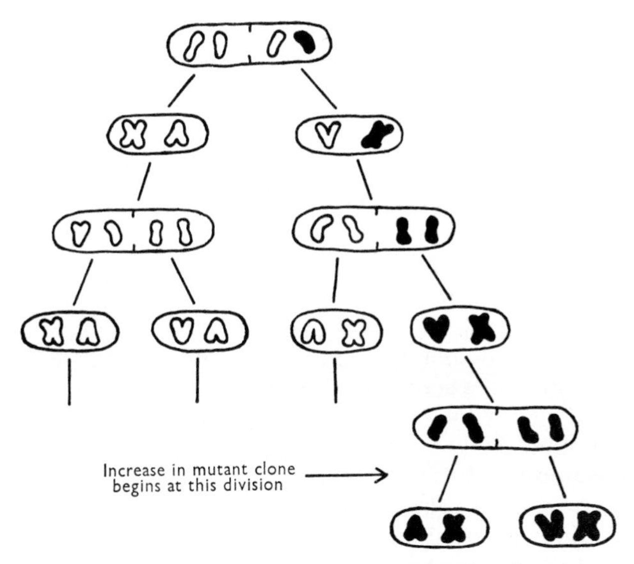

FIGURE 49. Diagram showing the segregation of a mutant nucleus from its non-mutant sister nuclei in a heterokaryotic cell. In the example shown, the mutation is dominant in heterokaryons and there is no phenotypic delay. (From Ryan and Wainwright, 1954.)

effects of parental cells on the growth of mutant cells has been demonstrated in a number of experimental studies. Such effects are not at all rare and in some instances may be drastic enough to hide the presence of a major proportion of certain mutant cells. For example, when different concentrations of streptomycin-sensitive (*ss*) *E. coli* cells are plated on media containing streptomycin, the following recovery of resistant (*sr*) mutants, indicated by the growth of colonies (clones) consisting of resistant organisms, may be obtained:

Number of *ss* cells plated:	10^8	10^9	10^{10}	10^{11}	10^{12}
Number of *sr* clones recovered:	0	0	1	5	18
Number of *sr* clones expected:	0	0	1	10	100

It is obvious that in this case some inhibitory factor prevents the multiplication of the majority of resistant mutants when the concentration of parental cells exceeds 10^{10}. Therefore, it is unwise, when attempting to isolate mutant types, to expose only one high concentration of parental cells to selective conditions permitting the survival of mutant cells. The parental concentration may actually be too high to permit the outgrowth of mutants or, alternately, in the case of low mutation rates, it may be too low to provide the chance for recovery of the rare mutant. Plating of ½ log dilutions, in concentrations bracketing the range from 10^8 to 10^{11} cells/ml, is usually advisable to assure recognition of the parental concentration that permits maximum recovery of a given mutant type. It has also been recognized that such interactions between parent and mutant cells are influenced by the parental genotype and by environmental conditions (Kraft and Braun, 1954). Consequently, the introduction of an arbitrary additional mutation (for example, resistance to Cu^{++}) into the parental genome, or growing the parent cells under unusual environmental conditions prior to the screening for mutants, can greatly alter the usual interactions between parent and mutant cells, and can thus permit the recovery of mutants not encountered under ordinary conditions.

Because many bacteria are multinucleate (p. 31) a *recessive* mutation occurring in one of the several nuclei cannot express itself until several divisions have elapsed (see Fig. 18). What would happen in the case of a *dominant* mutation in a cell with four nuclei? As can be seen from Figure 49, even though the mutational event may express itself in the first heterokaryotic cell containing the mutated nucleus, the number of mutant cells would not increase until two generations later when the mutant nucleus has segregated from the non-mutant nuclei. The *segregation lag* that will result under these conditions has been indicated most clearly in studies by Ryan and his co-workers (Ryan and Wainwright, 1954; Ryan *et al.*, 1954). By sampling the increase of h^+ mutants in h^- (histidine-requiring) populations of *E. coli* they determined that the rate of increase in the number of mutants did not take place at the theoretically expected rate of increase we tabulated on page 81. Rather, the observed rates matched a rate of increase that is predictable from a two-generation segregation lag as follows:

Generation	*Parents*	*Mutants* *New Old*	*Total number of mutants*
1	n	1	1
		↘	
2	2n	2+1	3
		↘ ↘	
3	4n	4+2+1	7
		↘ ↘ ↘	
4	8n	8+4+2+2	16

In this scheme new mutants do not double in number in the generation following their occurrence, but remain static in number for two successive generations until homokaryosis (p. 36) is achieved, as illustrated in Figure 49.

Another factor that must be considered in tests designed to estimate mutation rates is the limited growth of the parent cells that may occur in some selective screening media supposed to support only the growth of mutant cells (p. 67). This, in turn, may lead to the occurrence of additional mutations during the period of *residual growth* of parent cells, and may introduce an error in fluctuation tests when calculations are based upon the number of cells plated instead of the final residual growth of the parent cells. For example, plating of a population of streptomycin-dependent cells on a medium free of streptomycin not only will result in the growth of a few non-dependent mutants that might be present at time of plating, but will permit the dependent cells to divide a few times (residual growth), thus increasing the chances for the occurrence of additional mutations toward non-dependence. Bertani (1951) has found that the extent of such residual growth is mainly a function of the concentration of streptomycin in which the dependent cells have previously been cultured. In addition, he has shown that it is actually possible to utilize this phenomenon for a simple estimation of mutation rates from dependence to non-dependence. It is merely necessary to determine the number of colonies that develop from a streptomycin-dependent population during a known number of residual cell divisions on streptomycin-free agar. Each colony can be assumed to correspond to one non-dependent mutant which either arose during residual growth or was present in the original inoculum. Apparently, the number of mutants that may be carried over in the inoculum is usually very small in comparison with the number that will arise during residual growth. The approximate mutation rate, therefore, can be obtained by expressing the number of mutants present in the final population in terms of the known number of residual cell divisions. This simple method appears applicable to any system involving changes from dependence to non-dependence upon a certain growth factor. It has proved particularly useful in the analysis of certain environmental agents that are capable of enhancing the spontaneous mutation rate (p. 106).

MUTATION RATE VS. MUTANT FREQUENCY

All methods for the estimation of mutation rates have one important feature in common. This is the recognition of appropriate adjustments necessitated by the fact that mutants present at the time of screening in any bacterial population may represent mutants which arose just prior to screening as well as the progeny of mutants which arose several generations earlier (Fig. 50). Thus, mere inspection of cultures, even following growth from a single cell, cannot reveal the mutation rate. Such observations may indicate the frequency of certain mutants in a population (*mutant frequency*) but this does not necessarily reflect the rate at which such mutants arose (*mutation rate*).* It is also incorrect to conclude that differ-

*Only under special conditions can the mutant frequency reflect the mutation rate. For example, when a phage-susceptible population is plated on agar and phage is applied to different plates at different times after plating, the number of phage-resistant colonies that will develop after a known number of divisions of the parent cells will reflect the mutation rate. Under such conditions each mutant arising during the cell divisions that take place from the time of plating to the time of exposure to phage will give rise to one colony. The progeny of each of these mutants will remain within their respective colonies and hence every resistant colony corresponds to one mutational event. The last does not apply necessarily to the resistant cells that may have been present in the inoculum, but their number can be ascertained and subtracted by scoring the number of colonies that develop on plates exposed to phage immediately after inoculation.

A very useful extension of this procedure has been developed with the help of membrane filters (Matney, 1955). Replicate membranes, inoculated by filtering, for example, equal amounts of a heavy suspension of streptomycin-sensitive *E. coli* through each membrane, are placed on streptomycin-free nutrient agar. After various periods of time the individual membranes are transferred to streptomycin-containing nutrient agar, and at the same time, the population size is determined by washing off and diluting the growth from one of the membranes. In this manner the increase in the number of streptomycin-resistant mutant clones (mutant colonies) can be ascertained during a period of known increases in the parental population, and mutation rates can then be calculated according to the formula

$$a = (ln\ 2)\ (R_2 - R_1)\ /\ (N_2 - N_1)$$

where a is the mutation rate per bacterium per division cycle; R_1 and R_2, the average number of resistant clones at times 1 and 2; and N_1 and N_2, the average number of bacteria per culture at times 1 and 2 (Newcombe, 1948).

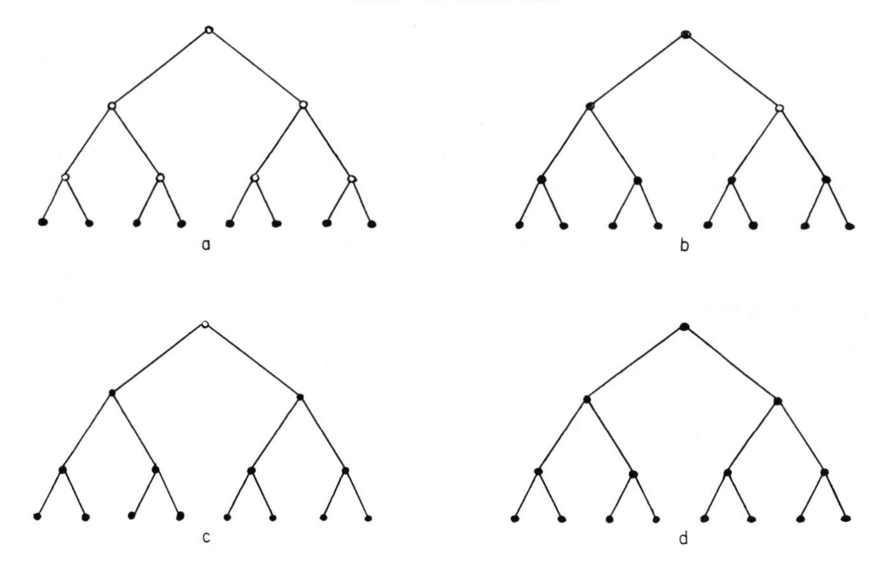

FIGURE 50. Diagram illustrating that the presence of eight similar mutant cells in a population could be due to (a) eight similar mutational events, (b) four similar mutational events one generation earlier, (c) two similar mutational events two generations earlier, or (d) one mutational event three generations earlier. ● is the mutant type; ○ is the parental type.

ences in mutation rates exist in cases where a comparison between cultures started from similar inocula and grown under different physiological conditions reveals that the second culture contains a significantly greater proportion of mutants than the first one. In such cases the altered physiologic conditions may have affected only the rate of establishment of the mutants arising at identical rates under either condition. We shall discuss such considerations again in Chapter 10.

MUTATION RATE AND CELL DIVISION

As stated previously, it has been customary to express mutation rates as the chance of mutation per bacterium per division (or per generation). The reason for this was entirely logical since it was assumed that cell division, and with it possible errors in gene replication, was required for the occurrence of mutational events. Later work carried out largely with the chemostat, a device which permits continuous growth of bacterial populations at different generation times, has shown that these assumptions have some validity as long as the rate of division is high, i.e., when generation times are short. Under these conditions (and they proved to involve generation times of 120 minutes or less in the case of *E. coli*) mutation rates are indeed dependent on generation time, being inversely proportional to it; the shorter the generation time, the greater the chance for mutation. However, when generation times are long (more than 120 minutes in the *E. coli* experiments with the chemostat), mutation rates have turned out to be no longer dependent on division time, but proved to be dependent on time itself (Novick and Szilard, 1951; Fox, 1955). In other words, when bacteria divide slowly, the chances for a mutation to occur can become a function of elapsed time and are independent of the number of division cycles that occur during that time. These facts, which at first sight seemed odd, started to make sense when it was proven that the rate of DNA replication can be independent of the rate of cell division, and that, in fact, DNA replication can occur even in non-dividing bacteria, at least for some time after cessation of multiplication (Ryan, 1959). It is probably because of such replication that mutational events can take place even in resting cell populations. The occurrence of mutants among resting cells was demonstrated by Ryan and his co-workers in an extensive series of studies in which they measured the rate of occurrence of h^+ mutants in non-dividing h^- populations maintained in histidine-free media (Ryan, 1959, 1961; Nakada *et al.*, 1960). They found that in the presence of an energy source, h^+ mutants arose at very low rates (about 40 times less than during growth) among the non-dividing h^- cells. Careful studies indicated that these events could not be due to any cryptic cell turnover; for example, penicillin, which should kill off all dividing cells (see p. 76), did not affect the appearance of the h^+ mutants in the non-dividing h^- culture. Ryan and his co-workers subsequently showed that mutants arose even after detectable residual DNA replication had ceased. This forced him to assume that faulty base sequences may arise under these conditions either by an undetectable replication of only minor portions of the DNA molecule, or by an exchange reaction involving individual bases.

We know too little about the control of DNA replication and DNA stability in multiplying and resting bacteria to form an accurate picture of all events determining spontaneous mutation rates. However, if we assume that most mutations involve alterations in nucleotide sequences, occurring either as an error in replication ("copy-error") or by an exchange reaction with a fraudulent base, we may sketch the following possible events: (1) DNA replication may be perfectly correlated with nuclear and cellular divisions in rapidly dividing bacteria—mutation rates are directly dependent on generation times under these conditions. (2) DNA replication becomes dependent on time, and must occur at regular intervals to preserve the existing information whenever the period between cell divisions exceeds a certain length—under these conditions mutation rates become dependent on time. (3) A different mode of replication of part of the DNA, or a substitution of some existing bases by others, might occur at regular intervals when metabolic events are slowed down below a critical point—under such conditions mutational events would also be dependent on time, but their rates would be lower than those typical under the usual conditions of DNA replication. But even if these assumptions should prove to be correct, the question still remains: what causes the copy-error or the incorporation of an "erroneous" base? Possible answers to this question have come from studies with specific environmental agents which are capable of increasing spontaneous mutation rates. These mutagenic agents, their modes of action and what they have taught us about the chemical basis of mutational events (mutagenesis) will be discussed in the following chapter.

[6]

MUTAGENIC AGENTS AND THE MOLECULAR BASIS OF MUTAGENESIS

Agents capable of increasing mutation rates are called *mutagenic agents* or *mutagens*. Mutations resulting from treatment with such agents are called *induced mutations* in contrast to the normally occurring *spontaneous mutations*. Mutagenic agents can increase mutation rates as much as 10- to 100,000-fold. The most widely investigated mutagens are base analogues, x-rays, ultraviolet rays (UV), nitrous acid and alkylating agents (i.e., agents, such as nitrogen mustard and diethyl sulfate, which are capable of transferring alkyl groups to other compounds) (see Freese, 1963 and Strauss, 1960, for general references). However, many other mutagens have been discovered in work with microorganisms; among them are organic peroxides and broth treated with H_2O_2 (Wyss *et al.*, 1948), carcinogenic substances (Demerec, 1949), certain purine derivatives (Greer, 1958), acridine dyes (Witkin, 1947; Brenner *et al.*, 1961), triazine and β-propiolactone (Demerec, 1954), certain simple chemical compounds (Demerec *et al.*, 1951) including $MnCl_2$ and ferrous ions (Catlin, 1953), certain conditions leading to a selective inhibition of DNA synthesis (Weinberg and Latham, 1956; Coughlin and Adelberg, 1956), and even visible light if the bacteria are sensitized with erythrosin prior to exposure (photodynamic effects) (Kaplan, 1948).

In view of the recognition that mutational events in bacteria seem to involve alterations in nucleotide sequences, it is possible to infer that the diversity of mutagenic agents is merely a reflection of the diversity of the reactions that can lead to altered nucleotide sequences; the action of a mutagenic agent may be on the DNA itself, it may affect precursors of DNA, or it may act even more indirectly by affecting systems on which DNA synthesis is dependent, including certain types of RNA and protein syntheses. While it is far from clear at which level the various known mutagens act, there are a number of examples of mutagens that, by virtue of their known chemical affinities and reactions, and also as a result of the reversibility of their effects by other agents, can be associated with either direct or indirect effects on DNA and DNA replication. Before we go into details regarding such examples, we shall first attempt to form a general, and somewhat simplified, picture of events that could give rise to new information by altering nucleotide sequences.

We have previously stated that the stability of the information existing in DNA appears to depend on the ability of a DNA's specific nucleotide sequence to replicate itself by forming complementary nucleotide chains, which involves the pairing of A with T, and of G with C. We can now imagine that these events may be upset dramatically if either a faulty base is incorporated at a given site in a new polynucleotide chain (A instead of G, C, or T; G instead of A, C, or T, etc.), or one or more nucleotide members of a DNA strand fail to replicate themselves. *A priori*, a number of different events leading to the incorporation of a faulty base in the new polynucleotide chain could be imagined: the normal attraction between A and T, or G and C, may be upset owing to a change in the base, which instead of attracting its complementary base (more precisely: nucleotide), attracts the wrong base, thereby altering all subsequent events at this site (Watson and Crick, 1953). For example (taking here into consideration only the replication of one strand and assuming an altered attraction by one thymine-containing nucleotide):

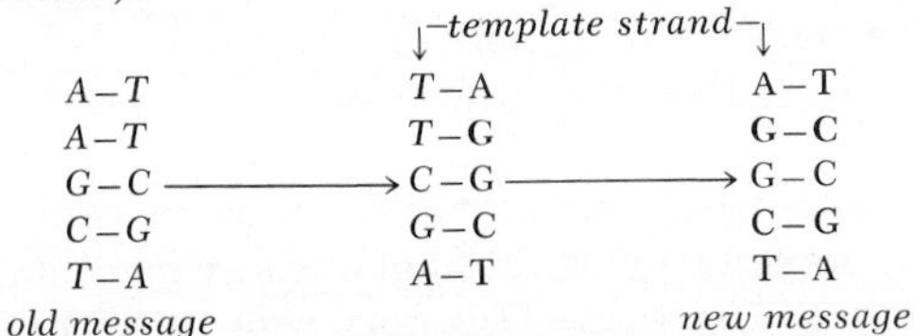

The new type of attraction, leading to the incorporation of the wrong base in the newly synthesized DNA strand, may be caused by either a rare, spontaneous shift in the tautomeric state* of the old base (T in our example) or the incorporation of a base analogue (e.g., a base that can take the place of T, because like T it is attracted to A, but which subsequently will attract not A, but a different base). It is possible to imagine that such shifts can occur more frequently when a high concentration of base analogues is present, or when there is a disturbance in the normal course of metabolic events leading to DNA replication, or when the nature and concentration of the pool of available "building stones" are dramatically altered. Furthermore, cells might possess some sort of repair mechanism that recognizes abnormal DNA sites and attempts to correct them, provided sufficient time for repair is allowed prior to the next cycle of DNA replication.

We can also imagine that errors in DNA replication may occur as a re-

*The four common bases in DNA may occasionally undergo rearrangements in the distribution of their electrons and protons. Such changes are known as tautomeric shifts and lead to structures that do not hydrogen-bond with their usual partner, but will pair with certain other bases. For example, a tautomer of thymine will hydrogen-bond with guanine instead of adenine, a tautomer of cytosine will pair with adenine instead of guanine; a rare tautomeric form of adenine will hydrogen-bond with cytosine, and a tautomer of guanine will pair with thymine (cf. Stahl, 1964).

sult of a failure of one or more nucleotides to replicate, possibly as a result of a "plugging up" process produced by certain agents with great affinities for purine or pyrimidine bases. Excess replication (addition) of a given base also is conceivable; such addition would upset the normal base sequence and would thus alter or make "senseless" the information in the affected DNA region. Finally, gross disturbances in the sugar-phosphate "backbone" of DNA also might cause faulty DNA replication and with it the transmission of a faulty or defective message. Our present knowledge of mutagens, their chemical characteristics and some of their modes of action supports the ideas just discussed, even though many details of the mutagenic processes remain obscure and, in some cases, even controversial (cf. Brenner *et al.*, 1961).

EFFECTS OF BASE ANALOGUES

The clearest picture of the probable events in mutagenesis has been obtained from studies of the mutagenic effects of certain base analogues (Freese, 1959). *5-Bromouracil* (BU), for example, is easily incorporated, in place of thymine, into the DNA of bacteria or bacteriophages (Zamenhof and Griboff, 1954; Dunn and Smith, 1954).* When BU replaces thymine in the DNA, the extent of survival of bacteria is high and in the case of many determinants there is, at first, no increase in the rate of mutation over the spontaneous rate. In these cases, then, mere incorporation of BU cannot be mutagenic; however, after cell division and DNA replication, specifically two DNA replications after analogue incorporation (Rudner, 1960), mutational events have been found to occur at rates that are significantly higher than spontaneous rates. This has been interpreted as being due to the ability of BU to pair most of the time with adenine (just as its analogue, thymine, which BU replaced, would have done), but occasionally BU shifts from its normal "keto" state, in which it pairs with adenine, to the tautomeric "enol" state in which it hydrogen-bonds with guanine (Fig. 51*A*). It appears that the shift leading to erroneous base pairing occurs more frequently in BU than in the thymine it replaces and this can account for the increased mutation rates that are typical for BU-containing DNA.

The mutational event is the consequence of the erroneous incorporation of G (instead of A), which, in turn, pairs with C at the next DNA replication, causing a more or less permanent base change from the original A-T pair to a G-C pair and with it an alteration in the message provided by the affected region (Fig. 52*B*). Note in the scheme of Figure 52 that the changed base pair (C-G) and its attendant mutant phenotype are expected to arise two generations (DNA replications) after the incorporation of the base analogues; this is exactly what has been observed in experimental tests. Note also that the mutant base-pair is expected to replicate itself after removal of the base analogue; this again is in agreement with the stability of mutant clones, as it was observed following the removal of BU in actual experimental tests (Strelzoff, 1961).

*To accomplish this, one has to either use a thymine-requiring bacterial mutant strain, or add BU to the growth medium in conjunction with sulfanilamide, aminopterin, or 5-fluorodeoxyuridine, all of which prevent the biosynthesis of thymine.

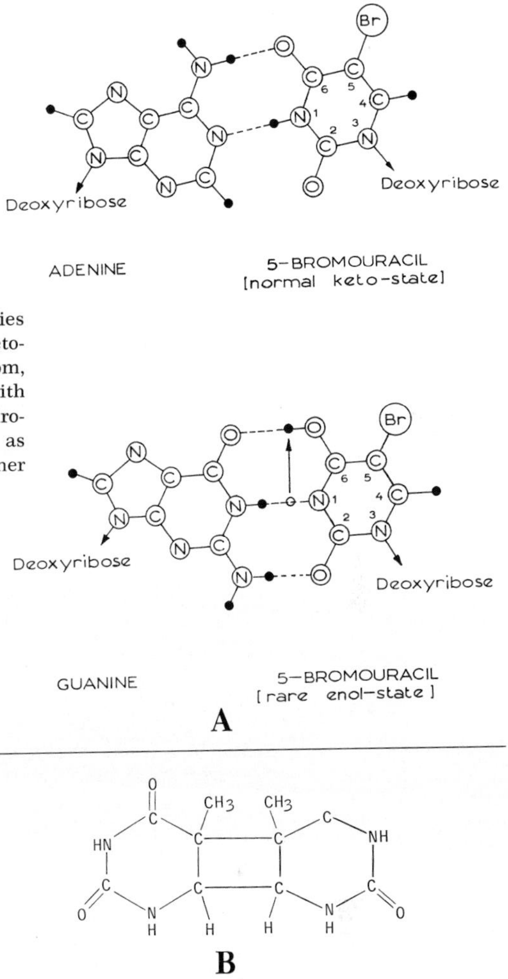

FIGURE 51. A, The base pairing properties of 5-bromouracil. Top, in the normal keto-state bromouracil bonds to adenine. Bottom, in the rare enol-state bromouracil pairs with guanine. Note the shift of one of the hydrogen atoms, which are here represented as black dots. (From Hayes, 1964.) B, A dimer of thymine.

If BU can occasionally hydrogen-bond with G instead of with A, then one must expect that, occasionally, BU may also take the place of C at the time of incorporation.* Figure 52*C* illustrates what could happen in this case.

2-*Aminopurine* (AP) is another mutagenic base analogue, which, if present in the environment, may occasionally be incorporated in the place of adenine (which it resembles). Like adenine, AP will usually pair with thymine, but it can also pair quite frequently with cytosine and thus cause base pair changes in the progeny.

*Remember: C normally pairs with G.

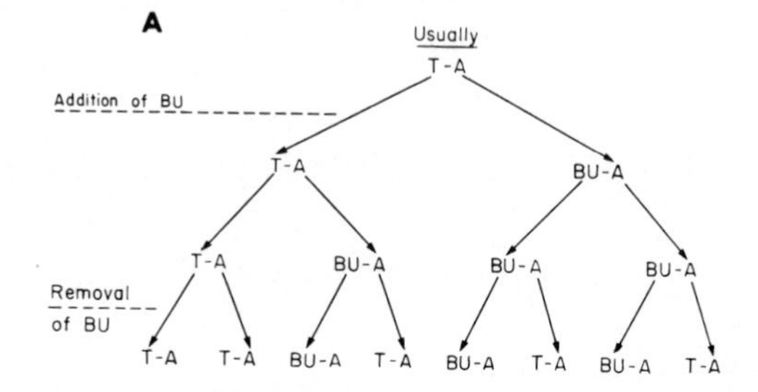

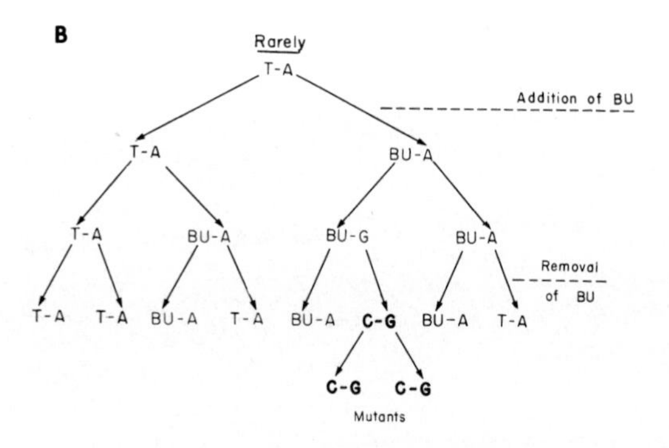

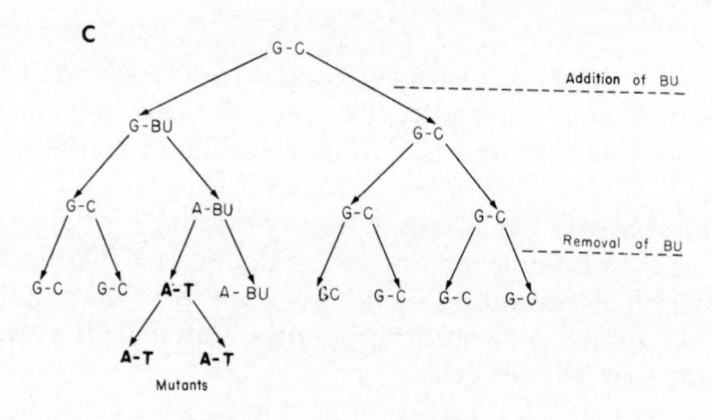

FIGURE 52. Transitions that may occur after addition of the base analogue 5-bromouracil. (After Freese, 1963.)

Such effects of base analogues were first proposed by Freese (1959), who based his ideas on the results he obtained following exposure of T_4 phages to base analogues. Subsequently, it was shown that comparable results can be obtained in tests with bacteria (Rudner, 1960, 1961; Strelzoff, 1961).

Freese proposed that two kinds of base alterations may occur as a result of errors in base pairing. The first kind, which he called *transition*, involves the replacement of a purine by another purine or of a pyrimidine by another pyrimidine:

$$\begin{matrix} A-T \\ \upharpoonleft\!\downharpoonright \\ G-C \end{matrix} \quad \text{or} \quad \begin{matrix} T-A \\ \upharpoonleft\!\downharpoonright \\ C-G. \end{matrix}$$

We can see such transitions occurring under the conditions which are proposed in the schemes in Figure 52. Another conceivable alteration in base pairing could occur when a purine is replaced by a pyrimidine or a pyrimidine by a purine; Freese has proposed the term *transversion* for such changes. The theoretical possibilities for transversion are:

$$\begin{matrix} A-T & \rightleftarrows & T-A \\ \upharpoonleft\!\downharpoonright & & \upharpoonleft\!\downharpoonright \\ C-G & \rightleftarrows & G-C \end{matrix}$$

As we discussed earlier, mutations not only can occur in one direction, but mutants may also occasionally revert to their original state. We may therefore ask: What is the influence of mutagenic base analogues on the reversion of analogue-induced mutations? In experimental tests with phages it was observed that thymine analogues like 5-bromouracil (BU) and 5-bromodeoxyuridine (BD), or the adenine analogue 2-amino purine, can induce mutations that can be reversed, at unusually high rates, to the original type by exposure to these base analogues.* In contrast, it was found that mutants that occur spontaneously or are induced by acridines cannot be forced, by subsequent exposure to BU or AP, to revert to the original state at rates higher than spontaneous rates (Freese, 1961).

Freese proposed that the difficulty of reversing spontaneous and acridine-induced mutants is due to transversions which may occur spontaneously or at higher rates after exposure to acridines, and which cannot be affected by transition-causing analogues like BU or AP. An alternate explanation assumes that agents like the acridines, which produce mutants that are "non-reversible" by base analogues, cause, instead of base substitution, a *deletion* or *insertion* of a base pair. They may do this by virtue of their ability to associate themselves with bases in such a manner ("sliding in between adjacent bases") that replication is altered at the affected site (Lerman, 1963). It should be noted that some circumstantial evidence for the occurrence of transversions has been obtained in studies with phages

*Figure 52 shows that once a transition has occurred, the subsequent occurrence of another transition, reestablishing the original base pair is an entirely conceivable event.

(Freese, 1961) in which suspected transversions, that had been refractory to AP and BD treatments reverted following exposure to either (a) ethyl ethane sulfonate, which is known to remove guanine from DNA, or (b) low pH (4.2), which is known to cause a depurination of DNA.

In the preceding section we referred to the relative insusceptibility to base analogues displayed by many spontaneous mutants. In this connection, it should be recalled that in addition to the just discussed "point mutations" affecting one base, spontaneous mutations may quite often occur as the result of major disturbances in the entire DNA structure (see Fig. 48). For example, Demerec (1960) has described the occurrence of deletions in spontaneous and UV-induced mutants of *Salmonella typhimurium*. It is evident that the major alterations in nucleotide sequence caused by deletions, by additions, or by the simultaneous alteration of many base pairs could not be expected to be repaired by agents responsible for only minor (single base) alterations in the DNA.

While it has been proven that some mutagenic base analogues, such as 5-bromouracil, are incorporated into DNA, others, like triethylene melanine (TEM), are not incorporated, and it is assumed that they react first with normally incorporated bases and thereby give rise to unusual bases, which are subsequently incorporated into DNA. These assumptions are supported by the kinetics of the mutagenic events following TEM exposure – the lack of dependence on DNA content but dependence on the concentration of low molecular cell components – and especially by the demonstration that TEM can react directly with thymine or thymidine, thereby yielding highly mutagenic materials (Szybalski, 1960). Still other base analogues, which are not incorporated, are non-mutagenic; they presumably cannot react with natural bases to yield analogues that can be incorporated.

EFFECTS OF AGENTS REACTING WITH DNA OR ITS PRECURSORS

Some mutagenic agents, such as nitrous acid and the alkylating agents, can cause chemical alterations in the bases, presumably even in intact DNA, since the transforming activity of "naked" DNA can be altered by exposure to these agents. However, in many instances these agents probably alter the composition of bases prior to their incorporation into DNA, and once altered, the bases may behave in the manner we just described for base analogues. Nitrous acid, which will deaminate amino groups containing purines and pyrimidines (substituting hydroxyl groups for amino groups) has been shown to be mutagenic for viruses, phage, and bacteria, and also for purified transforming DNA (Mundry and Gierer, 1958; Gierer, 1960; Kaudewitz, 1959; Litman and Ephrussi-Taylor, 1959). In studies with viruses, a maximum number of mutations have been obtained when dosages were used that lead to one deamination per 6000 nucleotides; higher dosages lead to inactivation (Gierer and Mundry, 1958). It is believed that adenine and cytosine are the sensitive bases that, when deaminated, may lead to mutagenic effects (Schuster, 1960).*

*Adenine is deaminated to hypoxanthine, which will pair with cytosine; cytosine is deaminated to uracil, which will pair with adenine.

Cytosine is also the target of another mutagen, hydroxylamine (Freese and Strack, 1962), the reaction leading to base changes that cause mutations (Freese *et al.*, 1961), presumably involving the transition from:

$$\begin{array}{c} C-G \\ \downarrow \\ A-T \end{array}$$

The mutagenic alkylating agents ethylethanesulfonate and ethylmethanesulfonate appear to react with guanine, possibly leading to depurination (Bautz and Freese, 1960). The specific site of attack of other alkylating agents, including the nitrogen and sulfur mustards, has been less precisely defined and may, in many instances, actually be less specific; possible reactions, in addition to the effect on purines, include effects on the DNA "back bone" itself, by an alkylation of phosphate groups and the crosslinking of DNA molecules (Bacq and Alexander, 1961). Formaldehyde has been recognized as a mutagen and its effect also appears to be related to its ability to react with aminated purines and pyrimidines, possibly giving rise to "dimers" of adenine (AA), which when incorporated into DNA could result in an altered base sequence.

EFFECTS OF BASE DEFICIENCIES

When thymine-requiring bacteria (e.g., *thy*$^-$ mutants of *E. coli*) are temporarily deprived of thymine, one observes a significant increase in mutational events (Coughlin and Adelberg, 1956; Weinberg and Latham, 1956). Such mutagenesis by thymine starvation may involve the production of "weak" spots in newly synthesized DNA, either through a deficiency of a pyrimidine unit or through the substitution of an unsuitable base. Alternately, it is possible that thymine starvation upsets general DNA synthesis by interfering with the normal synchronization of the metabolic events required for proper DNA replication and thereby causes misconstruction of the new DNA strand. It is conceivable, for example, that a lack of bases at an enzyme-controlled stage of nucleotide synthesis and polymerization may lead to faulty construction of the new nucleotide chain by drawing on unsuitable available substitutes. The extreme of such disorganization may be seen in the death by "*unbalanced growth*" that has been observed when RNA and DNA syntheses are grossly dissynchronized; thus, the death of thymine-requiring *E. coli* cells was observed when they were deprived of thymine for prolonged periods of time in the presence of precursors that permitted continued RNA synthesis (Cohen and Barner, 1954).

In this connection, it is of interest that an accumulation of N-methyladenine in DNA has been reported under conditions of thymine starvation (Dunn and Smith, 1955). The mutagenic effects of adenine, observed in studies with the chemostat (Novick, 1956), may conceivably also fall into the category of mutagenic events due to a critical unbalance among building stones available for DNA synthesis. Other mutagenic purines, like caffeine and theophylline, which are not incorporated in nucleic acids, are known to inhibit enzymes involved in nucleic acid metabolism and therefore may also produce their effects by upsetting normal rates of nucleic acid syntheses.

It is of considerable interest that the naturally occurring metabolite adenosine can counteract the mutagenic effects of the naturally occurring metabolite adenine (and also the mutagenic activity of many purine analogues) and can even reduce spontaneous mutation rates to about one-third their normal value (Novick, 1956). It is also noteworthy that only the riboside acts as an *antimutagen*; the deoxyriboside is inactive. In this regard, if, as Sager and Ryan (1961) have suggested, one assumes that too much adenine may interfere in some competitive way with the normal metabolism of adenosine, thus making mutation likely, then one may have in this competition between a naturally occurring base and its riboside a mechanism that could account for many natural (spontaneous) mutational events. There are many additional but less precisely defined examples of the influence of metabolism on mutational events, and we shall discuss some of these later (p. 110).

It has been established that heating (>60° C) can cause both *depurination* and very high (>10 per cent) mutant frequencies (Greer and Zamenhof, 1962). These effects can be demonstrated not only with whole cells, but also after heating naked transforming DNA. It has been calculated that mutagenic temperatures (exposure of naked DNA to 155° C for 15 minutes) can cause the liberation of 1.5 molecules of purine per 500 nucleotide pairs. It can be assumed that depurination may lead to a base-pair deficiency, or that the purine may be replaced by another purine when the apurinic site is "matched" during replication by the wrong pyrimidine, or, that the purine may be replaced by a pyrimidine when the apurinic site is "matched" by a purine. In any of these cases alteration in the base sequence, and with it alterations in the message of the affected region, would occur.

EFFECTS OF P^{32} DECAY

The decay of radioactive phosphorus (P^{32}), incorporated into DNA, not only can cause death ("suicide") in bacterial viruses and bacteria, but can also be mutagenic when the frequency of disintegrations is below that leading to lethal effects (Stent, 1960). These effects are due to the rupture of the DNA chain at the site of the P^{32} decay, which can result in a deletion or in total inactivation of the DNA when both chains are broken in the same region.

RADIATION EFFECTS

The most widely investigated, but (from the standpoint of modes of action) still relatively poorly understood, mutagens are x-rays and UV (see Zelle and Hollaender, 1955). The difficulty in analyzing their sites of attack is undoubtedly associated with the fact that there is more than one way in which these agents produce their mutagenic effects.

In the case of *x-rays*, the existence of a direct linear relationship between dosage and mutagenic effects on bacteria (Fig. 53*A*), a relationship that was also observed in earlier genetic studies with higher organisms, gave rise to the "single hit" interpretation of x-ray effects. In its simplest form, this interpretation assumed that a single hit or ionization of a sensitive target (presumably DNA) would cause a permanent alteration of the affected hereditary determinants and, consequently, of the characteristics these determinants control. The target theory was supported by (1) calculations on the target size, which turned out to match the assumed size of the genetic units, (2) the fact that x-ray effects are independent of wave length and intensity of radiation, and (3) the fact that the effects are additive when doses are applied intermittently. However, the subsequent discovery that quite a number of agents, including altered oxygen tension and reducing substances like 1,2-dithioglycerol (BAL) and $Na_2S_2O_4$, could greatly modify the lethal and mutagenic effects of x-rays (Hollaender *et al.*, 1951; Hollaender and Kimball, 1956), cast some doubt on the target theory and led to the assumption that the genetic effects of radiation may be of a more indirect nature. Actually, it is possible that both direct and indirect effects may play a role in x-ray-induced mutational events; the fact that the direct effects can be modified by certain environmental agents may reflect the existence of repair mechanisms that, subsequent to the damage to DNA, may cause the reestablishment of "normal" molecular conditions.

The idea that DNA may be, in many instances, the direct target of radiation effects persists because (1) DNA is the most radiosensitive component of cells (Szybalski and Lorkiewicz, 1962), (2) there is a correlation between radiosensitivity and DNA base composition (Kaplan and Zavarine, 1962), (3) it has been possible to demonstrate the direct effects of ionizing radiations on cytosine (yielding uracil) and on adenine (yielding hypoxanthine) (Ponnamperuma *et al.*, 1962), (4) the formation of hydroperoxides has been detected after x-radiation of purines and pyrimidines (Scholes *et al.*, 1960), and (5) direct effects of radiation on transforming DNA have been found (Pakula, 1962). In addition, it is possible to postulate a breakage of the DNA "backbone" as a result of ionization of the phosphate ester bonds.

Less direct effects of ionizing radiations on the initiation of mutagenic events may include the formation of altered bases prior to their incorporation into DNA. Also, some of the effects of x-radiation are probably associated with the formation of free radicals (such as HO_2) and with the formation of organic peroxide; the former is suggested by the protective effects of reducing compounds, and the latter is suggested by the finding that irradiation of media, leading to the formation of peroxides, can be mutagenic (Wyss *et al.*, 1948).

In the case of mutagenic effects following *ultraviolet irradiation*, exponential, rather than linear, dose-effect relationships have usually been observed (Fig. 53B). Following the absence of detectable responses at low dosages, a rapid increase of mutagenic effects with increasing UV doses tends to occur until an optimum level is reached, beyond which a further increase in dose fails to show a corresponding increase in the mutation rate; the type of dose response curve obtained is, however, greatly dependent on the strain used and can even be linear for some strains (Zelle *et al.*, 1958).

The nonlinear mutation dose response is believed to be due to the simultaneous occurrence of more than one effect in UV-irradiated cells: (1) effects that may lead to mutation and (2) inhibitory effects on general DNA synthesis (Witkin, 1956). The complex process of UV mutagenesis

(Text continued on page 102.)

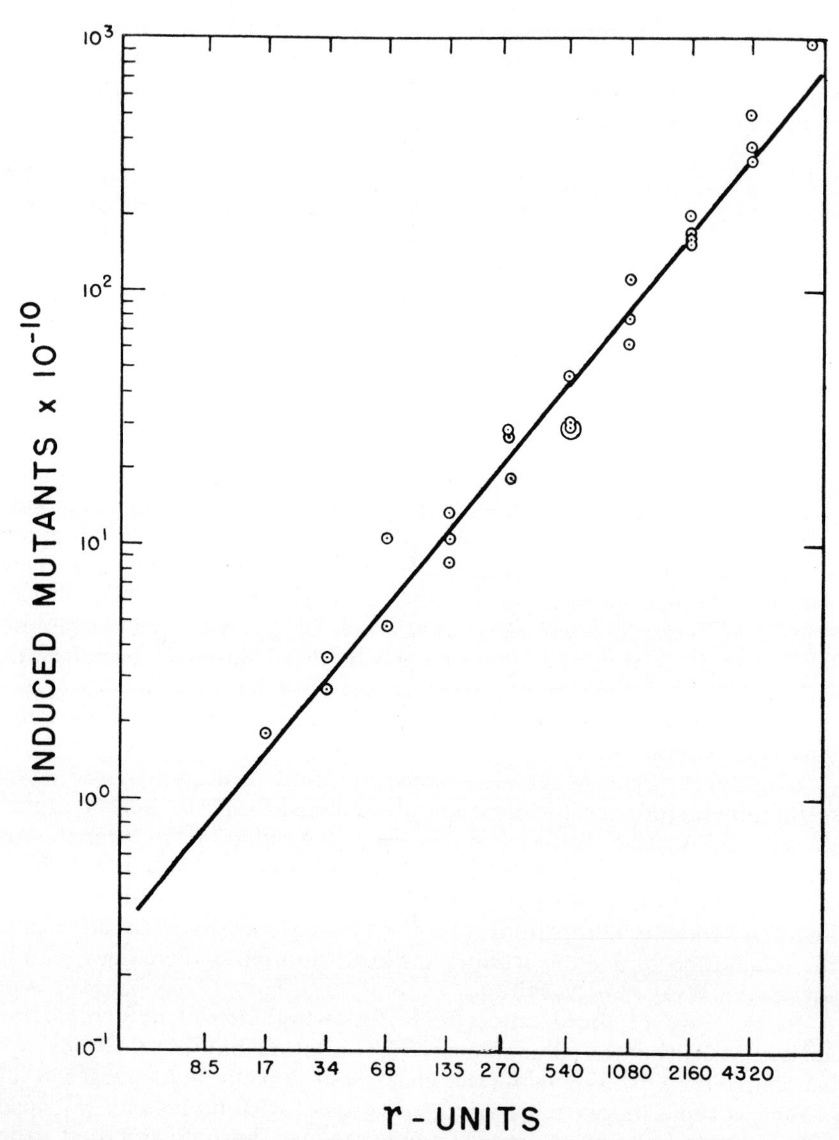

FIGURE 53A. Dosage dependence curve for x-ray-induced mutants. Frequency of reverse mutations (*arithmetic scale*) induced in methionine-requiring auxotrophs of *E. coli* by various doses of x-rays. (From Demerec and Sairns, 1959.)

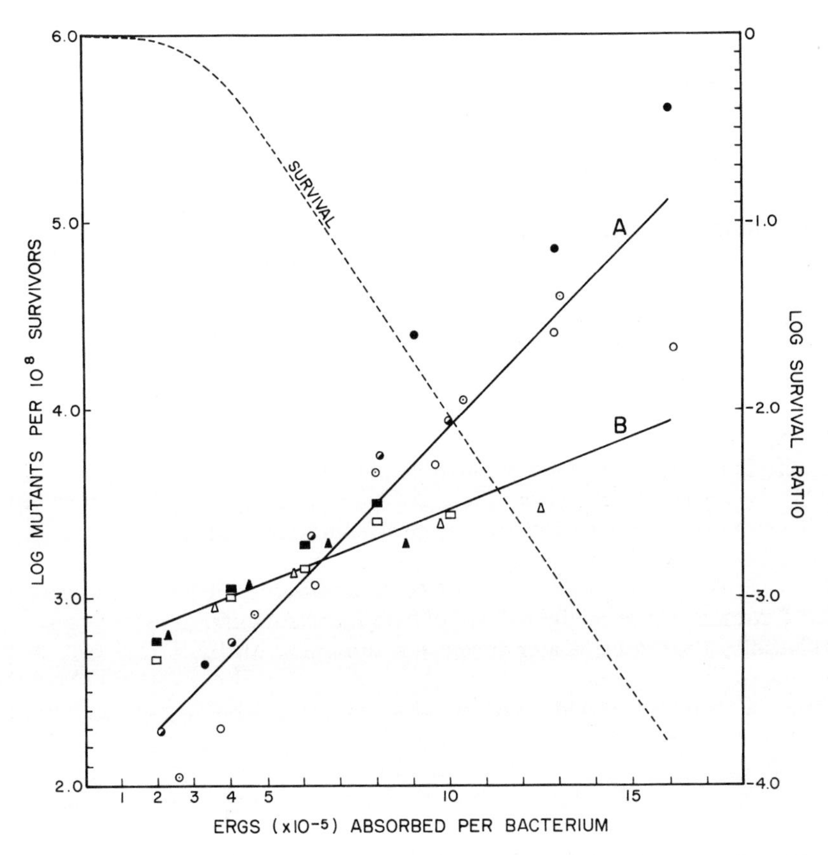

FIGURE 53*B*. Dosage dependence curves for UV-induced mutants. Frequency (*logarithmic scale*) of two different types of UV-induced mutants of *E. coli*, B/r. Circles indicate purine-independent mutants obtained after exposure of purine-requiring cells to 2650 Å; squares and triangles indicate streptomycin-independent mutants isolated after similar treatment of streptomycin-dependent cells. Data obtained from independent tests are indicated by difference in shading of circles, squares and triangles.

Line *A* shows the least square regression of log mutants on doses fitted to cases shown by circles (reversion of purine requirement); line *B* shows the regression fitted to cases shown by squares and triangles (reversion of streptomycin dependence). Statistical analysis indicates that the difference in the slope between lines *A* and *B* is highly significant. (Courtesy of M. Zelle and A. Hollaender.)

is greatly dependent on the time elapsing between UV exposure and the next replication of DNA (see p. 110). The lack of a linear increase in mutations at relatively high UV doses, therefore, probably reflects the disproportional increase in the inhibitory effects of UV on DNA synthesis, which, in turn, permits more time for the establishment of mutations following prolonged UV irradiation. By artificially prolonging the period between DNA replications at low UV doses, through the addition of non-mutagenic concentrations of caffeine, Witkin (1959) succeeded in producing a linear UV dose-effect curve. The effects of UV on survival and mutation, unlike those of x-rays, are not influenced by oxygen tension, but, as was the case with x-rays, DNA is among the most sensitive cell components. The action spectrum of mutation (which is the extent of mutagenicity at different wavelengths within the UV range) practically coincides with the absorption spectrum of DNA for these wavelengths (Zelle *et al.*, 1958). However, RNA, purines and pyrimidines have comparable absorption spectra and UV action on these cell components, leading to subsequent effects on base sequences in DNA, cannot be excluded at the present time.

As in the case of x-rays, chemical effects of UV on bases and on naked DNA (see Shuger, 1960), as well as biological effects on transforming DNA (Lerman and Tolmach, 1959) and on the DNA of certain phages (Kaplan *et al.*, 1960), have been demonstrated. Among the direct chemical effects of UV on bases, greatest attention has been paid to the hydration of uracil and cytosine (Shuger, 1960), and the formation of a dimer of thymine (Fig. 51*B*), which occurs after UV radiation either between adjacent pairs on the same strand or between bases of complementary strands (Beukers and Berends, 1961; Walker, 1963).* The most suggestive evidence for the probability that such dimer formation may play an important role in the biological effects of UV *in vivo* is the finding that these dimers disappear during a recovery period from the DNA of UV-resistant, but not from the DNA of UV-sensitive, *E. coli* strains (Setlow and Carrier, 1964). Furthermore, thymine dimers can be dissociated *in vitro* by temperature, and by light effects and also by exposure to the so-called photoreactivating "enzyme."

Reversal of the biological effects of UV by subsequent exposure to visible light (*photoreactivation*) has been known for a long time (Kelner, 1949): thermal reversal of UV effects (after mild—45° C—heat treatment) has been recognized more recently. In studies with UV-irradiated transforming DNA from *Hemophilus influenzae*, it was shown that it is possible to reverse a significant amount of the UV effects by exposing the bacteria to a protein fraction isolated from baker's yeast or *E. coli* (Rupert *et al.*, 1958), and it is this photoreactivating enzyme that has more recently been shown to cause a dissociation of UV-produced thymine dimers (Marmur and Grossman, 1961).

EFFECTS OF "MUTATOR GENES"

Since mutational events can be associated with alterations of base

*It should be pointed out that any cross-linking between complementary strands by means of dimer formation between thymines would presumably require that some sort of denaturation or distortion of the irradiated DNA molecule must occur first in order to place the bases involved opposite one another.

sequences, and since, in some instances, such alterations can occur more frequently when base analogues are present or when certain metabolic events are altered (see pp. 92 and 110), it is not surprising to learn that specific genetic changes can occur that will lead to significant increases in the mutability of other determinants. It may be assumed that critical metabolic events have been altered in cells carrying such a *mutator factor*, or *mutator gene*, so that, for example, faulty bases may be produced or some of the events controlling DNA synthesis are altered in a manner comparable to thymine starvation. Mutator genes can increase mutation rates for a great variety, perhaps all, other determinants. They have been described repeatedly, not only in bacteria (Treffers *et al.*, 1954; Skaar, 1956; Miyake, 1960), but also in higher organisms, and it has been possible through recombination tests to associate them with a specific region of the bacterial chromosome. Demerec (1960) has provided experimental evidence which shows that a mutator gene present in a strain of *Salmonella typhimurium* causes changes affecting single sites (single nucleotide pairs) in a manner comparable to the effects of base analogues.

DIFFERENCES BETWEEN INDUCED AND SPONTANEOUS MUTATIONS

Fairly often, but certainly not in the majority of cases, there appear to be certain differences between induced and spontaneous mutations, as indicated by the nature of the characteristics affected by the mutational event. For example, it has been observed that in a large group of spontaneously arising, phage-resistant mutants, all the independently isolated, auxotrophic mutants required tryptophan for growth; however, several phage-resistant mutants isolated following UV irradiations showed completely different requirements (Table 7) (Bryson and Davidson, 1951).

TABLE 7. *Phage resistance pattern and nutritional requirements of spontaneous and ultraviolet-induced phage-resistant mutants of* E. coli *isolated from strain B/r.**†

	SPONTANEOUS				INDUCED			
	Total	Non-deficient	Deficient: Tryptophanless	Deficient: Misc.	Total	Non-deficient	Deficient: Tryptophanless	Deficient: Misc.
B/r/1	72	20	52	0	9	7	1	1[a]
B/r/1,5	87	79	8	0	105	100	1	4[b]
B/r/1,3,4,7	4	0	4	0	0	0	0	0
B/r/1,3,4,7,6	1	0	1	0	0	0	0	0
Total	164	99	65	0	114	107	2	5

*From Bryson and Davidson, 1951.

†B/r/1 refers to mutants resistant to phage T_1 only, B/r/1,5 refers to mutants simultaneously resistant to phage T_1 and T_5, etc.

[a] methionineless

[b] thiamineless, aromaticless, purineless and serineless.

More recently, Böhme (1961b) contributed another example of such differences: among spontaneously arising, streptomycin-non-dependent (*ss*) mutants isolated from a streptomycin-dependent strain of *Proteus mirabilis*, 72 per cent required an additional growth factor, whereas among $MnCl_2$-induced *ss* mutants, only 30 per cent showed such new growth requirements. It is possible that such differences are attributable to the frequency of occurrence of point mutations after treatment with many mutagens, as opposed to the relatively more frequent occurrence of gross changes, such as deletions, in the case of spontaneous mutations. In addition, in cases in which only point mutations are involved, *different* genes leading to a *similar* phenotype (e.g., phage resistance) may be differently susceptible to spontaneous and induced mutational events.

SPECIFICITY OF MUTAGENS

Throughout the discussion of specific mutagens we have pointed out that some mutagens tend to affect purines (e.g., heat) and others react with pyrimidines (e.g., UV). Since we have good reason to believe that the purine and pyrimidine content of different polynucleotide regions of the bacterial DNA (controlling the formation of different proteins) can differ considerably, it would be entirely within the realm of expectation if some mutagens were to affect some polynucleotide regions (and thus some determinants) more than others. For example, a polynucleotide region (i.e., determinant) rich in cytosine would be more likely to be affected by nitrous acid than by heat; conversely, a region rich in adenine would be more susceptible to heat effects.

Such relative specificity of mutagens for different determinants is

TABLE 8. *Frequencies of reversions induced in nutritionally deficient strains of* E. coli *by treatment with x-rays, ultraviolet rays (UV), nitrogen mustard (NM), manganous chloride ($MnCl_2$), triazine and β-propiolactone (β-pl).**†

STRAIN	GENE	REVERSIONS $\times 10^{-8}$ INDUCED BY					
		X-rays	UV	NM	$MnCl_2$	Triazine	β-pl
M–1	leucine-a	[12]	1,200	0	[24]	[0]	[2]
Sd–4–55	trytophane-a	113	1,800	221	10,200	492	60
D–84	arginine	134	4,600	[4]	63	125	16
M–4	tryptophane-b	1,160	10,700	25	448	[0]	217
WP–12	tryptophane-c	1,563	3,110	397	14,700	4,430	291
Sd–4	streptomycin	1,700	7,140	3,990	7,220	5,500	2,052
12–72	phenylalanine	2,460	[100]	2,740	[11]	16,320	[3]
	leucine-b	[97]	[57]	31	594	165	158

*From Demerec, M.: Proc. Amer. Philos. Soc., 98:318, 1954.

†For each mutagen the two highest values are underlined and the two lowest are enclosed in boxes.

confirmed by experimental observations and is in contrast to the old belief that the effects of mutagens are entirely non-specific. As Table 8 illustrates, striking quantitative differences can be found in the efficacy of different mutagens in causing reversions in different genetic regions (loci) controlling different characteristics. For example, UV caused a high frequency of reversions in one of the loci controlling tryptophan synthesis and had little effect on the locus controlling phenylalanine synthesis; in contrast, nitrogen mustard produced remarkable mutagenic effects as far as the phenylalanine locus is concerned, without having much effect on the tryptophan locus.

It is interesting to note that the quantitative differences in response of different genes to different mutagens become clearly apparent only when tests are made on reverse mutations of mutants, such as when types having an added growth requirement ("auxotrophs") mutate to the "wild" type ("prototroph") having no such requirement. The mutagen specificity is inapparent when mutations from prototrophy to auxotrophy are studied. The reasons for this are easily understandable: as we pointed out before, each functional gene is made up of many purine and pyrimidine nucleotides (roughly several hundreds) and a change in any of these can lead to loss of function and thus, for example, to an added growth requirement. In contrast, an auxotroph that has arisen by point mutation, i.e., by a change in a single nucleotide, can revert to the original functional state characterizing the prototroph only when this very nucleotide is restored to its original reading. Thus, if in tests on mutagenic effects of different mutagens one starts out with a given auxotrophic strain and looks for prototrophic mutants, one measures only changes that have affected one specific A-T, T-A, C-G, or G-C pair; but if one measures mutations from prototrophy to auxotrophy, a change in any nucleotide pair belonging to the region under observation may yield the same result, irrespective of whether a purine or pyrimidine has been altered or lost. Hence, mutagen specificity cannot be revealed in this last test system.

The conclusion that differences in the response of given genes to different mutagens is due to differences in their base content and sequences is also supported by the finding that different genes can give different dose response curves to the same mutagen (Fig. 53) and by the observation that UV or x-irradiation of naked transforming DNA can produce different degrees of inactivation of different genetic markers (e.g., streptomycin resistance, erythromycin resistance, capsule formation), or even of similar markers (e.g., streptomycin resistance), in DNA isolated from different strains (Zamenhof *et al.*, 1957; Lerman and Tolmach, 1959; Rupert and Goodgal, 1960; Pakula, 1962).

It is the hope of many investigators that eventually the utilization of mutagens with known effects on specific base changes or substitutions, and the differential susceptibility of different genetic sites to such mutagens, will permit the spelling out of the base sequence of the different genetically functional regions of the DNA. A partial approach to this goal can be found in the studies of Benzer (1961), who has been able to map a region encompassing two cistrons (see p. 287) of the phage T_4 in terms of "mutational hotspots," i.e., sites responding specifically to one of several mutagens, which included nitrous acid, ethyl methane sulfonate, 2-aminopurine, 5-bromouracil and proflavine.

LETHAL EFFECTS AND MUTATION RATES

There are some mutagens, such as $MnCl_2$ (Demerec and Hanson, 1951) and ethyl methane sulfonate (Loveless and Howarth, 1959), which are highly effective at non-toxic concentrations. The majority of mutagens, however, cause both killing and mutagenic effects. Thus, as illustrated for UV in Figure 53, the larger the proportion of cells that fail to survive, the greater the increase in mutation rates. In assaying mutagenic agents it is, therefore, of great importance that the mutation rate be determined as the rate among the survivors, rather than as the rate for the total population exposed. In older studies, certain environmental agents were believed to have increased mutation rates, whereas they had merely caused a differential survival of mutants – killing a larger proportion of parent cells than of mutant cells.

The reactions responsible for the lethal effects are not necessarily always identical with those leading to mutagenesis, even though it can be assumed that at least part of the lethal and mutagenic effects are identical in respect to their action on DNA. The existence of differences is indicated, for example, in the case of UV irradiation: it has been found that following exposure of bacteria to low doses of UV, both the lethal and mutagenic effects can be greatly reduced by post-treatment with light (photoreactivation), whereas with high doses the mutagenic effect becomes stable and only the lethal effect can be reversed by photoreactivation (Newcombe and Whitehead, 1951). Also, mutagenic effects of UV have been detected at dosages that are nonlethal (Matney *et al.*, 1958).

DETERMINATION OF INDUCED MUTATION RATES

Increased mutation rates following exposure to mutagenic agents can be determined with the help of the fluctuation test applied to the survivors or their progeny. In a number of studies with *E. coli* (Demerec and Hanson, 1951; Demerec *et al.*, 1951) mutagenic effects have been tested with the help of Bertani's technique (p. 86): streptomycin-dependent cells are plated on streptomycin-free media following treatment with a suspected mutagen; the mutation rate is then calculated from the number of non-dependent mutants that develop into large colonies on the antibiotic-free medium during a known number of residual cell divisions of the dependent cells.

A widely used adaptation of this test system employs mutants requiring a specific growth-factor (auxotrophs). These are plated on media supplemented with *very small* amounts of the needed growth factor; the mutation rate is then calculated by scoring of the number of prototrophic mutants (= colonies developing from growth factor-independent mutants) that can grow during the limited period of multiplication of the parental auxotrophs.

DELAYED APPEARANCE OF INDUCED MUTANTS

The test systems just described have revealed that induced mutants usually will not manifest themselves until two or more generations after the time of exposure to mutagenic agents. This delay may be attributed to several factors: (*1*) In the case of copy errors, after incorporation of a fraudulent base such as BU, time will elapse between the incorporation of such a base and the permanent change in base sequence, giving rise to what we may call a *copy error lag*. As Figure 52 illustrates, and as confirmed by experimental data (Rudner, 1960a), two replications of DNA can elapse between the incorporation of a base analogue such as BUDR and the manifestation of the mutagenic effect. However, in some instances—for example, in the case of induction of try^{+} (tryptophan-independent) mutants in try^{-} (tryptophan-requiring) cell populations following an exposure to 2-aminopurine—incorporation of the base analogue itself is sufficient for the expression of the new phenotype (Rudner, 1960a).

(*2*) Another cause for a delayed manifestation of induced mutations is a *delay in cell division*, which may occur after heavy dosages of some mutagens (for example, UV). Mutations seem to occur most frequently in the cells that are most "injured" by the mutagen and thus delayed in the onset of renewed divisions; as a result, a delayed multiplication of mutant cells, preceded by the multiplication of non-mutated cells, may occur in mutagen-exposed bacterial cultures (Ryan, 1954).

(*3*) Nuclear segregation, following induction of mutation in one nucleus of multinucleated cell, can [as in the case of spontaneous mutations (p. 86)] cause a delayed expression of induced mutations, in other words, a *segregation lag* (Ryan *et al.*, 1954).

(*4*) The delay in phenotypic expression (*phenomic lag*), due to the time required to exhaust preformed products, also can delay the expression of an induced mutational change to the extent that it may delay the phenotypic manifestation of a spontaneous mutation (p. 84). For example, while mutants displaying a gain in biosynthetic activities (e.g., $try^{-} \rightarrow try^{+}$) can be isolated with little delay following mutagen treatment, mutants with added growth-factor requirements (e.g., $try^{+} \rightarrow try^{-}$) cannot be recovered if screening procedures for their isolation are applied shortly after mutagen exposure. This failure of early recovery of induced auxotrophs is due, in part, to their delayed phenotypic expression, which can be attributed to the time required for the exhaustion of preformed products; such preformed products, which mutant cells can no longer synthesize, are carried over from parent cells to mutant cells for some generations after the mutational event. The resulting delay in the expression of the mutant phenotype is independent of, and quite different from, the delays caused by a lag in copy error, by delayed onset of cell division, by segregation lag, or by a combination of these factors.

Delayed phenotypic expression of a mutational event, due to a carry-over of preformed materials from the non-mutant parental cells, also appears to play a role in the case of the delayed appearance of mutagen-induced, phage-resistant mutants. Thus, as illustrated in Table 9, after exposure of phage-sensitive *E. coli* cells to UV, the percentage of recoverable phage-resistant mutants (assayed as described on page 87) has been found to increase for several post-irradiation generations, returning to normal approximately eight generations after treatment. Experimental evidence indicates that this is due to a delayed phenotypic expression of a genetic alteration that has taken place several generations earlier (Newcombe, 1948). The cause of the resulting phenotypic lag is, in all prob-

TABLE 9. *Delayed appearance of phage-resistant (B/1) mutants after ultraviolet treatment of* E. coli, *strain B.**†

INCUBATED BEFORE PHAGING	PERIOD OF EXPOSURE TO UV						CONTROL		
	4 minutes			2 minutes					
	Total no. of bacteria	B/1	Mutant frequency x 10^8	Total no. of bacteria	B/1	Mutant frequency x 10^8	Total no. of bacteria	B/1	Mutant frequency x 10^8
0	1.12 x 10^7	19	170	1.23 x 10^7	6	49	2.42 x 10^7	0	
2 hrs	1.79 x 10^7	118		2.71 x 10^7	95		2.4 x 10^8	4	
Increment 0–2 hrs	0.67 x 10^7	99	1478	1.48 x 10^7	89	601	2.2 x 10^8	4	1.8
3 hrs	1.43 x 10^8	548		2.17 x 10^8	414		19.2 x 10^8	55	
Increment 2–3 hrs	1.25 x 10^8	430	344	1.90 x 10^8	319	168	16.8 x 10^8	51	3.0
4 hrs	11.44 x 10^8	2081		17.36 x 10^8	1234		153.6 x 10^8	295	
Increment 3–4 hrs	10.01 x 10^8	1533	153	15.19 x 10^8	820	54	134.4 x 10^8	240	1.8

*After Demerec, 1946.

†Cells were exposed to ultraviolet irradiation for 2 or 4 minutes and were subsequently incubated for various lengths of time before application of phage.

ability, a carry-over of phage-receptor sites on the cell wall, which, for some generations, permits phage adsorption and thus phenotypic phage-sensitivity, even though new receptor sites are no longer formed. At the point at which the number of these sites becomes too small to permit phage adsorption, phenotypic phage-resistance will ensue.

All the delays we have discussed so far have one very practical implication for studies designed to isolate an optimal number of mutants following exposure to a mutagen: in such studies, irradiated or otherwise treated bacterial populations should not be exposed immediately to screening conditions; instead, a growth period, involving approximately three to six divisions, should be allowed before screening (see p. 129).

(5) In addition to the four types of delays in the appearance of mutant clones that we have discussed so far and which involve the completion of a mutational event (copy-error lag), its appearance in cells that have been generally injured (cell division lag), or a lag in phenotypic expression due to nuclear segregation, or carry-over of preformed products, there seems to be a fifth delaying mechanism, namely, delayed mutation. Such a *mutational lag*, possibly caused by the prolonged intracellular survival of mutagen-induced base analogues, has been observed by Zamenhof (1961), in studies in which prolonged genetic instability followed the exposure of bacteria to mutagens, and earlier by Witkin (1951), in a study designed principally to demonstrate that nuclear structures are actually a major site of mutational changes in bacteria. A brief review of this study is of interest at this point.

NUCLEAR STRUCTURES AS SITES OF MUTATIONAL CHANGES

Witkin took advantage of the fact that, depending on the stage of a culture's growth, *E. coli* cells with either one, two, or four nuclei can be harvested; the cell's nuclear status can be checked by direct cytological observations. Using the change from the ability to ferment lactose (*lac*$^+$) to the inability to carry out this fermentation (*lac*$^-$) as an indicator of mutational events, Witkin checked the effects of UV irradiation on *lac*$^+ \rightarrow$ *lac*$^-$ mutations in predominantly uninuclear, and then in predominantly multinuclear, cell populations. *Lac*$^+$ cells can be easily recognized on eosin-methylene-blue (EMB) agar because they give rise to red colonies; in contrast, *lac*$^-$ cells develop into white colonies on EMB agar.

When a population of primarily uninucleate *lac*$^+$ cells was irradiated and plated on EMB agar, a few white colonies developed, i.e., colonies which were entirely *lac*$^-$. Obviously mutations to *lac*$^-$ which occurred in a few cells expressed themselves immediately, thus leading to the development of colonies which consisted entirely of *lac*$^-$ cells. However, when *lac*$^+$ populations consisting primarily of cells with two nuclei were irradiated, the development of several sectored colonies, half *lac*$^-$ and half *lac*$^+$, was observed (Fig. 54). In this case the mutation occurred in only one of the two nuclei of the cell. Since half of the subsequent colonial growth originated from the mutated nucleus and the other half from the unaffected nucleus, only half of each colony represented the progeny of the nucleus in which the mutation occurred. Similarly, irradiation at stages

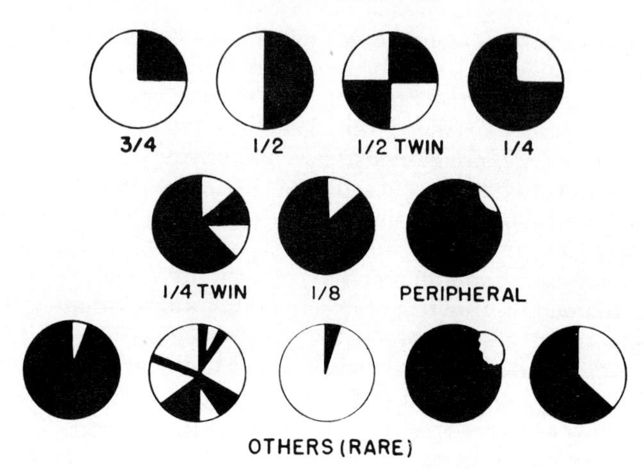

FIGURE 54. Diagrammatic representations of the types of lactose-negative sectored colonies obtained on EMB agar after treatment with ultraviolet light. (E. Witkin, 1951.)

where most cells contained four nuclei resulted in the development of a certain proportion of colonies showing quarter sectors of lac^- cells (Fig. 54).

While these results indicate that nuclear and mutational phenomena show a high degree of association, an additional observation is of interest because it is indicative of the existence of an occasional mutational lag: sectoring was observed in some of the colonies that developed from mutagen-exposed, uninuclear cells. Such sectoring is best explained on the basis of delayed mutational events.

EFFECTS OF METABOLISM ON "MUTATION FIXATION"

We have now discussed two major types of events that can play a role subsequent to mutagen exposure: (*1*) a series of unknown upheavals that may lead to a delayed alteration of the genotype and (2) the delayed phenotypic expression of earlier occurring changes in the genotype. A third possible event has been recognized in studies with certain mutagens, particularly UV, namely, the initiation of a chain of events that, depending on some metabolic processes, may or may not result in the subsequent occurrence of a mutation. In other words, mutagen exposure can set up "pro-mutational" reactions that may or may not result in a subsequent permanent alteration of the base sequence in a portion of the DNA molecule. The critical period determining the sequence of such pro-mutational events seems to be the time between mutagen exposure and the next replication of DNA; the critical metabolic processes during this period appear to be the rates of RNA and protein syntheses.

Some of the observations (Witkin, 1956, 1961; Doudney and Haas, 1960; Weatherwax and Landman, 1960; Lieb, 1960) that have led to such

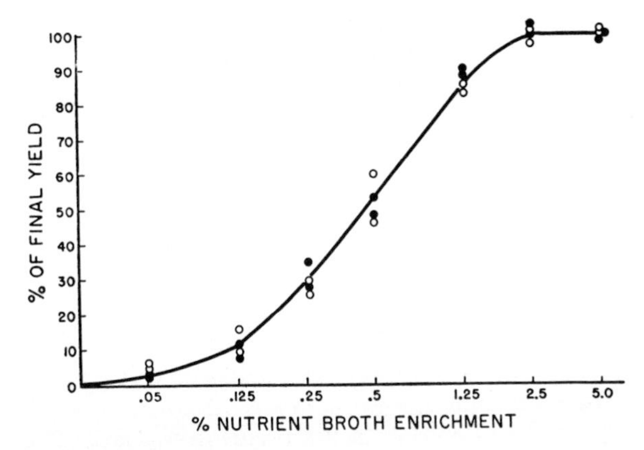

FIGURE 55. Expression of UV-induced *try*$^+$ prototrophs derived from a *try*$^-$ mutant strain of *E. coli,* on a minimal medium enriched with different amounts of nutrient broth. The open circles (○) represent irradiated cells plated at the enrichment levels indicated and then incubated for two days. Closed circles (●) represent irradiated cells plated at the enrichment levels indicated, incubated for three hours, and then transferred to plates to which 5 per cent nutrient broth had been added; they were incubated on these for two days. (From Witkin, 1956.)

conclusions can be summarized as follows: When auxotrophic bacteria (e.g., tryptophan-requiring, *try*$^-$, *E. coli* or *Salmonella typhimurium*) are exposed to UV, the frequency of recovered prototrophs (e.g., *try*$^+$), indicative of irreversible mutational events, is *increased* when a high rate of protein synthesis, made possible by supplementation of the post-irradiation medium with amino acids or nutrient broth (Fig. 55), is permitted prior to cell division. As Figure 55 also indicates, the critical factor is the early post-irradiation supplementation; transferring the irradiated cells to a differently enriched medium after three hours does not alter the final outcome. Mutant frequency is also increased when UV-irradiated bacteria are treated with basic dyes that, owing to their ability to complex with DNA, can retard cell division.* Mutation frequency is also increased if the cells are cultivated, prior to UV exposure or shortly thereafter, in media rich in adenine, guanine, cytosine, uracil, or their ribosides; deoxyribosides have no effect, thus implying the involvement of RNA synthesis. *Decreased* mutant frequency after UV exposure has been obtained when irradiated cells were exposed to inhibitors of protein synthesis (chloramphenicol, amino acid analogues) or of RNA synthesis (6-azauracil) during the critical early period after irradiation. All post-irradiation events are temporarily arrested, that is, both potential increases or decreases in mutational events triggered by the treatments cited previously are postponed, whenever a general inhibition of metabolic events is permitted to take place shortly after UV irradiation. Such general metabolic arrests

*On the other hand, thymine deprivation, leading to delayed DNA synthesis in a thymine-requiring strain, was found to interfere with the effects of enhanced protein synthesis on increases in mutation frequency.

can be produced either by placing the irradiated bacteria into saline or into a medium lacking a carbon source, or by adding dinitrophenol.

These seemingly complex observations start to make some sense if one considers (1) the ability of UV to alter DNA components, probably by thymine dimerization (see p. 102), (2) the probable ability of certain enzymes, comparable to the photoreactivating enzyme, to repair such alterations (p. 102), (3) the dependence of DNA synthesis on protein and RNA syntheses (see Lark, 1963, for references), and (4) the fact that DNA not only replicates itself but also furnishes the information required to produce the enzymes that must control DNA replication and the repair of thymine dimerization. Thus, when thymine dimerization, or other possible alterations of DNA occur after irradiation, the probability that such damage will lead to a permanent change in base sequence during the next DNA replication cycle will depend on whether or not repair takes place prior to renewed DNA synthesis. Lengthening the time prior to renewed DNA synthesis, without impairing the formation and action of repair enzymes, would increase potential mutational events; on the other hand, any inhibition of RNA and protein syntheses that affects the formation of repair enzymes preferentially would lead to an increased frequency of unrepaired mutational events.

We can now come back for a moment to the actual experiments concerning the influence of altered protein synthesis on post-UV events and gain an understanding of why one type of curve, showing changes in mutation frequencies, was obtained when irradiated bacteria were transferred from a medium supporting little protein synthesis to a medium supporting much protein synthesis, whereas another type of curve was obtained when the transfer was made in the opposite direction (Fig. 56). It is now possible to suggest, as Witkin has done, that the first curve (minimal medium → rich medium) shows the decline of mutation frequency (MFD) that results from

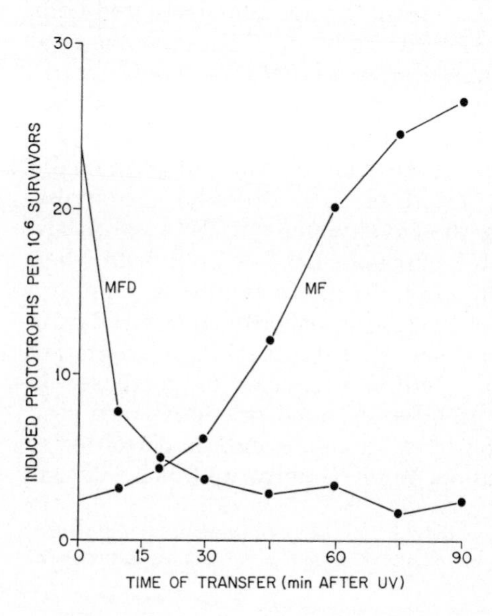

FIGURE 56. Mutation frequency decline (MFD) and mutation fixation (MF). Aliquots of irradiated *E. coli* suspension were spread on the surface of "glucose-salts-5 per cent nutrient broth" agar (SEM) and on minimal agar containing 1 μg tyrosine/ml (MT); the plates were incubated at 37° C and transfers were made at various times. For MFD, the transfers were from MT to SEM; for MF, the transfers were from SEM to MT. (From Witkin, 1961.)

the occurrence of a repair process prior to DNA replication. The second curve (rich medium → minimal medium), on the other hand, may reflect "mutation fixation" (MF), that is, the occurrence of DNA replication prior to repair and with it a fixation of the change initiated by the exposure to UV.

The enhancing effects produced by RNA precursors might be attributed to an interference, by modified RNA precursors resulting from irradiation, with the formation of the repair enzyme.* An alternate explanation has been proposed by Doudney and Haas (1960), who suggest that a unique mode of DNA replication may take place after UV exposure, transferring information (instead of directly from DNA to DNA) from irradiated DNA by way of RNA to newly formed DNA.

To conclude, as far as mutagenic effects of UV are concerned, at least three critical processes appear to interact in the determination of the events following UV irradiation: the extent of damage (probably thymine dimerization) to DNA, the length of time between irradiation and renewed DNA replication (controlled by enzymes including kinases), and the formation and activity of a repair enzyme. Since the last two events are subject to modification by agents affecting RNA or protein syntheses, or both, it is not surprising that altered metabolism can have a striking influence on the final results of an exposure to a mutagen like UV.

Not all determinants behave like the ones considered in the preceding section. Witkin and Theil (1960) showed that UV-induced mutations to streptomycin resistance were not modifiable by altered protein synthesis (including chloramphenicol treatment) following irradiation. This lack of response may be attributable to a difference in the DNA change which causes streptomycin resistance (a structural change instead of a point mutation?) or, possibly, to a difference in the base content of the polynucleotide region whose alteration leads to streptomycin resistance (possibly a lack of thymine, if repair of thymine dimerization is the chloramphenicol-sensitive, post-irradiation step). What has been observed for UV also may not apply to other mutagens, possibly because their action is not changeable by a repair enzyme. Thus, it was found that mutations triggered by exposure to alkylating agents (Strauss and Okubo, 1960) or caffeine (Glass and Novick, 1959) are not affected by subsequent modifications of protein synthesis induced, for example, by exposure of the treated bacteria to chloramphenicol.

However, the observations made in the case of UV irradiation furnish a clear example of the complexity of mutational events, whether spontaneous or induced. They illustrate that mutational events are not comparable to a mere decay of a molecular information-carrying structure, akin to the disintegration of radioactive atoms. Rather, mutation is a dynamic process involving a series of events, all of which have one end-result: the alteration of existing information in DNA by minor or gross changes in base composition and sequences. As we have seen, this end-result can be reached by a number of avenues, including the formation and incorporation

*See Chapter 16 regarding the role of RNA in transmitting information from DNA to protein-synthesizing sites.

of faulty bases, dimer formation, or structural changes in the DNA molecule. We have also seen that some of these changes are only the beginning of a chain of events, and can be made ineffectual by subsequent repair mechanisms.

Finally, we have seen that environmental condition can influence these processes and that susceptibility of different determinants (different regions of the polynucleotide chain, several hundred nucleotides long) to such changes can differ, presumably as a result of differences in the base content of the determinative regions. Mutation, therefore, must be regarded as a process that is relatively, but not completely, undirected, and which, though occurring spontaneously, is subject to a certain degree of modification by a few environmental conditions. It can be anticipated that our ability to modify mutational processes will increase as we learn more about the actual base-content and -sequence of genetically active DNA regions, about the specificity of action of different mutagens and antimutagens, and about the precise nature of the biochemical steps involved in the development and repair of altered information.

PART II

[7]

REPRESENTATIVE TYPES OF MUTANTS: I

Among bacterial mutants, obtained either spontaneously or with the help of mutagenic agents, certain types have been extensively analyzed by both geneticists and bacteriologists. They are mutants with altered resistance to inhibitory agents, especially antibiotics, mutants displaying novel growth-requirements or fermentation characteristics, and mutants involving changes in cellular or colonial morphology, virulence and antigenic characteristics.

MUTANTS RESISTANT TO INHIBITORY AGENTS

STREPTOMYCIN RESISTANCE PATTERN

One-step mutants exhibiting an absolute increase in resistance to certain inhibitory agents, for example, streptomycin-resistant mutants and phage-resistant mutants, have already been referred to in the foregoing chapters. The isolation of such one-step mutants is relatively simple; all that is required is exposure of large, predominantly sensitive populations to the inhibitory agent, e.g., phage or streptomycin, whereby all sensitive cells are inhibited and only the small proportion of resistant mutants, e.g., 1 in 10^9, continues to multiply. Thus plating of 10^9 cells from a phage-susceptible population on media containing phage will yield several colonies, each consisting of clones originating from a phage-resistant mutant. These mutants are absolutely resistant to the phage and thus represent one-step qualitative changes in properties which are undoubtedly connected with changes in some biosynthetic step. Similarly, in the case of streptomycin resistance, mutants can be isolated in one step that are resistant to the highest attainable concentration of the antibiotic. However, when a large streptomycin-susceptible population is plated on streptomycin-containing agar, mutants resistant to the highest level as well as mutants resistant to lower levels of streptomycin will be found. Thus plating on media containing, let us say, 100 μgm of streptomycin per ml will yield mutants resistant to an optimum concentration of streptomycin,

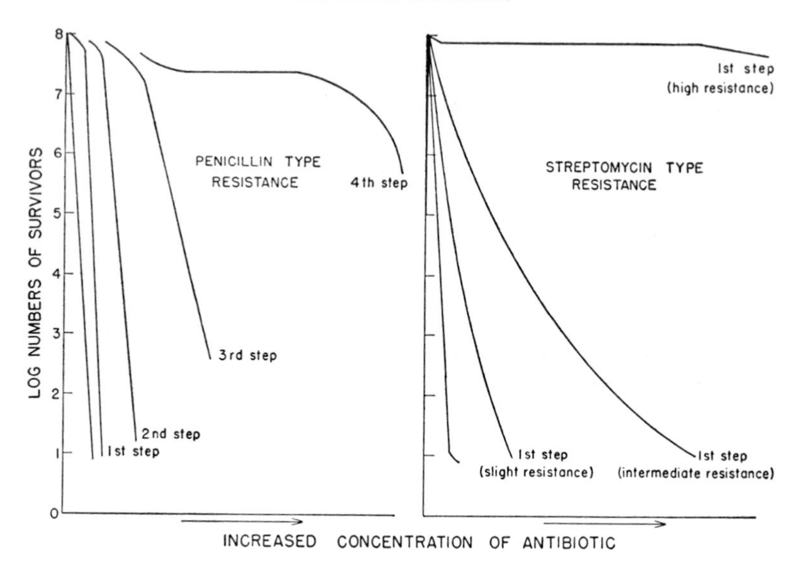

FIGURE 57. Comparison of survival curves, showing the penicillin and streptomycin types of resistance pattern. (From Bryson and Demerec, 1950.)

others which are only resistant to 100 μgm/ml of streptomycin, and still others which upon subsequent subculturing will be found to be streptomycin-dependent (Fig. 57).

Mutants resistant to different levels of streptomycin can arise at different rates (see Table 6). Demerec (1948) has proposed that this occurrence of mutants with different levels of streptomycin resistance involves mutations of genes with unequal potency, which means that in one cell a nucleotide region ("gene") may mutate and provide maximum resistance, whereas in another cell a different nucleotide region may mutate and thereby afford only intermediate resistance. Demerec's suggestion is supported by the recognition that streptomycin effects may involve more than one sensitive target in cellular metabolism (cf. Bragg and Polglase, 1962) and thus may be overcome by more than one type of genetically controlled metabolic alteration.* Furthermore, the results of recombination tests (see Chapter 12) following genetic transfers of streptomycin-resistance or -dependence "markers," either by transformation, transduction, or conjugation (cf. Hashimoto, 1960; Mitchison, 1962), have confirmed that different genetic sites can be involved in the control of low and high streptomycin resistance (*sr*) and also in streptomycin dependence (*sd*). However, at least in the case of *E. coli,* high resistance to streptomycin and *sd* can be controlled by closely linked sites within the same locus (nearby nucleotides within a given polynucleotide region). It is also interesting

*In general, drug resistance may develop when the genetic change permits either (1) an alternative or more efficient method for synthesizing an antagonized essential metabolite, (2) decreased affinity of the drug for cellular components, or (3) the synthesis of drug-inactivating enzymes (Bryson and Demerec, 1955).

to note that recombination tests revealed that in *E. coli* most reversions from *sd* to streptomycin independence do not involve reversions at the *sd* site, but rather mutations affecting other closely linked sites that lead to the activation of a suppressor interfering with the function of the unaltered *sd* site (cf. Böhme, 1961a).

Mutants which in one step acquire total resistance to a usually inhibitory agent also have been isolated in the case of isonicotinylhydrazine (isoniazid) and sodium-p-aminosalicylate (PAS) (Szybalski and Bryson, 1953a), as well as in the case of valine resistance in *E. coli*, K-12 (Manten and Rowley, 1953). This is in contrast to the pattern of mutational increases in the case of most antibiotics in which highly resistant mutants cannot be isolated in one step but require several mutational steps.

PENICILLIN RESISTANCE PATTERN

We shall choose penicillin resistance as an example of stepwise increases in resistance – an example that applies equally to mutational increases in resistance to most other antibiotics (e.g., Aureomycin, chloramphenicol, neomycin, Terramycin, etc). When a population of penicillin-sensitive cells is inoculated into a medium containing high levels of penicillin, no resistant mutants appear. However, if such a susceptible population is cultured in the presence of low levels of penicillin, mutants resistant to these low levels can be isolated and the latter cells when cultured in the presence of slightly higher levels of penicillin will permit the subsequent isolation of even more resistant mutants (Fig. 57). Thus penicillin resistance increases stepwise. Mutants resistant to high levels cannot be isolated in one step but require several mutational steps, each of which increases the resistance level in approximately geometric order.

Demerec (1948) has suggested that this stepwise increase in resistance involves changes of genes with equal or very similar potencies. To visualize this interpretation let us set the value of each mutational change (or the potency of the altered gene) at 2 units. A first mutational change would result in resistance to 2 units. A subsequent mutation, also of the potency 2, would raise the resistance level to 4, a further mutational change adding a third 2 potency would raise the resistance level to 8, the next change to 16, etc.

Again, as in the case of streptomycin resistance, recombination tests following genetic transfer have confirmed that many different genetic sites (not necessarily closely linked regions of the polynucleotide chain) can contribute to the development of resistance against a given antibiotic (Hotchkiss, 1951; Cavalli, 1962). A similar situation also has been found in the case of increased resistance to an analogue of an essential metabolite, namely, in the increased resistance of *Diplococcus pneumoniae* to amethopterin, an analogue of folic acid (Sirotnak *et al.*, 1960).

ISOLATION OF ANTIBIOTIC-RESISTANT MUTANTS

To accomplish the isolation of mutants highly resistant to antibiotics other than streptomycin or isoniazid, it is necessary to ascertain first the highest antibiotic concentration at which survivors can be isolated. Such survivors are usually first-step mutants. Doubling of the concentration used in the isolation of first-step mutants and culturing of the latter cells in this higher concentration will lead to the isolation of second-step mutants. In this manner, by increasing the antibiotic concentrations, isolation of survivors from each level used and subsequent exposure of such survivors to higher concentrations, mutants resistant to very high concentrations can be obtained. However, this method is cumbersome and shortcuts have been devised for cases where knowledge of the actual quantity of antibiotic used in each step can be neglected.

In one highly efficient technique, solid media are employed and each plate used for the isolation of mutants contains gradient concentrations of the inhibitory agent (Szybalski and Bryson, 1952). Such gradients are produced by pouring a layer of nutrient agar into a tilted Petri dish, permitting this layer to solidify, and subsequently pouring a layer of antibiotic-containing nutrient agar on top of the first layer while the plate is standing level (Fig. 58). During subsequent incubation, the downward diffusion of the antibiotic results in its dilution proportional to the thickness ratio of agar layers, and a uniform concentration gradient is thus established. In order to isolate resistant mutants a high concentration of susceptible cells (approximately 1×10^{10}/ml) is incorporated into the upper layer. Following incubation, a dense area of growth up to the limit of the tolerated, but unknown, antibiotic concentration will be noted. Beyond this region a few isolated colonies may be found in areas of higher concentration of the inhibitory agents (Fig. 59). These colonies represent clones from resistant mutants and they now may be restreaked towards areas of higher drug concentration or they may be used for the preparation of inocula for similar layer gradient plates with a two to five times higher antibiotic concentration.

A continuous culture device permitting the "automatic" isolation of

(10 cm. diameter; 2 x 20 ml. agar)

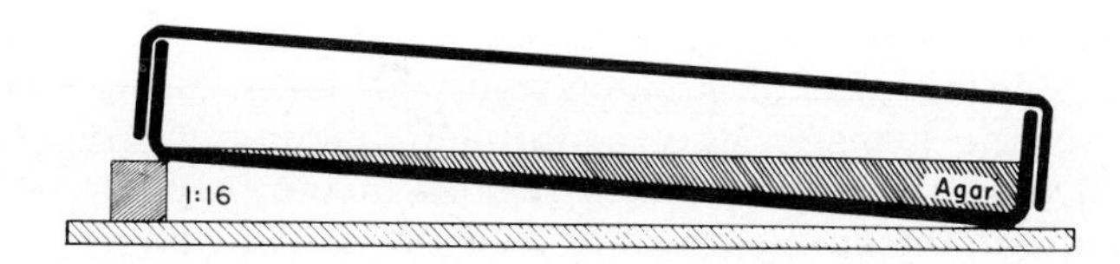

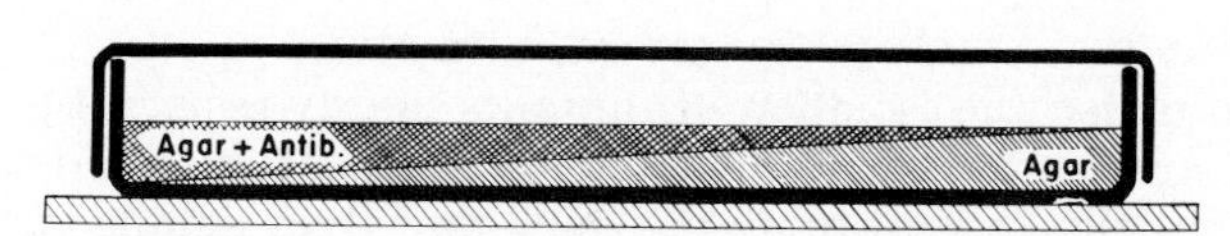

FIGURE 58. Preparation of a gradient plate. (From Szybalski and Bryson, 1952.)

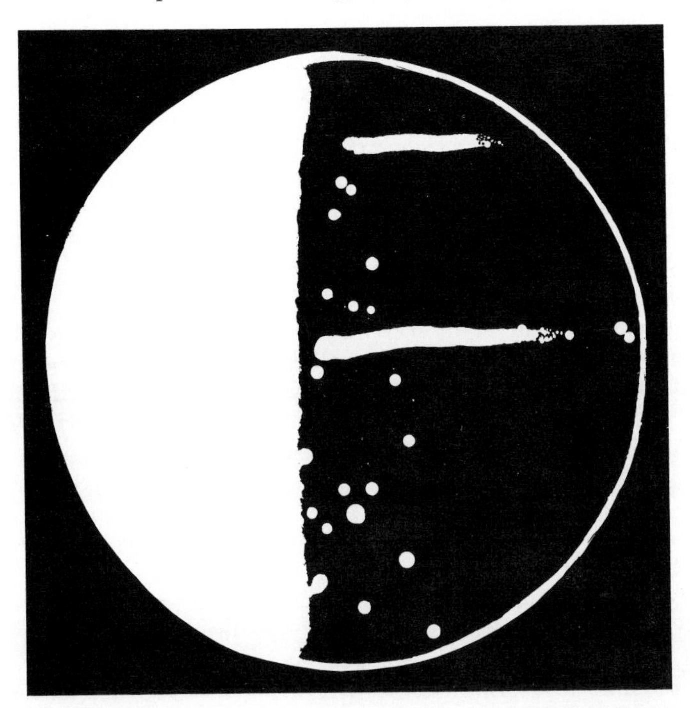

FIGURE 59. Growth of *E. coli,* strain B/r, on a gradient plate containing penicillin. The high concentration of the antibiotic is on the right side. Resistant colonies are seen beyond the boundary delimiting the inhibitory concentration for the majority of cells. Two resistant colonies have been streaked out, resulting in the production of second step resistant colonies in the area just to the right of the end of the confluent streaks. (From Szybalski and Bryson, 1952.)

highly antibiotic-resistant mutants has also been described (Bryson, 1952). In this "turbidostatic selector" a simple electronic circuit controls the periodic addition of nutrients to the growth-tube whenever the culture reaches a fixed turbidity, and a proportional-feed system automatically, and at a geometric rate, increases the concentration of the toxic substance in the nutrient in response to the reproduction of the cells.

Mutants resistant to inhibitory chemicals, such as dyes, metal salts, disinfectants, etc., or to analogues of some essential metabolites show a similar stepwise increase in resistance and can be isolated by repeated transfers in media containing increasing concentrations of the inhibitory agent or by the techniques just described.

In the isolation of resistant mutants it is prudent to remember that products of metabolism of the parental non-resistant type can interfere with the growth of resistant mutant cells (Saz and Eagle, 1953; Kraft and Braun, 1954) and that an excessive number of parental cells at the time of isolation of the mutants can, therefore, be detrimental rather than beneficial (see also p. 85). It has been established that growth of the parental population on unusual media, prior to the use of screening media, or a change of the genotype of the parents by the introduction of any one of a multitude of mutational changes can significantly alter the competition between parent cells and mutant cells, and can thus lead to an improved recovery of mutant cells (Kraft and Braun, 1954).

CROSS RESISTANCE AND COLLATERAL SENSITIVITY

The gradient plate technique described earlier can also be used for rapid determination of comparative resistance by streaking a bacterial suspension over the agar surface parallel to the axis of the concentration gradient. The length of the growing streak can then be used as a direct measure of the inhibitory concentration. In this manner Szybalski and Bryson (1952) have tested the degree of *cross resistance* among various antibiotic-resistant mutants of *E. coli.* As shown in Table 10, bacteria resistant to one antibiotic may display highly increased resistance to another antibiotic with which they had no previous contact. The cross resistance patterns fall into several distinct groups, as indicated by shading in Table 10. However, it appears that the patterns uncovered with derivatives of *E. coli,* B, are not always similar in other species, or even in other strains of *E. coli.*

It is possible to ascribe the occurrence of cross resistance to several factors: (1) the chemical similarity of the toxic agents; (2) their interference with the same metabolic pathway, in which case cells resistant through use of an alternative pathway would be immune to all agents affecting the original pathway; (3) the development of a non-specific biological change, such as decreased permeability; or (4) a change that affects a precursor reaction of several subsequent, diverse reactions. In addition, it has been observed that when a strain becomes more resistant to one antibiotic it may become considerably more sensitive to another (see fractions in Table 10). This phenomenon has been termed *collateral sensitivity* and may be regarded partly as the result of a selective process. In isolating strains resistant to one antibacterial substance, associated characteristics producing higher sensitivity to another antibiotic may be selected at the same time.

APPARENTLY UNRELATED CHANGES ASSOCIATED WITH ANTIBIOTIC RESISTANCE

As just stated, antibiotic-resistant mutants occasionally may display a change in one or more additional characteristics. These associated changes may not show an obvious connection with the increased antibiotic resistance, but they usually do have a causal relationship to it involving the occurrence of *one* fundamental change affecting both resistance and the other altered property. Thus, for example, highly isoniazid-resistant mutants of tubercle bacilli display lowered virulence for guinea pigs (Mitchison, 1954); similarly, many streptomycin-resistant mutants of *P. pestis* possess reduced virulence for mice (Brubaker and Surgalla, 1962). It can be assumed that such associated changes involve alterations of

So far, there has been no evidence that bacterial resistance or any other bacterial characteristic can be controlled by fairly automous *cytoplasmic factors*, like those responsible for some types of streptomycin resistance in the unicellular green alga *Chlamydomonas* (Sager, 1960), or the *petite* characteristic (tiny colonies due to a deficiency in respiratory enzymes) of yeast (Ephrussi, 1953). In the case of *Chlamydomonas*, a non-infective cytoplasmic factor without any known stage of integration with chromosomes is involved; in the case of yeast, the determinants associated with mitochondria appear to play a critical role. However, the absence of proof for the existence of such autonomous cytoplasmic determinants in bacteria does not necessarily imply the absence of such agencies of information transfer; it may be that we merely lack the appropriate techniques for recognizing their presence and function.

ANTIBIOTIC RESISTANCE IN RELATION TO THERAPY

Mutants resistant to antibiotics may establish themselves *in vivo*, e.g., in patients under treatment with antibiotics or in personnel exposed to aerosols containing low concentrations of antibiotics (Gould, 1957). In particular, streptomycin-resistant and isoniazid-resistant strains have been isolated fairly frequently from patients under treatment with these drugs – a fact which is not surprising in view of the one-step mutational increase to high resistance to these antibiotics. However, mutants resistant to other antibiotics, including those to which resistance increases stepwise, also have been isolated with increasing frequency since the advent of antibiotic therapy. The epidemiological problems that have been created by the emergence of antibiotic-resistant strains of staphylococci are a notorious example.

To avoid the undesirable occurrence of antibiotic-resistant mutants in therapy, it has been suggested that two antibiotics be given simultaneously, especially when streptomycin is one of the drugs employed. Since the mutation rate to antibiotic resistance is relatively low and since resistance to one antibiotic can be entirely independent of resistance to other antibiotics, e.g., Aureomycin-resistant mutants display no increased resistance to streptomycin, the chance of occurrence of mutants simultaneously resistant to both antibiotics should be as good as nil. Also, if antibiotics other than streptomycin or isoniazid are given singly, they should be employed at high levels because, as discussed above, resistance to these drugs develops by stepwise mutations, and low *in vivo* levels of the antibiotics, therefore, would favor the establishment of first-step mutants. High levels of the antibiotic *in vivo* should provide conditions under which first-step mutants are unable to survive.

Despite the theoretical soundness of these considerations, combination therapy (i.e., employing two or more antibiotics simultaneously) has not always prevented the emergence of resistant strains *in vivo*. One reason for such failure is the antagonism between certain antibiotics that can result when both are applied simultaneously (Jawetz *et al.*, 1954). For example, some staphylococci are inhibited less by the combination of bacitracin and terramycin than by bacitracin alone. Antagonism of this sort may be blamed, in part, on the weakly bacteriostatic effect of one of the drugs, which in turn interferes with the action of the other drug.* Such interference is also exemplified by clinical observations of the occasional emergence of isoniazid-resistant mutants in patients treated with isoniazid and PAS (see Mitchison, 1962), and by the observation that resistant mutants of *Mycobacterium ranae* can be isolated after exposure to high concentrations of isoniazid mixed with subinhibitory concentrations of streptomycin (Szybalski and Bryson, 1953b). Under these conditions, the decreased bacterial growth induced by streptomycin appears to protect the cells from the action of isoniazid; the prolonged residual growth permits the emergence of isoniazid-resistant mutants.

Simultaneous mutations in two DNA regions, each controlling resistance to one of two simultaneously applied antibiotics, also may occur occasionally and, for reasons not fully understood, the mutation rate for such a double event can be somewhat higher than that calculated from the product of the two individual mutation rates (Szybalski and Bryson, 1953a).† Finally, the occasional failure of multiple antibiotic therapy may also be attributable to cross resistance and to the occasional preexistence, at the time of initiation of chemotherapy, of mutants resistant to one or both of the drugs.

RADIATION RESISTANCE

Witkin (1947) first demonstrated that radiation-resistant mutants can be isolated from *E. coli*, strain B. This type of mutation is similar to that encountered in phage resistance, insofar as a one-step mutation is involved. However, in contrast to phage resistance, this increase in resistance is not absolute, but only relative. Witkin's technique for the isolation of radiation-resistant mutants is an interesting example of methods that may be applicable whenever one-step mutants leading to partial resistance are involved and techniques such as gradient plating are inapplicable.

Figure 60 shows survival curves for radiation-susceptible (B) and more radiation-resistant (B/r) cells of *E. coli* following exposure to increasing intensities of ultraviolet irradiation. It can be noted that the survival curves differ strikingly in the region of lower irradiation, but differ less in the area of high irradiation intensities. Exposure of a strain B population to intensities which suffice to eliminate the sensitive parent cells, therefore, would also affect the survival of the few B/r mutants present in a large population (1 in 10^5 cells).

In order to isolate the B/r mutants effectively, Witkin devised the multiple irradiation method. A population of sensitive cells is first exposed to an intensity of ultraviolet irradiation capable of killing 50 per cent of the B cells. As Figure 60 shows, B/r cells are not affected at this level of irradiation and their proportion in relation to the sensitive parent cells, therefore, increases among the survivors. In addition, the initial division of the surviving B cells is retarded so that the proportion of B/r cells will

*Remember, many antibiotics are only effective on actively metabolizing, multiplying bacteria.

†See also page 124 for an additional instance of involvement of more than one genetic site in one mutational event.

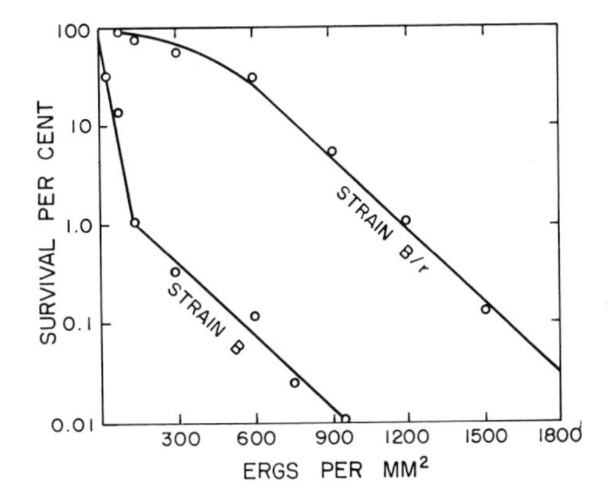

FIGURE 60. Sensitivity of strains B and B/r of *E. coli* to ultraviolet irradiation. (After Witkin, 1947.)

increase further during a subsequent growth-period of 24 hours. Samples of the 24-hour culture of survivors from the first irradiation are then exposed to another ultraviolet irradiation capable of killing 50 per cent of the B cells but none of the B/r cells. The survivors of the second irradiation are again permitted to grow for 24 hours and by now the proportion of B/r cells in the population has increased sufficiently to permit a third exposure to ultraviolet irradiation, this time to intensities which will kill all the sensitive B cells but will permit the survival of a sufficient fraction of the B/r cells.

We already discussed some likely mechanisms responsible for increased resistance to UV, namely, repair enzymes capable of removing thymine dimers (p. 102). Other conceivable mechanisms involve increased intracellular levels of catalase and cytochromes, which in deficient *E. coli* mutants proved to affect resistance to UV (Ogg *et al.*, 1956). Changes of this type may also account for the fact that mutants with increased UV resistance are usually more resistant to peroxide, nitrogen mustard, crystal violet, safranin, potassium tellurite and proflavin (Bryson, 1951). In fact, it has been demonstrated that radiation-resistant *E. coli* mutants can be obtained simply by isolating crystal violet- or proflavine-resistant mutants by means of the simple techniques previously described for obtaining antibiotic-resistant mutants.

BIOCHEMICAL MUTANTS

Even though all mutational changes must involve in one way or another a change in biochemical processes, the term *biochemical mutants* has been used in a more restricted sense to denote mutants that have lost or gained a nutritional requirement or show changes in other easily recognizable enzymatic processes, e.g., fermentation and capsule formation. Fundamentally, all mutational alterations affect either the formation or the function of specific enzymes, which in turn, control all of the cell's biosynthetic and metabolic processes. We shall see later how it has become possible to distinguish between so-called "structural genes" and "regulatory genes," the former controlling the specificity of a protein (i.e., its amino acid content and sequence), the latter determining whether or not the message from the "structural genes" will be translated into action (Chapter 17). At the moment, we shall not concern ourselves with the details of such control mechanisms, but shall take a look only at the end result of permanently altered information affecting either the formation or the functioning of enzymes.

Auxotrophic Mutants

The most widely investigated group of biochemical mutants includes the so-called *auxotrophic mutants*, an auxotroph being a mutant that requires growth factors not needed by the parent cells, or *prototrophs*. For example, prototrophic or wild-type cells of *E. coli* are able to grow in a *minimal medium* of the following composition:

	grams/liter
Glucose	1
KH_2PO_4	2
K_2HPO_4	7
Na citrate · $5H_2O$	0.5
$MgSO_4 \cdot 7H_2O$	0.1
$(NH_4)_2SO_4$	1

A mutant requiring leucine or thiamine, for example, cannot grow in this minimal medium but will grow if the medium is enriched with the specific requirement or if a *complete medium* is used. A complete medium can be prepared from commercially available nutrient broth or agar or can be made up as follows:

	grams/liter
Casein digest (NZ case)	10
Yeast extract	5
KH_2PO_4	1
K_2HPO_4	3
Glucose	5

ISOLATION PROCEDURES

It is relatively simple to isolate a prototrophic mutant from a population of auxotrophs by plating a sufficiently large population on minimal agar. The parent cells will be unable to grow, whereas any prototrophic mutant present, usually 1 in 10^8 cells, will develop into a visible colony. However, in order to isolate auxotrophs from prototrophic populations more complicated methods must be employed.

The oldest, simplest but least efficient method is to isolate at random a large number of colonies from an irradiated culture plated on complete medium. Each colony is subcultured on complete medium as well as on minimal medium. If growth fails on minimal medium but occurs on complete medium the isolate may represent an auxotrophic mutant. Less than 1 per cent of the colonies tested in this random isolation procedure is likely to be auxotrophic.

A more efficient method for the isolation of auxotrophic mutants is the delayed enrichment or layer plating technique. In contrast to the random isolation method in which one colony is tested at a time, the delayed enrichment method permits the simultaneous screening of several hundred colonies. A thin layer of unseeded minimal agar is poured into a Petri dish and, after it has solidified, a second layer of minimal agar containing 200 to 300 cells from a primarily prototrophic population is added. A third layer of minimal agar is then poured over the solidified second layer. Following incubation, prototrophic cells will give rise to visible colonies which will not spread because of the unseeded bottom and top layer. Mutant cells (auxotrophs) will fail to develop into visible colonies because their growth-requirements are not met by the minimal medium. However, if a fourth layer consisting of complete medium is now poured on top of the plates the required growth factors will diffuse through the other agar layers and stimulate growth of the auxotrophic cells into visible colonies. Several hours later the auxotrophs can be identified by the smaller size of their colonies. As illustrated in Figure 45, replica plating provides another simple method for isolation of auxotrophic mutants.

One of the most efficient methods so far developed for the isolation of biochemical mutants is the "penicillin method" discovered simultaneously by Lederberg (1948) and Davis (1948) (Fig. 61). This method is applicable to all bacterial species sensitive to penicillin and depends on the fact that penicillin is bactericidal only for dividing cells. Hence when a population of prototrophs is suspended for 12 to 24 hours in minimal medium containing bactericidal concentrations of penicillin, most of the prototrophs will be killed because they divide in this medium. At the same time, any auxotrophic mutants present will fail to grow in this deficient medium and, therefore, will survive despite the presence of penicillin. Subsequent plating of the penicillin-treated population onto complete medium will yield a high proportion of mutant, auxotrophic colonies as determined by their inability to produce growth when subcultured on minimal media. However, for some reason as yet unknown, as many as one-third of the apparent mutants may turn out to be prototrophs after renewed subculturing. Despite this erratic behavior of some isolates, the "penicillin method" represents a most useful tool for the isolation of auxotrophs.

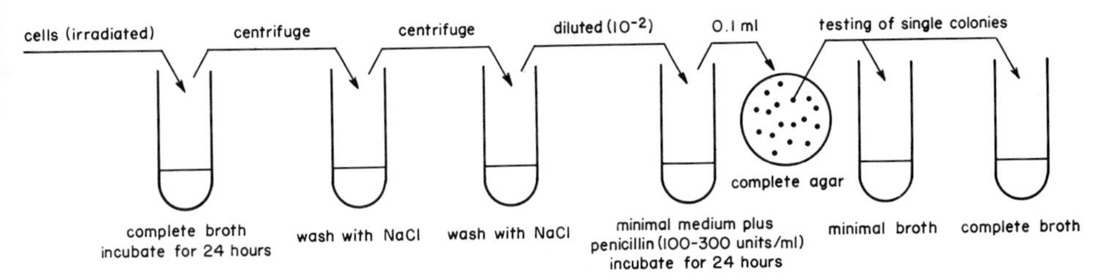

FIGURE 61. Isolation of auxotrophic mutants by the penicillin screening method. The lengths of incubation periods indicated are for *E. coli* and may require modification for work with other species.

Certain modifications which increase the efficiency of the penicillin method even further have been developed. One such modified procedure utilizes a greatly shortened period of exposure to penicillin, thus preventing excessive cross feeding and growth of auxotrophs from products released during prolonged penicillin lysis of prototrophs (Gorini and Kaufman, 1960).

In another improved procedure the whole process is carried out in solid medium instead of liquid medium (Adelberg and Meyers, 1952). First, a layer of minimal agar containing irradiated cells is poured into plates. After a few hours of incubation a layer of minimal agar containing penicillin is added. The penicillin is inactivated after 24 hours of incubation by the pouring of an additional layer of minimal agar containing penicillinase. The plates are reincubated and finally a layer of complete agar is poured on top of the previous layers. Renewed incubation will now promote the growth of auxotrophic mutants into colonies. The yield of auxotrophic mutants is very high in this procedure, and whereas in the liquid cultivation method several of the phenotypically identical auxotrophs may have originated from one original mutant cell, in this modified method each auxotrophic colony corresponds to one mutational event.

Matney and Goldschmidt (1962) have circumvented the somewhat laborious use of different agar layers by impinging cells on membrane filters, placing the membranes first on minimal agar, irradiating the impinged cells, and then placing the membranes, in turn, onto minimal agar and penicillin, minimal agar (to permit residual penicillin to diffuse away), and minimal agar and nutrient broth. The colonies which develop are picked and tested for their nutritional requirements.

The penicillin method also lends itself to the isolation of specific classes of mutants; this is accomplished by adding to the minimal agar layer, or to the penicillin-containing minimal liquid medium, specific growth factors that will not support the growth of undesired mutants, thereby eliminating them along with the prototrophs.

The penicillin method is not suitable for the isolation of all types of auxotrophs. Thus, one type, namely, thymine-requiring mutants, (which are of particular interest for genetic and biochemical studies, since thymine is found exclusively in DNA) is extremely difficult to isolate by the penicillin technique. This is due to the inability of the thymineless (*thy*$^-$) mutants to survive in a thymine-free medium (see p. 97). However, a procedure for their isolation has been discovered through the utilization of the selective survival of *thy*$^-$ mutants in a medium containing high concentrations of aminopterin and thymidine (Okada *et al.*, 1961). Both *thy*$^+$ and *thy*$^-$ cells are inhibited by aminopterin, but apparently this inhibition can be overcome by thymidine in the case of *thy*$^-$ cells.

Another technique for the isolation of auxotrophs utilizes the fact that 8-azaguanine is far more bactericidal for susceptible multiplying cells than for non-multiplying cells (Wachsman and Mangalo, 1962). Thus, this base analogue can be employed to isolate, with high efficiency, auxotrophic mutants from 8-azaguanine-susceptible strains, including strains with which the penicillin method is inoperable by virtue, for example, of the cells' production of penicillinase. The general procedure in the case of

8-azaguanine is similar to that described for penicillin: irradiation followed by a brief period of growth on enriched medium (to allow for delayed appearance of mutants), transfer to a minimal medium, addition of 8-azaguanine, incubation in the presence of the base analogue for two to five hours, and plating on minimal versus enriched media.

Another method employs the killing effects of tritium-labeled thymidine, which in a minimal medium is incorporated into the DNA of multiplying cells (prototrophs) far more rapidly than into the DNA of non-multiplying cells (auxotrophs); as a result, auxotrophs are killed at a far slower rate during subsequent storage at 5° C for 6 to 13 days. The method produces as much as a 4000-fold enrichment of auxotrophs over prototrophs (Lubin, 1959).

Additional use of the principle of selective suicide for prototrophs has been made in procedures in which the parental prototroph is diaminopimelic acid (DAP)- or thymine-dependent and thus, when growing in a DAP-free or thymine-free medium, is killed off by virtue of either the requirement of DAP for cell wall synthesis or of thymine for the prevention of thymineless death (see p. 97). In a minimal medium (in which they are unable to grow) auxotrophs will remain relatively unaffected by the respective absence of DAP or thymine and thus can be rescued by subsequent growth in a supplemented medium (Bauman and Davis, 1957).

In the case of spore formers, it has been found feasible to enrich cultures in favor of auxotrophic mutants by heat-treating germinating cultures (Iyer, 1960). Since spores and vegetative cells have quite different temperature sensitivities, germinating prototrophs are killed in a minimal medium, while non-germinating spores survive and can be caused to germinate subsequently in an appropriately enriched medium.

ASSAYING GROWTH REQUIREMENTS

Once mutants with increased growth requirements have been isolated, the specific nature of their requirements can be ascertained by several methods. One method consists of inoculating the mutant into minimal medium to which one of the following complex supplements has been added: (1) vitamin-free hydrolyzed casein which will support growth if the mutant requires a specific amino acid; (2) a mixture of water soluble vitamins which will support growth if one of these vitamins is required; (3) hydrolyzed yeast nucleic acid which will satisfy growth requirements for purines, pyrimidines, nucleosides and nucleotides; and (4) yeast extract which will stimulate the growth of certain vitamin-requiring mutants. Once the growth-response of a mutant to any of these general groups has been ascertained, the specific requirements can be determined by testing for growth in minimal media supplemented with either specific amino acids or specific vitamins, etc. Detailed suggestions for such tests have been compiled by Lederberg (1950).

Beijerinck's *auxanographic method* is another helpful technique for the characterization of biochemical mutants. The cells to be tested are incorporated into a layer of minimal agar and individual supplements, either in the form of crystals or as drops of a solution, are placed on the surface of the agar. The response to a specific supplement can then be recognized by growth in the area where the needed growth factor diffused into the agar. This method also permits the identification of complex requirements yielding growth in areas where the boundaries of two or more supplements overlap.

The replica plating technique (p. 72) also can be used for assaying the nutritional requirements of auxotrophic mutants.

POLYAUXOTROPHIC STRAINS

From auxotrophic mutants displaying one added growth requirement, e.g., leucine, additional mutants may be isolated showing still other growth-requirements, e.g., from a leucine-requiring mutant one might isolate a mutant requiring leucine plus arginine. In this manner polyauxotrophic strains can be "built up" and such strains have proven to be of considerable experimental value in recombination studies (see p. 292).

REVERSE MUTATIONS

Auxotrophic mutants are apt to revert to nutritional competence, i.e., the prototrophic characteristics may be restored by a mutational event. Thus prototrophic mutants, which no longer require the formerly needed growth substance, may occur in a population of auxotrophs and may selectively replace the auxotrophic cells. Such changes from populations requiring specific growth-factors to populations capable of growing in minimal media have all the aspects of adaptation in the sense of "training" bacteria to dispense with formerly needed growth factors. However, experimental studies of the type discussed in Chapter 5 indicate that this is a case of mutation and selection. The actual nature of these reverted mutants may differ. Some represent true reverse mutants in which the original prototrophic condition is restored not only physiologically but also genetically. Others represent only apparent reversions, that is, they involve mutants which phenotypically resemble the prototrophic parent type but in which the activity of the mutated gene has been altered by an additional *suppressor mutation* (see p. 79). The resulting apparent reversions, leading to mutants that merely mimic the original parent type but are not genetically identical with it, are of some importance for considerations which we shall discuss later under the subject of changes in antigenic characteristics. In any event, prototrophs may occur in auxotrophic populations and it is, therefore, important to maintain stocks of biochemical mutants under conditions which would give such reverse mutants the least chance of establishing themselves once they arise. A complete medium that adequately supplies the growth requirements of the auxotrophic mutant should be chosen for maintaining such cultures. If prototrophs are found in auxotrophic stock cultures, they can be eliminated fairly rapidly with the help of the penicillin technique described earlier.

BLOCKING OF BIOSYNTHETIC STEPS AND SYNTROPHISM

Auxotrophic mutants displaying a similar requirement may be dissimilar both genetically and biochemically. The possible genetic differences, which will be the subject of later discussions, are based on the fact that within a given polynucleotide region (genetic *locus*) specifying the formation of a specific enzyme, the alteration of any one of the several hundred different nucleotides (genetic *sites*) can result in the inactivity or alteration of the enzyme controlled by this locus. The biochemical differences between auxotrophs with identical growth requirements could be due to the fact that mutations at different loci may affect different steps (each controlled by a different enzyme) in one chain of biosynthetic processes. Such problems have been investigated extensively with *Neurospora* mutants and with bacterial mutants (see Davis, 1950; Adelberg, 1953; Wagner and Mitchell, 1964). From the vast storehouse of available information we shall choose the terminal steps of tryptophan synthesis to illustrate possible biochemical (and genetic) differences among auxotrophs with similar growth requirements.

Part of the synthesis of tryptophan proceeds through the following steps, all of which can be carried out by prototrophic cells: X $\xrightarrow{1}$ anthranilic acid $\xrightarrow{2}$ indole glycerol phosphate $\xrightarrow{3}$ indole $\xrightarrow{4}$ tryptophan. A mutation blocking step 4, by affecting the activity of the enzyme tryptophan synthetase, will lead to a requirement for tryptophan, which can be repaired only by the addition of tryptophan itself. However, another mutation which blocks step 3 will produce auxotrophs whose requirement for tryptophan can be compensated for by the addition of indole or tryptophan. Similarly, a mutation that interferes with step 1 may cause a tryptophan requirement which can be remedied by the addition to the minimal medium of either anthranilic acid, indole glycerol phosphate, indole, or tryptophan.

Blocking at different steps is usually due to the action of different genes. When such a mutational block occurs, the precursor tends to accumulate; e.g., anthranilic acid will accumulate if step 2 is blocked in the scheme shown in the preceding paragraph. The accumulated substance may be excreted into the medium, frequently in sufficient quantities to supply the needs of another mutant blocked at an earlier step. This second mutant can then grow and supply the final product to the first. This mutual feeding is known as *syntrophism*. Thus two mutants with similar requirements, each incapable of growing by itself in a minimal medium, may grow when placed together in minimal media because the accumulating intermediate of one mutant may be able to stimulate growth of the other which in turn supplies the end product to the first. For example, two tryptophan-requiring mutants, one blocked at step 3 of the above scheme, the other at step 2, may both grow when placed on a minimal medium. Syntrophic growth also can be employed for testing whether two mutants with similar nutritional requirements are blocked at different steps in the synthesis of the growth factors. However, Davis (1950) has pointed out that absence of syntrophism between two mutants with a common requirement does not always prove that they are blocked at the same enzymic site, "since precursors may fail to accumulate because of instability, diversion along an alternative path, or the inability of the cell to build up a concentration adequate for excretion."

"LEAKY" MUTANTS

The mutational blocks in biosynthesis are not always complete blocks (i.e., a complete absence of activity of a specific enzyme); frequently, genetic changes may result in a quantitative deficiency of a specific enzyme, or in a qualitative alteration that produces lower enzyme efficiency (see Chapter 14). In either case, the rate of production of a required growth factor can fall below the level necessary for normal growth; supplementation then becomes necessary, even though the presence of the substance required to reestablish normal growth can be demonstrated (in obviously insufficient quantities) within the cells.

DIFFERENT CAUSES OF AUXOTROPHY

An added growth requirement is not necessarily the result of a mutation directly affecting the information available in DNA for the formation of a particular protein (enzyme). The auxotrophic condition may also arise by virtue of a mutation affecting the various control mechanisms that influence the formation and function of an enzyme. We shall discuss the nature of some of these controls in Chapter 17, and we shall then see that among them are "repression" mechanisms (blocking of the *formation* of an enzyme) and "feedback" mechanisms (inhibition of an early enzyme reaction by the product of a metabolic pathway). Mutations affecting either of these control mechanisms can result in enzyme inactivity despite the presence of unaltered DNA information for enzyme specificity.

Other indirect mechanisms by which enzymatic reactions may be absent despite the intracellular presence of the required enzyme include (1) mutational alterations of the intracellular environment (cofactors, pH) required for enzyme activity, (2) interactions among enzymatic reactions belonging to the same or different pathways, and (3) alterations of the "active uptake" of required metabolites (Cohen and Monod, 1957).

SOME APPLICATIONS OF AUXOTROPHIC MUTANTS

The ability of auxotrophic mutations to block biosynthetic reaction chains at different steps has made them extremely useful for studies on the biosynthesis of growth factors. Although a great deal of this work has been carried out with the help of *Neurospora* mutants, bacterial mutants have also been used widely (see Wagner and Mitchell, 1964). The principal method in such studies is the identification of intermediates which are capable of substituting for the requirement of an end product; e.g., the ability of anthranilic acid and indole glycerol phosphate to satisfy the growth requirements of certain tryptophan-requiring mutants indicated that these compounds must play a role in the biosynthesis of tryptophan. The sequence of the biosynthetic steps is reflected by the requirement of different mutants. For example, if two mutants requiring tryptophan are found and both can grow on indole glycerol phosphate but only one can grow on anthranilic acid, it follows that anthranilic acid is the precursor of indole glycerol phosphate in the biosynthesis of tryptophan. Similarly, auxotrophic mutants have been used in the analysis of the biosynthetic steps involved in light production by luminous bacteria (McElroy and Farghaly, 1948), in nitrogen fixation by *Azotobacter* (Wyss and Wyss, 1950), in pigment production of *Serratia marcescens* (Green and Williams, 1957), in the development of bacterial spores into mature vegetative cells and as a tool for studying the biosynthesis of lipids (see Wagner and Mitchell, 1964).

As already indicated, auxotrophic mutants also have been vital for the elucidation of control mechanisms of enzyme formation and for the analysis of some of the complex interactions within and among biosynthetic pathways. They have made it possible to confirm that the original "one gene-one enzyme" hypothesis of Beadle and Tatum, broadly speaking, remains valid, even though it is no longer possible to define a gene in absolute terms, and even though there are important exceptions to the rule. Thus, cases are known in which one enzyme, apparently consisting of two components, can be altered by changes at either one of two distinct genetic loci; enzyme molecules may contain functionally distinct regions that are determined by different sites within one gene locus; and changes occurring in one mutational event (and apparently affecting one genetic locus) may affect two different enzymes. In the latter case the dual effect seems to involve a structural effect on one enzyme and a regulatory effect on another enzyme. We shall discuss these aspects in more detail in Chapter 14.

In addition to their usefulness in the analysis of "gene action" and control mechanisms, auxotrophic mutants can be used for biologic assays of various amino acids, vitamins, and nucleic acid derivatives, just as naturally occurring exacting mutants of lactobacilli have been used for such purposes. Nutritional requirements also can serve as excellent "markers" in studies on population dynamics (Ryan and Schneider, 1949) and in the analysis of the problems of intercellular transfers of genetic materials. We shall discuss their use in these studies in more detail in later chapters.

Meiotrophic Mutants

For cases in which naturally deficient strains (such as *Pasteurella pestis*, which normally requires cystein, methionine, phenylalanine, valine and isoleucine for growth) give rise to mutants that can dispense with one of these requirements ("gain mutation"), the term *meiotrophic* mutant has been proposed (Englesberg and Ingraham, 1957). This permits a differentiation between auxotrophs (requiring additional growth factors) and meiotrophs (requiring fewer growth factors) derivable from relatively fastidious prototrophs.

Fermentation Mutants

Variability in fermentative characteristics represents one aspect of bacterial variation that has been well recognized by bacteriologists since the days of Pasteur. In fact, one of the earliest contributions to bacterial genetics, dating back to 1907, had as its subject changes in fermentative characteristics of *E. coli* strains. Massini (1907) showed in these early investigations that a non-lactose-fermenting strain (nowadays labeled lac^-) gave rise to lactose-fermenting (lac^+) variants which could be recognized by cultivating the cells on lactose agar containing an indicator that turned red when acid was formed. Thus lac^- cells appeared white, whereas lac^+ cells, which fermented the sugar to acids, appeared red. When lac^-

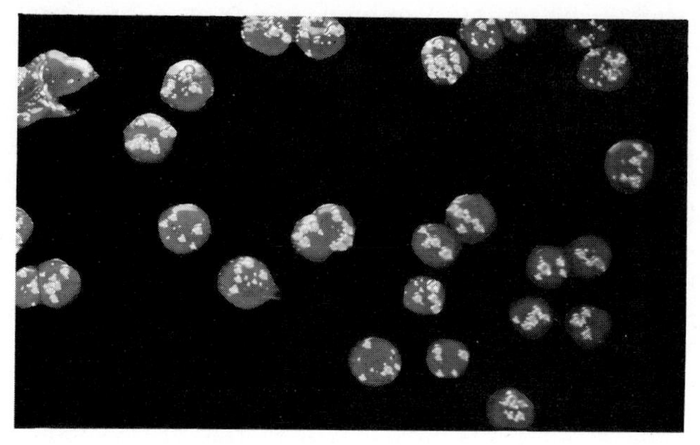

FIGURE 62. *Lac*$^+$ papillae on *lac*$^-$ colonies of *E. coli*. (Courtesy of Parr.)

cells were plated on an indicator medium, white colonies first developed but upon continued incubation red (*lac*$^+$) papillae appeared (Fig. 62). Upon subculturing from such papillae stable *lac*$^+$ strains could be isolated. Massini recognized such variants as mutants and later work by Lewis (1934) revealed that *lac*$^+$ mutants occurred at a constant frequency of approximately one *lac*$^+$ cell per 100,000 *lac*$^-$ cells.

Various other fermentation mutants have since been studied, especially those of Enterobacteriaceae, e.g., mutants differing in the utilization of citrate (Parr and Simpson, 1940), maltose (Doudoroff et al., 1949), galactose (E. M. Lederberg, 1960; Soffer, 1961), arabinose (Englesberg, 1961), or raffinose (Lester and Bonner, 1957). However, the utilization of the galactoside lactose, involving the formation and activity of the enzyme β-galactosidase, has remained one of the most widely investigated fermentation characteristics and has been instrumental in the recognition of the genetic factors controlling carbohydrate utilization (for references, see Jacob and Monod, 1961; Lowe, 1960).

INDUCIBLE AND NON-INDUCIBLE ENZYME SYNTHESIS

As in the case of mutations affecting steps in biosynthesis, the utilization of carbohydrates is under the control of specific enzymes (see example in Table 11), and the formation, as well as the function, of these catabolic enzymes is controlled by DNA in much the same way as are those of biosynthetic enzymes. Thus we find that fermentation characteristics are dependent on structural genes (which determine the specificity of enzyme formation), on regulatory genes (which determine whether or not an enzyme is formed) and on genes controlling the active transport of the respective substrate into the cell ("permease"-controlling genes).

As we shall see in greater detail later (Chapter 17), the regulatory mechanisms that control the formation of an enzyme can be influenced by environmental conditions in two directions: either in the direction of enzyme *repression* or in the direction of so-called enzyme *induction*. It is now believed that these two opposing phenomena have, in reality,

TABLE 11. *Utilization of galactose by* E. coli *K-12 (Leloir pathway)**

1. Galactose + ATP $\xrightarrow{\text{galactokinase}}$ galactose 1-phosphate + ADP
2. Galactose 1-phosphate + uridine diphosphate glucose $\overset{\text{galactose 1-phosphate uridyl transferase}}{\rightleftharpoons}$ uridine diphosphate galactose + glucose 1-phosphate
3. Uridine diphosphate galactose $\overset{\text{uridine diphosphate galactose 4-epimerase}}{\rightleftharpoons}$ uridine diphosphate glucose

Sum: Galactose + ATP → glucose 1-phosphate + ADP

*After Kalckar *et al.*, 1959.

a common basis (see pages 347 to 349). Briefly, it is believed that the regulator gene controls the formation of a cytoplasmic repressor which can interfere, by a sort of clogging mechanism, with the transcription (or, possibly, with the translation from RNA to protein) of the message produced by the structural DNA gene; the result is a lack of formation of the enzyme (see Fig. 154).

The only way in which an enzyme can be formed in a repressor-carrying cell is to divert the repressor from its clogging function—to occupy it, so to speak, by tying it up with a material for which it has high affinity—thereby freeing the polynucleotide region of the structural gene (or, possibly, the messenger RNA) to do its job of transcribing its information into the formation of the specific enzyme protein. The material that can tie up the repressor—resulting in de-repression—is the *inducer*, usually the substrate itself or a molecule closely related to it. Thus, in the presence of the substrate in the cell, the enzyme capable of breaking down this substrate can be formed. The continued presence of the substrate within the cell (requiring the additional activity of the "permease"-controlling genes) is needed in order to assure continued formation of the enzyme. As soon as the substrate is removed, the repressor will again assume its clogging functions, and enzyme production will cease. This dependence of enzyme formation on the presence of the substrate, or on a product closely related to it, has been variously called "induced enzyme synthesis," "adaptive enzyme formation," or "enzymatic adaptation." It is preferable to refer to it as induced enzyme synthesis or enzyme induction.

Some enzyme systems, active in catabolism, will function very nicely even in the absence of the substrate; in contrast to the "adaptive enzymes," they have been referred to as "constitutive enzymes." These substrate-independent enzyme systems are now regarded as having escaped from the controlling functions of the repressor system, and will occur in cells that have an inactive regulator gene, and thus no repressor. It has been possible to isolate constitutive mutants from inducible strains, and conversely, inducible mutants (possessing an active repressor system) have been isolated from strains forming a given enzyme constitutively.

From all this we can see that mutations affecting fermentative characteristics may do so by affecting any one of a number of "sensitive spots." They may alter the enzyme structure-specifying polynucleotide region, they may alter the function of the regulatory genetic system, or they may alter the genetic system controlling the entrance of the substrate into the cell.* In addition, non-chromosomal DNA elements (see p. 291) have been shown to be occasional carriers of the determinants of fermentative capabilities (Falkow and Baron, 1962). In some cases, fermentative properties can also be altered phenotypically by infection with a temperate bacteriophage (Li *et al.*, 1961).

It remains a matter of speculation whether such multiple potential sites of genetic alterations, capable of influencing fermentative characteristics, are responsible for the usually relatively high rates of mutation (1×10^{-7} to 1×10^{-5} per generation) encountered in the case of fermentative mutants. We are faced with a similar lack of genetic stability (in comparison to mutations involving auxotrophy or resistance) in the case of pigmentation and many antigenic mutants. As we shall see, certain high rates of antigenic instability ("phase variation") have been attributed to an undefined cytoplasmic state that can interfere with the functioning of a specific gene (p. 170). Whether a similar situation plays a role in the instability of some fermentation mutants remains to be seen.

Earlier we referred to the fact that the ability of bacteria to produce a specific enzyme requires, in the case of inducible enzymes, the presence of a specific substrate. Such environmentally controlled enzymatic induction may be distinguished from mutational changes in a very simple way: it can occur without multiplication of cells, and, instead of affecting merely *one* out of many cells, it causes changes in *all* cells of a genetically competent bacterial population. But remember, even though in adaptive enzyme formation a particular phenotype, e.g., lactose-fermentation of *lac*⁺ cells, will not express itself unless specific environmental conditions prevail, the potential capacity for this phenotypic change is always under genic control.

KINETICS OF INDUCED ENZYME SYNTHESIS

Some interesting data have been obtained regarding the kinetics of the process of induced enzyme synthesis, i.e., of the manner and rate with which de-repression (p. 348) may manifest itself. Of these we shall refer here only to one example of the competitive interactions which can occur in the synthesis of different specific enzymes. *B. subtilis* cells grown in the presence of D-fructose and L-arabinose display two successive growth cycles ("diauxie"), separated by a period of lag or even decrease (Fig. 63). According to Monod (1947), each of these cycles corresponds to the exclusive utilization of one compound at a time; the second compound is not attacked until the first has been exhausted. Experimental data indicate that this is due to inhibitory effects produced by the first compound on the

*In this third case, bacteria may possess active enzymes, demonstrable in cell homogenates, but fermentation does not occur because the substrate cannot enter the cell. Such cases, e.g., the presence of β-galactosidase in lactose-negative *Shigella* (Rickenberg, 1960), are referred to as involving *cryptic enzymes*.

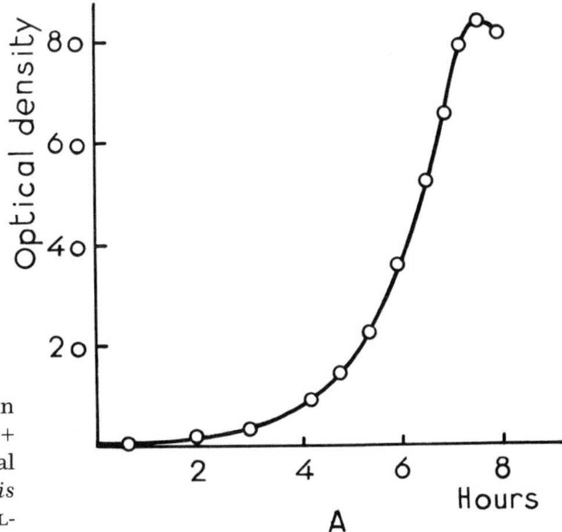

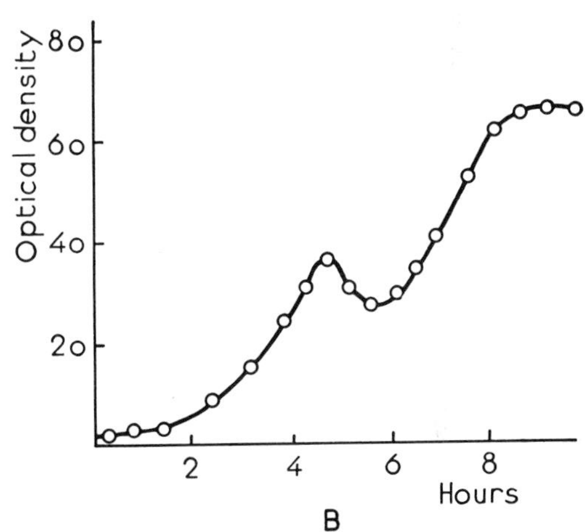

FIGURE 63. A, Growth of *B. subtilis* in synthetic medium with saccharose + D-mannose as carbon source; normal growth curve. B, Growth of *B. subtilis* in synthetic medium with D-fructose + L-arabinose as carbon source; "diauxic" curve. (From Monod, 1947.)

formation or activity of the induced enzyme attacking the second compound.

SEQUENTIAL INDUCTION

Specific polynucleotide regions (cistrons) control the potential for the formation of specific inducible or non-inducible enzymes; we should not expect, therefore, that any *one* specific gene (cistron) change may endow a mutant with the ability to attack simultaneously a group of *non-related* substrates. However, bacteria that can respond with induced synthesis of one particular enzyme, in the presence of its particular substrate, may thereby produce intracellular intermediates that in turn can serve as substrates for the induced synthesis of certain other inducible enzymes (provided the cells possess the inherent potential to form such enzymes in the presence of the appropriate inducer). In this instance, the provision of *one* external substrate can initiate a kind of chain reaction causing the successive induction of a series of specific enzymes, each reacting with one of a number of *related* substrates. Each one of the required substrates is formed as the result of the prior activity of an inducible enzyme. This phenomenon, initially christened "simultaneous adaptation" by Stanier (1947), nowadays goes under the term of *sequential induction*. Stanier pioneered the use of this phenomenon in the determination of the nature of intermediates in metabolic pathways involving inducible enzymes.

To illustrate the principle of this method, a metabolic pathway requiring catalysis by a series of specific inducible enzymes may be represented as follows:

$$A \xrightarrow[E_A]{} B \xrightarrow[E_B]{} C \xrightarrow[E_C]{} D \xrightarrow[E_D]{} \text{etc.} \quad \text{etc.}$$

where E_A, E_B, etc. represents the specific enzymes catalyzing each step. These enzymes are not apparent unless the cells are exposed to specific substrates, A, B, etc. Exposure to substrate or condition A will cause the production of E_A, thereby catalyzing step $A \longrightarrow B$. The formation of B will in turn stimulate the activity of E_B, causing the formation of C, etc. Therefore, cells "adapted" to metabolite A will simultaneously also be "adapted" to metabolites B, C, D, etc. Similarly, the initial "adaptation" of cells to any intermediate in the pathway will cause the full "adaptation" to later intermediates in the same reaction chain. In view of its specificity this phenomenon permits testing whether a presumed intermediate actually belongs in a given reaction chain consisting of a series of steps which involve induced enzyme synthesis. In the actual tests an organism is exposed to a primary substrate and is then tested for its ability to dissimilate the presumed intermediate. If the compound under investigation is immediately attacked by the cells "adapted" to the primary substrate A, but is not similarly dissimilated by control cells "unadapted" to A, then it is highly probable that the compound is a member of the reaction chain. Metabolic processes of bacteria which have been analyzed, partly or entirely, by an analysis of inducible enzyme patterns include oxidation of acetate and Krebs-cycle compounds, oxidation of aromatic compounds, oxidation of tryptophan and of tyrosine and the fermentation of purines (Stanier, 1951).

UTILITY OF FERMENTATION MUTANTS

Fermentation mutants are useful tools for genetic studies with bacteria. They can be readily recognized by plating on indicator media such as eosin-methylene blue (EMB) agar or triphenyltetrazolium agar containing the appropriate carbohydrate. On EMB agar, colonies that ferment the carbohydrate produce a dark purplish color; non-fermenters fail to do so. On tetrazolium agar, non-fermenters appear bright red and fermenters remain uncolored. The reaction is sufficiently sensitive to permit the easy identification of non-fermenter sectors in fermenter colonies, or vice versa. This simplicity of identification makes fermentation mutants extremely useful for studies on recombination (p. 294) and for population studies where the fate of two easily distinguished types is determined. A specific example of the application of this "marker" technique has already been cited in connection with studies on the delayed appearance of mutants (p. 109).

Pigmentation Mutants

Another group of biochemical mutants that has received some attention due to the ease of identification is the one involving changes in pigmentation. For example, both Bunting (1946) and Lincoln (1947) have made extensive use of differences in pigment production displayed by various *Serratia marcescens* and *Phytomonas stewartii* mutants, respectively, to analyze mutation rates and phenomena of selection. Their investigations have supplied substantial evidence indicating that changes in pigmentation can be attributed to mutations, and recombination studies have confirmed that nuclear determinants are involved in the control of pigment production (Belser and Bunting, 1956). Such control is again exerted through the formation and function of enzymes involved in the biosynthesis of pigments. Different steps in these biosynthetic events have been recognized with the aid of a series of independently isolated *Serratia* mutants with pigment deficiencies; the occurrence of syntrophism (see p. 133) between two such mutants has been observed (Green and Williams, 1957). In the case just referred to, two pigment-deficient mutants (A, B) formed pigment when grown together (A+B) indicating that the lack of enzyme formation or function in these two mutants involved two different steps, and that during joint growth A was able to supply B with the lacking intermediate, or vice versa.

Pigmentation is a characteristic that can be greatly altered by temporary modifications due to environmental changes. For example, changes in the medium such as a shift in pH can cause changes in pigmentation. In contrast to mutations, such temporary modifications affect all members of a homogeneous population and will last only as long as the changed environment persists. Pigmentation mutants, on the other hand, arise as individual variants among a large number of genetically different parent cells. Thus, it is important to distinguish between pigmentation variants due to mutation and those caused by temporary modification. The use of constant environmental conditions is one of the necessary requisites in studies on pigmentation.

Mutation rates of most pigmentation mutants thus far studied differ widely and can be very high; rates varying from 1×10^{-3} to 1×10^{-7} have been observed. The cause of the relative instability of some of these mutants is still unknown.

[8]

REPRESENTATIVE TYPES OF MUTANTS: II

MUTATIONS AFFECTING CELLULAR MORPHOLOGY

Heritable alterations of a variety of morphological cellular characteristics have been observed and analyzed. Among these are changes in cell appendages (such as flagella and pili or fimbriae), in spore formation, in cell wall synthesis and in cell size.

FLAGELLA

Members of normally flagellated species, such as *Salmonella typhimurium* or *Listeria monocytogenes*, can display environmentally induced, temporary phenotypic modifications, as well as spontaneously occurring, more permanent genotypic changes in presence, motility and morphology of flagella. With the aid of transduction (see p. 265), it was demonstrated that several genes (*Fla* genes) are required for the synthesis of flagella in *Salmonella* (Stocker *et al.*, 1953).* These *Fla* genes, however, do not control the specificity of the fibrous protein, called *flagellin,* which is the main constituent of flagella. Other genes, i.e., those that are concerned with so-called phase variation (p. 170), appear to control the structural composition (amino acid sequence) of the flagellar protein, and with it, the antigenic specificity ("phase") and shape of the flagella (Iino, 1962). We shall later see that phase variation of *Salmonella* populations represents an alternate manifestation, in individual cells, of either one of two antigenic properties (H_1 or H_2) of flagellar H antigens; this variability in H antigens, in turn, reflects some unique interactions between the genetic determi-

*In the presence of these genes, "mobility-conferring particles" (possibly identical with the flagellum itself or equivalent to the basal granule that determines the production of a flagellum) are produced and these, though unable to reproduce, can be transferred, *in the absence of the genetic determinants,* from one cell to another (Stocker, 1956).

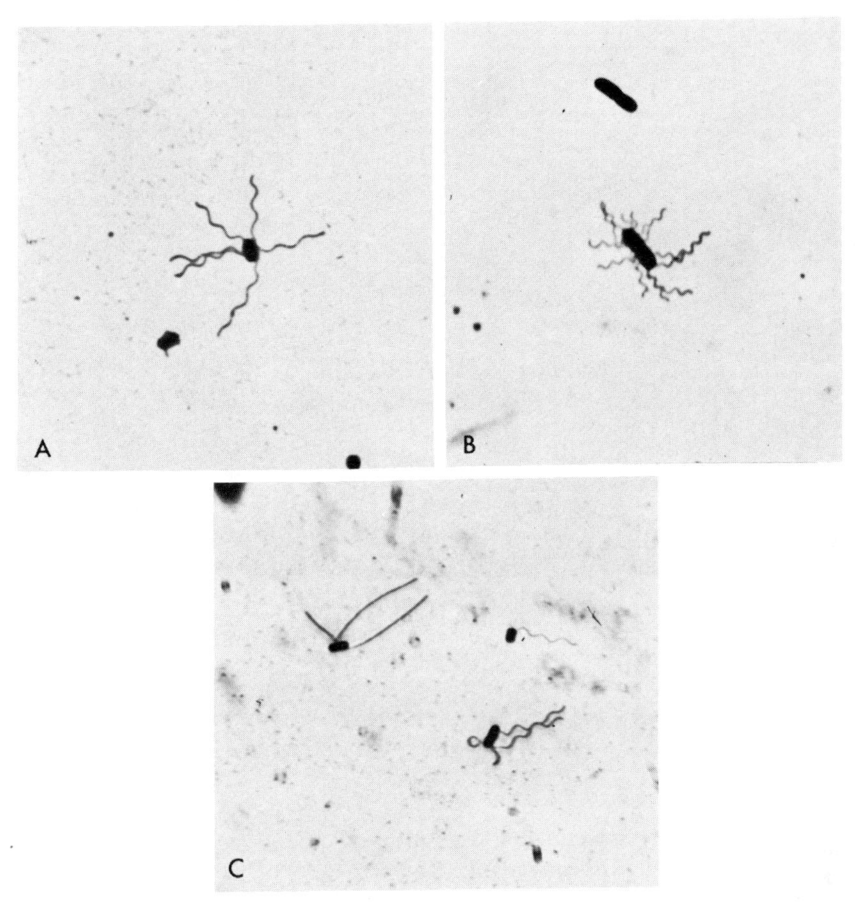

FIGURE 64. Shapes of flagella. **A**, *Proteus mirabilis*, normal flagella. **B**, *Proteus mirabilis*, curly flagella. (Both photomicrographs × 3600.) **C**, *Listeria* strain showing two organisms with normal flagella and one with straight flagella. (Magnification: × 1800.) (From Leifson *et al.*, 1955; and Leifson and Palen, 1955.)

nants of H_1 and H_2 (p. 172). Since the antigenic properties of flagella are associated with flagellar morphology, instabilities in flagellar morphology, corresponding to those in H antigenicity, can be observed in *S. typhimurium* (Iino, 1962).

The protein-dependent morphological alteration of flagella expresses itself in the tightness of the helical shape assumed by most flagella. This has been referred to as "wavelength" (Leifson *et al.*, 1955) (Fig. 64), but variants with straight flagella also have been observed (Leifson and Palen, 1955) (Fig. 64). In *Listeria*, separate mutations for flagellation and motility have been observed (i.e., not all flagellated strains are motile), and these changes were found to occur at rates of 10^{-8} to 10^{-9} per cell division (Leifson and Palen, 1955).

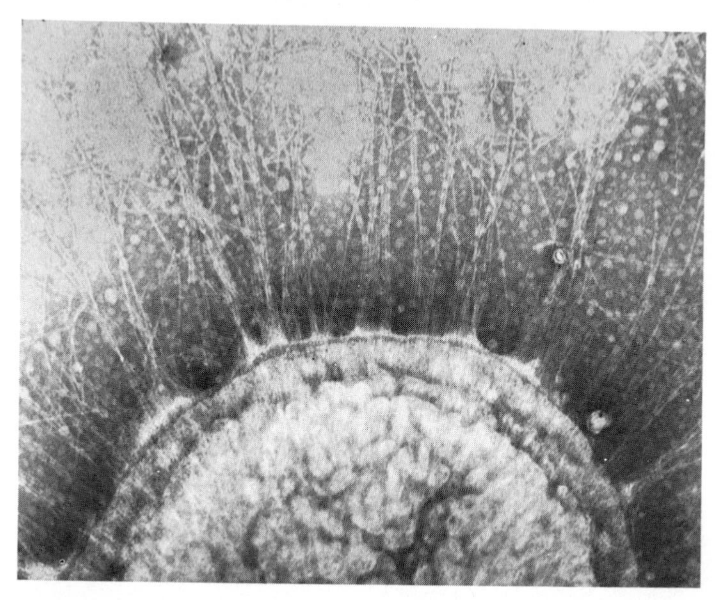

FIGURE 65. Electron micrograph of fimbriae of *Klebsiella*. The bacteria have been negatively stained by phosphotungstate. (Magnification: × 75,000.) (From Thornley and Horne, 1962.)

Pili or Fimbriae

Non-flagellar, proteinaceous, filamentous appendages with a diameter of 80 to 100Å, called fimbriae or pili (Fig. 65), have been observed in many Enterobacteriaceae (Brinton, 1959; Duguid, 1959), and their presence is associated with the appearance of new antigenic cell surface properties and with the ability of fimbriate organisms to cause hemagglutination (Shedden, 1962). As in the case of flagella, cultural conditions can modify the phenotypic manifestation of genotypically fimbriate organisms, but non-fimbriate mutants, unable to develop fimbriae even under conditions that normally favor their development, have been described. Fimbriate or piliate mutants of *Proteus* have been shown to have a selective advantage under anaerobic or relatively anaerobic conditions, whereas non-fimbriate mutants tend to become dominant under aerobic conditions (Shedden, 1962). Mutation rates from piliation (P^+) to non-piliation (P^-) in *E. coli* are high (4×10^{-4} per bacterium per generation); mutation rates from P^- to P^+ are extremely low (Brinton, 1959). Recombination tests have permitted the identification of the region of the *E. coli* chromosome controlling the development of pili (Brinton *et al.*, 1961).

Spores

Most strains of spore-forming species of bacilli will form spores when environmental conditions become unfavorable for vegetative growth. As early as 1881, Pasteur described the occurrence of asporogenous variants of *Bacillus anthracis*, and numerous papers have since reported on both relatively unstable asporogenous variants (i.e., variants that are capable of reverting to spore formation) and extremely stable variants which have not reverted during years of laboratory cultivation. The genetic basis of spontaneous variation in spore formation has been partially elucidated by recent studies utilizing transformation tests (p. 239) among sporogenous and asporogenous mutants of *B. subtilis* (Schaeffer *et al.*, 1959; Jacob *et al.*, 1960; Spizizen, 1961). Spontaneously reverted, asporogenous mutants of *B. subtilis* arise as frequently as 1 in 10,000, and can be easily recognized and isolated owing to the fact that their colonies, instead of turning brown after 48 hours of incubation, remain white after prolonged incubation. Mutants in which the process of sporulation is blocked at either one of several different steps have thus been isolated (Fig. 66).

Transformation with DNA from the sporogenic parent type or even with DNA from another, differently blocked, asporogenous mutant will yield sporogenic transformants. In addition, the property of non-sporulation (Sp^-) has been reported to be transferable by transformation to spore-forming cells. These observations suggest that, at least in certain types of asporogenous mutants, the information for spore formation is not lost, but suppressed owing to the presence of some additional (Sp^-) information. Mutable determinants controlling the rapidity with which sporulation may occur also have been described.

The already mentioned stable asporogenous variants have not been transformable by DNA from spore-forming strains, a fact which has served to support speculations that sporulation also may be controlled by episomes (see p. 291) (Jacob *et al.*, 1960). It has been argued that since the phenotypic manifestation of the sporulation trait takes place only during certain stages, this may reflect an ordered, environmentally controlled alternation of detachment of an episome from its chromosomal sites (preceding sporulation), and its subsequent reintegration during spore germination. So far, however, such assumptions remain purely hypothetical.

Cell Wall

Among the several alterations in cell wall structure that can occur either as the result of temporary environmental modifications or as the consequence of relatively permanent mutational changes, we shall consider here only those causing a major deficiency in cell wall components. More subtle changes giving rise to changes in antigenic characteristics will be dealt with in the next chapter.

PROTOPLASTS

To understand the basis of spontaneous and permanent mutational changes in cell wall formation, we must first review some of the more drastic changes in cell wall integrity that can be caused by environmental agents. In 1952, Tomcsik and Guex-Holzes described the formation of a spherical body following lysis of the cell wall of a gram-positive bacillus by lysozyme; the resulting *protoplast* rapidly lysed in the usual hypotonic

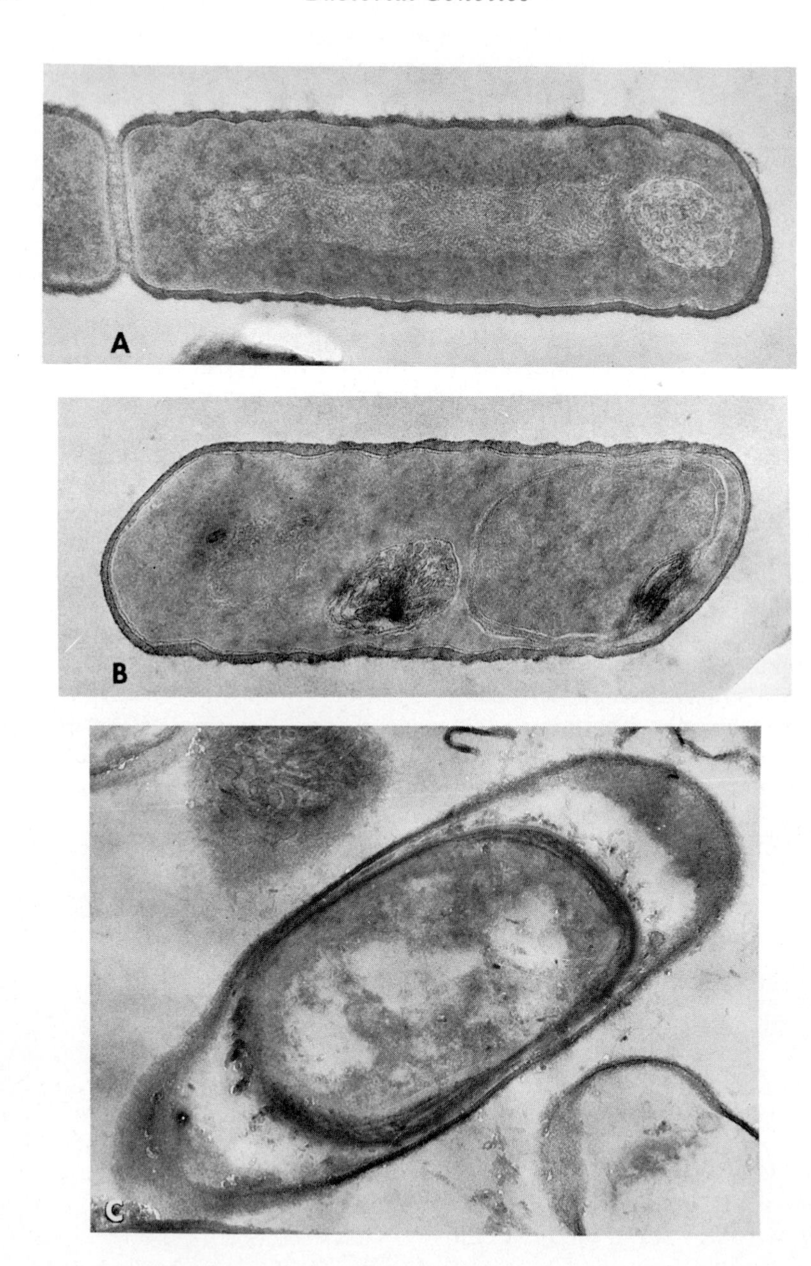

FIGURE 66. Electronmicrographs of three non-sporulating mutant types derived from *Bacillus subtilis* (Marburg strain) showing some of the various stages at which sporogenesis may be blocked as the result of mutation. **A**, Mutant Osp C in which sporogenesis is blocked at a very early stage; a mesosome is visible at the right but no typical prespore is visible (× 84,000). **B**, Mutant Osp 4UV in which sporogenesis is blocked at a somewhat later stage; a prespore in a deficient envelope and a mesosome are clearly discernible (× 91,000). **C**, Mutant Osp 91/1 in which the prespore, having reached a quite advanced stage, lyses (× 96,000). (Courtesy of A. Ryter.)

media. In 1953, Weibull demonstrated that it is possible to maintain such protoplasts for prolonged periods of time in a hypertonic medium, e.g., in 0.3 M sucrose. Under the latter condition, the hypertonic environment assumes the "corsetting" functions usually delegated to components of the cell wall.

Protoplasts of gram-positive bacteria have been demonstrated to be truly deficient in cell wall materials. They lack attachment sites for bacteriophage and are therefore phage resistant; they do not react with antisera prepared against isolated cell walls; they lack DAP (an amino acid found mainly in the cell wall fraction of bacteria), but they retain essentially all normal biochemical and biological activity except the ability to multiply (cf. Weibull, 1953). Protoplasts rarely revert spontaneously to normal bacillary forms, but they may do so, with high frequencies in some species, under specific environmental conditions, e.g., after plating in 30 per cent gelatin (Landman and Halle, 1963). In the case of spontaneous reversions, only a very few cells of a protoplast population revert following removal of the condition that led to protoplast formation; in reversions "induced" by specific environmental conditions, all protoplasts may revert to the bacillary form.

SPHEROPLASTS

Osmotically fragile, spherical elements, similar to the protoplasts just discussed, also can be produced, by a variety of treatments, from gram-negative bacteria. Lederberg (1956) was the first to demonstrate that protoplast-like bodies can be produced after exposure of growing *E. coli* cultures to high levels of penicillin in the presence of 0.3 M sucrose (Fig. 67). Penicillin is now known to interfere with the formation of the rigidity-producing, mucopeptide-containing, inner layer of the cell wall of gram-

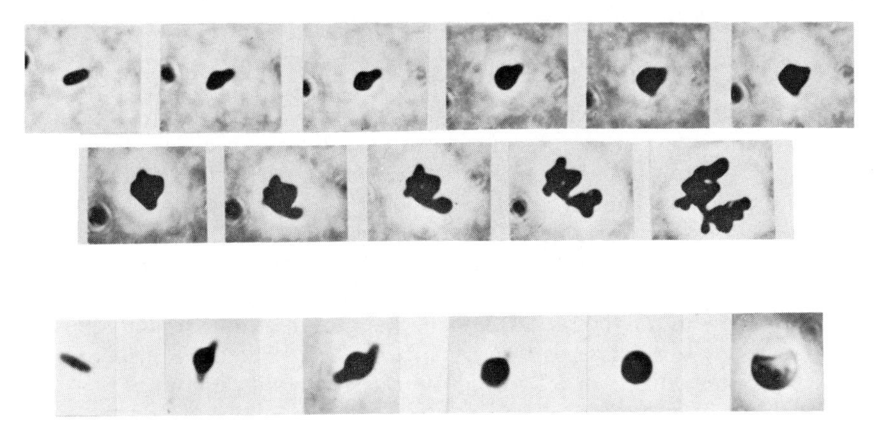

FIGURE 67. Phase contrast time-lapse photomicrographs showing formation and multiplication of *E. coli* spheroplasts (0 to 4 hours). Top, colony development from a single bacterium in penicillin + sucrose agar. Bottom, successive stages of spheroplast formation from an individual cell in penicillin + sucrose-containing broth. (From Lederberg and St. Clair, 1958.)

negative bacteria, presumably as the result of its effect on the cell membrane—the site of cell wall synthesis (cf. Landman, and Ginoza, 1961).

Many other agents and conditions affecting the synthesis or integrity of cell wall components are now known to be capable of producing similar protoplast-like structures; these include serum factors (Michael and Braun, 1959), glycine (Welsch and Osterrieth, 1958), lithium ions (Pizzura and Szybalski, 1959), enzymes isolated from leucocytes (Weibull, 1953), lytic enzymes or unbalanced growth occurring in old cultures (Chatterjee and Williams, 1962; Sinkovics, 1957), phage enzymes (Carey *et al.*, 1957) and lysozyme, provided that access to the lysozyme-susceptible inner mucopeptide layer of gram-negative bacteria is made possible by either chelation, trypsinization, or freezing and thawing (Kohn, 1960). The osmotically fragile spheres thus produced from gram-negative bacteria differ from the lysozyme-produced protoplasts of gram-positive bacteria in an important respect: they retain parts of the cell wall. Accordingly, to distinguish them from true protoplasts, they are referred to as *spheroplasts* (Brenner *et al.*, 1958). The presence of cell wall residue or of modified cell wall components on spheroplasts is reflected by the fact that they retain phage adsorption and antigenic sites and are usually capable of multiplication.

Evidence has been provided indicating that the nature of the wall lesion can be distinctly different following the use of different spheroplasting agents. Thus 20 per cent sucrose can protect penicillin spheroplasts or serum spheroplasts, but it cannot protect spheroplasts produced by penicillin and serum together (Michael and Braun, 1959). This has been interpreted as an inability of the hypertonic environment to compensate for the larger wall lesions produced by the combination of penicillin and serum. Stabilization of spheroplasts and protoplasts in *hypo*tonic media with the aid of spermine (10^{-3} M) and other polyamines has been reported (Tabor, 1962), but the mode of action of these stabilizing agents is not yet clear. Spheroplasts can revert to the normal bacillary form when the conditions leading to spheroplast formation are removed.

WALL-DEFECT MUTANTS

We have already referred to the fact that the amino acid α, ϵ-diamino pimelic acid (DAP) is found almost exclusively in the cell wall of many bacteria. It therefore will come as no surprise to learn that DAP-requiring *E. coli* auxotrophs lyse in DAP-free, hypotonic media (Bauman and Davis, 1957; Kandler and Zehender, 1957), but can be stabilized and grow as spheroplasts in DAP-free, hypertonic media (Lederberg and St. Clair, 1958). These mutants obviously behave like permanent spheroplasts: unable to grow in a hypotonic DAP-free medium owing to wall deficiency, but able to grow as spheres in a hypertonic DAP-free environment or as normal bacillary forms in a DAP-containing hypotonic medium.

L-FORMS

One of the more puzzling bacteriological problems of the 1940's and 1950's was the significance of the so-called L-forms ("L" in honor of the

Lister Institute), or "large bodies," first noted by Klieneberger (1935) in cultures of *Streptobacillus moniliformis*. These forms were soon recognized as descendants of typical bacteria, and it was demonstrated, particularly in studies with *Proteus* and *Salmonella*, that they are apt to arise either spontaneously or following exposure to penicillin (see Dienes and Weinberger, 1951). Their true significance, however, remained controversial for many years.

A number of investigators regarded L-forms as stages in an orderly life cycle and thus coined the term "L-phase." Bacteria in this "phase" were described either as large round bodies or small granular forms; they were recognized principally by their unusual growth in soft 10 per cent serum-agar. The so-called 3A type L-forms yielded tiny compact colonies with granular subsurface growth (Fig. 68); the so-called 3B type was characterized by relatively large colonies containing spherical elements

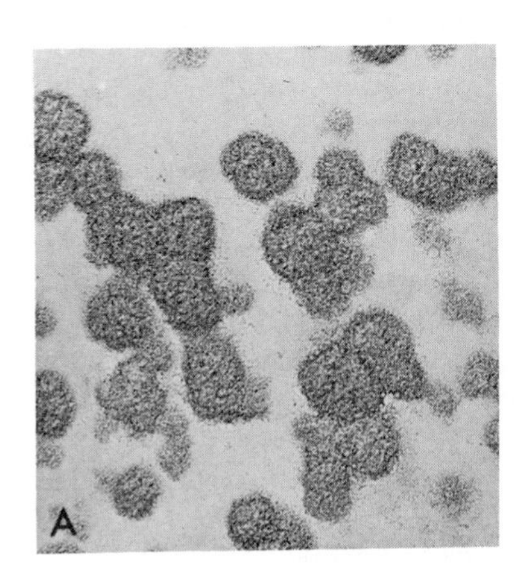

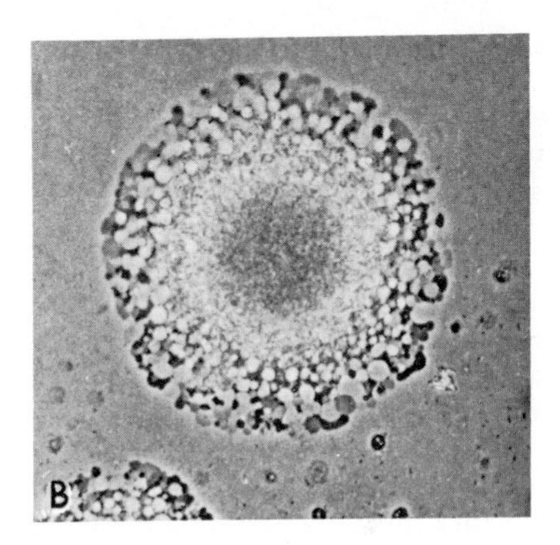

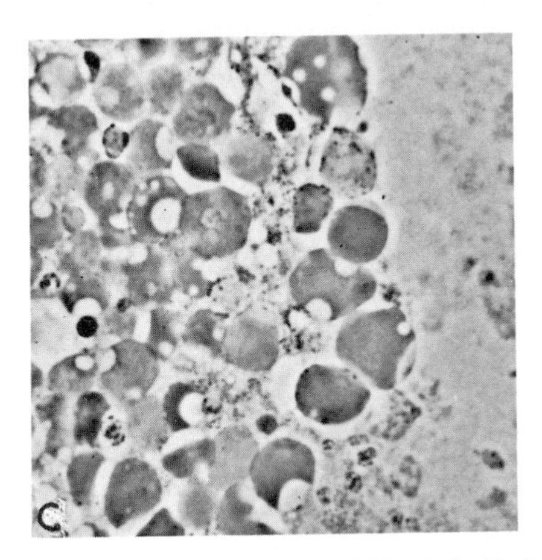

FIGURE 68. Colonies of L-forms of *Proteus mirabilis*. A. Stable L-form, Type A. (Magnification: × 220). B. Labile L-form, Type B. (Magnification: × 220). C. A section of the margin of a Type B colony. (Magnification: × 1100). (From Taubeneck, 1962.)

of different sizes (2 to 10 μ in diameter) (see Fig. 68). Various investigators confirmed that in addition to serum, penicillin was required in the medium to sustain the unusual morphology and the budding growth of the 3B type, which reverts to typical bacillary form and multiplication in the absence of penicillin. In contrast, the 3A type usually remains stable in the absence of penicillin, although this antibiotic in *high* concentration serves to induce the abnormal morphology and growth (cf. Taubeneck, 1962). Reversions of the 3A type to the bacillary form have never been observed in some cases (*E. coli*); they do occur rarely, e.g., at frequencies of less that 1 in 10^9 in others (*Salmonella*), and more frequently in still others (*Proteus*). It is now known that specific environmental conditions, such as 30 per cent gelatin, can foster high frequencies of reversions in L-form populations that would fail to revert under ordinary penicillin-free conditions (Landman and Halle, 1963).

With the discovery of penicillin-induced spheroplasts, the tendency grew to regard L-forms as more or less stable spheroplasts (Lederberg and St. Clair, 1958). However, a number of workers soon recognized that the story was somewhat more complicated. Only the 3B forms are really comparable to multiplying spheroplasts, representing temporarily cell-wall deficient elements with a cell membrane sufficiently tough that they can persist in the absence of hypertonic media. In contrast, the spheric elements present in the 3A type colonies, which are known to have suffered a greater cell wall loss than 3B forms,* apparently owe their stable existence to a unique type of bacterial variation, namely, to an inability to reconstitute a normal cell wall (Altenbern and Landman, 1960; Landman and Ginoza, 1961; Taubeneck, 1962).

The exact mechanism responsible for this essentially irreversible loss of the cell envelope in 3A type forms remains a matter of speculation, but the fact that conversion to the stable L-form can occur without a requirement for multiplication, and can simultaneously affect the majority of the members of a penicillin-exposed population, demonstrates that conventional mutation of a nuclear determinant is not involved. Taubeneck has suggested that the relative irreversibility of the loss of cell wall may be due to the loss of all the cell wall residues that could serve as matrix for the structural assembly and incorporation of the gene-controlled building stones. Landman has suggested that the cell membrane is a critical site for both wall synthesis and cell division, and that agents, like penicillin, that damage the membrane lead to stable L-forms because either (a) a component ("primer") of a self-sustaining reaction chain required for septation and wall-formation is lost,† or because (b) the ability of the membrane to accumulate a critical metabolite essential for its repair is destroyed. Critical soft agar concentrations are required for the multiplication

*The differences in loss of cell wall material between 3A and 3B types is indicated by the fact that 3B forms retain bacteriophage receptors, while 3A forms lack these.

†One possible candidate for the hypothetical primer is the mesosome (p. 26), which may be lost or critically reduced in numbers as a consequence of wall removal, "perhaps in the manner in which a wrinkle in an inner tube is lost when the tire is removed"; new folding of the membrane (mesosome formation) may be induced mechanically by the solid media that cause reversions (Landman and Halle, 1963).

of the stable L-forms, and it has been suggested that such agar concentrations can support an artificial sort of division: "The burgeoning protoplasm of the multinucleate large bodies oozes between, and is pinched off and supported by, the agar fibers in such a way that further growth of the nucleated cell fragments can occur" (Landman and Burchard, 1962).

Whatever the ultimate explanation for the mode of damage to cell wall synthesis in these stable L-forms might be, they do furnish an outstanding example of the occasional loss of cellular properties due to a loss of cell organelles that appear to be relatively independent of control by chromosomal genes. It will be recalled that a somewhat comparable example is provided by the older observations on the loss of certain respiratory functions in "petite" (small colony) variants of yeast (Ephrussi, 1953), in which such loss is associated with the spontaneous or acridine-induced loss of mitochondria-like particles.

To recapitulate, three types of wall-deficient variants of gram-negative bacteria giving rise to L-type growth have now been recognized: (1) spheroplast-like temporary variants, (2) true mutants that have suffered a gene-controlled impairment of the synthesis of a wall constituent, such as DAP, and (3) an unusual type of relatively stable variant that, having suffered a total or near-total loss of cell wall, is usually, but not always, unable to regenerate new cell wall and thus can remain in the form of a naked protoplast capable of multiplication only under specific environmental conditions.

Cell Size and Ploidy

In Chapter 3 we referred to the fact that the information-carrying chromosomal structures of higher organisms occur as duplicate sets within a single nucleus (diploidy) or may be present in gametes as a single set (haploidy). We also pointed out that bacterial nuclei are as a rule haploid, although transient stages of partial diploidy have been recognized following bacterial conjugation (see p. 289). Studies with higher organisms have revealed that the nuclei of some species may contain more than two homologous chromosomes. Such polyploids may contain three identical sets of each chromosome (triploid), four sets (tetraploid), five sets (pentaploid), or even more than that (see Fig. 16). Although such polyploidy may occur naturally in higher organisms, it can also be induced by certain chemicals, such as colchicine and camphor, which prevent normal splitting of the chromosomes during meiosis or mitosis. Polyploids usually have giant cells and the polyploid condition can be maintained indefinitely.

Bacterial variants with large cell size, suspected of being caused by a polyploid-like condition, have been described occasionally. For example, the formation of a *Pasteurella pestis* strain with giant cells following treatment with camphor, a known polyploidizing agent, has been reported (Won, 1950). Large cells also have been found to occur transiently in cultures of staphylococci, either spontaneously or, at higher frequencies, following exposure to UV, formaldehyde and certain antibiotics (Clark and Webb, 1955). A further indication of the polyploid nature of these transient elements is the difference in their survival following x-irradiation; with normal, haploid cells a "single hit" type of exponential inactivation is observed, whereas the suspected polyploid cells yield a very different, "multiple hit" type of sigmoidal survival curve. However, the instability of these large forms of cocci suggests that they are rather temporary variants in which, because of environmental conditions, nuclear changes (possibly involving nuclear fusion within a multinuclear cell) may have occurred.

More stable, and presumably diploid, large cell types have been isolated from *E. coli* cultures after exposure to camphor vapors (Ogg and Zelle, 1957). These large cells also showed atypical, sigmoid survival curves after x-irradiation, had twice the normal DNA content per cell, and yielded small cell segregants after cultivation under particular environmental conditions (Ogg and Humphrey, 1963). The presumably haploid segregants could be reconverted to the presumably diploid, radiation-resistant state by growth in the presence of camphor vapors. Partial diploidy revealed by segregation of markers following haploidization has been detected in cells resulting from conjugation in *E. coli* (p. 289). In such studies, certain strains (called *Het*) were found in which partial diploidy was not just transient after mating, as is the case for the majority of sexually fertile *E. coli* strains, but was persistent over several generations following mating (Lederberg, 1949).

[9]

REPRESENTATIVE TYPES OF MUTANTS: III

Variability in colonial morphology, antigenic characteristics and virulence has been of particular interest to investigators concerned with bacteria that belong to pathogenic or potentially pathogenic species. There is good evidence that changes in these properties are frequently the result of spontaneous mutations, and that most mutations affecting one of these characteristics also affect the other two characteristics. For example, a change in virulence is usually, though not necessarily, associated with changes in colonial morphology and antigenicity. Similarly, environmental conditions capable of modifying, for example, antigenic properties are also likely to cause temporary changes in colonial morphology and virulence. Such associations are not surprising when it is recognized that in many instances changes in antigenic, colonial and pathogenic properties merely reflect a change in one element, namely, the cell surface. However, the story is not always so simple; we are quite often confronted with independent changes in these three properties, indicative of the fact that virulence and colonial morphology are not always dependent on cell surface characteristics.

In view of the occurrence of both independent and associated changes in colonial morphology, antigenic characteristics and virulence, we shall, in the following section, consider first the more specific aspect of each class of mutants and refer subsequently to some of their common features, including mutation rates and the influence of extra-chromosomal factors.

MUTATIONS AFFECTING COLONIAL MORPHOLOGY

DETECTION

Cells placed singly or in groups on solid media will develop into visible colonies that may differ in appearance not only between species but within species. Many factors may contribute to such differences in colonial morphology. Among them are the morphology and the surface structure of the individual cells and their arrangement within the colony. The latter is partly determined by the manner in which the cells move following division on solid media. For example, Bisset (1950) has shown that when cells grow under the severe mechanical restraint imposed by a solid medium "smooth bacteria grow and elongate against the pressure of the surrounding medium. When separation is complete, the daughter cells [occurring singly (see p. 40)] may be forced back again, side by side, by the elasticity of the agar." In contrast, "rough bacilli remain attached at the point of division and the filament, constrained in the same manner, is compressed concertina-fashion, bending at the points of division" (Fig. 69).

Many differences in colonial morphology can be detected with the unaided eye; additional differences become apparent if a dissecting microscope is used for inspecting colonies. However, the most sensitive system for the detection of otherwise inapparent differences in colonial morphology consists of microscopic observations with the help of obliquely transmitted light (Henry, 1933) (Fig. 70). In addition to this critical illumination

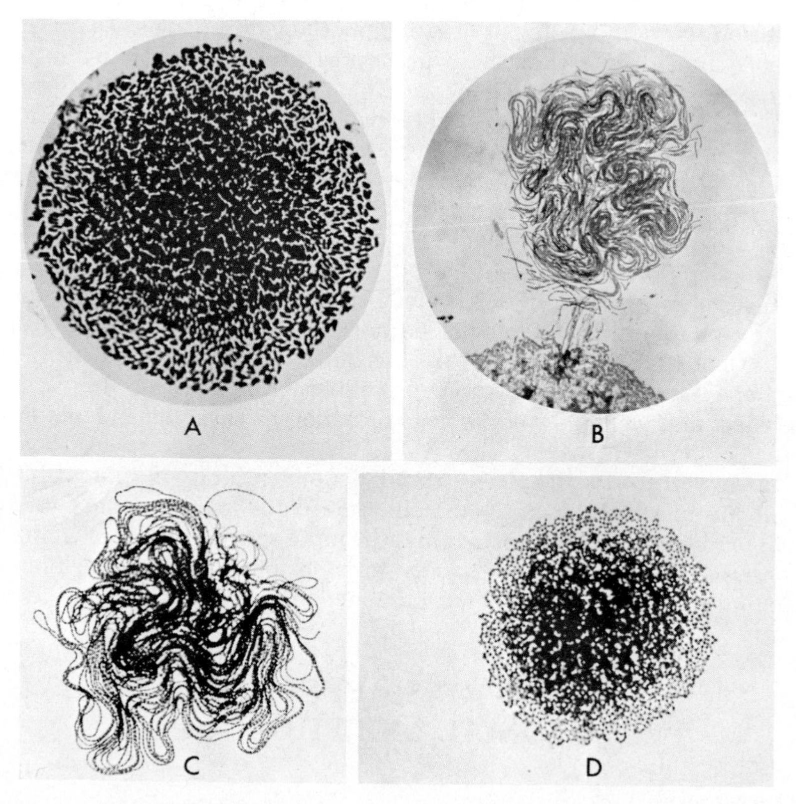

FIGURE 69. Smooth and rough colonies. A, Smooth colony of *E. coli*, impression preparation (×500); B, rough colony arising from the perimeter of a smooth colony of *Shigella dysenteriae* (×300); C, long-chained rough colony of streptococcus (×300); D, short-chained smooth colony of streptococcus. (Magnification: × 300.) (Photos by Bisset, reproduced by courtesy of the Journal of Pathology and Bacteriology and the Journal of General Microbiology.)

FIGURE 70. Arrangement of mirror and lighting source for inspection of colonial morphology by obliquely transmitted light.

an appropriate transparent medium is required, because many differences may be inapparent on one medium but show up clearly on other media. To illustrate what may be accomplished with such techniques, Figure 71 shows some of the colonial types of *Bacterium tularense* which have been detected on glucose-cysteine-peptone agar with the help of the oblique lighting technique (Eigelsbach *et al.*, 1951). Such differences as those visible in Figure 71 are of considerable value for recognizing differences in antigenicity and virulence (see p. 183), but remained undetected until the proper lighting and medium were employed. In studies with various enteric organisms and with *Brucella* species, a nutrient medium containing 1 per cent dextrose and 2 per cent glycerol, 2 – 1 agar (Henry, 1933), has been found particularly suitable for the differentiation of colonial types. In some other studies the use of oblique lighting and MacConkey's agar has proved helpful (see p. 159). Unfortunately, most workers have not employed such improved techniques, but, nevertheless, the literature on differences in colonial morphology between species and within species is very voluminous (see Hadley, 1927, 1937; Braun, 1947). The major reason for this intense study of colonial characteristics is the frequent association between changes in colonial characteristics and changes in other less readily determined characteristics such as virulence, antigenicity and immunogenic potency.

COLONY TYPES

Several characteristic groups of colony variants have been noted within most bacterial species and they have been referred to as smooth (S), rough (R), mucoid (M), and intermediate (I). Smooth colonies are usual-

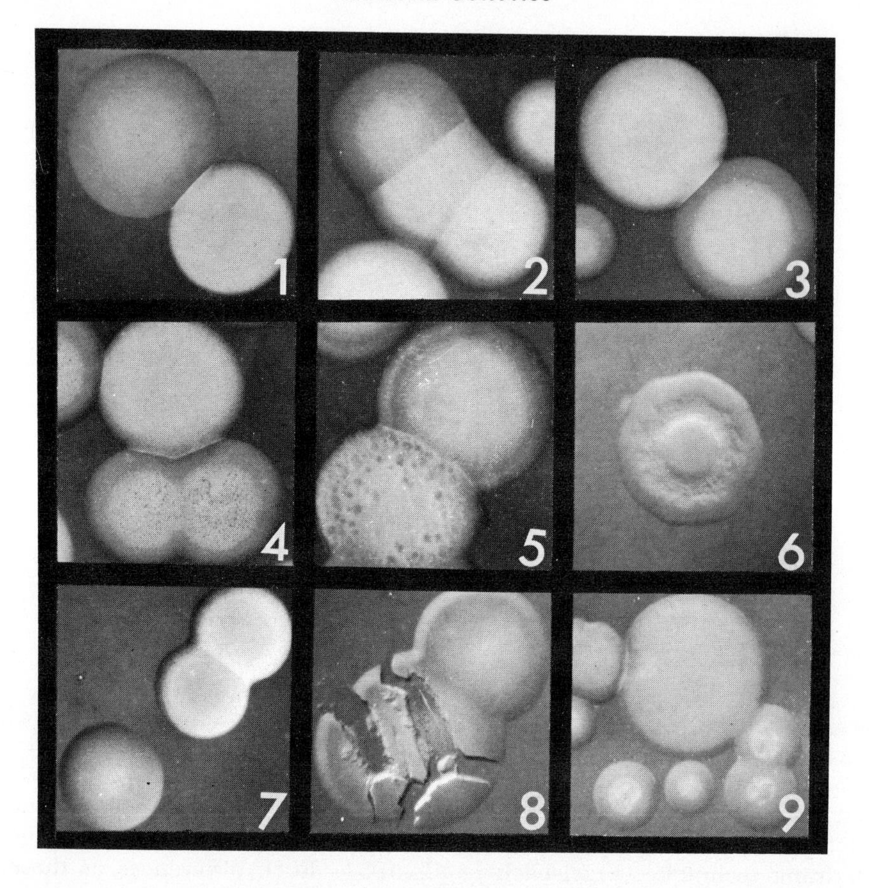

FIGURE 71. Various colonial types of *P. tularense* as revealed by the oblique lighting technique. The majority of colonies shown give smooth acriflavine reactions. Non-smooth acriflavine reactions are produced by the two lower colonies in 4, the upper one in 7, the smaller colonies in 9, and the colonies shown in 8. The colonies in 8 are extremely brittle, and when touched with a wire break into several pieces, as illustrated in the lower portion of the photograph. (From Eigelsbach *et al.*, 1951.)

ly round and glistening; rough colonies have a granular or wrinkled appearance with a tendency towards irregular margins; mucoid colonies are commonly round, transparent, and because of the mucopolysaccharide capsule of their constituent cells, have a slimy consistency; intermediate colonies, which are usually round, opaque or slightly granular, have an appearance intermediate between smooth and rough colonies. Careful inspection, especially with oblique lighting, has revealed the occurrence of an enormous number of different colonial types within each of these major groups. For example, various types of intermediate (such as I_1, I_2, I_3) smooth (such as S′, S″, etc., or smooth-S, smooth-Sy, smooth-F, etc.) have been described in the literature. In addition, other groups of colony types frequently described in the older literature are the so-called G type consisting of minute colonies claimed to contain filterable elements, a dwarf (D) type characterized by small colonies usually containing diphtheroid forms, and the L-type, which has been discussed in the preceding chapter.

In a few species still other colonial types have been described; for example, virulent hemolytic streptococci occur in a form designated "matt." In many species mutants with unchanged cellular morphology have been described which give rise to small colonies (Fig. 72). Such "small colony variants" appear to have a lowered metabolism (Colwell, 1946), in some cases possibly due to a decrease in cell wall permeability (Clowes and Rowley, 1955), or they may have a partial requirement for certain growth factors (Gillespie, 1952). In *Staphylococcus aureus*, small colony mutants with respiration deficiency, altered cytochromes and a deficiency in enzymes controlling thymine synthesis have been observed (Gause and Kochetkova, 1962). Small colony variants of *E. coli* have been studied in recombination tests and these tests confimed that the majority of such variants are due to changes in either one of several genetic loci (Clowes and Rowley, 1955).

Accurate classification into any major group of colonial types, such as S, R, M, etc., by means of visual inspection cannot always be accomplished, since no objective standard can be applied and all visual observations are subjective in nature. However, as long as it is recognized that changes in colonial morphology do not represent definite steps in a life-cycle as envisaged by some investigators (Hadley, 1927, 1937), but are merely indicators of undirected, spontaneous changes in other associated characteristics (Braun, 1947), it becomes relatively unimportant to identify each colonial form with one specific type.

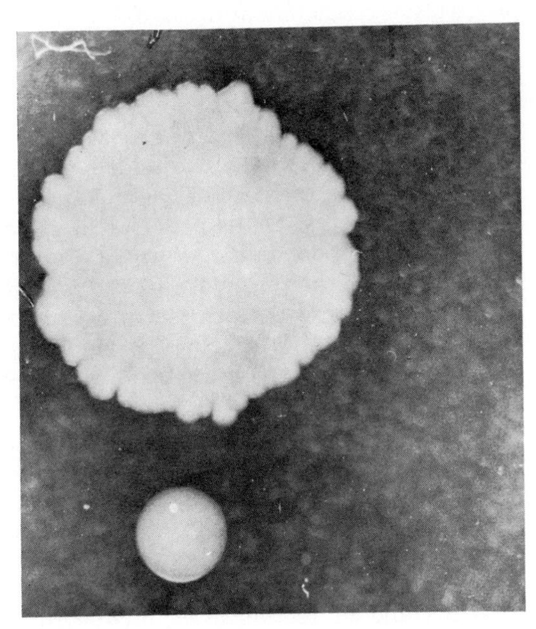

FIGURE 72. Normal colony type and small colony mutant of *E. coli* (obtained after exposure to copper ions) on nutrient agar. Incubation period was five days at 37° C. (From Hirsch, 1961.)

THE SIGNIFICANCE OF CHANGES IN COLONIAL MORPHOLOGY

Despite the absence of objective criteria for the identification of specific colony types, the approximate classification of colonial types of pathogens into general groups, represented by S, R, or M, has proved very useful in relation to the natural occurrence of certain colony types. Thus the pathogenic forms found most frequently in nature are of one colonial type only, usually the S type (for example, the Salmonella species) or the M type (for example, the pneumococcus species as classified according to Dawson's terminology).

In a few species, such as *B. anthracis,* it used to be claimed that the pathogenic type recovered on primary isolation may be found as an R type. This has turned out to be an artifact; the virulent type of *B. anthracis* does produce capsules of glutamyl polypeptide when grown *in vivo* and also when grown *in vitro* in the presence of bicarbonate or in an atmosphere rich in CO_2. However, when this type grows in the absence of CO_2 or bicarbonate, the capsule fails to develop and the resulting colonies, though they may contain genotypically smooth type cells, manifest a rough phenotype (Sterne, 1938). Genotypically rough cells unable to form capsules even in the presence of CO_2, can arise spontaneously in smooth *B. anthracis* populations *in vitro*, as well as *in vivo* (Thorne, 1961).

When primary isolates of the S or M type are grown under laboratory conditions, population changes involving the establishment of mutants with altered colonial morphology are usually observed. This phenomenon also has been referred to as *bacterial dissociation.* The observation that such *in vitro* population changes usually proceed from S → R → M or from M → S → R has led to the claim that this represents a definite life-cycle of the culture. It is now known that such trends are due merely to the progressive replacement of the initial type by mutants possessing certain properties which endow them with successively higher selective value and with which changes in colonial morphology may be associated (see Chapter 10). Similarly, the "normal" type found in natural habitats merely represents a particular mutant in which the properties causing a specific colony type are associated with other properties that favor the cells' survival in nature. In the case of pathogenic bacteria some of these properties can be identified with the presence of certain surface components of the cells which render the bacteria more resistant to the defense mechanism of the host and thereby contribute to greater virulence. The same surface components may also determine antigenic properties of the cell in addition to the morphology of the colony of which they are a part. Changes in colonial morphology, therefore, are primarily useful as indicators of changes in associated characteristics.

COLONIAL MORPHOLOGY AS INDICATOR OF CHANGES IN RESISTANCE AND GROWTH REQUIREMENTS

Undoubtedly most of the smooth, rough, mucoid, etc., changes are in the nature of a biochemical mutation. Even though we have just begun to learn something about the steps involved in the biosynthesis of surface antigens and of factors associated with virulence, it is clear that any change in such characteristics must involve some change in the presence or activity of an enzyme controlling, directly or indirectly, the formation of a surface component. This has been confirmed by recent studies on *D. pneumoniae* and *Salmonella* mutants that show altered biosynthetic events in the formation of capsular material (pneumococci) or other cell surface components (salmonellae). In these studies some of the specifically blocked, enzymatically controlled steps in cell surface biosynthesis have been identified (cf. Mills *et al.*, 1961; Mills and Smith, 1962; Osborn, 1963; Nikaido, 1962; Nikaido *et al.*, 1964).

In addition, it has been found that even biosynthetic changes that are not known to have primary effects on cell surface components can affect colonial morphology. Thus, the biosynthetic changes that occur in auxotrophic mutants and resistant mutants of *E. coli* can also cause minor but significant changes in colonial morphology (Braun and Lewis, 1950). To detect such changes it is necessary to employ the oblique lighting system and, preferably, a medium containing a dye. Thus, inspection of the colonial morphology of more than 20 different *E. coli* auxotrophs cultured on MacConkey's agar revealed distinctly different colonial types for almost every one of the mutants tested. Differences between radiation-resistant and radiation-sensitive mutants, as well as between streptomycin-sensitive, -resistant, and -dependent mutants, were also observed.

Such easily detected differences in colonial morphology are useful in at least three ways: (1) they permit the simple and relatively rapid recognition of characteristics such as radiation-resistance, which would otherwise be more difficult to detect; (2) they allow the rapid determination of the fate of two mutants with different growth requirements or with absolute differences in resistance during growth in a non-selective medium (for example, competition between streptomycin-resistant and streptomycin-sensitive mutants can be tested without the use of streptomycin as a screening agent which would eliminate one of the mutant classes); and (3) they make possible a rapid determination of the heterogeneity or homogeneity of a culture.

Although, as just stated, characteristic colonial differences can be found among most mutants so far tested, it has also been recognized that different colonial types may occur in a mutant culture apparently homogeneous for a given characteristic, e.g., histidine requirement. In such cases it must be assumed that histidine-requiring mutants differing in some other characteristic, such as growth rate or phage-resistance, are coexisting in the culture. The use of one stable colonial type isolated from such a culture is preferable for experimental work.

The aforementioned use of MacConkey's medium has also revealed significant, previously unrecognized, colonial differences in species other than *E. coli*. For example, it was found in studies with *Salmonella typhimurium* that antigenically identical threonine-resistant and threonine-sensitive mutants, differing in virulence, can be detected with ease following growth on MacConkey's agar (see Fig. 73 and p. 217). Other observations have shown that similar significant differences between antigenically similar but immunogenically different types of various enteric organisms can be observed on MacConkey's agar. One note of caution in regard to

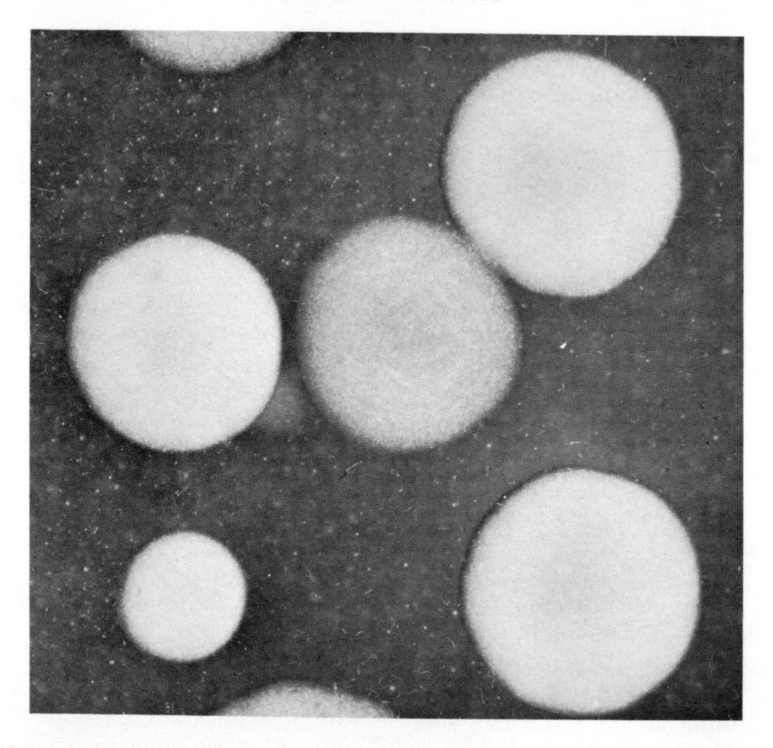

FIGURE 73. Four S^o (threonine-susceptible) colonies of *Salmonella typhimurium* surrounding an S^t (threonine-resistant) colony. (From Page *et al.*, 1951.)

the use of MacConkey's agar is in order. It has been noted that on this medium certain mutants of *E. coli* will develop into colonies showing a multitude of papillae (secondary colonies) after 48 hours of incubation (see Fig. 86). Similar changes do not occur on nutrient agar. The actual cause for this instability, involving either selective growth of new mutants or their increased occurrence, is still unknown. Naturally, subculturing from such heterogeneous colonies would result in heterogeneous cultures. Therefore, in cases like this it is advisable to use the appearance on MacConkey's agar as a useful indicator but to choose for subculturing corresponding colonies from parallel plates with nutrient agar, the latter preferably produced with the help of the replica plating technique.

INHERENT AND ENVIRONMENTAL FACTORS AFFECTING COLONIAL MORPHOLOGY

The available evidence indicates that changes in colonial morphology may be produced by mutations affecting nuclear determinants, by the presence of prophage or phage in the bacterium and by environmental influences.

The involvement of *chromosomal factors* is more frequently assumed than proven; yet it is strongly supported by various demonstrations of the transferability of information for the specificity of colony type by way of the nuclear elements, for example, in transformation (see Chapter 13) and in recombination following conjugation (Clowes and Rowley, 1955; Subbaiah and Stocker, 1964). However, determinants other than those conventionally associated with chromosomal elements can also cause sudden and relatively stable alterations in colonial morphology. This has been demonstrated in the case of *conversion of colony type by phage* or more exactly by prophage.

As illustrated in Figure 74, infection of a bacterium with an appropriate bacteriophage may lead to one of two alternatives: (a) vegetative multiplication of the phage genome, maturation of the phage particles, and lysis of the bacterium; or (b) in the case of *temperate phages*, an immunity reaction may occur (in some, but not all of the infected cells) that prevents vegetative phage multiplication and bacterial lysis, thus permitting the production of the *lysogenic state* in which the phage genome persists as a prophage in direct association with the bacterial genome (apparently inserted into the bacterial chromosome, see page 265). Certain phage genes, either by direct action (i.e., by controlling the formation of a specific enzyme) or by interaction with bacterial genes, may alter the phenotype of a phage-infected cell; therefore, alterations of the bacterial phenotype can occur in lysogenized bacteria. This phenomenon of *viral conversion** (see also pp. 267 to 277) can affect enzymes controlling the formation of cell components and with them alterations of colonial morphology may occur. Thus the lysogenization of rough strains of mycobacteria has been found to result in the production of smooth colonial types (White *et al.*, 1962).

A still different type of alteration of colonial morphology by phage has been observed in the case of *Brucella abortus* (Jones *et al.*, 1962): When cells of an intermediate bluish gray colony type are exposed to brucellaphage, "sticky white" colonies develop. It appears that this phenomenon is not due to the presence of a prophage since phage antiserum abolishes the phenomenon.† Rather, in this case, bacterial lysis following phage infection seems to be abnormally delayed so that it does not occur until the infected cell has divided, thus giving rise to both free phage and dividing bacteria in the same colony. An enzyme produced by the free phage, in turn, seems to act on components of the bacterial cell wall, thus producing cells and colonies with altered morphology.

A great number of *environmental conditions* can cause alterations in colonial morphology that frequently mimic those caused by mutation or viral conversion. Several criteria can help in determining whether an alteration in colonial morphology is the result of an environmentally in-

*It is important to distinguish viral conversion from transduction. In the former, each phage-infected bacterium may manifest the new phenotype controlled by phage genes, as long as the phage or prophage is present; in other words, the change is due to phage-associated information and may affect a *great many* bacterial cells. In transduction, on the other hand, an occasional phage (bacterial virus) may carry bacterial genes from one bacterium to another and, as a result, an occasional bacterium may undergo recombination with the phage-carried piece of bacterial information; in other words, the change is independent of the subsequent presence of phage or prophage; it is due to *bacterial* rather than viral information.

†Note that antiserum can only act by virtue of its reaction with the protein coat of whole phage.

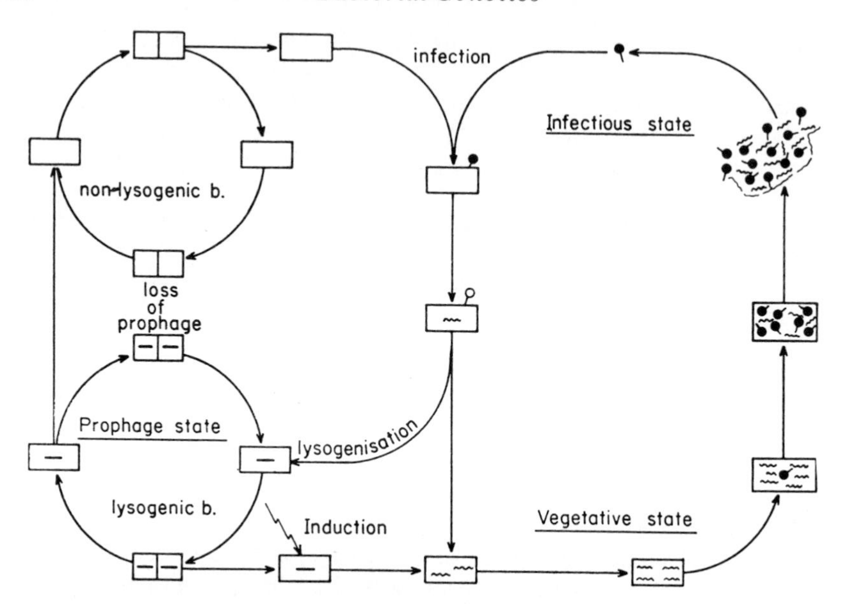

FIGURE 74. Diagram showing the cycle of a temperate bacteriophage in inducible lysogenic bacteria. (After Lwoff, 1953, from Jacob and Wollman, 1961.)

duced, temporary modification or a mutational change: (1) If an initially homogeneous population consisting of one colonial type is subcultured under altered environmental conditions and all developing colonies show a different appearance, a temporary modification must be suspected. The return of such a population to the original environmental conditions should restore the original phenotype. In contrast, mutational changes are likely to be involved if subcultures from a population of uniform colonial appearance yield several different appearing colonies in addition to colonies predominantly of the original type.

(2) The occurrence of two or more different colonial types in a population kept under identical conditions, e.g., on the same plate, is indicative of genetic differences between the colonies under observation, provided the colonies are of equal age and evenly distributed over the plate; crowded growth or differences in age of colonies can lead to differences in appearance that are not genetically controlled. Differences that are not due to age or crowding may become inapparent when the same population is grown under different environmental conditions. Of course, this does not indicate a disappearance of the genetic differences between the cells which previously led to dissimilar colonial types; it means merely that such differences cannot be detected phenotypically. Return to the original conditions should restore the differential appearance. For example, on minimal synthetic agar phage-resistant mutants of *E. coli* produce a colony type different from that produced by phage-sensitive cells. These differences become inapparent when the two types of cells are permitted to grow on a complex agar medium.

It also happens frequently that specific environmental conditions cause changes in colony morphology that copy in all details the appearance of certain colonial types which can arise by mutation. Such modifications can be classified as phenocopies (see p. 5). For example, in studies with *Lactobacillus* spp. it was observed that cells which normally develop into rough colonies on an adequate tomato juice agar will produce smooth colonies when sorbitan monooleate is added to the medium (Rogosa and Mitchell, 1950). This smooth phenotype disappears immediately upon subculturing on media without sorbitan monooleate. Similarly, virulent strains of *Mycobacterium tuberculosis* develop into colonies characterized by smooth contour and glistening surface when grown on the surface of agar media containing Tween 80; however, on the surface of media without Tween 80 the same cultures yield much smaller colonies with an extremely ragged outline (Dubos *et al.*, 1946). Alterations of pH or the addition of glycerine can also cause temporary modifications in the colonial appearance of *M. tuberculosis* (Fregnan *et al.*, 1961). It is likely that in these modifications of lactobacilli and mycobacteria the altered environmental conditions, including the presence of surface-active agents, modified the restraining effects of the solid medium upon dividing cells (p. 154), thus causing a different arrangement of cells within the colony and consequently a change in the colony's appearance.

A third example of temporary modifications of colonial morphology is the change that occurs when genetically smooth cells of *Brucella* spp. are grown in the presence of non-inhibitory concentrations of penicillin (Braun *et al.*, 1952). Under such conditions, smooth cells will produce rough or mucoid colonies, the actual phenotype depending upon the strain and the penicillin concentration employed. Subculturing on penicillin-free media or the addition of penicillinase will reverse this effect immediately and will reestablish the smooth phenotype. In this case the biosynthesis of cellular surface components responsible for S characteristics presumably is inhibited in the presence of penicillin. A final example of a phenocopy of colonial types is the production of mucoid colonies of *E. coli*, strain W, which are found when the wild, usually non-mucoid, type is grown at 15° C, instead of 25° C or 37° C; the same phenotype, reflecting the formation of capsular material by the cells, is found in a number of mutants that develop mucoid colonies at 15, 25 and 37° C (Beiser and Davis, 1957).

ANTIGENIC MUTANTS

Like colonial characteristics, antigenic or serologic characteristics, especially of pathogens, represent one of the useful taxonomic and diagnostic tools in bacteriology. Therefore, it is not surprising that variation in antigenic characteristics has been known and studied for a long time. Indeed, much of our knowledge regarding the antigenic structure of bacteria has been obtained through studies on the nature of antigenic changes which may occur in bacterial populations *in vitro* as well as *in vivo*. The literature on the manifestations of these changes, dating back almost 50 years, is immense (see Raffel, 1963), but the underlying causes of antigenic variability were, until quite recently, either obscure or subject to extremely contradictory interpretations. The studies of the last 20 years have helped greatly to remove this subject from its obscurity and there is now ample evidence that while environmental conditions can greatly influence quantitative fluctuations in antigenic properties, most qualitative changes in antigenic characteristics are either mutational in origin or due to viral conversion.

ANTIGENIC TYPES

Adequate descriptions of the antigenic characteristics of bacteria can be found in most textbooks (Dubos, 1958; Raffel, 1963) and do not need much elaboration here. There is no uniform nomenclature for these characteristics; the complexity of the different schemes of symbols is matched only by the complexity of the antigenic component themselves. In general, many gram-positive species possess surface antigens that are predominantly polysaccharide, usually occurring in the form of distinct capsules, and their sugar composition and sequence determines their type-specificity. S → R variation in these species is accompanied by a loss of the capsular polysaccharide, S → I variation by a quantitative reduction in capsular material. In addition, cells of gram-positive species may possess specific somatic antigens, of proteinaceous nature, and the virulent strains of some species possess antigenic capsules that are of a polypeptide structure (examples: the glutamyl polypeptide capsule of virulent *Bacillus anthracis*; the M antigens of streptococci).

In gram-negative species, antigenic components which react with antisera against whole organisms are found in the surface complexes that consist of lipids, proteins and polysaccharides. In many, but not all, cases the antigenic properties of these complexes are principally referable to the polysaccharide moeity. It has, for example, been established that in the so-called *O (somatic) antigens* the low molecular weight sugar constituents, situated at the terminal end of the side chains attached to the polysaccharide molecules, determine antigenic specificity (F. Kaufman *et al.*, 1961). In addition, antigenic properties can be associated with surface proteins (e.g., in certain *P. pestis* strains); also, the so-called *H (flagellar) antigens* of flagellated organisms are protein in nature. It has been known for a long time that (1) a loss of O antigen can account for the S → R variation, (2) a reduction in O antigens will yield antigenically intermediate (I) types, and (3) replacement of the O antigen by a surface antigen with a high mucopolysaccharide content will result in the so-called M types.

Variation in H antigens has long been known to be a rather frequent event—so frequent that individual cultures started with one H type may contain, after a relatively short period of multiplication, many cells displaying a different H antigen. As a result, mass cultures may agglutinate in either of two H antisera. The variability in H antigens has been referred to as *phase variation* and has been recognized as a unique variation since it always involves alternate sets of antigens, rather than random variational events. For example, cells displaying antigens a, b, c, or d (phase 1 or "specific" antigens) may spontaneously give rise to variants displaying either antigens "1.2," "1.5," or "1.7" (phase 2 or "group" antigens) and thus lead to mixed cultures that reveal in serological typing the presence of two different H antigens (see Kauffman, 1961). But while any phase 1 antigen may be found associated with any phase 2 antigen in naturally occurring so-called "species" of salmonellae, one cannot find, either under natural conditions or following the transduction of H determinants (Lederberg and Edwards, 1953), a combination of two different phase 1 antigens or of two different phase 2 antigens in individual cells, or in a culture of related organisms. We shall discuss the genetic basis for this restricted variability (or substitutive variation) a little later.

The H antigen variation just described is independent of the O antigen variation previously discussed, but, as already mentioned on page 142, a third variation can occur in the flagellated Enterobacteriaceae, namely, a complete loss of the flagella, giving rise to the so-called H → O variation.*

The surface antigens are responsible for the readily detectable antigenic properties of a cell, but there may be additional antigenic characteristics that do not become detectable until the surface antigen is removed, either by chemical means or by spontaneous variation affecting the biosynthesis of the specific surface substances. This antigenic multiplicity can be understood best by comparing the bacterial cell surface to the layers of an onion where the peeling away of one layer will uncover another layer or antigenic surface. Although this is a helpful picture, like most simplifications, it does not agree entirely with the facts. As we shall see now, the loss of an O antigen can merely consist of the loss of a monosaccharide from the polysaccharide structure.

THE CHEMICAL BASIS FOR ANTIGENIC VARIATION

Even prior to the recent recognition of the chemical basis for some antigenic changes, it was possible to assume that the loss of an antigenic component may represent a process similar to that of biochemical mutation, (i.e., a loss of the ability to perform previously possible biosynthetic steps, either by the loss of information for the structural synthesis of the enzyme or by a change in factors controlling the activity of the enzyme). A number of studies with different organisms have confirmed that this assumption was correct. To illustrate this point, we shall choose two examples: (1) changes in the biosynthesis of capsular material of pneumococci, and (2) changes in the O antigen of salmonellae.

Among S pneumococci, nearly 80 different types differing in immunologically distinct capsular polysaccharides are known. The composition of several of these polysaccharides has been established; that of Type *III*, for example, has been found to be -[3)-β-D-glucuronic acid (1 → 4)-β-D-glucose $(1\rightarrow]_n$. Studies by Mills, Smith, Austrian and Bernheimer (cf. Mills and Smith, 1962) have established that the biosynthesis of this Type *III* capsular polysaccharide proceeds by way of the uridine diphosphoglycosyl (UDPG) compounds, as shown in Figure 75. Non-capsulated

*H comes from the German word "*Hauch*," which was used by Weil and Felix (1917) to designate the growth of motile forms on solid media where they spread like the mist produced by breathing (*Hauch*) against a cool glass surface; O stands for "*ohne* (without) *Hauch*."

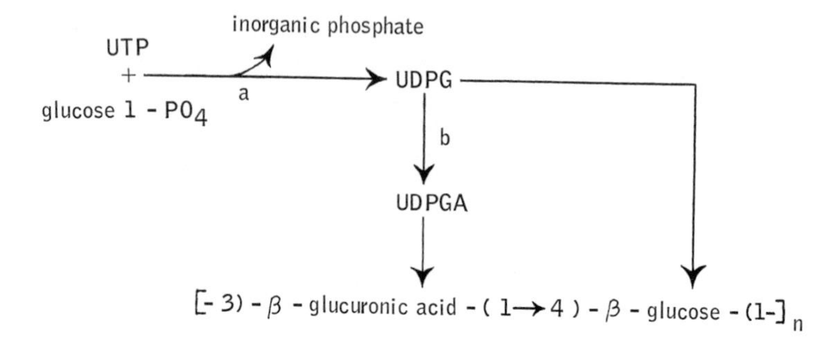

FIGURE 75. Metabolic pathway in Type *III* capsular polysaccharide synthesis of pneumococci. UTP = uridine triphosphate; UDPG = uridine diphosphate glucose; UDPGA = uridine diphosphate glucuronic acid; a = uridyl transferase; b = UDPG dehydrogenase. (After Mills and Smith, 1962.)

strains derived from Type *III* show no UDPG dehydrogenase activity (i.e., they do not produce UDPGA from UDPG), while the polymerizing system synthesizing Type *III* capsular polysaccharide from UDPG and UDPGA remains functional, as revealed by tests with enzyme extracts. Thus the S*III* → R mutation can be attributed in this case to a genetic block affecting the UDPG → UDPGA step, or, in other words, to the absence of proper information for the synthesis or functioning of the enzyme UDPG dehydrogenase catalyzing this step. Similarly, in the case of non-capsulated mutants derived from Type *I* pneumococci, the absence or inactivity of a single enzyme, either UDPG dehydrogenase or, in some other mutant, UDPGA 4-epimerase (controlling the step UPDG → UDP Gal), has been established.

In studies with *Salmonella* it has been determined that the various O antigens occurring in the 700 different known "species" of this genus have a basic polysaccharide structure containing heptoses, glucosamine, galactose and glucose, and that the O antigens of many species contain, in addition, one or more of the following sugars: mannose, fucose, rhamnose, colitose, abequose, paratose and tyvelose (the last four are rare sugars that have been identified as stereoisomeric 3, 6-didesoxyhexoses) (cf. Kauffman, 1961; Kauffman *et al.*, 1960; Staub and Tinelli, 1960; Robbins and Uchida, 1962). Many of these sugars appear in unique sequences in side chains which are responsible for the antigenic specificity of these heteropolymers (for example, O-1 antigen appears to involve the structure 6-α-glucosyl-galactosyl-mannosyl-rhamnosyl; O-9, the structure 3-tyvelosyl-mannosyl; and O-12a involves 4-α-glucosyl-galactosyl-mannosyl-rhamnosyl) (Staub, 1960). The main antigenic determinant is usually a terminal sugar, but changes in the terminal disaccharide or in subterminal linkages also can evoke alteration in antigenic specificity (Staub, 1964).

It is interesting to note that the more recent chemical analysis of the polysaccharides of different *Salmonella* "species" permits a chemical grouping of "species" which is identical with the earlier grouping based on serological criteria (Kauffman-White scheme). Chemical analyses have revealed that variations in O antigens involve the loss of certain sugars usually present in side chains (Nikaido, 1962; Osborn *et al.*, 1962). It should be noted that contrary to the old idea that an S → R change in enterobacteria involved the unmasking of an already present underlying antigen following the loss of the S "layer," the newer data, as shown in Figure 76, indicate that the S → R change may involve a simplification of the polysaccharide component of the O antigen (Beale and Wilkinson, 1961).

Sometimes S → R variation can involve the addition of a new sugar, rather than a loss; e.g., in *Shigella dysenteriae*, R types show a loss of rhamnose and the gain of aldoheptose (Davis, 1957). In the case of the so-called "M" *S. typhimurium* (really a rough type equivalent to Rc in Figure 76 and not to be confused with mucoid mutants) it has been possible to attribute the absence of galactose, and of sugars attached to it, to the absence, or lack of activity, of the enzyme UDP-galactose-4-epimerase (Nikaido, 1962; Osborn *et al.*, 1962). Just as an auxotrophic mutant can

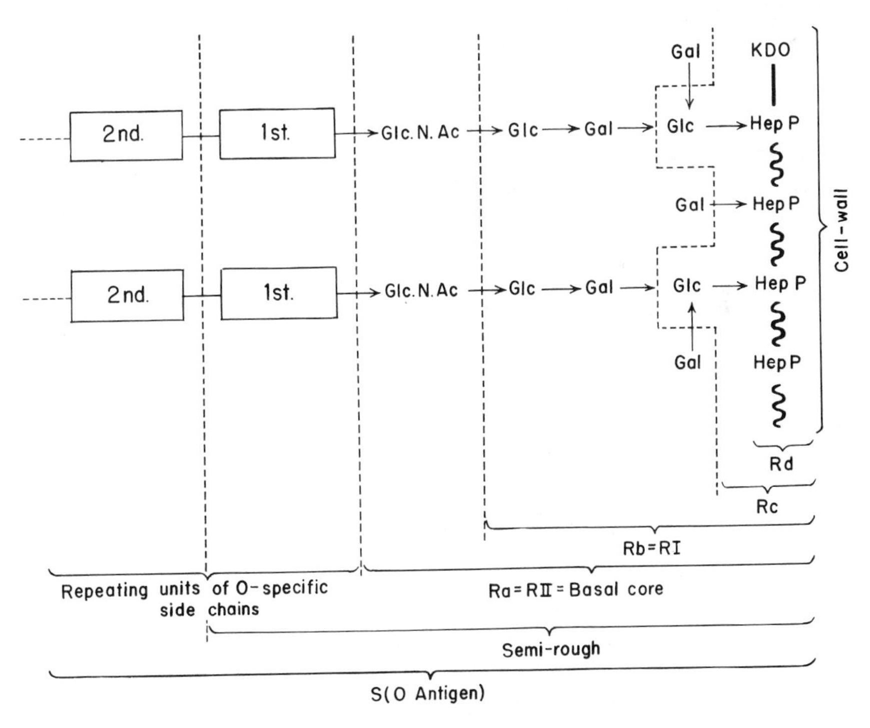

FIGURE 76. Suggested structure of *Salmonella* O and R antigens. The dotted lines indicate where biosynthesis is blocked in different R mutants derived from S strains; the respective R mutants (chemotypes Ra, Rb, Rc, etc.) synthesize only the part of the O antigen that is on the right side of the respective dotted line. Depending on the chemotype (or serotype), the repeating units of the O-specific side chains contain sugars such as mannose, rhamnose, galactose and abequose. The semi-rough mutant contains only one repeating unit in the polysaccharide of its cell wall. Hep = heptose, KDO = 2-keto-3-deoxyoctonate, Glc = glucose, Gal = galactose, Glc. N. Ac. = N-acetylglucosamine. (From Lüderitz *et al.*, 1965.)

be made to grow on a minimal medium if the non-synthesized compound is added to the medium, the O antigenicity can be restored to the epimeraseless mutants when the non-synthesized galactose is supplied exogenously. "M" mutant cells grown in the presence of galactose show a sugar composition that is indistinguishable from the wild O type of its *S. typhimurium* ancestor. Incidentally, such phenotypically modified mutant cells also regain the capacity to adsorb certain O-specific phages, a property that is lacking in mutant cells grown in the absence of galactose (Fukasawa and Nikaido, 1960). This phenomenon illustrates the frequent but not necessary association between phage adsorption sites and O antigens, and also furnishes a good example of the chemical basis of changes in phage susceptibility.

Two earlier discovered examples of the fact that antigenic characteristics can be subject to temporary modifications under the influence of environmental conditions are (1) the ability of R cells of various *Salmonella* species to develop S antigenic characteristics following growth on solid media containing carbohydrate supplements (Hayakawa, 1937; Crossley *et al.*, 1946) and (2) the formation of new cell surface components ("capsule") by certain *E. coli* mutants under the influence of alkaline substances engendered by other mutant cells (Zamenhof, 1946). Without much doubt, the first case, like the case of the epimeraseless mutants, can be ascribed to the fact that the necessary carbohydrates normally synthesized by the S cells were made available to the enzyme-deficient mutants, which retained the ability to incorporate such compounds into their cell surface even though they had lost the ability to synthesize them. Removal of the required supplements restored the original R phenotype.

GENETIC CONTROL OF ANTIGENIC VARIATION

It is now known that hereditary alterations in antigenic characteristics of bacteria can be caused by: (1) mutations affecting chromosomal determinants (i.e., spontaneously altered nuclear information); (2) changes in the activity of nuclear genetic sites, which occur in the absence of any altered nuclear information; (3) the presence of phage or prophage in the bacterial cell (conversion); or (4) introduction of, as well as changes in, determinants associated with non-chromosomal replicons (see p. 291), such as the F replicons of *E. coli*.

CHROMOSOMAL CONTROL. The control of antigenic characteristics by the information associated with chromosomal DNA has been demonstrated amply with the aid of genetic transfers by, for example, transformation in pneumococci (cf. p. 240), transduction in *Salmonella* (Lederberg and Edwards, 1953), and conjugation in *E. coli* and *Salmonella* (Subbaiah and Stocker, 1964). All these tests showed that like other nuclear determinants, information for antigenic characteristics can be transferred from cell to cell by naked DNA, by phage-protein-carried DNA, or by the polynucleotide structure that migrates during conjugation from the donor to the recipient cell.

CONVERSION. Phage infection can lead to altered antigenic properties in lysogenized bacteria and even in phage-susceptible bacteria that subsequently lyse (cf. Barksdale, 1959; Luria, 1962; LeMinor *et al.*, 1961). This finding shows that the information for antigen synthesis does not necessarily have to reside within the *bacterium's* normal polynucleotide information. The DNA of some phages is obviously endowed with the capacity to furnish the information necessary for the formation (or activation) of an enzyme that influences the synthesis of bacterial cell surface components, even when such informative DNA is not fully integrated into the bacterium's DNA. Thus it has been recognized that infection of *Salmonella* with phage epsilon-15 initiates the production of somatic antigen 15, and phage ϵ-34 initiates the production of antigen 34. The latter conversion, however, can occur only in bacteria that already carry phage ϵ-15 and thus possess antigen 15, which is needed as substrate for the processes initiated by ϵ-34 (Uetake *et al.*, 1958; Uetake and Hagiwara, 1961). Also, for adsorption of phage ϵ-15, the presence of O antigen 10 is required; for the adsorption of phage ϵ-34, O antigen 15 is the receptor. With the appearance of antigen 15 in ϵ-15-infected bacteria, antigen 10 disappears, but a virulent variant of ϵ-15 also has been isolated which, in infected bacteria, produces an antigen 15 with the persistence of antigen 10.

Infection of *Salmonella* with phage PLT22 will initiate the production of O antigen 1 (Zinder, 1957). Chemical and serological analyses described by Staub and Tinelli (1960) have shown that in this conversion the specificity of antigen 1 is produced by the formation, in the lysogenized bacterium, of a new enzyme capable of attaching glucose to the galactose of the preexisting trisaccharide side chain; thus, in non-lysogenized *S. typhimurium* there is an α galactose-mannose-rhamnose side chain, but in PLT22-infected *S. typhimurium* there is an α glucose-α galactose-mannose-rhamnose chain.

Similarly, information introduced into the bacterial cell with phage ϵ-34 has been shown to control the addition of glucose to the trisaccharide β-galactose-mannose-rhamnose (Robbins and Ushida, 1962). In the case of the conversion of *Salmonella* 3,10 into *Salmonella* 3,15 by phage ϵ-15, the trisaccharide α galactose-mannose-rhamnose is replaced by the trisaccharide β galactose-mannose-rhamnose, showing that the information introduced into the bacterial cell with the phage genome causes an attachment of the galactose in the β instead of the α position. Even in the case of a more complex conversion by phage 27, in which the new antigenic properties in the phage-infected cells were found to differ with the antigenic type of *Salmonella* that had been infected, it appears likely that phage 27 causes in all instances only one basic alteration, namely, an attachment of rhamnose to the mannose of a side chain (Staub and Forest, 1963). These and several other examples of antigenic changes by phage conversion in *Salmonella, Shigella*, and possibly also in staphylococci,* all indicate that antigen-determining phage genes can control the production of enzymes that catalyze specific steps in the biosynthesis of surface polysaccharides (Luria, 1962). The actual conversion is very rapid: the new antigen appears within a few minutes after infection and is produced as long as the lysogenic state persists, or, in the case of virulent phages, until lysis occurs.

*It is possible that the alteration of phage susceptibility, in the lysogenized *Staphylococcus*, including the acquisition of sensitivity to phages to which the non-lysogenized bacterium is resistant, represents another example of conversion leading to altered cell surface components (Rountree, 1959).

It is of interest that defective mutants of phage ε-15 have been found that lysogenize and produce antigenic alteration in their bacterial hosts, but can no longer be induced to produce mature lytic phages (Uetake, 1959). In this case, a new bacterial property (antigen 15) becomes permanent, without any residual evidence of its phage origin. Luria (1962) has suggested that the converting genes of phages may be understood on the basis that either "the phage consists of a fragment of bacterial chromosome which, by regressive or progressive evolution, has become a virus, or the phage has acquired bacterial genes by recombination with the host."

It appears that identical antigenic specificities can be evoked by the action of phage genes and by chromosomal genes of a non-lysogenized bacterial genome. Thus antigen 1 of certain *Salmonella* strains is due to a prophage, but the same antigen 1 also can be present (even though there are some differences in its overall chemical composition) independent of any apparent prophage in *Salmonella* of another group (Stocker *et al.*, 1960).

EFFECTS OF F FACTORS AND OTHER REPLICONS. We have already referred to some genetic elements that can exist either independent of the bacterial chromosome or in direct association with it (see p. 124). Prophage is one such element, but there are also others that in genetic tests show a similar behavior as far as transient association with the chromosome is concerned, and which, together with prophages, can be classified as episomes. It now appears more likely, however, that many of these episomes actually represent membrane-associated, replicating DNA elements ("replicons") that, though smaller, are very similar in many respects to the big bacterial replicon which commonly goes under the name of "chromosome" (see pp. 315 to 319).

In many *E. coli* cells a small replicon can be found which carries the F factor responsible for the initiation of conjugation (p. 297). This F factor also determines the presence of specific, carbohydrate-containing surface antigens (Ørskov and Ørskov, 1961; Sneath and Lederberg, 1961). Also, bacteriocins including colicins–proteinaceous antibiotic substances that kill susceptible bacteria (see p. 314)–have been recognized as being intimately associated with the lipopolysaccharide antigens of the cell surface of gram-negative bacteria (Amano *et al.*, 1958). The production of these surface structures, which in all probability contribute to a cell's antigenic properties, also is controlled by separate replicons which, when present in a bacterium, can alternate between a chromosome-associated and -non-associated state (see p. 315). Thus many of the genetic elements that used to be classified as episomes contain determinants that can cause changes in antigenic components.

PHASE VARIATION. Earlier we referred to the fact that changes in the flagellar H antigens of *Salmonella* ("phase variation") occur spontaneously at very high rates. Stocker (1949), working with *S. typhimurium*, analyzed mutation rates typical of such phase variation. He detected the H variants by pouring sloppy (0.35 per cent) nutrient agar containing antibody for one phase on the surface of agar plates on which colonies had grown. This resulted in narrow, dense zones of opacity around colonies consisting of cells of the agglutinated phase, whereas colonies of the other phase displayed diffuse zones due to swarming organisms. This method permitted the rapid analysis of the proportion of phase variants that established themselves in liquid cultures originally inoculated with cells of one phase only and maintained, by repeated transfers, in continuous logarithmic growth. Under such conditions, and provided that the growth rates of parent cells and mutant cells are identical, the proportion of mutant cells will increase linearly with the number of generations at a rate proportional to the mutation rate (Luria and Delbrück, 1943). These prerequisites are fulfilled in the case of the H antigen variation of *S. typhimurium*. Thus Stocker was able to calculate the mutation rates from the slope of increase in proportion of mutant cells (see p. 191 for further details of this method). In nine strains tested, the mutation rates from group to specific phase (see p. 164 for definition) ranged from 1×10^{-4} to 4.7×10^{-3} per bacterial generation cycle, and the rates of mutation from specific to group phase ranged from 1×10^{-5} to 8.6×10^{-4}. In all cases the mutation rate from group phase to specific phase was higher than the rate of reverse changes.

Additional tests involving replicate cultures and patterned after Luria and Delbrück's fluctuation test (p. 69) substantiated the assumption that the occurrence of phase variants is a spontaneous and undirected event, likely to take place once within approximately 1×10^4 cell divisions. But despite the fact that from the standpoint of spontaneity and independence of environmental influences phase variation mimics events that involve spontaneous alterations of chromosomal information, experimental evidence indicates that the mechanism responsible for these spontaneous changes does not involve any altered information. Rather, it involves a shift in the ability of unaltered information to express itself.

The uniqueness of phase variation was already suggested by the fact that it involves (as we discussed on page 164) variability affecting, as a rule, only two alternative, mutually exclusive sets of antigenic properties. Transduction experiments by Lederberg and Edwards (1953) then demonstrated that the antigens of phase 1 are controlled by a set of alleles (or genetic changes within a locus) at a locus labeled H_1, and the antigens of phase 2 by a set of alleles at a different locus, H_2. Next it was determined that it is possible to transduce the antigenicity of one H_1 allele to a recipient with a different H_1 allele, thereby substituting the former for the latter; it was similarly possible to substitute by transduction one H_2 by another H_2. However, it was not possible to produce by transduction combinations of different H_1 or of different H_2 in one cell*; this was shown by sampling of the progeny of individual, transduced cells (Fig. 77). Since the two antigenic phases that may manifest themselves in the progeny of a cell [H_1 (H_2)† → H_1 (H_2) + (H_1) H_2] are determined at separate loci, it is clear that phase variation cannot represent a mutation from one specific allele to another [$H_1 \rightarrow H_2$ or $H_2 \rightarrow H_1$]. Instead, some factor must deter-

*One very rare exception is a case in which, following transduction, two H_1 loci could coexist (Iino, 1959).

†The gene in parenthesis does not express itself.

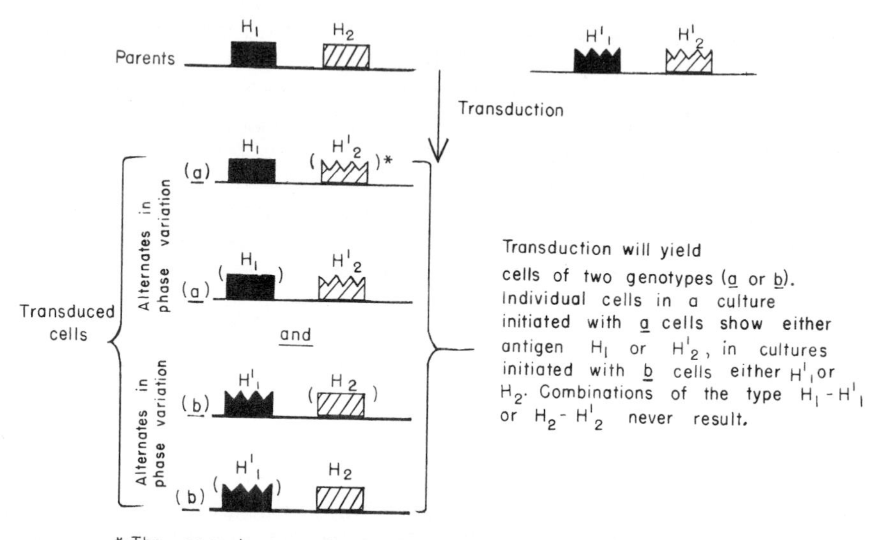

FIGURE 77. Diagram of the results obtained in transduction tests with phase variants.

mine whether or not the information produced by the already present H_1 and H_2 loci can express itself. The problem thus became: What controls the state H_1 (H_2) and the alternative state (H_1) H_2? By using again the analytical tool of transduction, Lederberg and Iino (1956) demonstrated that the ability of a transduced H_2 locus to express itself depended on the phase of the donor. Thus, if the transducing phage was obtained from (H_1) H_2 cells, the new H_2 antigen manifested itself in the transduced cells. If, on the other hand, the donor was H_1 (H_2), the recipients did not manifest the new H_2 antigenicity (i.e., until such a time as phase variation occurred in the progeny of the transduced cell). We can illustrate this as follows:

$$\left.\begin{array}{ll} & (H'_1)\ H'_2 \text{———x*}\ (H_1)\ H_2 \\ \text{or} & (H'_1)\ H'_2 \text{———x}\ \ H_1\ (H_2) \end{array}\right\}\ (H_1)\ H'_2\ [\text{also}\ (H'_1)\ H_2]$$

$$\left.\begin{array}{ll} & H'_1\ (H'_2) \text{———x}\ \ (H_1)\ H_2 \\ \text{or} & H'_1\ (H'_2) \text{———x}\ \ H_1\ (H_2) \end{array}\right\}\ H_1\ (H'_2)\ [\text{also}\ H'_1\ (H_2)]$$

The conclusion was that the antigenic H phase is governed by two alternative states of the H_2 locus: when the H_2 locus is in its active (*epistatic*) state, it initiates the formation of the H_2 antigen while, at the same time, it suppresses the function of the H_1 locus; alternatively, when the H_2 locus is inactive (*hypostatic*), it permits the expression of the H_1 locus.

*Symbol for transduction. Thus, A———x B indicates that A is the donor of the phage lysate, containing the transducing phage, and B is the recipient.

It is still not clear precisely what it is that determines the "state" of the H_2 locus, and whether it might possibly involve the absence and presence of an extra-chromosomal element ("episome") attached to the H_2 region (Jacob and Wollman, 1961). It is clear, however, that phase variation represents a unique type of spontaneous variation in which information is not altered but suppressed. Whether this variation involves a sort of repression by an intermediate or end product that builds up slowly and steadily to effective, repressing, intracellular concentrations, thereby acting in a manner akin to repressors of enzyme synthesis (see Chapter 17), is something that remains to be elucidated.

The case of phase variation is instructive from still a different viewpoint. It shows that the techniques of genetic transfers are required in order to distinguish whether a spontaneous, environment-independent alteration in hereditary characteristics involves altered chromosomal information, inactivity of such information due to still unknown causes, or extra-chromosomal elements.

The antigenic flagellar substance altered by phase variation of *Salmonella* is a protein (flagellin) which undergoes chemical alterations, presumably in amino acid sequence, when mutation alters an H locus (McDonough, 1962). Flagellin contains in addition to 18 conventional amino acids an unusual amino acid, ε-N-methyl-lysine, which has not been observed elsewhere in nature (Ambler and Rees, 1959). A gene closely linked to the H_1 locus has been found that determines the presence or absence of ε-N-methyl-lysine (Stocker *et al.*, 1961). Mutations affecting this gene alter antigenic flagellar properties and occur independent of phase variation.

PHENOTYPIC CHANGES IN ANTIGENIC PROPERTIES

Many of the environmental effects that lead to a temporary modification of colonial morphology (p. 163) affect antigenic cell surface structures, and may therefore also serve as examples of environmentally modified antigenic properties. Many additional illustrations (cf. Meynell, 1961) could be cited, such as the dependence of the development of certain *Pasteurella pestis* antigens on temperature and pH of the growth medium (cf. Burrows, 1962), the destruction of M antigen of streptococci by a protease formed during growth in media of low oxidation-reduction potential (Stamp, 1953), and the interfering effects of sublethal concentrations of penicillin on the development of certain S antigens (p. 163). The problem of recognizing whether a change in antigenic properties is due to a temporary modification by environmental influences, or a more permanent genetic change involving altered DNA elements, is identical to that already discussed under changes in colonial morphology.

SIMPLE INDICATORS OF GROSS ANTIGENIC CHANGES

The methods of identifying antigenic characteristics are frequently cumbersome. Even under ideal conditions they involve tests on large populations of cells rather than on single cells or their immediate progeny. This undoubtedly has introduced errors into the literature where certain antigenic characteristics have been described as representative for certain cells, whereas they may really represent the overall antigenic characteristics of heterogeneous populations consisting of several antigenically dissimilar cell types. Considerable work is required to identify the antigenic characteristics by serological methods; the *in vivo* testing of associated immunogenic properties is even more time-consuming. For these reasons, correlated characteristics have been useful as rapid indicators of certain types of antigenic constitution or changes. One of these is colonial morphology. Even though the terms "smooth" and "rough" were originally applied to colonial morphology (De Kruif, 1921), it was soon recognized that changes in colonial morphology were usually associated with changes in antigenic characteristics. Because of the medical importance of the latter, most of the studies on population changes among pathogens were undertaken in an effort to analyze antigenic changes rather than changes in colony morphology. To what extent the use of colonial characteristics as indicators of antigenic characteristics is justified depends on the species under investigation. In some species, changes in these two characteristics are closely linked; in others independent changes in colony morphology and antigenicity are frequent.

In the case of several gram-negative species (e.g., *Brucella* species, *B. tularense*, *Salmonella* species, *E. coli*) the acriflavine test has proved to be a far more reliable indicator of antigenic characteristics than mere observation of colony morphology (Allessandrini and Sabatucci, 1931; Braun and Bonestell, 1947). This simple test consists of suspending cells, preferably from individual colonies, in a drop of saline; a small amount of a 1:1000 solution of neutral acriflavine is then added with the help of an applicator stick. If the cells in the suspension are antigenically smooth they will remain suspended; antigenically rough cells will yield clumps, and antigenically mucoid cells will produce slimy precipitates upon contact with the acriflavine (Fig. 78). Whenever the result of this test differs from the colony appearance, this should be so indicated in the description of the mutant. Thus, the symbol S describes a type that is antigenically and colonially smooth, whereas a smooth colony with R antigenic characteristics, as indicated by a rough acriflavine test, should be labeled S^R. Similarly, S^M would describe a colonially smooth mutant with M antigenic characteristics. Failure to observe such a differentiation between antigenic and colonial characteristics has resulted in considerable confusion in the existing literature since the terms smooth, rough, mucoid, etc., and the symbols S, R, M, etc., often have been applied loosely to either colonial morphology or antigenic characteristics.

The suggestion which has been offered by some authors to designate, whenever possible, antigenic characteristics by the symbols S, M, R, etc., and colonial characteristics as smooth, rough, mucoid, etc., appears to be of distinct merit, especially in view of the frequently encountered independent changes between the two characteristics (see p. 183).

REVERSIONS

In the literature on antigenic changes many references can be found to mutational changes in two directions as represented by progressive and

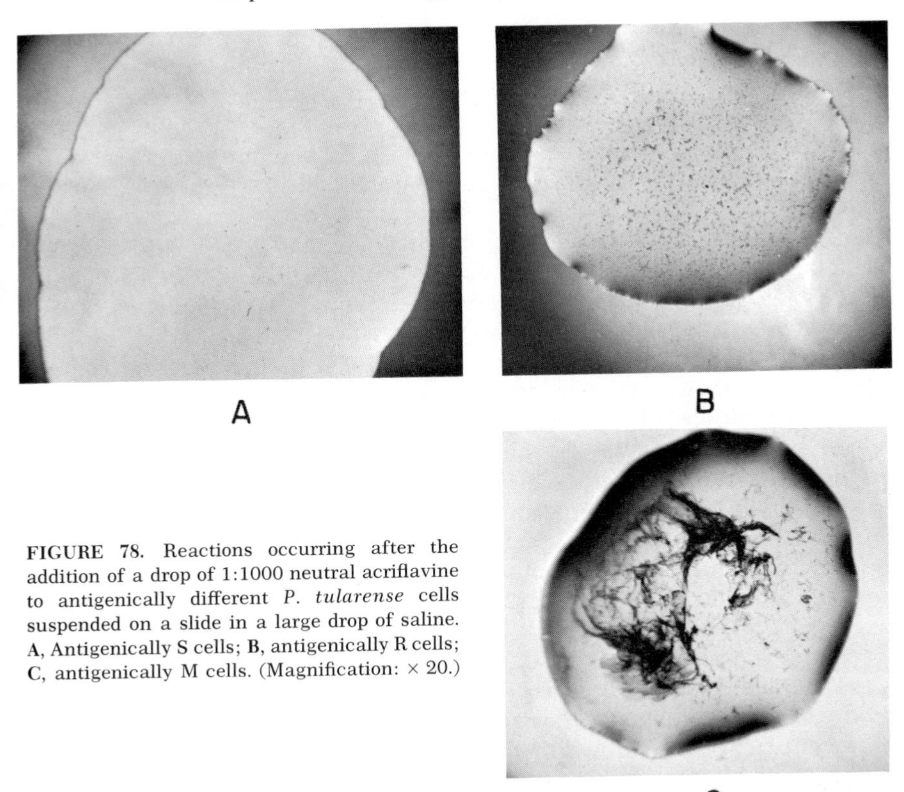

FIGURE 78. Reactions occurring after the addition of a drop of 1:1000 neutral acriflavine to antigenically different *P. tularense* cells suspended on a slide in a large drop of saline. A, Antigenically S cells; B, antigenically R cells; C, antigenically M cells. (Magnification: $\times$ 20.)

reverse changes in antigenic characteristics, e.g., $S \rightleftarrows R$. Evidence exists which indicates that such changes in two opposite directions do not *necessarily* involve reverse genetic changes but may be due to progressive genetic changes involving a reversal in phenotype only (Braun, 1947). For example, genetic changes yielding a phenotypic picture of S to R and back to S ($S \rightleftarrows R$) in aging cultures of *Brucella abortus* were shown to be more correctly represented as changes from S to R to S′ ($S \rightarrow R \rightarrow S'$) where S′ was antigenically similar to S but the mutant S′ differed significantly from the parent S type in the associated characteristic of alanine resistance (Goddlow *et al.*, 1951). Thus, just as in the case of "reverse" mutations from auxotrophy to prototrophy (p. 79), phenotypic reversal is not always indicative of genotypic reversal, i.e., a return of the altered gene to its original status. A change involving another locus, e.g., a suppressor gene, or a different allelic state of the same gene may cause a phenotype which mimics that of the original parent type.

MUTANTS WITH ALTERED VIRULENCE

Virulence expresses the ability of certain types of bacteria to produce a pathological state in a particular host. It is the end result of interactions between host and parasite, and is governed by certain inherent properties of the bacterium and of the host. Therefore, it is not quite accurate to refer to the virulence of a bacterium *per se* without referring to the host. Nevertheless, such oversimplification is convenient for descriptive purposes, provided it is understood that whenever we talk about properties associated with the virulence of a bacterial cell we are actually referring to properties that affect its relation to the host.

The variability of bacterial properties associated with virulence has been known for a long time and it has been of great basic as well as applied interest to medical bacteriologists (cf. Braun, 1947; MacLeod, 1958). Numerous studies have shown that *in vivo* passage of pathogenic bacteria may often increase their virulence and it is well known that a loss of virulence is likely to occur following prolonged cultivation under laboratory conditions. All available evidence clearly indicates that most of these changes involve the establishment of mutants with altered virulence in initially virulent populations (see p. 198). In many instances, the actual nature of the inherent properties which are altered in such mutants remains relatively unknown. However, a number of complex properties affecting virulence have been described and they may undergo either simultaneous changes or vary independently of each other.

INHERENT PROPERTIES AFFECTING VIRULENCE

Pathogenic bacteria differ from saprophytic bacteria in their ability to invade the tissues of a host and to cause symptoms of disease. These symptoms will ensue unless the invaders are quickly defeated by the host's defense mechanisms, which include the activity of the reticulo-endothelial system. The invasiveness of pathogenic bacteria, therefore, is one of the properties which determine their virulence, and this property depends partly on the manner in which the bacterium can protect itself [e.g., through the possession of a polysaccharide capsule (pneumococci), smooth surface antigens (gram-negative pathogens), or a type-specific M protein and a capsule of hyaluronic acid (hemolytic streptococci)] against the action of phagocytes. Surface structure also can influence the bacterium's ability to resist other antibacterial host factors, such as serum factors, including specific antibodies and components of the complement system, that can lyse gram-negative bacteria (Michael and Braun, 1959).

Another interesting cell-surface-dependent property associated with virulence is suggested by Jenkin (1962), who obtained some evidence indicating that virulent strains of *S. typhimurium* share an antigen with susceptible hosts (but not with resistant hosts), while the avirulent variants lack this common antigen. Since, as a rule, animals do not form antibodies against their own antigens, susceptibility may involve, at least in this particular case, an inability of the host to form a class of antibodies (opsonins) that assist in phagocytosis. It has also been demonstrated that in the case of intracellular parasites, such as *Brucella*, the ability to multiply within monocytes (a phenomenon presumably associated with virulence) is dependent on the presence of S surface antigens; non-S mutants fail to undergo intracellular multiplication (Braun *et al.*, 1958). These and many other observations show that changes in the surface structure of bacterial

TABLE 12. *Virulence for guinea pigs of several mutants of* Brucella suis *differing in colonial morphology**

Brucella suis TYPE	DOSAGE (ORGANISMS)	INFECTION RATIO (INFECTED / TOTAL)
S = Smooth	14	9/9
	140	9/9
I_1 = Intermediate$_1$	12	4/8
	120	10/10
	1200	8/8
I_2 = Intermediate$_2$	10	0/10
	100	1/10
	1000	2/9
I_3 = Intermediate$_3$	8.2	0/10
	82	0/4
	820	6/10
R = Rough	8.6	0/8
	86	0/6
	860	5/9
M = Mucoid	9.4	0/9
	94	1/8
	940	2/7

*From Braun, 1950.

cells, including changes from smooth to non-smooth, often are associated with simultaneous changes in virulence (Table 12).

Still another property that contributes to the virulence of many pathogens is the production of toxins. It is of interest that in a number of cases such toxigenicity is due to phage conversion, the most famous case being the toxigenicity of *Corynebacterium diphtheriae* (Groman and Lockart, 1953; Barksdale, 1959); lysogenic strains produce a toxin which is not produced by the non-lysogenic bacteria. It is suspected that toxin of staphylococci may also be produced under the influence of a phage (cf. Groman, 1961). Toxigenicity can be lost either by curing bacteria of the phage (in cases like *C. diphtheriae*) or by spontaneous mutation in cases in which phage is not involved.

Many additional inherent factors can contribute to the virulence of bacteria. Some of these are poorly understood; others have been described as associated with the production of hemolysins, leukocidins, coagulase, lecithinase, fibrinolysins, or hyaluronidase (see Burrows *et al.*, 1959; Raffel, 1961). It is noteworthy that hyaluronidase production by streptococci is also inducible by phage conversion occurring after the infection of susceptible bacteria with a lytic phage (Kjems, 1957).

The complexity of the many factors, including antigenic surface components, that may be required to bring out full virulence is illustrated by the analysis of the factors that are required for virulence of *Pasteurella pestis* (Burrows, 1962). For full virulence of *P. pestis* strains for mice and guinea pigs the bacteria must possess *(1)* antigen F_1 forming a proteinaceous envelope (probably controlled by two different genetic loci); (2) antigens *V* and *W* causing resistance to phagocytosis (probably controlled by one locus); (3) a determinant P^+, probably associated with iron utilization and recognized by the ability of P^+ strains to develop pigmented colonies; (4) a determinant, Pu^+, which permits the organism to grow independent of an exogenous source of purine (for lack of virulence of purine-requiring mutants, see page 182); (5) toxigenicity; and (6) an additional virulence determinant as yet unidentified. The unidentified determinant must be assumed to be necessary because strains that are F_1^+, VW^+, P^+, Pu^+, T^+ but nevertheless possess reduced virulence for the mouse have been encountered. A smiliar multiple factor control of virulence also has been demonstrated for *Agrobacterium tumefaciens* in which transformation tests revealed several loci whose joint activity were required for full virulence (Klein, 1956).

Virulence-determining properties of bacteria are obviously under the same sort of genetic controls as the other cellular properties that depend on the formation and activity of specific enzymes. It can be hoped that most of the constituents of pathogenic bacteria which are related to the outcome of their interactions with animal or plant hosts can be described ultimately in biochemical terms (for progress in this area, see Braun, 1960). Changes in these properties can then be analyzed, recognized, and—one may hope—systematically modified by environmental and genetic influences, just as similar processes involving gene-controlled biosynthetic processes have become amenable to modification in other biochemical mutants.

ASSOCIATED CHANGES

Most studies on changes in virulence which can be subjected to genetic analysis have utilized easily identifiable associated changes, for example, altered antigenicity or colonial morphology, as indicators. This has been necessary because of the cumbersome techniques associated with titrations of virulence in animals or plants and seems justified for species in which there is a high degree of association between these characteristics. Such studies (cf. Braun, 1947) have revealed that changes in virulence occur spontaneously and without a directing influence of the environment, just as in the case of changes in colonial morphology and antigenicity. They manifest themselves initially only in a few cells of a population consisting predominantly of cells with different virulence. Therefore, changes in virulence behave as mutational changes, and much of the information reviewed in the preceding sections on antigenic and colonial mutants also applies to virulence characteristics including the fact that the spontaneous occurrence of altered types may in some cases involve extra-chromosomal DNA factors, including conversion, rather than altered intra-chromosomal nucleotide sequences.

The usual close association between virulence and colonial morphology has permitted the isolation of mutants with altered virulence on the basis of differences in colonial appearance. For example, a systematic isolation of clones differing in virulence was easily accomplished in *Bacterium tularense* when it was found that differences in colonial morphology could be detected with the help of the oblique lighting system (Eigelsbach *et al.*, 1951). Cultures which in animal titrations had revealed unequal virulence were found to consist of mixtures of cells with different virulence which could be separated on the basis of colonial morphology (Fig. 71). Most of the resulting clones displayed considerable stability in virulence and colonial characteristics. Similarly, clones with differences in virulence have been isolated on the basis of colonial morphology in a number of bacterial species. An additional interesting example is provided by studies with *Salmonella typhimurium* in which clear-cut differences in colonial morphology became apparent when mixed cultures, streaked on MacConkey's agar, were viewed with oblique lighting (Page *et al.*, 1951). Two colonial types (Fig. 73), differing significantly in virulence but not in their acriflavine reactions or antigenic formulae, were recognized and isolated. This also represents one example of the occasional occurrence of associated changes in virulence and colonial morphology without changes in antigenic characteristics.

ENVIRONMENTAL EFFECTS ON VIRULENCE

The high degree of association among colonial morphology, antigenic and virulence characteristics immediately tells us that many of the examples we have cited for environmentally induced, phenotypic modifications of the other properties (pp. 163 and 173) also apply, in many cases, to temporary modifications of virulence. For example, genotypically VW^+ cells of *Pasteurella pestis* grown at 28° C produce no VW antigens and are of low virulence, but they do develop, even in the absence of multiplication, significant amounts of VW antigen and virulence when subsequently incubated at 37° C (Fukui *et al.*, 1960). Also, intracellularly grown brucellae display a greater resistance to serum bactericidins than their genotypically identical sister cells grown on agar media (Stinebring *et al.*, 1960). Furthermore, the susceptibility of enterobacteria to serum bactericidins is greatly affected by the cells' growth phase and by the composition of the culture medium (Michael and Braun, 1959). These altered susceptibilities to one of the important components of the antibacterial defense systems of the host, measured *in vitro* in the two examples just cited, undoubtedly reflect phenotypic changes that would alter host-parasite interactions.

Any environmental condition that slows down bacterial multiplication may intially reduce infectivity because it may reduce the pathogen's ability to establish a foothold *in vivo*. On the other hand, a reduction of metabolic rates can be of benefit in some situations because, it has been shown, the bactericidal activity of serum is strongest against fast-growing cells and weakest against slow-growing cells (Michael and Braun, 1959).*

SOME GENETIC PROBLEMS COMMON TO COLONIAL, ANTIGENIC AND VIRULENCE MUTANTS

The foregoing descriptions have illustrated that in many instances the available information pertaining to colonial mutants is also applicable to

*Many other examples of the role of phenotypic variability of bacteria in infection could be cited, including the contribution of phenotypic heterogeneity in genotypically (relatively) homogeneous bacterial populations, but the interested reader is referred to a good review of this topic by Meynell (1961).

phenomena associated with mutants differing in antigenicity or virulence, and vice versa. In the case of some problems associated with these mutants the extent of such overlapping information is particularly pronounced; problems belonging in this category will be considered now.

MUTATION RATES

Evidence for the spontaneous origin of variants differing in colonial morphology, antigenicity and virulence is convincing (Braun, 1947), but direct proof and reliable data on mutation rates as supplied by fluctuation tests are scarce. It will be recalled that the principal feature of the fluctuation test is the ability to recognize small numbers of mutants among an overwhelming number of parent cells by the specific elimination of the non-mutant background. For example, streptomycin-resistant mutants can be separated easily by the lack of growth of streptomycin-susceptible parent cells in the presence of the antibiotic. Such specifically selective agents, capable of eliminating all cells of one type in favor of variant cells, are relatively unknown as far as colonial morphology, antigenicity and virulence are concerned.

However, selective agents *and* the fluctuation test have been employed for the estimation of mutation rates involving antigenic and colonial changes from S→R in *Brucella abortus*. In this species it had been found that S cells are far more susceptible to the growth-inhibitory effect of D-alanine or salicylate than R cells (p. 202). Therefore, soft (0.75%) agar media, containing D-alanine or salicylate, could be used as screening media on which S cells developed into microcolonies only, whereas R cells

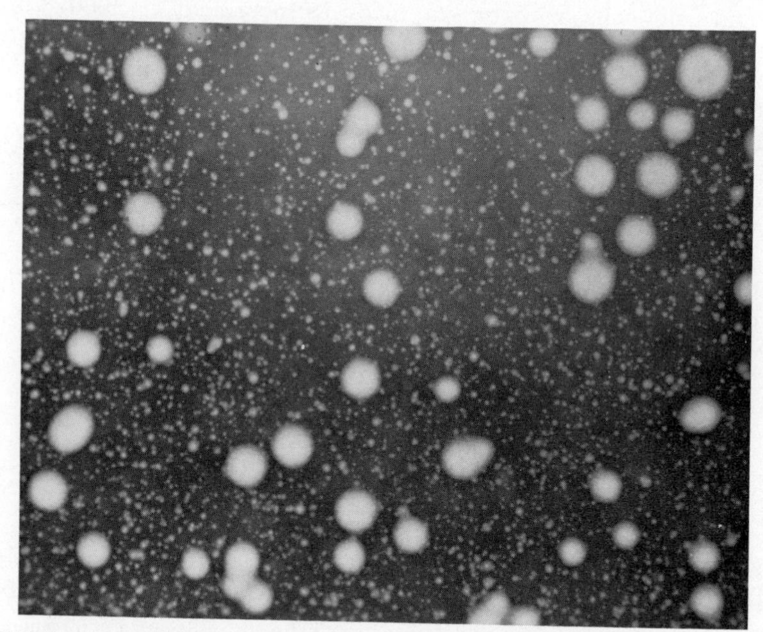

FIGURE 79. Colonies which developed from S and R cells of *Brucella abortus* on soft (0.75 per cent) agar containing 3.0 mg/ml of DL-alanine. Tiny colonies developed from S cells, large colonies from R cells. (Magnification: × 15.)

developed into colonies of normal size (Fig. 79). With the help of such screening media and the fluctuation test (Fig. 44) a spontaneous mutation rate of 1×10^{-7} was obtained for S→R changes (Braun and Ciaccio, 1952). It also has been reported that S and R variants of intestinal pathogens display differential susceptibility to deoxycholate (Brodie and Shepherd, 1949), and an association of resistance to bile salts and virulence has been described in *S. typhimurium* (Thomas and Wilson, 1960). So far, however, these correlations have not been exploited for fluctuation tests.

In the absence of effective means for eliminating the predominant parent cells, visual inspection of easily recognized differences between mutants and the parent type has been used in a few cases to gain information on mutation rates (e.g., Page *et al.*, 1951; Lincoln, 1947; Zelle, 1942; Burrows, 1962; DeKlerk and Coetzee, 1962); rates ranging from 1×10^{-3} to 1×10^{-10} per generation were observed. This makes it evident that mutations affecting colonial morphology can occur at greatly different rates. Rates of mutation affecting antigenic and virulence characteristics presumably may vary over a similarly wide range, depending partly on the species, the strain and the actual cellular component involved. This conclusion appears justified on the basis of (1) the frequent correlation among changes in colonial morphology, antigenicity and virulence, (2) the limited evidence available from fluctuation tests, and (3) the many indicative observations on the variable stability of these characteristics during prolonged cultivation. However, it must be kept in mind that the latter evidence, i.e., cultural stability, is not necessarily conclusive, since in observations based upon population changes it is often difficult to separate the effects of selection from those of mutation. In addition, mutants affecting antigenicity, virulence, or both are often difficult to recognize; many of them may remain undetected unless environmental conditions permit their establishment within the parent population. These problems will be discussed in more detail in Chapter 10.

As far as the underlying genetic changes leading to these mutation rates are concerned, we now have good reason to suspect that unusually high rates may reflect alternate expression of unaltered information, as in the case of phase variation or, possibly, viral conversion. However, since elucidation of the nature of such changes requires the use of genetic transfers for proper analysis, it will probably be a long time before it becomes possible to categorize most spontaneous changes in colonial, antigenic and virulence characteristics.

ANTIGENICITY AND VIRULENCE OF AUXOTROPHIC MUTANTS

The capacity of a pathogen to establish itself in a susceptible host depends, in part, on its ability to propagate *in vivo* at sufficiently high rates (p. 176). Therefore, it could be anticipated that mutants unable to synthesize a required growth factor would be at a disadvantage in hosts or tissues that do not supply this growth factor. This has been confirmed in a series of studies with auxotrophs derived from pathogenic strains of *Salmonella typhimurium* (Gowan *et al.*, 1951; Furness and Rowley, 1956), *S. typhi* (Bacon *et al.*, 1951), *Klebsiella pneumoniae* (Garber *et al.*,

1952), *Pseudomonas pseudomallei* (Levine and Maurer, 1958) and *Erwinia* (Garber *et al.*, 1956; Garber, 1960).

Gowen *et al.*, used radiation and the penicillin screening technique for the isolation of 70 different, serologically unaltered, auxotrophic mutants of *S. typhimurium*. Several of these mutants displayed altered virulence (either decreased or increased) which sometimes was, and sometimes was not, associated with altered immunogenicity. For example, adenine-, hydroxyproline- and arginine-requiring mutants displayed a loss of both virulence and the capacity to immunize mice; in contrast, leucine- and serine-requiring mutants were low in virulence, but high in their immunogenicity. Furness and Rowley (1956) later demonstrated that an adenine-dependent strain of low virulence could be transduced to adenine-independence and with this change attained virulence for mice.

Bacon isolated 25 different auxotrophs from *S. typhi* and found that the majority of the mutants retained full virulence for mice. Among those that showed changes in virulence, the most notable loss of virulence was associated with mutants deficient in their ability to synthesize purines, para-aminobenzoic acid (PAB), or aspartic acid, and with certain cystine- (1 of 11) or histidine-requiring (2 of 10) mutants. Purine-requiring mutants of *P. pestis*, *Klebsiella* and *Ps. pseudomallei* later also were found to be avirulent for mice, and it has been established that the limited availability of this growth factor in the host prevents the *in vivo* multiplication of these mutant cells to toxic levels. In contrast, mice were found to contain ample levels of growth factors required for those auxotrophic mutants which failed to show a loss of virulence. As expected, full virulence of the purine-, PAB-, and aspartic acid-requiring mutants was restored in mutant-infected mice by the injection or, in some cases, by the feeding of the specific growth factor. Evidence indicated that a seasonal variation which had been observed in the virulence of these mutants was due to seasonal changes in the availability of the specific nutrilites in the host. Also, dissimilar mutants of low virulence exerted a synergistic effect when mixed suspensions of such mutants with different growth factor requirements were injected into mice (Table 13). This increased virulence probably resulted from the mutual feeding of the mutants, i.e., mutant A

TABLE 13. *The synergistic effect of purine-requiring and PAB-requiring mutants of* Salmonella typhosa *tested in mice**

TOTAL DOSE OF ORGANISMS	DEATHS OUT OF 20 MICE INJECTED WITH		
	purine-requiring mutant #479	PAB-requiring mutant #20063	#479 + #20063
1 x 10^8	0	0	2
2 x 10^8	0	1	17
4 x 10^8	2	1	18
8 x 10^8	9	10	20

*From Bacon, Burrows and Yates, 1951.

supported the growth of mutant B by excreting the specific growth factor required by B, and vice versa. Such mutual feeding was also observed when mixed suspensions of these mutants were grown *in vitro*. It may well be that these findings on seasonal variations and synergistic effects of auxotrophs on virulence reflect a mechanism for changes in virulence that can occur in natural infections.

The studies with *S. typhi* auxotrophs also furnished some observations regarding antigenic characteristics in these mutants: Mutants with lowered virulence retained the polysaccharide Vi antigen, but there was a reduction of this antigen in a histidine- and a cystine-requiring strain. The O antigen, as a rule, also remained unaltered except for its reduction in the two histidine-requiring mutants; these mutants also displayed an altered morphology.

INDEPENDENT AND ASSOCIATED CHANGES IN COLONIAL, ANTIGENIC, VIRULENCE AND OTHER CHARACTERISTICS

Throughout this chapter repeated reference has been made to the frequent occurrence of simultaneous changes in colonial morphology, antigenicity and virulence. There are still other characteristics which are apt to change in association with the above named characteristics, e.g., cell morphology, stability in saline, sensitivity to bacteriophage, biochemical activities, antibiotic resistance, and ability to sporulate (see Braun, 1947). The occurrence of such associated changes attained considerable significance in the discussions that raged at one time in regard to the nature of changes involving colonial, virulence, antigenic and other associated characteristics. As has been pointed out in Chapter 2, De Kruif, Mellon, Hadley and others regarded such changes as part of a regular life-cycle. The demonstration of the fairly frequent occurrence of independent changes in these characteristics served as important evidence against the concept of regular life-cycles in the days preceding the introduction of genetic techniques into studies with bacteria.

Table 14 shows some representative examples of the independent changes that have been observed in studies on the characteristics mentioned previously. In inspecting this table it should be kept in mind that the characteristics cited in the first column are identical with those which frequently show associated changes in the same species.

The question still remains why the various characteristics discussed in this chapter may show either independent or associated changes. In an attempt to answer this question it must be stated first that a great number of constantly associated changes undoubtedly can be attributed to the occurrence of one basic change. For example, merely the loss of the polysaccharide components in cell surface materials can account for several of the usual characteristics of the R mutants, such as (1) loss of type-specific antigenicity; (2) increased agglutinability by salt through increase of lipid instead of polysaccharide components at the cell surface; (3) altered sensitivity to bacteriophage, and, (4) a loss in virulence. This situa-

TABLE 14. *Examples of independent changes among characteristics that frequently show associated changes*

CHARACTERISTICS INVOLVED	SPECIES	REFERENCE
Cell morphology, instability in saline, inagglutinability in anti-sera, and colonial morphology	*Klebsiella pneumoniae*	Yale J. Biol. Med., *16*:629, 1944
Cell morphology, colonial morphology, production of somatic antigen, and pigment production	*Serratia marcescens*	J. Bact., *34*:255, 1937
	Gaffkya tetragena	J. Bact., *31*:407, 1936
Cell morphology and colonial morphology	*Bacillus megatherium*	J. Bact., *38*:41, 1939
Colonial morphology and capsular polysaccharide production	*Streptococcus sp.*	J. Inf. Dis., *79*:148, 1946
Colonial morphology and fermentative abilities	*Shigella sonnei*	J. Bact., *31*:309, 1936
	Bacillus anthracis	J. Bact., *25*:49, 1933
Colonial morphology, antigenicity, and fermentative abilities	*Escherichia coli*	J. Bact., *31*:453, 1936
Colonial morphology, carbohydrate fermentation, toxin production, and virulence	*Streptococcus sp.*	J. Bact., *32*:105, 1936
Colonial morphology and virulence	*Corynebacterium diphtheriae*	J. Bact., *25*:97, 1933
	Pasteurella pestis	J. Inf. Dis., *73*:124 1943; J. Bact., *76*:41, 1958
	Myocobacterium tuberculosis	J. Bact., *82*:517, 1961
Colonial morphology and antigenicity	*Noguchia granulosis*	J. Inf. Dis., *59*:244, 1936
	Brucella abortus	Amer. J. Vet. Res., *8*:386, 1947
	Salmonella typhosa	J. Hyg., *35*:428, 1935
Virulence and polysaccharide antigens	*Salmonella typhimurium*	J. Bact., *40*:197, 1940
Virulence, agglutinability, growth requirements, hemagglutination, alum precipitability, and protective antigenicity	*Hemophilus pertussis*	J. Gen. Microbiol., *5*:531, 1951
Toxigenicity and colonial morphology	*Clostridium botulinum*	Mikrobiol. Zhur., *7*: 63, 1940
	Shigella dysenteriae	Compt. rend. Soc. biol., *136*:478, 1942
Phage sensitivity and colonial morphology	*Streptococcus sp.*	Arch. inst. biol. (São Paulo), *6*:121, 1935
Virulence and pigment production	*Staphylococcus aureus*	J. Bact., *73*:685, 1957

tion appears similar to the previously mentioned correlation between ultraviolet-resistance, nitrogen mustard-resistance and H_2O_2-resistance in certain *E. coli* mutants, which probably reflects the occurrence of only *one* basic change. However, changes such as those cited in Table 14 must be of a different nature because in these cases a group of characteristics may undergo either associated or independent changes. Several different mechanisms may be postulated for such phenomena. First, it is possible to assign the cause to a single mutational change affecting either one of different levels of gene-controlled processes, a scheme that has been useful in the interpretation of genetic studies on higher organisms and that has also been applied to explain the metabolic changes which may or may not occur simultaneously with changes in phage-resistance of *E. coli.*

Figure 80 illustrates the manner in which the interpretation just described can be applied to the occurrence of associated or independent changes in an arbitrarily chosen set of characteristics involving colony morphology, cell morphology, stability in saline and virulence. It can be assumed that a common precursor, *a*, exists for the biosynthetic processes leading to the development of these characteristics. Mutation A affecting process *a*, and thereby all subsequent processes, will cause simultaneous changes in all four characteristics; another mutation, B, may affect process *b* only and thus cause a change in virulence without changing colony morphology, cell morphology, and stability in saline; at another time, a mutation C, which affects process *c*, may occur and cause changes in colony morphology, cell morphology, and stability in saline without altering virulence; and so on. The bacteriological literature contains many examples supporting this type of interpretation (see Braun, 1947). The discovery of branched biosynthetic pathways with common precursor reac-

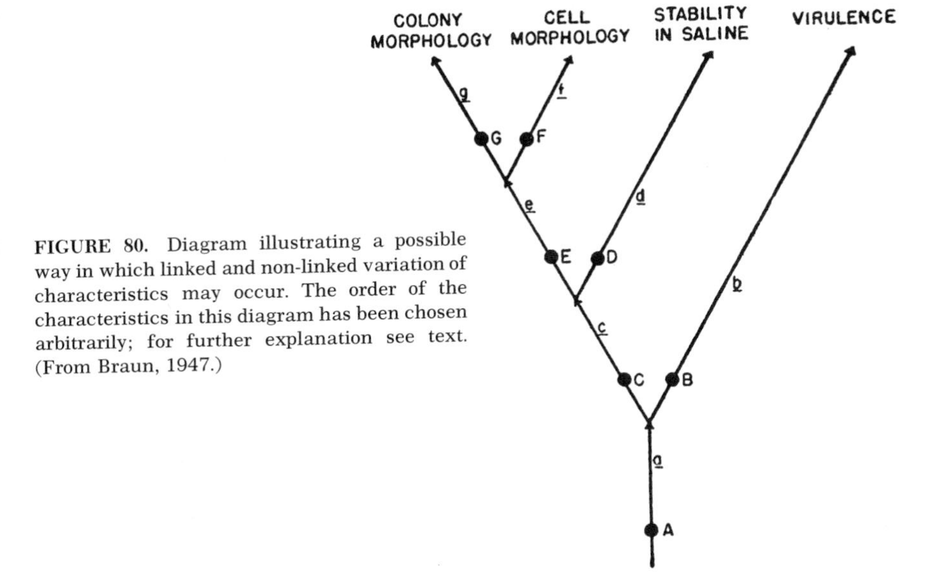

FIGURE 80. Diagram illustrating a possible way in which linked and non-linked variation of characteristics may occur. The order of the characteristics in this diagram has been chosen arbitrarily; for further explanation see text. (From Braun, 1947.)

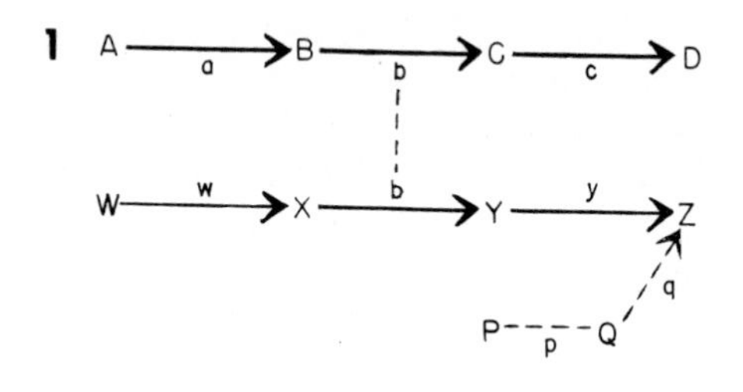

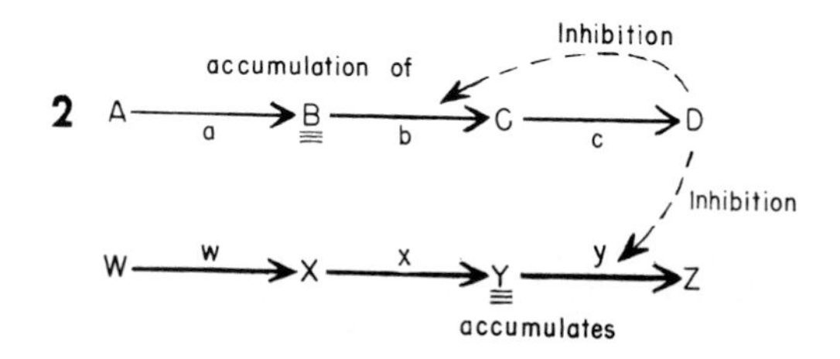

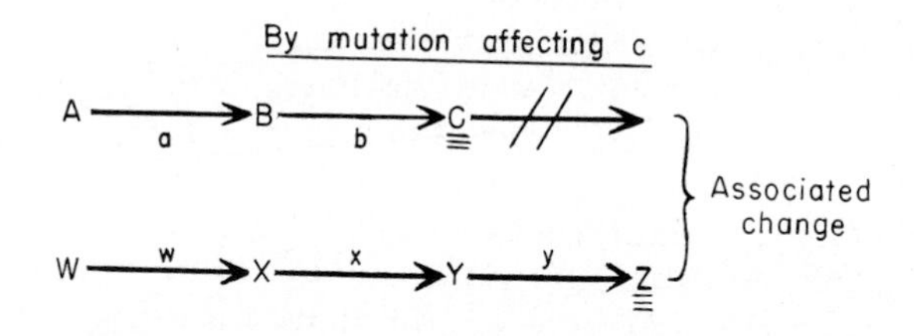

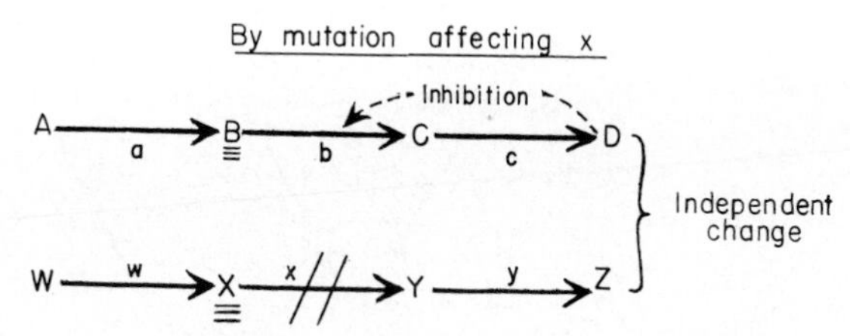

FIGURE 81. Diagrammatic representation of some theoretically possible mechanisms that may lead either to associated or independent changes in a set of characteristics. A, B, C, D, etc., are intermediates in a biosynthetic pathway; a, b, c, etc., are gene-controlled enzymes.

tions (e.g., in the synthesis of aromatic amino acids) furnishes a factual example of the type of scheme suggested in Figure 80. The involvement of the same enzyme in catalyzing two similar reactions in two entirely different pathways [e.g., in the pathways of isoleucine and valine (Figure 155)] furnishes another mechanism whereby one mutation affecting the forma-

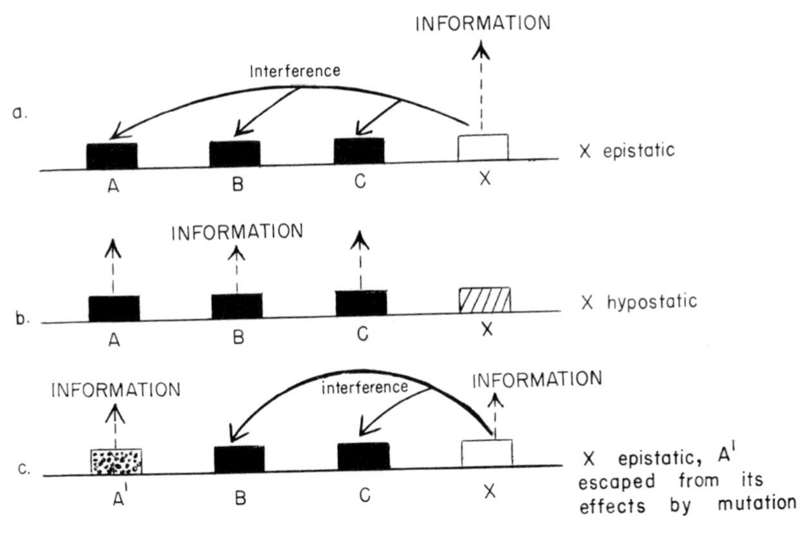

FIGURE 82. Diagrammatic representation of a phase-variation-like mechanism that may lead to associated (b) as well as independent (c) changes in the manifestation of information controlled by several separate cistrons.

tion or activity of one enzyme may cause changes in two separate properties (lack of enzyme b in Figure 81-1); independent changes may occur whenever an alternate pathway to one of the end products becomes activated (enzyme q in Figure 81-1).

Phenomena akin to certain types of repression and feedback inhibitions (see p. 345) also may serve as an example of simultaneous inhibitory effects on several separate pathways. In this case, the information for these pathways persists while the ability for utilizing this information is prevented by mechanisms discussed in Chapter 17. An independent change in one of several mutually inhibited pathways may occur when a mutation affects the information required for the synthesis of an enzyme controlling one of the steps in one of these pathways (Fig. 81-2).

Finally, we may have phenomena resembling phase variation in which the state of one gene may control the expression of one or more other genes. When, for example, the gene X is epistatic to genes A, B and C, they will not manifest their information, and we obtain a sudden and simultaneous change in several, biosynthetically unrelated characteristics (Fig. 82a, b). An independent change in one of these characteristics may occur when its controlling gene (A, B, or C in our example) escapes from the overall control of gene X by mutating from A to A′, B to B′, or C to C′, (Fig. 82c).

An essentially similar situation may exist in cases in which the control by X permitting the alternate expression of genes A, B, and C is not changed by alterations in the "state" of the non-mutated gene X, but is changed by an actual mutation of X to X′. Many years ago, Luria (1945) described an example of mutations affecting the resistance of *E. coli* to phage, in which the wild type allele of one gene (X) appeared to act as a suppressor for manifestations of the effects of another gene (Y); by mutation (X→X′) this block disappeared, permitting Y to manifest its effect. We thus have quite a number of conceivable genetic mechanisms that can account for the occasional occurrence of associated, as well as independent, changes in a set of characteristics. This removes a once puzzling and confusing phenomenon from its obscure state and supports the general conviction that the mechanisms of control and changes of different hereditary bacterial characteristics, though they may be very complex, are basically identical.

[10]

POPULATION CHANGES: I

So far we have considered primarily changes which occur in the genetic make-up of individual cells. We have seen how such changes can be detected most conveniently when environmental conditions are adjusted in such a manner that only the progeny of these altered cells and none of the parent cells can survive. Although such specifically selective conditions do occur occasionally in nature, e.g., after exposure of pathogens to antibiotics, they do not represent the more common condition where cells with different genotypes compete within a population.

Since specific mutants may arise at an "average" rate of 1 in 10^9 cells and since most bacterial populations reach such a population density very rapidly, it is evident that after a brief period of growth practically all bacterial populations, even if started from a single cell, contain one or more mutant cells. If a mutant cell is better adapted to the existent environmental conditions than the parent cells, i.e., if it can survive better and propagate faster, its progeny will constitute an ever increasing proportion of the total population and the genotypic and phenotypic complexion of the population will change. Thus, in dealing with bacteria, population changes are likely even if clones are used as starting material, i.e., if the inoculum of a culture consists of a *homogeneous* population, containing only genetically identical cells. This situation becomes even more complex if the inoculum constitutes a *heterogeneous* population, i.e., contains cells with different genotype, a situation which is most frequently encountered in bacteriological work. In the case of initially heterogeneous cultures, immediate selective growth of certain, already present, mutants may occur in addition to the selective establishment of mutants arising following growth of the culture. Therefore, population changes are even more likely to occur, and occur more rapidly, if heterogeneous rather than homogeneous inocula are used. In microorganisms, population changes represent an ever-present problem. The recognition of population changes and an understanding of population dynamics may be considered prerequisite to any study with bacteria.

In dealing with bacterial population changes due to the selective establishment of genetically altered individuals,* one has to consider at

*While we shall refer in the following section to the selective establishment of "mutants," it should be kept in mind that the phenomena of population changes and selection apply just as well to cells that have attained a different genotype and phenotype by events other than mutation, e.g., by genetic transfers or by conversion.

least two types of representative conditions: (1) changes occurring under relatively constant environmental conditions, and (2) changes occurring when the environment continuously changes, as the result of natural or artificial exposure to new cultural conditions or as the result of alteration in cultural conditions produced by the metabolic activity of the bacteria themselves.

POPULATION CHANGES DURING CONTINUED GROWTH UNDER RELATIVELY CONSTANT ENVIRONMENTAL CONDITIONS

POPULATION EQUILIBRIA BETWEEN MUTANTS OF EQUAL GROWTH RATE

Constant environmental conditions may occasionally prevail for relatively long periods in nature but they are rarely found under normal laboratory conditions. An approximation of such conditions can be achieved if cultures are frequently transferred to fresh media, e.g., every day. Constant environmental conditions can be achieved more successfully if a continuous culture apparatus such as the chemostat (see p. 88), permitting logarithmic growth indefinitely, is used (Malek, 1958; Moser, 1958; James, 1961). If mutants arise within a population growing under such constant conditions, and if such mutants have the same growth rate as the parent cells, then the rate of establishment of such mutants will be proportional to the mutation rate. Actually it will diminish with time since the percentage of the original cell type susceptible to mutation will gradually decrease. *Mutation pressure* is a term applied to the cause of population changes under conditions where the continued though infrequent occurrence of mutants alone is responsible for changes in the population and where there is no specific selective advantage for either the parent cells or the mutant cells since both grow at equal rates. In a preceding chapter we have referred to the fact that back-mutations are apt to occur. Such back-mutations, occurring after the proportion of mutant cells is sufficiently large to yield mutant cells of their own, will further reduce the increase of mutants in a growing population. This will ultimately cause the attainment of an equilibrium level between the proportion of mutant type to parent type. This was pointed out by Bunting (1946) in her studies on color mutants of *Serratia marcescens*. She showed that at the time of equilibrium the ratio of the two cell types will equal the ratio of their respective mutation rates. Thus, in populations where cells undergo mutation at the rate m, and back-mutation at the rate b

$$\frac{\text{number of cells of parent type}}{\text{number of cells of mutant type}} = \frac{b}{m}$$

at time of equilibrium.

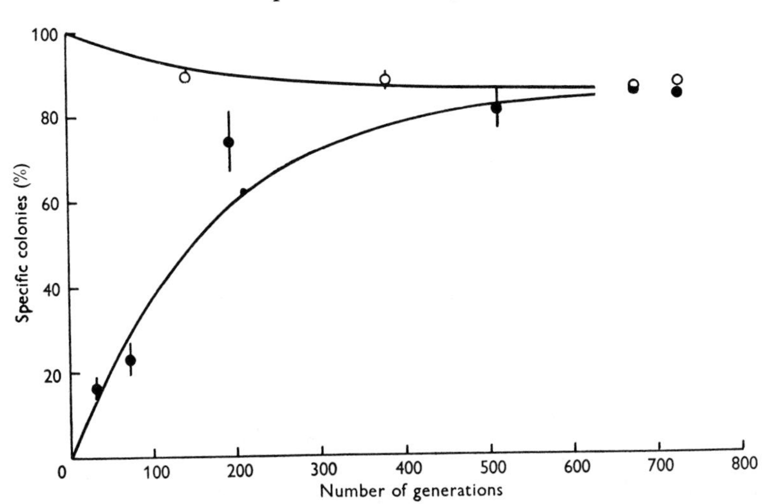

FIGURE 83. Attainment of an equilibrium state between group and specific phase "mutants" of *S. typhimurium* after prolonged logarithmic growth. Observations on "mutation" from group to specific phase are represented by closed circles; observations on "mutation" from specific to group phase by open circles. Lines correspond to "mutation" rates of 5.2×10^{-3} and 8.8×10^{-4}. (From Stocker, 1949.)

This will hold true only if the growth rates of parent and mutant types are equal, a situation which is infrequently met. Fairly high mutation rates are also required for the observation of this phenomenon, because more than 400 generations are required for the attainment of this population equilibrium if the mutation rates are as high as 1×10^{-4}. Nevertheless, Stocker (1949), in his studies on rates of "mutation" of H antigens in *Salmonella typhimurium* (see p. 171), was able to provide an additional experimental demonstration for such population equilibria, controlled by the ratio between forward and back "mutation" rates. For example, under conditions of continuous logarithmic growth one strain yielded after 600 generations about 14 per cent group-phase cells and 86 per cent specific-phase cells, regardless of whether the initial culture contained specific or group cells only (Fig. 83). This is in accordance with the theoretically calculated expectation of an exponential approach towards an equilibrium state involving cells with a mutation rate of 5.2×10^{-3} for the change from group to specific phase and a rate of 8.8×10^{-4} for the reverse change. The actual mutation rates found were in close agreement with those postulated; they turned out to be 4.7×10^{-3} and 8.6×10^{-4}, respectively.

"PERIODIC SELECTION"

In some of these population studies Stocker noticed an anomalous decrease in the proportion of mutant cells after about the 500th generation of continued growth and a renewed increase in their proportion after an

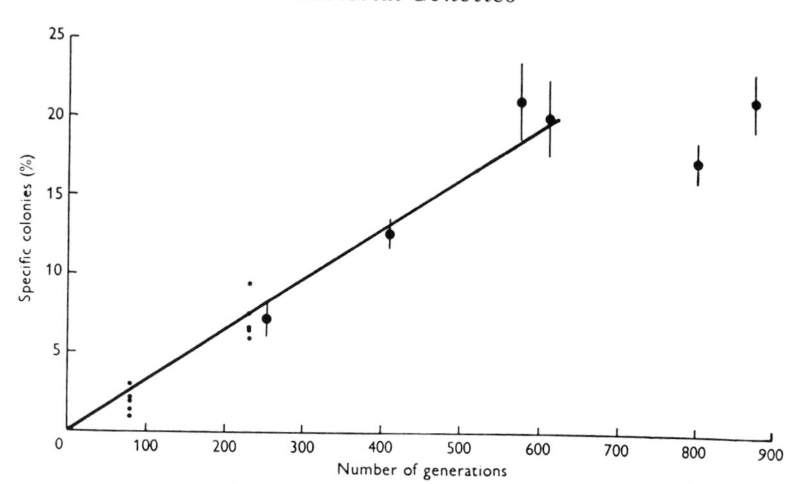

FIGURE 84. Increase in the proportion of *specific phase* cells during prolonged logarithmic growth of *S. typhimurium* cultures started with *group phase* cells. Note that the increase is linear up to the 574th generation; thereafter a temporary fall in the proportion of specific cells occurs. (From Stocker, 1949.)

additional 200 generations (Fig. 84). He assumed that this may have been due to the appearance of a faster growing mutant with antigenic characteristics similar to those of the parent cells. Such mutants with shorter generation time would be able to replace the original cells and their slow-growing antigenic mutants fairly rapidly. However, after continued growth the fast-growing cells might give rise to equally fast-growing antigenic mutants which now could establish themselves under mutation pressure and thus the proportion of mutants would begin to rise again. To illustrate this somewhat complex phenomenon let us assume that from slow-growing cells A equally slow-growing mutants B with altered characteristics (e.g., antigenic properties) arise at a constant rate. B cells will gradually replace A cells, proportional to the mutation rate from A→B. After continued growth A′ mutants may arise from A cells, differing from A in growth rate only. A′ will outgrow both the A and the B cells which established themselves in the initially A population and thus cause a decrease of the proportion of B cells. Eventually, fast-growing B′ mutants will arise from the fast-growing A′ cells and because of the constantly occurring mutations from A′→B′, B type cells will again increase in proportion to A type cells. This can be summarized with the help of the following diagram:

$$\begin{array}{ccc} A & \rightarrow & A' \\ \downarrow & & \downarrow \\ B & & B' \end{array}$$

Atwood, Schneider and Ryan (1951) confirmed Stocker's assumptions in studies with histidine-independent (h^+) and histidine-requiring (h^-) mutants of *E. coli*. They observed that during continuous serial transfers of cultures containing initially various proportions of h^- and h^+ cells an equilibrium level between h^+ and h^- was attained but it exhibited periodic fluctuations. Also, the mean equilibrium level in cultures started with primarily h^- cells was not equal to the mutational equilibrium, i.e., $\frac{\text{mutation rate } h^- \rightarrow h^+}{\text{mutation rate } h^+ \rightarrow h^-}$ (see p. 190), but was in favor of the h^- cells. By isolating h^+ cells at various stages of the continued growth and placing them in competition with h^- cells used originally in initiating the serial transfers, it was confirmed that a phenomenon involving the replacement of the original h^- cells by faster growing h^- cells had taken place. A continuous replacement of mutants in the manner outlined in the preceding paragraph was found to take place. The mutation pattern appeared to be as follows:

$$\begin{array}{cccccccl} h_0^- & \rightarrow & h_1^- & \rightarrow & h_2^- & \rightarrow & h_3^- & \\ \downarrow & & \downarrow & & \downarrow & & \downarrow & \text{etc.} \\ h_0^- & & h_1^+ & & h_2^+ & & h_3^+ & \end{array}$$

The average time elapsing between the periodic replacement of one h^+ type by another appears to be 300 generations. The investigators have proposed the term "periodic selection" for this phenomenon. Periodic selection, by permitting the periodic establishment of selectively advantageous, faster growing, mutants resembling the originally predominant type, tends to maintain a high proportion of cells with characteristics similar to those of the initially predominant cells. It thus acts to stabilize bacterial populations under conditions that are not specifically selective for the type of mutants labeled B or h^+ in our examples. This may explain why under laboratory conditions involving continuous transfers on complex media initially prototrophic bacterial populations remain essentially prototrophic, and initially auxotrophic populations will remain predominantly auxotrophic. Periodic selection thus appears to postpone the establishment of mutational equilibria. It must be reiterated that these phenomena apply only when there is no significant selective advantage for the mutant differing from the predominant parent cells in properties other than growth rate, i.e., if there are no selective advantages for the antigenic or auxotrophic mutants arising in the examples discussed above.

Essentially similar information has been obtained in population studies on phage-resistant and phage-susceptible cells growing in the absence of phage in the chemostat (Novick and Szilard, 1950). As mentioned previously, the chemostat is a device that permits the continuous growth of bacterial populations under constant environmental conditions and at a constant rate. Under these conditions it was observed that following prolonged growth repeated population change-overs occur, involving the establishment of mutants differing from the previously predominant cells merely in growth rates. At least two such shifts were observed in an experiment extending over 450 successive generations.

POPULATION CHANGES IN THE ABSENCE OF CONSTANT ENVIRONMENTAL CONDITIONS

In general, bacterial populations do not grow for prolonged periods under the ideal constant conditions described in the preceding section. Under most laboratory conditions, and probably in their natural environment as well, bacterial populations fail to propagate at constant rates. Exhaustion of nutrients, the accumulation of toxic metabolic products, changes in the pH of the environment due to the metabolic activity of the bacteria, and defense mechanisms of the host in the case of pathogenic bacteria, are some examples of environmental factors which will interfere with continued growth. Therefore, in most cases the propagation of initially homogeneous populations is inhibited long before changes due to mutation pressure can exert themselves. Under conditions of limited growth of the parent cells the selective growth and survival of mutants especially fitted to survive under the existing environmental conditions becomes a major factor in population changes.

ABSOLUTELY SELECTIVE CONDITIONS

The most extreme type of change in environmental conditions involves absolutely selective agents which completely inhibit continued propagation of the original cell type. Such conditions are ordinarily not encountered as the result of gradual changes in the environment of bacteria but occur when bacteria are placed in the presence of inhibitory agents; for example, antibiotics, phage or disinfectants. We repeatedly referred to such conditions in Chapters 5 and 7. Population changes can occur in the presence of agents that are completely inhibitory for the majority of originally present cells if a few resistant mutants are present at time of exposure to the inhibitor. Theoretically, all subsequent growth should be due to the growth of the resistant mutants only. However, in practice it is sometimes observed that even following exposure to inhibitory conditions the original cells may multiply for a few generations, side by side with the resistant mutants and their progeny. We have discussed such residual growth previously in connection with the problem of determining mutation rates (p. 86).

Population changes following exposure to absolutely selective conditions sometimes may exhibit a lag period between the time of cessation of growth of the original type and the detectable appearance of renewed growth due to resistant cells. This becomes especially apparent when growth in liquid media is measured turbidimetrically. This delay is due to the period of time required for a sufficient increase in resistant clones, to turbimetrically detectable levels, from the few resistant mutant cells present at time of environmental change.

RELATIVELY SELECTIVE CONDITIONS

We shall now consider the types of population change most frequently encountered in experimental studies, where constant environmental conditions are not assured and where the resulting shifts in environment may favor the establishment of mutants without completely suppressing the further multiplication of the parent cells. Such conditions exist during the standard type of cultivation in liquid media and in solid media in which growth invariably ceases after a period of time. This cessation of growth is undoubtedly due to changes in the environment, even though the actual restricting factors are not always known; exhaustion of nutrients often appears to play a very minor role. In contrast to absolutely selective conditions, relatively selective conditions fail to suppress the growth of the parent cells entirely but provide an opportunity for the establishment of mutants with equal or greater selective value under the prevailing conditions. The coexistence of both parent and mutant cells during periods of population shifts is characteristic of such changes.

Population Changes on Solid Media

In the course of the development of a bacterial colony on solid media a single cell may give rise to 10^7 to 10^8 cells. Mutants arising at high rates, therefore, may establish themselves within single colonies, provided their growth rates are equal to or greater than that of the unaltered parent cells. If the mutations involved affect morphological, color or fermentation characteristics, such population changes become easily visible on appropriate media. They may lead to variously sectored colonies if the mutants arise during the period of active multiplication of the parent cells (Shinn, 1939).

Depending on the time of occurrence of the mutation during the development of the colony and depending on the growth rate and stability of the mutant cells, colonies may display different types of sectors. Figure 85 shows some examples of non-lactose fermenting (*lac*$^-$) sectors in colonies developing from *lac*$^+$ cells. The *lac*$^+$ cells were exposed to ultraviolet irradiation to increase the mutation rate.

As pointed out previously (p. 110), certain sectored colonies, especially those displaying half- or quarter-sectors extending to the center of the colony, may not necessarily owe their formation to a mutation that occurred following the propagation of the initial cell from which the colony developed; such sectors may be due to nuclear segregation occurring after multiplication of an initially multinucleate cell containing one "mutated nucleus."

Frequently a mutant has little selective value when it has to compete with the actively growing parent cells and does not find the proper condition for growth until active multiplication of the non-mutant cells has ceased. Under these conditions mutant cells may give rise to secondary colonies growing in the form of papillae on the old colony (Fig. 86). An analysis of the secondary colony formation by *Bacillus subtilis* (Shah and Iyer, 1961), which may serve as an example, revealed a gradual restriction of the growth of parental cells by acids produced from the glucose

FIGURE 85. Sectored colonies of *E. coli* which developed after exposure of lac^+ cells to ultraviolet irradiation. Cells were plated on EMB agar. A to D are various lac^- mutant sectors. E and F show double sectoring: E shows a dark and a light mutant sector, neither of which would be scored as lac^- and F shows sectoring for colonial morphology mutation and for mutation to lac^- (the white edge on the upper side of the colony is due to reflection from the lamp used for illumination). (Courtesy of H. B. Newcombe.)

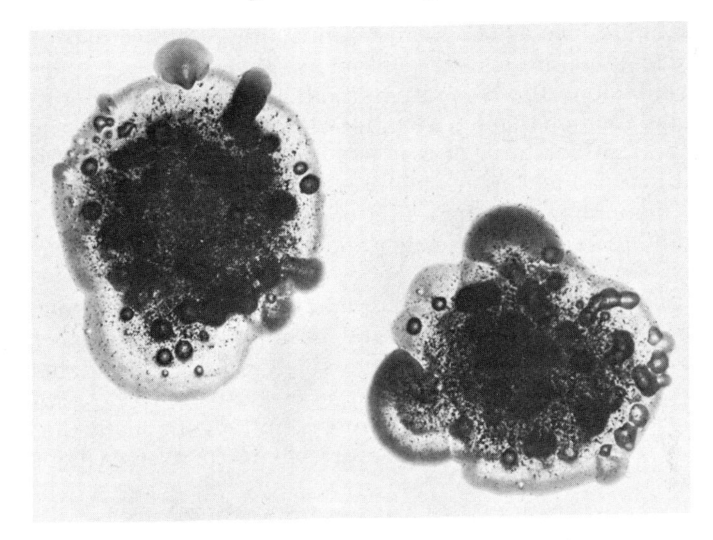

FIGURE 86. Papillae (daughter colonies) on colonies that developed from B/r cells of *E. coli* on MacConkey's agar. Incubation time was 3 days at 37° C plus 3 days at room temperature. (Magnification: × 8.) (V. Bryson, 1952.)

and the amino acids of the medium. Reversal of this pH change by decarboxylation of the amino acids, leading to the formation of alkaline amines, is slow in the case of the parent type, but more rapid in the case of the mutants. Thus the greater decarboxylase activity of the mutants provides them with a selective value under conditions in which the parental type is at a disadvantage owing to the acid environment. Prevention of pH changes in the medium prevents the formation of secondary colonies.

As a rule, subcultures made from secondary colonies or from mutant sectors of colonies will continue to breed true. One exception to this rule may occur when the growth of the mutant cells is dependent on some metabolic product produced by the parent cells. Transfers from the mutant portion of the colony then may not yield any growth in the absence of the parent cells or may cause the preferential growth of a parent cell accidentally carried over to the new medium during the attempted isolation of the mutant clone.

Metabolites inhibitory for the parent cells but permitting the growth of mutant cells also may play a role in the formation of secondary colonies. Thus, it has been reported that the constitution of the medium, e.g., the carbohydrate source used, may affect the frequency of formation of secondary colonies of *Bacillus megatherium* (Delamater, 1951). Such effects are similar to those observed in liquid media where, as we shall see later, changes in the nutrient source may affect the rate of population changes by causing quantitative and qualitative changes in the production of metabolites selectively favoring the establishment of mutant cells.

In general, population changes are less frequent on solid media compared to changes that may occur in populations of comparable size maintained in liquid media. The factors contributing to this improved stability of populations maintained on solid media are not too well understood but they must include the decreased effectiveness of metabolites that may affect population changes. The latter difference can be illustrated by the fact that in broth cultures of *Brucella abortus* 100 μgm/ml of DL-alanine, a normal metabolite, suffices to inhibit the multiplication of smooth cells, whereas more than 10 times this concentration is required to cause a similar inhibition of smooth cells growing on solid media containing 2 per cent agar.

The improved stability of bacterial populations on solid media makes such media the preferred substrate for maintenance of stock-cultures. Also, the preparation of inocula from single colonies is a highly desirable procedure, since in most cases there is a relatively good probability that cells recovered from one colony are more similar genetically than an equal number of cells taken from different colonies or from a liquid culture.

Population Changes in Liquid Media

TYPICAL GROWTH CYCLE

The typical laboratory culture of bacteria maintained in a test tube or flask in an appropriate liquid medium at proper temperature displays a characteristic growth cycle. In discussing this cycle we have to distinguish between two types of cell count: (1) the *viable cell count* which measures the number of cells capable of reproduction and which can be obtained by determining the number of colonies which develop after plating of appropriately diluted cell suspensions, and (2) the *total cell count* which can be determined by direct counts of aliquots in a counting-chamber under the microscope or, less accurately, by turbidimetric measurements. Figure 87 illustrates the usual course of the viable and total cell counts after inoculation of a liquid medium which, as is usually the case, does not supply (at least for any prolonged period of time) the optimum growth conditions for the inoculated cells. Following a lag period both viable and total cell counts will increase equally and logarithmically. After this period of logarithmic growth the viable cell count reaches a maximum which is retained as long as growth persists. During this period the total cell count may continue to increase at a gradually decelerated rate until the nutrient supply is exhausted (Jordan and Jacobs, 1944). As a result, there is a nonlinear relationship between maximal cell *numbers* attainable in a culture and the initial concentration of limiting nutrients; however, there is a linear relationship between cell *mass* and the initial concentration of limiting nutrients (Ecker and Lockhart, 1961).

POPULATION PRESSURE

At the point of population growth where the total number of cells becomes steadily greater than the number of viable cells, population pressure will start. After this point not every cell that arises will be capable of further multiplication. Therefore, population pressure can act as selection pressure permitting the establishment of any mutant that possesses a faster growth rate or better "viability" under the existent environmental

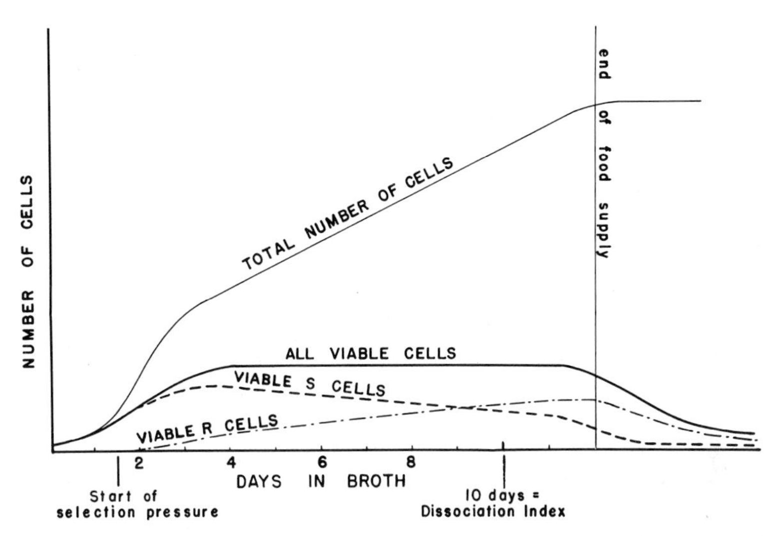

FIGURE 87. A graphic representation of the total number of cells and of the number of viable cells during growth of bacterial populations in a closed system and following the cessation of growth as the result of an exhaustion of food supply. (From Braun, 1946.)

conditions. The replacement of the original members of the population by mutants with faster growth rates is easily comprehended, but the importance of the differential between the total number of cells and the number of viable cells (viability) may need some explanation. As an example, let us assume that for the original members of a population two out of every six cells arising under given conditions retain the ability to propagate, whereas two out of every three cells of a spontaneously arising mutant propagate under the same environmental conditions. Since the total viable population usually is limited to a maximum number per unit of the environment, the higher "viability" of the mutant will suffice to replace the original type even though the mutant type may actually have a slower growth rate (Braun, 1946).

FACTORS INFLUENCING THE RATE OF POPULATION CHANGES

We thus can list several inherent factors that can influence the rate of population changes in a bacterial culture under restricted growth conditions:

1. Rate of mutation from the original type to a type better "adapted" to the existent environmental conditions.
2. Growth rate of the mutant type in relation to that of the parent type.
3. Viability of the mutant type in relation to that of the parent type.
4. Growth rate of the parent type.
5. Viability of the parent type.

Both growth rate and viability of the parent type affect the time at which population pressure starts and since mutants find little opportunity to establish themselves prior to this period, a shift in the time of onset of population pressure will affect the rate of population changes (Braun, 1946). The factors listed under 2 to 5 are capable of modifying the rate of population changes even in the presence of constant mutation rates. Any environmental agent capable of modifying these factors can also affect the rate of population change.

Experimental data supporting such considerations have been obtained with various bacteria, but especially in studies on population changes of *Brucella abortus* involving mutants with altered antigenic and colonial characteristics. Following inoculation of smooth cells into broth, population changes involving the gradual establishment of non-smooth mutants usually can be observed after the maximum viable cell count has been reached. The rate and extent of such population changes can be determined by periodic plating of aliquots on solid media and determining the percentage of smooth and non-smooth colonies that develop. Data thus obtained have confirmed that the inherent properties of viability and growth rate, listed under 2 to 5 above, affect the rate of establishment of spontaneously arising mutants. In addition, various environmental conditions which are capable of modifying these inherent properties were found to modify the rate of population changes. In the bacteriological literature on population changes involving mutants with altered antigenic characteristics these facts have frequently been reflected in different terms, such as "a rapidly dissociating culture," or "a strain with slow rate of dissociation," or "a high dissociation index (= percentage of non-smooth cells in an originally smooth population after a certain period of incubation)," etc.

POPULATION CHANGES AS RESULT OF DIFFERENTIAL METABOLIC CAPACITIES OF PARENT AND MUTANT TYPES

Many population changes undoubtedly take place because certain mutants can cope more efficiently than their parental cells with conditions that influence energy-yielding reactions and other vital mechanisms. Thus, in studies with certain strains of *Brucella abortus* it was recognized that oxygen tension plays a very important role in population changes from smooth → rough (Braun *et al.*, 1956), probably owing to the differences between smooth and rough cells in their synthesis of the heme enzymes involved in terminal oxidation (Altenbern *et al.*, 1957; 1959).

Under conditions of reduced oxygen availability, rough cells, arising spontaneously in originally smooth cultures, will rapidly outgrow their parental smooth type cells. This accounts for the long known ability of antisera against smooth cells to accelerate smooth → rough population changes in liquid cultures. In the presence of such antisera, the agglutinated smooth cells fall to the bottom of the culture vessel where low oxygen availability puts them at a selective disadvantage in competition with rough mutants. If, however, the oxygen availability for the smooth cells is improved in antiserum-containing cultures either by agitation, which prevents the cells from remaining at the bottom of the culture vessel, or by reducing the distance between the bottom of the culture vessel and the liquid-air interphase, no accelerated population changes occur, even in the presence of very high antiserum concentrations. It can be assumed that many other environmental effects on population changes, particularly the effects of pH and temperature (Braun, 1946), also involve quantitative differences in the susceptibility of related cell types as a result of inherent differences in enzyme systems controlling critical biosynthetic events.

The influence of oxygen availability on population changes has been demonstrated not only for *Brucella* but also for *Pasteurella pestis*. However, in this case, aerobic conditions favor the avirulent cells (which have a more effective oxidative metabolism), whereas in the absence of oxygen (in the presence of N_2), the virulent cells grow as rapidly as the avirulent cells. Consequently, cultures started with mostly virulent cells will retain virulence under N_2, but will undergo population changes under aerobic conditions involving the gradual establishment of avirulent mutant cells and their progeny (Delwiche *et al.*, 1959).

THE ROLE OF METABOLITES IN POPULATION CHANGES

Usually population changes will not take place *in vitro* until the culture inoculated with cells of one genotype has started to age. Two factors may be responsible for this delay: (1) Cells inoculated into a new type of medium will for relatively prolonged periods of time behave as if they were still in their previous environment, a phenomenon which can be ascribed in part to a "carry-over" of preformed materials (Braun, 1958) and in part to the time required for the organisms to switch over from one type of predominant enzymatic activity to another (Richmond and Maaløe, 1962); selective influences imposed by the new environment therefore will express themselves only with a delay. (2) The selective conditions may develop as the result of the growth and metabolic activity of the organisms. This gradual change in environmental conditions, in a closed culture system like the test tube, can lead to a cessation of logarithmic increases in the viable count of the original cell type, and at the same time any mutant displaying greater viability under the existing environmental condition may start to outgrow the parental type.

The factors causing the cessation of logarithmic growth include, apart from the gradual exhaustion of growth-limiting nutrients, toxic factors that may accumulate as the result of the cells' metabolic activities and which may inhibit the continued propagation of members of the original population. Extensive investigations regarding such inhibitory factors have been carried out with *Brucella* species, and the data obtained, which we shall now review, may serve as examples of the general mechanisms of population changes that appear to be of widespread occurrence.

Smooth *Brucella* cells growing in a synthetic medium containing DL-asparagine as the sole source of nitrogen displayed the typical logarithmic increase in the number of viable cells which ceased after four days (Fig. 88). During the next five days of incubation the viable count dropped; there then followed a renewed rise in viable count resulting from the growth of progeny of rough mutants. As Figure 88 illustrates, the addition of 10 per cent by volume of a Seitz-filtrate from a 24-day-old culture to a freshly inoculated smooth culture resulted in a marked effect on the subsequent growth and population change. The increase of the viable smooth organisms was repressed, and an earlier and more rapid establishment of rough cells occurred. Analysis of culture filtrates by paper partition chromatography (Fig. 89) revealed that the amino acid alanine, not previously present in the culture medium, started to accumulate just prior to the time when non-smooth cells started to establish themselves (Goodlow *et al.*, 1950).

Addition of D- or DL-alanine to smooth cultures caused an inhibition of smooth cells and earlier establishment of non-smooth cells similar to that observed in cultures to which old culture filtrates had been added. Addition of L-alanine had no effect on growth or population changes (Goodlow *et al.*, 1951a). It was determined that DL-alanine in a concentration of 100 μgm per ml or more exhibited a significant growth-depressing effect on the smooth cells, whereas the rough cells remained unaffected until a concentration of 1000 μgm of alanine per ml of medium was reached. The significance of these results was underlined by the demonstration that *Brucella abortus* cells produce alanine by direct amination or transamination (Altenbern and Housewright, 1951).

The experiments thus revealed that the accumulation of a specific metabolite, alanine, limits the increase in viable smooth cells and at the same time creates an environment favorable for the progressive establishment of non-smooth cells with greater resistance to this inhibitory metabolite. It will be recalled that non-smooth mutants arise in smooth populations at the rate of 1×10^{-7} (p. 181), and we have now seen how such mutants attain an opportunity to establish themselves in originally smooth populations because of their greater resistance to alanine. Prior to population

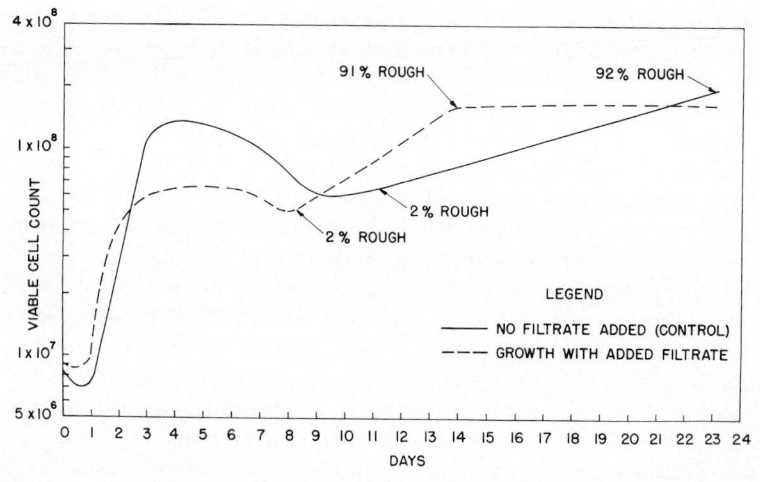

FIGURE 88. Growth (viable cell counts) and population changes in initially smooth *Brucella abortus* cultures maintained in synthetic medium with or without filtrates from old cultures. (From Goodlow *et al.*, 1950.)

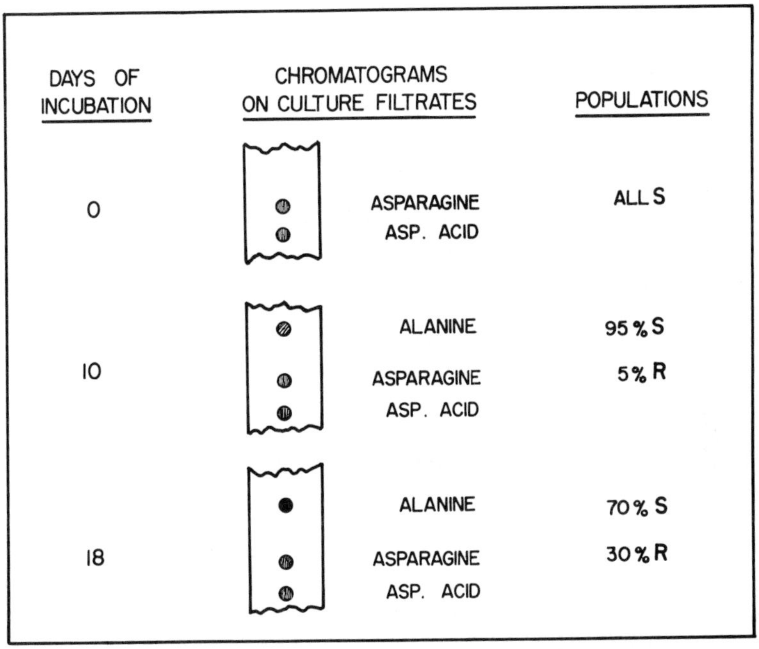

DAYS OF INCUBATION	CHROMATOGRAMS ON CULTURE FILTRATES	POPULATIONS
0	ASPARAGINE ASP. ACID	ALL S
10	ALANINE ASPARAGINE ASP. ACID	95 % S 5 % R
18	ALANINE ASPARAGINE ASP. ACID	70 % S 30 % R

FIGURE 89. Alanine accumulation tested by paper partition chromatography, and population changes in initially smooth *Brucella abortus* cultures.

changes in a closed system, such as a test tube, the parent cells can thus create conditions that may be termed "suicidal" and thereby set up specific environmental effects that will favor the establishment of metabolite-resistant mutants. These mutants, as illustrated in the case of *Brucella*, may display altered antigenic, colonial and virulence characteristics.

Similar effects of metabolites upon population changes seem to occur in various species. Evidence for this conclusion is available for *Salmonella typhimurium* (Page *et al.*, 1951) where the metabolite threonine causes the selective establishment of more virulent mutants with increased threonine-resistance (see p. 217), and *Bacterium tularense*, where a metabolite that is as yet unidentified affects the establishment of mutants with altered colonial morphology and virulence. Limited evidence indicates that similar phenomena may play a role in population changes of *Mycobacterium tuberculosis*, *Corynebacterium diphtheriae*, *Shigella dysenteriae*, and crown gall bacteria. In addition, Bunting's data obtained in earlier population studies with color variants of *Serratia marcescens* (Bunting, 1942) suggest the possible involvement of a metabolic factor. She observed that in aging broth cultures mixed populations change in a reproducible manner from cells producing predominantly dark red colonies to pink and white colony-forming cells. It could be shown that in fresh broth conditions prevailed which favored the establishment of cells that developed into dark red colonies, but this initial growth produced changes in the environment which in turn caused an increase in pale variants. An increase of pale variants could be effected in fresh broth cultures by adding autoclaved filtrates of old broth cultures or of autolyzed dark red cells. The actual nature of the responsible factor, however, has remained undetermined.

APPARENT CYCLES AND REVERSE POPULATION CHANGES

It was determined in the *Brucella* studies that alanine production continued during prolonged incubation of cultures in which rough cells with greater alanine resistance than that of the original smooth population had become established. When the alanine concentration of the culture liquid reached a level that was inhibitory for these rough cells, still other antigenic mutants with higher alanine resistance established themselves progressively in such cultures. The actual antigenic characteristics displayed by these mutants with increased resistance to a specific metabolite depended upon the strain and species employed. In a *Brucella abortus* strain, dwarf rough mutants were found after 60 days of incubation which were not only highly resistant to alanine but actually required alanine for optimal growth. Therefore, in a closed culture system the continuous quantitative and qualitative alteration of metabolite concentration can create a constantly changing environment that successively favors different mutants as long as reproduction continues. The concurrent increase of toxic metabolite level and successive establishment of mutants with higher resistance can cause what appear to be *progressive* population changes, a phenomenon that was regarded as a life-cycle by many earlier bacteriologists.

Again in studies with *Brucella abortus*, a type of population change frequently reported in the older literature was elucidated. It involves population changes from smooth to rough and eventually back to smooth (S⇄R), or more precisely the gradual establishment of R variants in a population originally consisting of S cells only and the subsequent establishment of S mutant cells in this R population. It was determined that the S mutants arising in the R population are similar in colonial morphology, virulence, and antigenicity to the original S cells but differ from them in one important respect: they are more resistant to alanine than either the original S or the R cells (Goodlow *et al.*, 1951b). Thus what had appeared to involve reverse changes from S→R→S, actually involved a population change from S→R→S′, where S′ cells simulate the phenotype of the S cells in most respects except the property which gives a high selective value in an aged culture containing a high concentration of alanine. Many older observations recorded as reverse changes, or the establishment of reverse mutants, may represent similar progressive mutational changes.

THE INFLUENCE OF PARENTAL NUTRITION ON POPULATION CHANGES

The recognition of the role of metabolites in population changes has revealed that the parent type can actually influence the direction in which population changes may occur since its metabolic products can determine which of the many spontaneously arising mutants will have the greatest survival value at any given time of a culture's growth. This was confirmed in studies with *Brucella* in which D- or L-asparagine instead of DL-asparagine was used as the source of nitrogen in the liquid synthetic medium (Goodlow *et al.*, 1952). When grown in media containing L-asparagine, most smooth strains yielded a high viable count, failed to produce alanine and failed to show population changes. In contrast, alanine accumulation, an early inhibition of viable S counts, and population changes took place in media containing D-asparagine, similar to what had been observed in DL-asparagine cultures. The most interesting effects were observed when smooth cells of a *Brucella suis* strain were used as inocula for D- or L-asparagine cultures (Table 15). Alanine accumulated in the media containing D-asparagine and population changes involving the progressive establishment of alanine-resistant rough cells took place. However, in L-asparagine media no alanine but another amino acid, valine, accumulated and the progeny of valine-resistant mucoid mutants established themselves in the originally smooth population. This represents a clear example of how changes in the nitrogen source can qualitatively alter the accumulation of metabolites and population changes.

TABLE 15. *Population changes and metabolism in initially smooth* Brucella suis *cultures maintained in a synthetic medium with* D- *or* L-*asparagine as the sole source of nitrogen*

CONFIGURATION OF ASPARAGINE	PERCENTAGE OF VARIANTS ON THE FOLLOWING DAYS					AMINO ACID METABOLITES
	5th	8th	12th	16th	20th	
L	0	0	42M*	52M	41M	Valine
D	16R†	55R	84R	90R	97R	Alanine

*M = Mucoid
†R = Rough

ADDITIONAL CORRELATIONS BETWEEN METABOLITE ACCUMULATION AND POPULATION CHANGES

In addition to the qualitative correlation between metabolite accumulation and population changes just described, several examples illustrating quantitative correlations between the accumulation of metabolites and the degree of population changes were observed in the work with *Brucella*. For example, it was noted that a reduction of the concentration of DL-asparagine in the culture medium will result in decreased accumulation of alanine and a corresponding reduction in the rate of population changes. Thus, apparently minor changes in environmental conditions can have a significant effect upon growth, metabolite production and population changes. This emphasizes the necessity for rigid control of cultural conditions in all bacteriological studies, especially in studies that employ cultivation in liquid media beyond the period of logarithmic growth of the original population. Without due attention to such effects it becomes difficult to compare data obtained in different experiments or in different laboratories.

Certain environmental agents suppress population changes in smooth *Brucella* cultures. For example, the addition to broth cultures of 5 per cent normal serum from *Brucella*-susceptible animals, of 0.03 M pyrophosphate, or of chelating agents such as ethylene diamine tetra-acetic acid prevents the establishment of non-smooth mutants in smooth cultures (Braun, 1949; Cole and Braun, 1950). However, these agents do not inhibit the growth of non-smooth cells when added to pure R or M cultures. Evidence is available indicating that these effects may also be attributed to an effect upon metabolite production by smooth cells, since in smooth strains alanine production is suppressed in the presence of the environmental agents that suppress population changes. However, Altenbern *et al.*, (1957), in studies with one strain of *B. abortus*, collected evidence suggesting a still different mechanism for these effects of serum and of chelating agents, namely an inhibition of cytochrome systems and the simultaneous activation of an alternate hydrogen transport mechanism in smooth organisms, and a lack of such an alternative in the case of rough organisms. But whatever the causal mechanism, similar effects of normal serum also have been observed with *Staphylococcus aureus* (Hoerlein, 1948), *Salmonella* species, and *Bacterium tularense*.

CORRELATIONS BETWEEN POPULATION CHANGES AND INHERENT DIFFERENCES IN METABOLISM

Under identical environmental conditions different strains, or clones, isolated from apparently homogeneous cultures can display persistent differences in rate of population changes (Braun, 1946). For example, in the case of *Brucella abortus*, cultivated in beef-extract broth, smooth clones were isolated that consistently yielded 80 per cent non-smooth variants after 10 days of incubation, whereas other clones isolated from the same smooth stock-culture never showed more than 5 per cent non-smooth cells following 10 days of incubation. Such inherent differences in rate of population change were found to be correlated with inherent differences in rate of alanine production.

The most striking case of correlation between inherent differences in metabolism and population changes was seen in studies with a certain smooth strain of *Brucella melitensis* (Braun *et al.*, 1952). This strain was found to utilize D-alanine. Therefore, when grown under conditions that led to extracellular alanine accumulation and population changes in all other *Brucella* strains tested, it failed to show any accumulation of alanine in culture filtrates, did not display any population changes and continued to increase in viable count long after other strains had reached their maximum viable level. In the presence of non-inhibitory concentrations of penicillin, the metabolism of this *B. melitensis* strain was modified, alanine accumulated in the culture fluid, and population changes occurred involving the progressive establishment of non-smooth mutants with increased resistance to alanine.

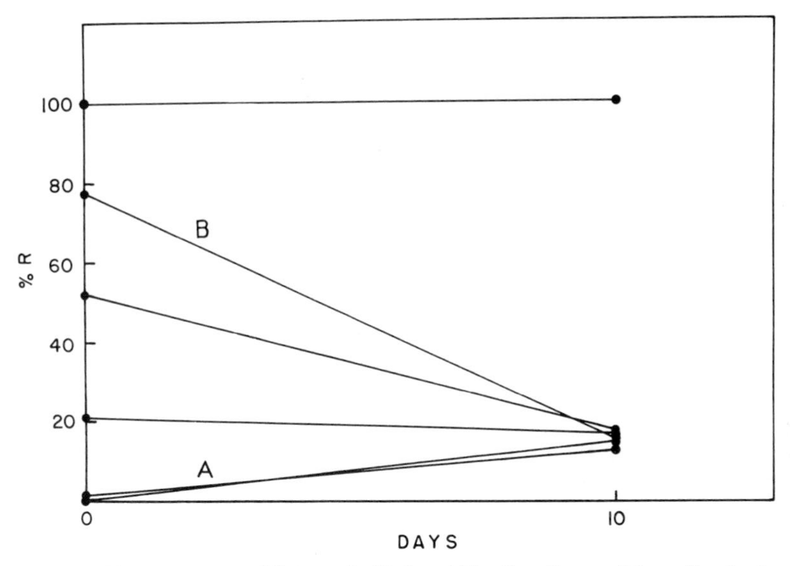

FIGURE 90. The percentage of R types in 10-day-old broth cultures of *Brucella abortus* originally inoculated with various mixtures of S and R type cells. Note that the lines connecting the 0-hour and 10-day values are diagrammatic only and do not necessarily represent the true values of the proportion of R types at intermediate points. (From Braun *et al.*, 1951.)

INTERACTIONS BETWEEN MUTANTS IN MIXED POPULATIONS

The bacteriological literature contains several references to the fact that regardless of the initial proportion of two types, such as S and R cells, in a mixed inoculum, all broth cultures will display the same ratio of types after a relatively short period of incubation. Similar observations were made with *Brucella abortus* and are illustrated in Figure 90. It can be seen that regardless of the initial proportion of R cells in cultures inoculated with a mixture of S and R cells, all cultures displayed the same proportion of R cells after 10 days of incubation. The cause for the attainment of such a population equilibrium is quite different from that described on page 191, in which forward and reverse mutations bring about an equilibrium between mutants and parent type after continuous and prolonged growth involving as many as 500 generations. The type of equilibrium (more preceisely, a transient equilibrium) to which we now refer occurs in cultures maintained under conditions of limited growth and is achieved so rapidly that mutation pressure cannot be held responsible.

Equilibria such as those illustrated in Figure 90 are apparently due to interactions between the two cell types involving their respective rates of production of an inhibitory metabolite and differential resistance to this inhibitory substance. This has been shown to be the case with *B. abortus* in which S and R types differ not only in their susceptibility to the inhibitory effects of alanine, but also in their rate of alanine production. S cells produce alanine at a greater rate than R cells and are more sensitive to it (Braun *et al.*, 1951). Thus, a culture which initially contains a high percentage of S type cells (line A in Fig. 90) will soon attain an alanine level inhibiting S cells and favoring the establishment of R cells. Consequently the percentage of R types will show a significant increase during a 10-day period of incubation. In contrast, there is much slower alanine accumulation in cultures which initially contain a high percentage of R cells. In the absence of high alanine levels it is the faster growing S type which is selectively favored over the R type; consequently the percentage of R type cells will decrease in such cultures during the initial 10-day period of growth (line B in Fig. 90). These population changes can take place very rapidly as indicated in Figure 91. Viable cell counts of homogeneous S and homogeneous R cultures grown in the absence or presence of DL-alanine have confirmed that S cells have a greater survival value than R cells in the absence of significant alanine levels, whereas R cells yield higher viable counts than S cells in the presence of alanine. Such data serve to demonstrate that the selective value of any given mutant may differ under different environmental conditions. It is noteworthy that in the well analyzed case of population changes in *Brucella* this shift in selective values can be referred to environmental changes produced by the cells themselves.

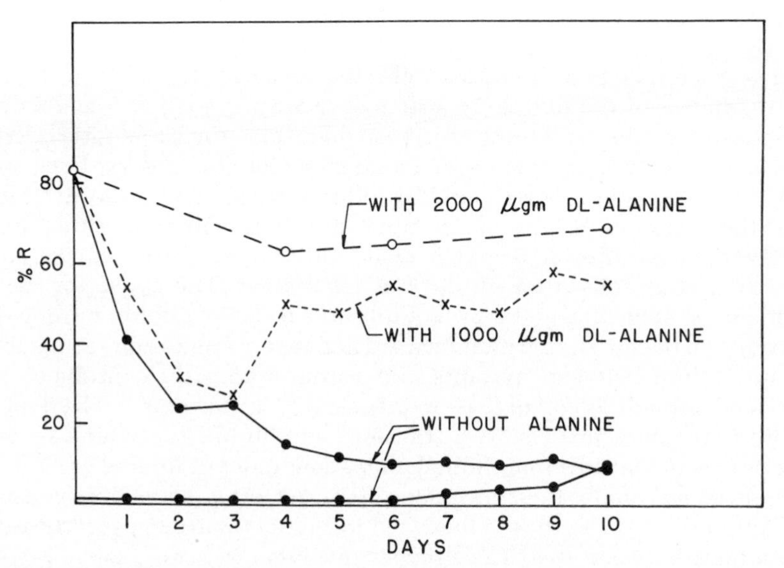

FIGURE 91. Daily changes in proportions of S and R types in broth cultures of *Brucella abortus* started with mixed inocula, and the effect of the initial addition of DL-alanine upon such population changes. (From Braun *et al.*, 1951.)

It has also been established in these studies that the level of the early population equilibrium can be affected by a number of factors: the genotype of the cells, the environmental conditions existing in the mixed culture, and the conditions under which the inoculum has been grown previously. Thus, when different S clones are used the level of the equilibrium differs, an effect that can be attributed to clonal differences in the rate of alanine production. A similar shift in the S/R equilibrium can also be produced by environmental influences. For example, initial addition of DL-alanine to mixed S + R cultures results in S/R equilibria with a larger proportion of R cells than those found in control cultures without added alanine (Fig. 91). When agents that interfere with alanine accumulation, such as pyrophosphate, are added to the cultures, the S/R equilibrium will be shifted in favor of S type cells.

Shifts in the equilibrium also occur when the S cells used are pregrown in different media. Thus mixed S + R cultures in standard broth, prepared from S cells pregrown for three days in a medium enhancing alanine production, will show a higher proportion of R cells in the S/R equilibrium than corresponding cultures prepared from S cells pregrown in a standard medium. Similarly, the S/R equilibrium is shifted in favor of the S cells if, prior to growth in the standard medium, the latter are pregrown in a medium inhibiting alanine production. Such "carry-over" effects are probably due to the ability of cells to store metabolic products and to utilize or to excrete them for a number of generations after transfer to a new environment. Wherever metabolic products play a role in population changes such effects must be kept in mind; environmentally induced temporary modifications of metabolism may persist for limited periods after transfer to new environmental conditions, and the degree of early population changes can thus be modified, depending on the previous growth conditions.

INFLUENCE OF OLIGONUCLEOTIDES ON POPULATION CHANGES

Up to this point we have concerned ourselves principally with factors that influence the establishment of less virulent (non-smooth) mutants of pathogenic species in cultures that originally consisted primarily of virulent (smooth) cells. For many years this was the only known direction of population changes *in vitro*, whereas it was well established that *in vivo*, i.e., in susceptible hosts, population changes took place in the opposite direction—from non-smooth → smooth. More recently, it has been discovered that non-smooth → smooth (e.g., M → S or R → S) population changes also could occur *in vitro* provided cultures were supplemented with enzymatic digests of DNA (Braun and Whallon, 1954; Braun, 1958; Firshein and Braun, 1960).

These effects of breakdown products of DNA, which are independent of the source of DNA and are now known to involve oligonucleotides (cf. Braun, 1965), were first observed in studies with *Brucella abortus*, but later were also found to occur in pneumococci, *Shigella*, *Clostridium botulinum*, *Vibrio cholera* and apparently also in *Pasteurella pestis* (see Firshein and Braun, 1960, for references). Thus it appears that these effects are a general phenomenon, even though the mechanisms respon-

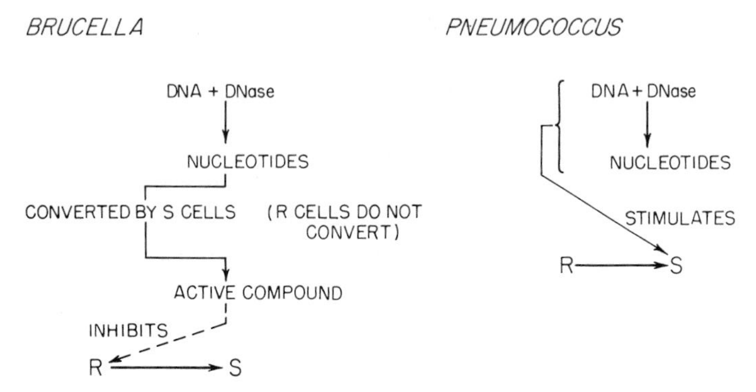

FIGURE 92. Mode of action of DNA + DNAase on *Brucella* and pneumococcus populations. (From Braun, 1958.)

sible for the selective effects of enzymatic DNA digests (DD) in gram-positive and gram-negative bacteria may be somewhat different, as indicated by comparative studies with *Brucella* and *D. pneumoniae*. Figure 92 shows that in *Brucella* the presence of DD causes S cells to form an inhibitor that suppresses the growth of R type cells without interfering with the multiplication of S cells, whereas in *D. pneumoniae*, DD has a direct stimulating effect on S cells without having a comparable effect on R cells.

The direct stimulation of S cells under conditions in which they are ordinarily at a disadvantage, resulting in R → S population changes in DD-supplemented cultures which were initiated either with S or with 99 per cent S plus 1 per cent R populations, is indicated in more detail in Figure 93. This figure also shows that in the presence of DD, additional supplementation of the cultures with deoxynucleosides and deoxynucleotides enhances the selective stimulation of the multiplication of S cells. This selective stimulation of the gram-positive S cells has turned out to be directly associated with a selective stimulation of DNA synthesis by DD, as measured in resting cells (Firshein, 1961).*

It is interesting that virulent staphylococci are able to produce their own DD by means of the nuclease produced by coagulase-positive virulent cells and the presence, in most cultures, of DNA from lysed cells (McKee and Braun, 1962). This ability may account for the fact that, in contrast to most other bacterial species, population changes of staphylococci *in vitro* are in the direction of avirulent → virulent, instead of virulent → avirulent.

POPULATION CHANGES INVOLVING INHIBITORY EFFECTS PRODUCED BY THE PARENT TYPE

In discussing the effects of alanine on population changes of *Brucella* we furnished an example of the inhibitory effects of a parental metabolite on parental cells. In discussing the influence of DD on M → S population changes of *Brucella* we pointed out that materials produced by the mutant type can inhibit further multiplication of the parental type. Still other

*The mechanism by which oligonucleotides can influence DNA synthesis is not yet entirely clear, but it may involve a stimulation of kinase activity.

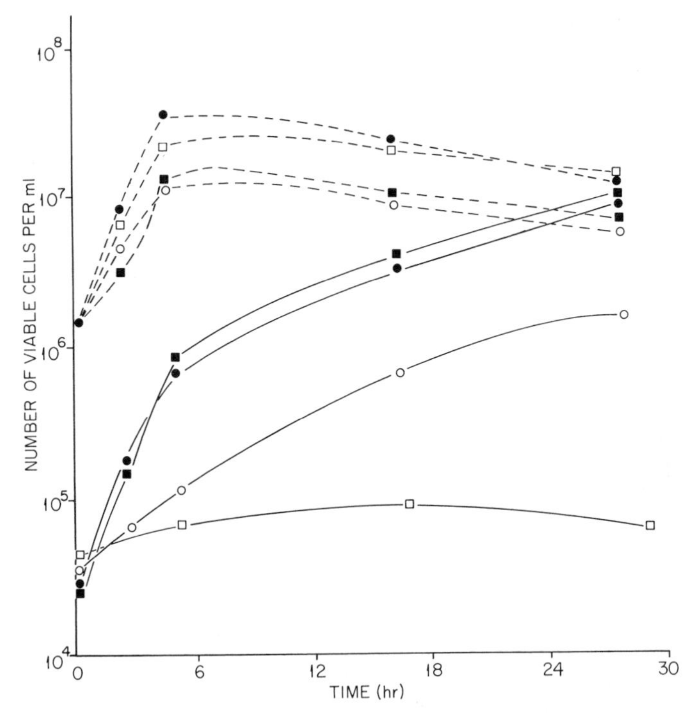

FIGURE 93. Viable counts of S and R pneumococci (Type I) in BHI-blood broth in the presence and absence of various nucleic acid degradation products. The cultures were started with an inoculum consisting of 99 per cent S + 1 per cent R cells. In the presence of enzymatic digests of DNA (DD) the S cells become the dominant component of the population 48 hours later. ● = DD + deoxynucleosides + deoxynucleotides + nucleoside diphosphates; ■ = DD + manganese (55 μg/ml); ○ = DD; □ = unsupplemented control cultures. —— = S; - - - = R. (From Braun, 1958; based on data by Firshein and Braun.)

kinds of interactions between parental and mutant cells can occur and Table 16 summarizes some of these.

The analysis by Ryan and his co-workers (1948, 1949a, b, c) of population changes in test tube cultures initiated with histidine-requiring *E. coli* mutants provides a good example of cases in which mutants may be inhibited by the growth products of parental cells. It was shown that the establishment of histidine-independent (h^+) mutants in a culture started with histidine-requiring (h^-) cells is dependent on the activity of the parental h^- cells. As one might expect, in the presence of suboptimal concentrations of histidine, selection is strongly in favor of h^+ cells since h^- cells cease to grow when the histidine content of the culture is exhausted. At that time the h^+ component of the culture continues to grow, but the extent to which such growth proceeds depends upon the activity of the h^- bacteria in the stationary phase. In aerated cultures the h^- cells continue to consume glucose in the stationary phase and the exhaustion

TABLE 16. *Some types of interactions between parental and variant cells**

CONDITION	PRODUCED BY Parental cells	PRODUCED BY Variant cells	AFFECTING Parental cells	AFFECTING Variant cells	EXAMPLE
Inhibitory metabolite	+	−	+	−	Goodlow *et al.*, 1950
	+	−	−	+	Saz *et al.*, 1953
	−	+	+	−	Cavalli-Sforza and Lederberg, 1953
	+ in conjunction with	+	+	−	Braun *et al.*, 1957
Depletion of a critical growth factor	+	−	+	−	
	+	−	−	+	Ryan, 1953
	−	+	+	−	Ryan, 1953

*From Braun, W.: J. Cell. Comp. Physiol., 52(Supp. 1):345, 1958.

of glucose causes a cessation of growth of h^+ cells. In unshaken cultures the glucose supply does not become limiting, but the h^- cells in the stationary phase continue to produce acid and an inhibitor of unknown constitution, active at any pH range, both of which limit the amount of growth of h^+ cells. Thus the establishment of h^+ cells in h^- populations can be inhibited by different means (the production of acid and an inhibitor or the exhaustion of glucose) all of which involve a modification of the medium by bacteria in the stationary phase. These findings explain why h^+ cells establish themselves rapidly in h^- populations with initially low histidine concentration, but fail to establish themselves at high histidine concentrations. The amount of histidine determines the size of the stationary population of h^- bacteria, and the more h^- bacteria in the stationary phase, the sooner will the medium fail to support growth of h^+ organisms.

Similar inhibitions of the growth of mutant cells in the presence of inhibitory conditions produced by cells of the original population have been reported. For example, Zamenhof (1946), investigating the establishment of citrate-fermenting mutants of *E. coli* in populations of non-fermenters, found that the mutants are specifically inhibited by some unidentified product of the metabolism of the parent type. Guthrie (1949) reported that the frequency of reversion of cultures of a purine-requiring *E. coli* mutant is greater in low concentrations of purine when the number of parent bacteria is lower. Also, inhibition of phage-resistant or streptomycin-resistant mutants of *E. coli* in the presence of increasing concentrations of sensitive parent cells has been observed (for example, Bertani, 1951).

We referred earlier (p. 85) to the fact that an alteration in the background genotype of parental cells can alter competitive interactions between mutant and parent cells to such an extent that a class of mutants which ordinarily has little or no survival value in the presence of inhibitory parental cells, can now establish itself. The same end result may also be achieved through changes in environmental conditions. Thus, the use of culture conditions that are unfavorable for the parental type frequently permits the recovery of mutant types which are ordinarily not encountered. This does not mean that the altered environmental conditions caused the occurrence of novel types of mutants; it merely means that the new environment permitted the propagation of mutant types which ordinarily cannot grow in the presence of parental cells.

DETERMINATION OF THE SELECTIVE VALUE OF A MUTANT

The foregoing examples, as well as the type of interaction described on page 207, clearly illustrate that it is not always possible to determine the selective value of a mutant by comparing its growth and viability in pure cultures with those of the parent type grown in pure culture. So many examples are now known of significant modification of selective values when a mutant grows in association with its parent type that inferences from data on separate growth to behavior in mixed populations become at least questionable. Nor can evidence derived from artificial mixtures of mutant and parent types be entirely relied upon. The early literature on mutagenic agents contains several examples where investigators, in order to demonstrate the absence of selective values of certain mutants, followed the fate of the mutant type cells in artificial mixtures of parent and mutant cells. It is evident that conclusions from such "reconstruction experiments" may not necessarily be valid since, as illustrated in Figure 90, different initial proportions between two types may result in different, even opposite, selective value. In addition, since growth of one cell type can continuously modify the environmental conditions, the relative selective value of a mutant may differ depending on the time in a culture's growth at which it is introduced or arises. Thus, it would be extremely difficult to reconstruct accurately selective conditions that exist under natural circumstances when a mutant may occur at different stages of the culture's growth as approximately 1 cell among 10^8 parent cells.

DIVERSITY OF ENVIRONMENTAL AGENTS AFFECTING POPULATION CHANGES *IN VITRO*

In addition to the various environmental agents cited in this chapter, there are many others, including naturally occurring materials, that can influence population changes *in vitro*. Examples of some of these selective agents, which are of interest to medical bacteriology because they favor the establishment of mutants with altered antigenic or colonial characteristics, are: bacteriophages, tissue extracts, pleuritic and ascitic fluids, Atabrine, ferric chloride, substances produced by one species affecting population changes of other species, barium chloride, phenol, and penicillin (for references, see Braun, 1947). It remains to be established how many of these agents exert direct selective effects (i.e., inhibit growth or viability of the parent type while favoring those of the mutant cells) and how many act indirectly, for example, by influencing the accumulation of metabolites that are responsible for selective effects.

[11]

POPULATION CHANGES: II

Population changes due to the selective establishment of spontaneous mutants or of otherwise altered genetic types can take place not only *in vitro*, but also *in vivo*. The events *in vivo* are of particular interest when members of pathogenic bacterial species are involved. In the present chapter we shall review some examples of such population changes. In addition, we shall discuss some of the relationships between population dynamics and problems of bacteriological procedures, and we shall also refer briefly to population changes that do not involve the selection of genetically altered types.

POPULATION CHANGES *IN VIVO*

A considerable number of reports attest to the fact that heterotrophic bacteria may undergo population changes within their host environment. It is common experience that such population changes *in vivo* may differ from those observed *in vitro* as to both rate and mutant type selected. Factors that can account for some of these differences include: (1) the presence of specifically selective host factors, such as tissue factors, and, in the case of pathogens, defensive factors, including antibodies; (2) the usual lack of a closed system in which inhibitory metabolic products of the bacteria, affecting the survival value of parent cells or mutants, could accumulate; (3) the occasional availability of a constant supply of nutrients which may permit a pattern of growth resembling that occurring in a chemostat (p. 88) rather than that observed in test tubes.

EXAMPLES OF POPULATION CHANGES *IN VIVO*

Except for the reports on the establishment of drug-resistant bacterial populations in patients under treatment (see p. 125), most investigations on population changes *in vivo* have concerned themselves with changes involving mutants with altered virulence and antigenic characteristics. The following are typical examples.

It has been reported that after inoculation of I type cells of avian or human tubercle bacilli into hens, populations containing S cells subse-

TABLE 17. *Comparison between selective effects in chicks and guinea pigs inoculated with S, M, and R mutants of* Brucella suis.*

HOST	INOCULUM: 51% M + 49% S % M recovered from spleens of individual animals after 1 week			INOCULUM: 48% R + 52% S % R recovered from spleens of individual animals after 1 week		
Chick	99	93	32	66	98	92
Guinea pig	<0.01	<0.01	<0.01	<0.1	<1	<0.01

*Number of cells inoculated intraperitoneally into each animal: 2×10^9.

quently could be isolated from the host, whereas predominantly R populations were isolated following passage of these strains through guinea pigs (Buonomini, 1938). In other studies with avian tubercle bacilli it was noted that isolations from chickens always yielded S populations regardless of the antigenic type inoculated, whereas isolations from rabbits generally were of the same antigenic type as that inoculated (Ferreira, 1942). Population changes involving the establishment of virulent S mutants have been recorded following the inoculation of relatively avirulent M cells of *Brucella suis* into guinea pigs (Jones and Berman, 1951).

These and similar observations indicate that in the case of pathogenic bacteria the virulent type is most apt to establish itself within susceptible hosts, a tendency which is easily understood since virulence is usually associated with properties that appear to protect these types from the defense mechanisms of the host and thus endow them with high selective values (see Braun, 1947, for further references). For example, it has been demonstrated repeatedly for various species that relatively avirulent, non-smooth cells are far more easily phagocytized than virulent S cells. Also, in the case of intracellular parasites, like *Brucella*, S type cells will multiply in monocytes of susceptible hosts, whereas non-S mutants fail to do so (Braun *et al.*, 1958). In contrast to this selection against mutants with decreased virulence in susceptible hosts, mutants with lower virulence seem able to maintain themselves in resistant hosts. For example, after inoculation of mixed suspensions of S + M cells of *Brucella suis* into highly susceptible embryonated eggs, population changes involving the disappearance of the less virulent M cells occur rapidly (Kraft and Braun, 1952). In contrast, mixed S + M populations are maintained for prolonged periods after inoculation into more resistant chicks (Table 17). This ability of mutants with decreased virulence to persist in normally resistant hosts is paralleled by various observations on the establishment of relatively avirulent mutants in immunized hosts and in asymptomatic carriers.

THE NATURE OF SELECTIVE HOST FACTORS

The actual nature of the host factors that may exert a specific selective effect upon bacterial population changes *in vivo* has been determined in a few cases only. We have previously mentioned that DNA breakdown products can produce a selective stimulation of the growth of virulent S pneumococci and virulent coagulase-positive staphylococci *in vitro* (p. 209). It has been shown that these breakdown products, which presumably may occur naturally at sites of infection, also can produce a significant enhancement of the growth of virulent cells *in vivo* (Firshein and Braun, 1958; McKee and Braun, 1962). On the other hand, some agents that influence population changes *in vitro* are without effect *in vivo*.

In studies with *Brucella* it has been possible to recognize a serum factor which is present in susceptible animals and prevents population changes without affecting growth when added to virulent smooth cultures *in vitro*. Sera obtained from resistant species and from immunized or infected animals of susceptible species do not produce this selective effect but permit the rapid establishment of relatively avirulent non-smooth mutants during cultivation *in vitro*. At one time it was believed that these serum effects might play a significant role *in vivo* as well as *in vitro*. However, repeated trials failed to confirm this (Braun *et al.*, 1951). Non-smooth mutants could not be isolated with any consistency from guinea pigs infected with smooth cells even during periods when these animals lacked the selective serum activity. This result is understandable in view of the demonstration *in vitro* that the accumulation of alanine can contribute to the selective establishment of non-smooth mutants in originally smooth cultures, and the finding that the selective serum factor prevents population changes by interfering with the production of alanine by the cells. A similar accumulation of alanine presumably does not occur *in vivo* since the host presents an "open system" from which bacterial metabolites can be removed as efficiently as metabolic products of the host. Therefore, in contrast to the situation during cultivation *in vitro*, conditions favoring the establishment of metabolite-resistant mutants with altered virulence normally are not created within the animal. However, it is interesting to note that non-smooth *Brucella* mutants have been recovered from walled-off abscesses of animals infected with smooth cells (Braun *et al.*, 1951). These abscesses contained a significantly higher level of amino acids, including alanine, than the surrounding "open" tissue. Thus it appears that population changes similar to those occurring in test tubes may occur *in vivo* when bacteria find themselves within a closed environment such as is represented by walled-off abscesses.

It is evident that the factors contributing to population changes *in vivo* are highly complex. Not only does the establishment of mutants with altered virulence *in vivo* depend on the susceptibility of the host and its ability to support or to inhibit the growth of the parasite in general and that of specific mutants in particular, but it appears also that the specific site of propagation may influence population changes.

THE EFFECTS OF AMINO ACIDS ON POPULATION CHANGES *IN VIVO*

It has been established in a few cases that specific amino acids can affect population changes not only *in vitro* but also *in vivo*. Thus alanine, which in the case of *Brucella* is associated with the selective establishment of more alanine-resistant mutants with altered virulence *in vitro*, can cause *in vivo* population changes of *Brucella* (Mika *et al.*, 1952). It was found that the administration of alanine (400 mg per day for 14 days) to guinea pigs infected with S cells resulted in an increase of virulence due to population changes involving the establishment of more virulent, more alanine-resistant S′ mutants. Alanine-resistant R mutants, which had been found consistently after accumulation or addition of alanine in S cultures maintained *in vitro*, were not observed in isolates from alanine-treated animals. Such R mutants, although they may arise *in vivo*, presumably have little chance to establish themselves in animals because of their greater susceptibility to destruction by host factors.

A similar modification of virulence due to population changes *in vivo* under the influence of a specific amino acid has been reported for *Salmonella typhimurium* (Page *et al.*, 1951). It was observed that, after infection of guinea pigs with 4×10^5 cells from a stock culture of *S. typhimurium*, 60 per cent of all animals died within 15 days, whereas 100 per cent died when animals were injected with 50 mg of DL-threonine at time of infection. Also, the average time of survival after infection was significantly shorter when threonine was given, compared to the time elapsed before death occurred in animals that did not receive threonine. This enhanced virulence after injection of threonine was found to be due to the *in vivo* selection of a more virulent, threonine-resistant mutant that had been present in the original stock culture. It was established that the *Salmonella* suspensions used for inoculation into the animals contained less than 1 per cent of such threonine-resistant (S^t) cells, in addition to threonine-susceptible (S^0) cells (Fig. 94). S^t and S^0 types also differ in colony morphol-

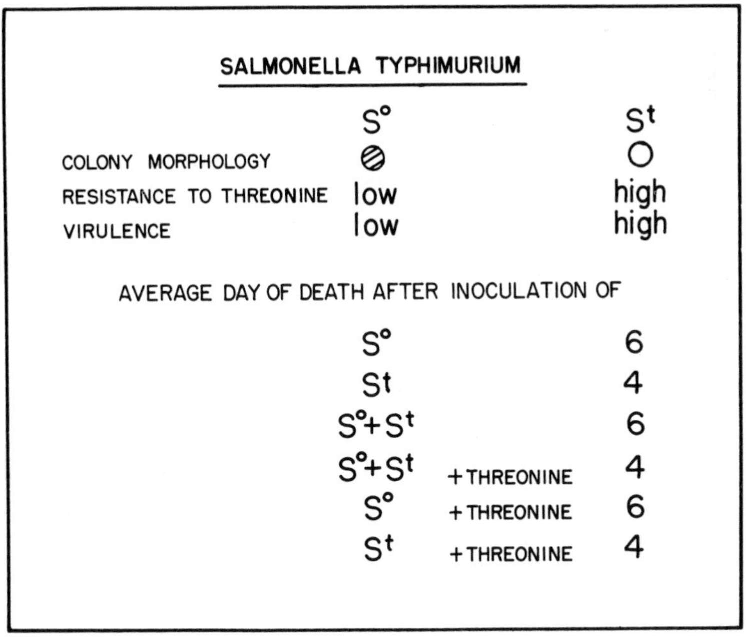

SALMONELLA TYPHIMURIUM

	S^0	S^t
COLONY MORPHOLOGY	⊘	○
RESISTANCE TO THREONINE	low	high
VIRULENCE	low	high

AVERAGE DAY OF DEATH AFTER INOCULATION OF

S^0		6
S^t		4
S^0+S^t		6
S^0+S^t	+THREONINE	4
S^0	+THREONINE	6
S^t	+THREONINE	4

FIGURE 94. Properties of S^t and S^0 types of *Salmonella typhimurium*, and the effects of threonine upon the severity of infection in guinea pigs infected with approximately 1×10^6 cells of these types.

ogy (see Fig. 73) but are identical in their antigenic and in almost all of their biochemical reactions.

In vitro, S^t mutants, arising at the rate of approximately 1×10^{-6}, established themselves rapidly in originally S^o populations. Similarly, the proportion of more virulent S^t cells increased rapidly in threonine-treated animals infected with mixtures of S^t and S^o, whereas S^o cells predominated at the time of death in similarly infected animals that received no threonine. The increase in virulence of *S. typhimurium* in threonine-treated animals, therefore, can be accounted for on the basis of originally heterogeneous populations containing small numbers of more virulent, threonine-resistant S^t type cells which will be selectively favored in threonine-treated animals. It is interesting to note (see lower part of Fig. 94) that threonine injections failed to produce an effect on survival when animals were infected with homogeneous S^o populations. This result, which is in contrast to the experience with S^o populations containing a few S^t cells, has been explained on the basis that average time of death is too rapid (6 days), even after infection with the less virulent S^o cells, to permit the selective establishment of S^t mutants which arise at a relatively low rate. However, if a few S^t cells are present initially in S^o populations, they will be selected immediately after infection of threonine-treated animals. Such differences in results after use of initially homogeneous or heterogeneous populations of bacteria may account for many controversial observations regarding the effects of diet on infection (see Clark, 1950). Schneider (1949) previously demonstrated that nutritional modifications of *Salmonella* infections can be achieved only if inocula (and hosts) are genetically heterogeneous.

MUTATION AND SELECTION IN RELATION TO SOME PROBLEMS OF BACTERIOLOGICAL TECHNIQUE

The recognition that a bacterial culture is not just a conglomeration of similar cells that metabolize and propagate, but represents a population that is constantly subject to changes in inherent properties, demands certain precautions in the execution of bacteriological studies. We already have referred to some of these applied problems during the description of specific phenomena; we shall reiterate some of them here and add a few others.

MAINTENANCE OF BACTERIAL STOCK CULTURES

Each period of growth provides an opportunity for the occurrence and establishment of mutants. Consequently, in preparing stock cultures a growth period as brief as feasible prior to storage under conditions unfavorable to growth should be employed. In general, the time of pre-storage incubation should not exceed the period of logarithmic growth. In addition, media least favorable for population changes should be used. In this respect solid media are superior to liquid media. Frequent transfers should be avoided, since each growth period furnishes renewed opportunity for mutation and selection of new or already present mutants.

If a series of seed cultures is required, it is far more advantageous to prepare and store a large series of simultaneous subcultures from one parent culture instead of making repeated serial transfers. Storage at low temperature is always preferable to storage at elevated temperatures, e.g., room temperature, even if the bacteria are suspended in a medium that does not support growth. If the latter procedure is employed, as has been the case in the storage of certain live vaccines, renewed growth may eventually ensue because of the supply of growth from dying cells. This renewed growth may furnish mutants with a selective opportunity for growth and can lead to rapid population changes. Theoretically, storage in the frozen-dried state should be the ideal condition for the maintenance of bacterial cultures. However, it has been observed with bacteria (Braun, 1950) as well as with fungi (Subramaniam, 1951) that after reconstitution of apparently homogeneous lyophilized cultures a small percentage of previously undetected variants may be present. The reason for such changes following lyophilization is still undetermined; it may possibly involve the destruction of an inhibitor which had prevented the growth of mutants already present in the population prior to lyophilization.* This effect of lyophilization should not prevent its use as a desirable technique for the preservation of bacterial cultures. But it suggests that single colony isolates, insuring the reisolation of the predominant parent type, rather than mass-cultures should be employed after reconstitution of lyophilized cultures for the preparation of new inocula.

In general, transfers made from single colony isolates increase the probability of maintaining homogeneous cultures, since even in the presence of a small proportion of mutant type cells in the parent culture it is more likely that these cells are excluded in transfers made from single colonies. Mass transfers are apt to carry over such mutant cells and thus preserve existing heterogeneity as well as enhance the potential degree of cultural heterogeneity by giving these mutant cells further opportunity to establish themselves during subsequent growth periods. However, since *unselected single colony transfers* may occasionally result in the accidental isolation of a mutant colony, it is advisable to check, whenever possible, the properties of cells belonging to the colony which is used for the transfer.

Media providing the desired type with optimal growth conditions should be employed in order to reduce the opportunities for improved survival and growth of undesirable mutants.

PREPARATION OF INOCULA

The majority of stock cultures propagated over a period of time by arbitrary mass transfers can be assumed to be fairly heterogeneous. Since this genetic heterogeneity may involve all types of characteristics (e.g., growth rate, nutritional requirements, metabolite production, fermentative, antigenic and virulence characteristics), it is often difficult to ascertain the degree of heterogeneity. However, as pointed out repeatedly in preceding chapters, colonial morphology on transparent solid media, viewed with oblique lighting, constitutes a simple indicator for many

*Experimental studies have indicated that the effect is not due to selective killing.

organisms of the relative degree of heterogeneity, since many types of mutational changes appear to produce changes in colonial morphology. For the preparation of inocula from any stock culture it becomes again desirable to utilize material grown from single colony isolates (keeping in mind, however, the dangers of unselected single colony transfers pointed out above). Although this does not necessarily result in the isolation of a clone, especially when practiced with species in which cells tend to associate in clumps or chains, it is still likely to reduce any existent heterogeneity. Such single colony isolates should be made from colonies that have not reached their maximal size. Furthermore, under conditions of growth that lead to a maximal level of viable cells, i.e., maintenance in test tubes or flasks without transfer, the size of the inoculum must be taken into consideration. The number of cells in the inoculum can affect potential population changes, because the larger the inoculum the earlier will competitive conditions be attained in the culture.

Unless efforts are made to control the homogeneity of inocula for cultures or animals, erroneous conclusions can easily result. This is exemplified in results obtained in studies on the immunogenic potency of *B. tularense* cultures where it was demonstrated that immunogenic differences between cultures could be attributed to the degree of heterogeneity existing within the cultures under comparison (Eigelsbach *et al.*, 1951). In other words, differences which had been observed in immunogenicity of various cultures were found to be due to the relative proportion of highly immunogenic and weakly immunogenic cells in the heterogeneous cultures. The identification of mutants with different immunogenic potency was made possible by the detection of colonial differences among these mutants (see Fig. 71). In work with various other species, a similar heterogeneity has been detected in cultures used for the preparation of vaccines. In every case, subsequent isolation and maintenance of the highly immunogenic component of the population resulted in greatly improved vaccines.

Similar considerations apply to *in vitro* work with bacteria, for example, metabolic studies. Unless the homogeneity of the inoculum is assured, a rapidly growing minority component (*a*) of the population may be responsible for the detectable reactions under one set of conditions (A), whereas the majority component (*b*) of the tested population may propagate under a different set of conditions (B) and manifest its reaction. It is clear that such differences would be difficult to detect if a single criterion such as growth is used as sole indicator of metabolic competence. The ultimate conclusion that a given type may be capable of growth under conditions A and B may be entirely erroneous, since it was type *a* that was responsible for reactions noted under condition A, whereas a completely different type, *b*, accounted for the reactions observed under condition B.

PROBLEMS ARISING DURING CULTURAL GROWTH

The problems just described apply equally when cultural heterogeneity is not present in the inoculum but develops during subsequent growth. Let us refer again to the last cited example in which nutritional competence under conditions A and B is to be tested, but this time in a population consisting of type *a* cells only. If, as customary in most metabolic studies, the development of turbidity during a given period of growth is used as indicator, one might find equal increase in turbidity under both conditions A and B. Yet a more careful analysis of the final population may reveal that *a* cells grew under condition A, whereas the progeny of a mutant, *b*, which arose during the initial but limited growth of the *a* population, is responsible for the turbidity that developed under condition B. The initial growth of *a*, sufficient to permit the occurrence of mutant *b*, may have been due to previously discussed "carry-over" effects which permit cells to propagate initially in an adverse environment at the expense of stored products. Such cases have been observed and they show that a careful analysis of the final population should be made in order to avoid what would have been an invalid conclusion in this case, namely that one given type is capable of growing as well under condition A as under condition B.

Similar erroneous conclusions can be drawn if turbidity is used as sole indicator of nutritional competence and growth is observed to occur after a prolonged lag period. The problem involved in such cases, namely the occurrence of a competent mutant during "invisible" growth and the subsequent development of turbidity due to growth of the mutant's progeny, has been clearly demonstrated in appropriate experimental studies (e.g., Fildes and Whitaker, 1948).

The occurrence of population changes due to the selective growth of a mutant is much more likely to be detected if viable cell counts (plate counts) are employed and it is unwise in any bacteriological study to neglect such viable counts. If feasible, both viable and total cell counts should be obtained in studies with bacterial populations, at least whenever unfavorable cultural conditions exist at the start of the culture.

Since selection pressure does not manifest itself significantly prior to the stationary phase in cultures grown under conditions adequate for the growth of the initially inoculated type, population changes are not too likely to occur during the initial growth of cultures inoculated with a homogeneous population. But whenever such cultures are incubated beyond the point of cessation of logarithmic growth, the possibility of increasing cultural heterogeneity must be recognized.

PRIMARY ISOLATIONS

The existence of selective host factors favoring the establishment and growth of certain mutants *in vivo* can account for population changes that may occur rapidly during the propagation of isolates under laboratory conditions. There may be not only a lack of the selective host factors *in vitro*, but also altered cultural conditions permitting the accumulation of inhibitory metabolites which favor the rapid establishment of mutants dissimilar to the type which was best adapted to conditions *in vivo*. Therefore, special care must be taken in isolation procedures to insure the propagation of the type or types present *in vivo*. Whenever feasible, primary isolates should be cultivated in agar media rather than in liquid media, since population changes are generally less apt to occur on solid media than in liquids, provided unduly prolonged incubation is avoided. However, sometimes it is difficult to obtain a positive culture upon first inoculation onto solid media and initial cultivation in liquids becomes necessary. Under such conditions transfer to solid media should be made as soon as feasible in order to avoid drastic population changes. For example, it is customary to make primary isolations of many pathogens in blood cultures. In this case the organisms are propagating in the presence of antiserum, a condition known to support rapid population changes in liquids. In comparison, the presence of antiserum is far less effective in solid media. Unless the likelihood of such population changes during primary isolations is recognized, false conclusions may result regarding the identity of the type present *in vivo*.

POPULATION CHANGES THAT ARE DUE TO TEMPORARY MODIFICATIONS

Not all popluation changes in bacteria involve mutation and selection. In Chapters 7 and 9 we referred to the occurrence of modifications, i.e., non-heritable changes of the phenotype under the influence of environmental agents. Usually such modifications affect all cells of identical genotype simultaneously. However, occasionally cells of identical genotype are not equally affected because not all of them are necessarily in a comparable physiological state required for identical response.

Several previously cited examples (e.g., pp. 163, 173 and 179) illustrate that after transfer to certain environmental conditions all cells in a population may alter their characteristics and maintain these modified characteristics as long as they are kept under these particular conditions. Sometimes the altered phenotype may even be maintained for short periods after return of the cells to the original environment, an effect that may involve metabolic lag and intracellular storage of intermediate products as discussed on page 209.

In contrast to population changes due to mutation and selection, in which repeated sampling of growing cultures will reveal the gradual progressive establishment of the progeny of favored mutants, modifications will produce simultaneous changes in all or the majority of members of a population. There can be an exception to this overall population change; it occurs when a population consists of cells with different genotype, all of which display one phenotype under one environmental condition but show differences in detectable characteristics under altered environmental conditions. For example, genetically non-identical cells *a* and *b* may give rise to colonies of similar appearance on medium A but develop into distinctly different colonial types on medium B (Fig. 95). Such an apparent population change, detectable on medium B, is obviously not due to mutation and selection following transfer from medium A to medium B. This can be confirmed by noting the immediate reversion to phenotypic homogeneity upon transfer to condition A or by isolation of the two types from medium B and subsequent study of the changes in phenotype of the population's components during altered environmental conditions (see Fig. 95).

Another case of modification that may lead to erroneous conclusions regarding the appearance of a new type involves the occasionally observed ability of one mutant in a heterogeneous population to modify the pheno-

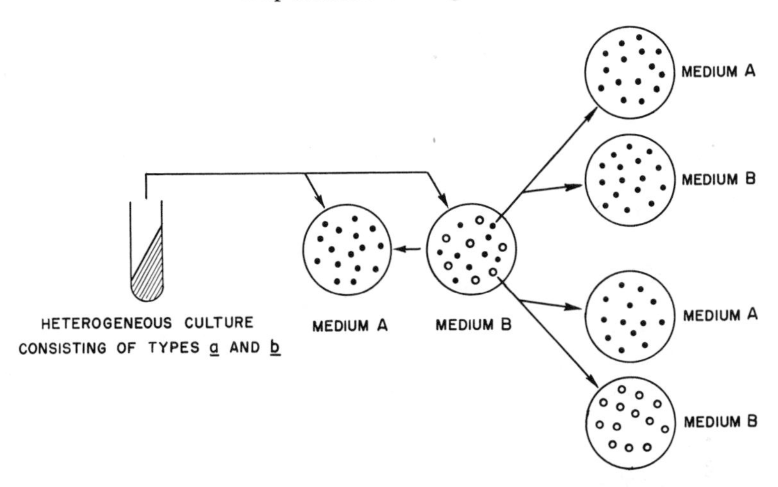

FIGURE 95. Diagram illustrating apparent population changes that may be caused by the phenotypic similarity of two genetically different types of bacteria (*a* and *b*) when grown on one medium (A), compared with their dissimilarity on another medium (B).

type of another mutant present. Thus, cells giving rise to one distinct colonial type may give rise to a completely different looking type of colony when grown in the presence of certain mutants (Fig. 96). This modification is of the same order as the previously described ability of certain prototrophs to "feed" auxotrophs when they are jointly inoculated into a minimal medium (p. 130). Again, the true situation can be detected by isolating the two distinct components of the population and observing their characteristics when they are grown independently of each other (see Fig. 96).

In the category of modification also belongs the widely investigated phenomenon of *induced enzyme synthesis*, to which we have already referred in Chapter 7. You will recall that this involves the activation of specific enzymatic activities of a cell under the influence of specific extracellular substrates; for example, genotypically *lac*$^+$ *E. coli* cells may form the enzyme β-galactosidase only in the presence of the appropriate substrate, lactose. The actual mechanisms for such induced enzyme formation

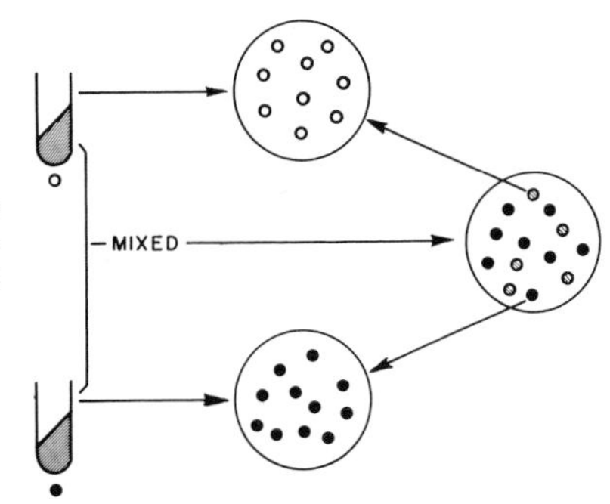

FIGURE 96. Diagram illustrating the phenotypic modification of colonial morphology which may occur occasionally when one type is grown in the presence of another colonial type.

in the absence of any genotypic alterations of the cell were quite mysterious for many years, until the pioneering studies of Vogel, Monod, Jacob and others (see Chapter 17) indicated that a de-repression of repressed enzyme synthesis in genotypically competent cells was at the root of this phenomenon. We shall reserve more detailed discussions of enzyme repression until Chapter 17. However, of principal interest to our present discussion is the fact that a population which contains a certain proportion of cells genotypically capable of forming a specific enzyme under the influence of the proper environment may appear phenotypically homogeneous under one set of environmental conditions e.g., in the absence of the specific de-repressing substrate, and heterogeneous under another environmental condition, e.g., in the presence of the substrate. Thus in the process of induced enzyme synthesis the existent genetic heterogeneity of the population is revealed; under these conditions the detectable characteristics of certain members of a population will be changed even though their genetic constitution remains unaltered.

How can one differentiate population changes due to induced enzyme synthesis in genetically competent cells from population changes that are due to mutation and selection? First, induced enzyme synthesis frequently can occur in the absence of growth, under conditions where selection is entirely eliminated. Thus the exposure of a resting population to the substrate and observation of the subsequent occurrence of the specific metabolic activity constitutes unequivocal proof of the occurrence of induced enzyme synthesis. Second, in cases in which induced enzyme synthesis occurs only in the presence of growth, a condition which makes it difficult to eliminate selection as a causative factor, presumptive evidence against the involvement of mutation can be obtained by the application of the fluctuation test of Luria and Delbruck (p. 69). If the variance obtained in this test is high, mutation must be suspected; if it is low, induced enzyme synthesis is indicated. In addition, a single subculture in the absence of the specific substrate usually suffices to de-adapt cells, i.e., to reestablish the original repressed state of enzyme formation.

PART III

[12]

GENETIC TRANSFERS I: GENERAL CONSIDERATIONS

The ability of a living organism to survive and to multiply under drastically altered environmental conditions depends on its reaction range, that is, on its genotypically controlled potential. In the preceding chapters we have encountered many examples of the ability of mutants to multiply under conditions that were unfavorable or even lethal for their parent types. Until now we have considered only one major mechanism that can lead to alteration of inherent information, namely, mutation. From the standpoint of the species, it would obviously be of considerable value to have mechanisms permitting the pooling and redistributing, within *one* clone, of different bits of information that have arisen by spontaneous alterations of the genotype in *different* but related clones. Thus, if the combined information XY would lead to high survival value of its carrier, the pooling of X and Y into a single descendant of two cell lines, one of which carried information X and the other Y, could be more efficient than the chance occurrence of a mutation to Y in a line already provided with information X. Such pooling, and also reassorting, of slightly different information between related organisms occurs in higher organisms as a result of sexual reproduction. Since it provides the offspring with new and varying sets of information, sex can be regarded as a sort of defense mechanism providing organisms with a greater plasticity to respond to changing environmental conditions.

In bacteria, too, mechanisms have evolved that permit a pooling and reassorting of preexisting information between *related*, but genotypically slightly different, organisms. However, these mechanisms of intercellular genetic transfers are somewhat less complex and less complete in bacteria than in higher organisms, and (as we have already indicated in Chapter 1) involve, in transformation, transduction and conjugation, a unidirectional transfer from a donor cell to a recipient cell of only a fraction of the total information existing in the donor cell. In bacteria the addition of only a portion of the information of the donor cell to the total information of the recipient cell does not result in a typical diploid *zygote*, but only in a partially diploid zygote, which has been termed a *merozygote*.

The basic feature of all intercellular genetic transfers in bacteria (and in higher organisms) is that usually the transferred information is not added *in toto* to the preexisting information of the recipient cell; instead an exchange occurs between the donor's and the recipient's information during a transient period of partial diploidy, as illustrated in Figure 97. The outcome is the maintenance of an equal amount of total genetic information, even though the quality of information, i.e., the nucleotide sequence of a limited region, may be altered by the prior exchange of informative nucleotide regions. In this respect events in bacteria resemble recombinational events in the gametes and somatic cells of higher organisms; however, in higher organisms an entire haploid set of DNA information of each parent can participate in the events leading to recombination, whereas in bacteria only a portion of the donor's haploid genome tends to be involved in recombination.

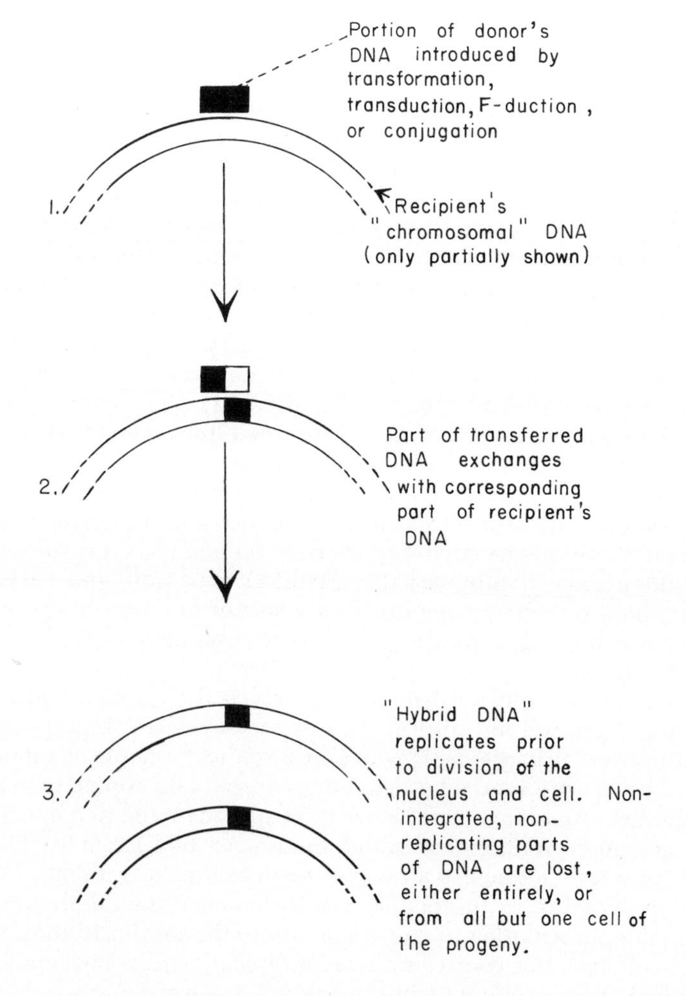

FIGURE 97. Diagram illustrating how in genetic transfers between bacteria a small amount of information (= nucleotide sequences) of the donor may be exchanged for information existing in the recipient's "chromosomal" DNA.

SEGREGATION AND CROSSING-OVER IN HIGHER ORGANISMS

Let us briefly recall some of the basic features of sexual reproduction and recombination of information in higher organisms. First of all, these processes occur only between related organisms; in fact, the very delineation of a species of higher organisms is based on whether or not two organisms are inter-fertile. Within each sexually reproducing species the pooling of haploid sets of the chromosomes (the carriers of nuclear DNA and information) results, after fertilization, in a zygote (diploid) in which both male and female have made equal contributions in terms of the total chromosomal complement, which in the vast majority of species consists of more than one pair of non-homologous chromosomes. The information carried by each partner in a "homologous pair" of chromosomes, however, can be unequal, because the nucleotide sequence (and thus the genetic determinants) of one parent may be slightly different from that of the other. During the subsequent maturation divisions (haploidization), which precede the formation of the gametes, information carried in different, non-homologous chromosomes may be segregated at random, which, as illustrated in Figure 98, can give rise to new *inter*-chromosomal combinations and thus to a new assortment of information in the gametes and in the zygotes resulting after fertilization.

However, for our discussion of genetic transfer and recombination of information in bacteria we do not have to concern ourselves any further with a review of the events involving information (determinants, "genes,"* markers) carried on *different* chromosomes. The reason is that in all of the well-investigated cases of bacterial recombination only one major DNA element corresponding to a chromosome of higher organisms has been recognized until now.† This permits us to focus our attention on the fate, during sexual reproduction, of information carried on *one* chromosome.

Experimental studies with higher organisms established long ago that each chromosome contains information for the specification of many different enzymes (in the classic genetical language: each chromosome contains a large number of genes controlling different characteristics), and since chromosomes are usually transmitted as complete units, all the information within one chromosome is likewise transmitted as a unit to the progeny. Accordingly, geneticists have talked about *linked genes*, and linkage groups of individual species have been identified as being equivalent to the number of non-homologous chromosomes that are typical for that species. However, the linkage of genes located on a given chromosome is far from absolute. The occurrence of a process known as *crossing-over* was recognized in studies with higher organisms almost 50 years ago.

*We shall use the term "gene" quite frequently in this chapter, but it should be remembered that what we are really talking about is a functional, distinct polynucleotide region of the chromosome of higher organisms or of the equivalent DNA structure in bacterial cells.

†For the moment, we may disregard other bacterial replicons (p. 291) which, when present, represent relatively minor elements, in terms of both size and informational content, and do not segregate at random.

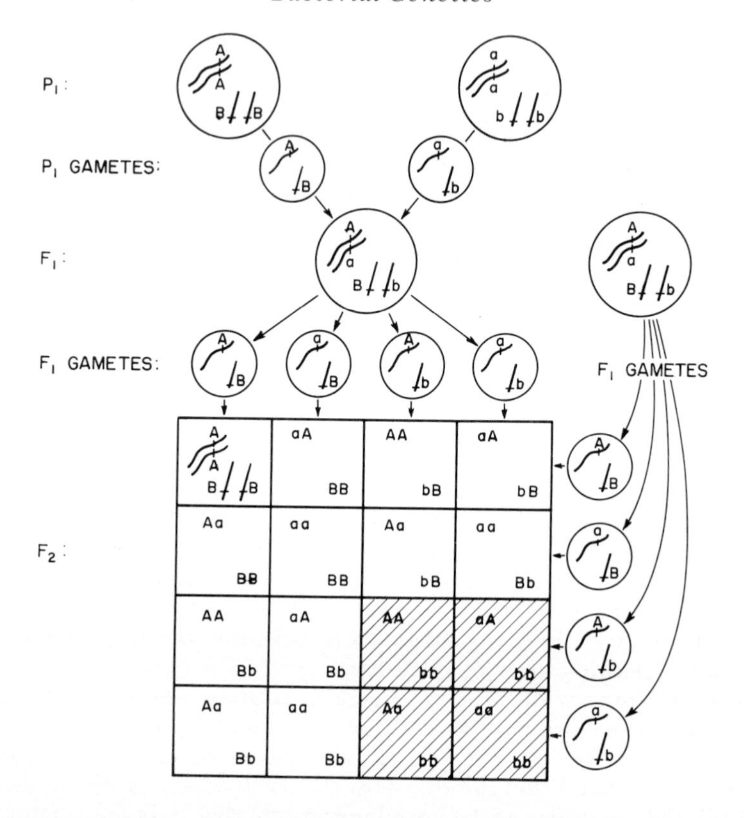

FIGURE 98. Diagram showing the segregation, during meiosis in higher plants and animals, of genes associated with homologous chromosomes, as well as the independent assortment of genes associated with non-homologous chromosomes. The results of random union among the four types of gamete formed by the F_1 heterozygote are shown in the F_2 checkerboard. The shaded areas in the checkerboard indicate that only one fourth of the F_2 will be homozygous for the recessive gene b and thus will manifest the gene's phenotypic effects.

This particular process, leading to new combinations (*recombinations*) of linked genes, involves a reciprocal exchange of parts between the two members of each (diploid) chromosome pair. The actual occurrence of such chromosomal exchanges, which was first indicated by the results of breeding experiments, has been confirmed in plants and animals by cytological observations of cells in which the individual members of chromosome pairs differed either structurally or as a result of radioactive labeling.

Briefly, and considerably simplified, this is the manner in which an exchange of parts of the chromosome can take place in higher organisms during meiosis (Fig. 99):

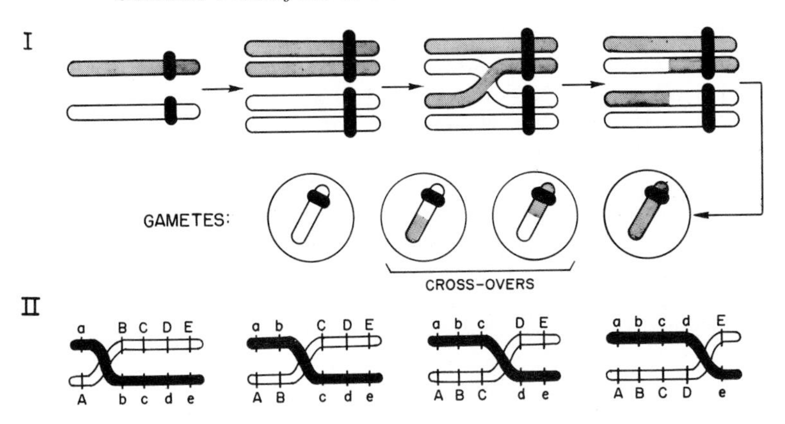

FIGURE 99. I, Diagrams illustrating the process of crossing-over in higher organisms. From left to right: Two homologous chromosomes before meiosis; each chromosome becomes double as it forms two chromatids; one chromatid from each chromosome exchanges a portion with the homologous chromatid of the other chromosome; crossing-over is completed—two of the four gametes resulting at the end of meiosis carry cross-over chromosomes. II, Diagrams illustrating the likelihood of the occurrence of crossing-over among five pairs located at different sites on a chromosome pair. The distant genes A and E are separated from each other by all of the possible crossing-overs, the likelihood of crossing over between A and E equaling the sum of the occurrence of crossing-over between genes A and B, B and C, C and D, and D and E. Similarly, the probability of crossing-over occurring between genes A and C is greater than that between genes A and B.

Prior to segregation of the members of each chromosome pair, the two chromosomes are in intimate contact. At this time each homologous chromosome splits longitudinally into two chromatids and corresponding parts of each chromosome are exchanged in a process that presumably involves breakage and immediate fusion. As Figure 99 illustrates, only two (any two) of the four chromatids in each pair of chromosomes are usually involved in this exchange; consequently, two of the four gametes resulting at the end of meiosis will contain chromosomes with the recombination of genes brought about by the crossing-over of chromatids. If one member of a chromosome pair carries genes A B C D E F and the other member carries genes a b c d e f, crossing-over between the sites of genes B and C or b and c will result in the creation of new chromosomal gene-combinations, namely A B c d e f, and a b C D E F. The resulting gamete transmits the new gene-arrangement to succeeding generations where the previous occurrence of the crossing-over can be recognized by the novel phenotype corresponding to the novel genotypic intra-chromosomal assortment.*

Since cross-overs are more likely to occur between genes that are located far apart it has been possible to establish the relative position of genes within a chromosome on the basis of cross-over frequencies. As shown in the second part of Figure 99, crossing-over will occur more fre-

*In addition to taking place during meiosis, prior to sexual reproduction, crossing-over can occur during *mitosis* in filamentous fungi ("parasexual cycle"; cf. Pontecorvo, 1962) and apparently also, but very rarely, during the division of somatic cells of higher organisms and in tissue-culture cell lines.

quently between distant genes A and E than between neighboring genes A and B. Morgan, who did the pioneer work on these problems with the fruit-fly in 1915, found that the analysis of cross-over data from breeding experiments permitted the construction of *linkage maps* for individual chromosomes on which genes were located in a linear fashion according to the distance indicated by "cross-over units." For example, mutant genes a, b, and c giving rise to such easily detected phenotypes as cinnabar eye color, short wings, and curved wings were known to belong to the same linkage group, i.e., were located on the same chromosome, because they usually segregated together in crosses with the wild type. Yet, the appropriate breeding experiments revealed that occasionally genes a, b, and c may separate from each other and this separation occurs with a constant frequency. Ten per cent of the progeny showed the occurrence of segregation between characteristics a and b, and 18 per cent between a and c. Accordingly, on the linkage map genes a and b are plotted at a distance of 10 units from each other, and genes a and c are separated 18 units from each other.

MAPPING OF LINKED GENES

To explain the mapping of linked genes further, let us consider the following simplified example from studies with the fruit fly. We have one (diploid) parent with the genotype $\frac{+\,b\,+}{a\,+\,c}$* which we mate with $\frac{a\,b\,c}{a\,b\,c}$. The non-cross-over classes of the progeny would be: $\frac{+\,b\,+}{a\,b\,c}$ and $\frac{a\,+\,c}{a\,b\,c}$ (phenotypes + b + and a + c, since a, b and c are recessive determinants); the phenotypes of the cross-over classes (which always must add up to less than 50 per cent) would be: a b +, + + c, a + +, + b c. The progeny a b + and + + c represent the offspring derived from gametes in which, during reduction divisions, a cross-over occurred between a and b; the progeny a + + and + b c are the result of crossing-overs between b and c.†

Now let us fill in some actual figures for the number of individuals found in these different classes:

+b+	810	1638 (parental classes)
a+c	828	
ab+	62	150
++c	88	
a++	89	192
+bc	103	
Total	1980	

*In genetic "shorthand" one writes $\frac{+\,b\,+}{a\,+\,c}$ instead of $\genfrac{}{}{2pt}{}{+\,b\,+}{a\,+\,c}$, the information associated with one partner of a chromosomal pair being written as the numerator and that of the other partner as the denominator; + is used as the symbol for the "wild-type," i.e., for the normal allele of the mutant locus.

†In addition to single cross-over, double or even multiple cross-overs may occur, but because of their infrequencies we shall neglect them for the moment.

To calculate the frequency of recombination of a and b (= crossing-overs between a and b), we determine the frequency of individuals belonging to these classes, i.e.:

$$(150 \times 100)/1980 = 7.6\%$$

and, accordingly, for cross-overs between b and c:

$$(192 \times 100)/1980 = 9.7\%$$

The three determinants a, b and c can now be mapped:

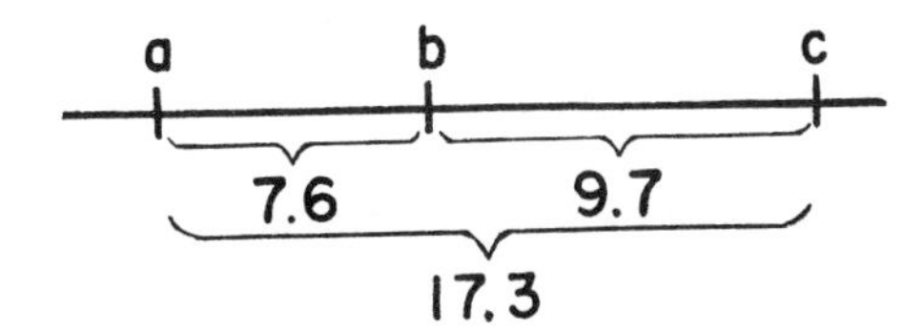

The order of chromosomal arrangement a b c is already indicated by the fact that the percentage of crossing-overs between a and c adds up to 17.3 per cent. If the order were c a b, the percentage of crossing-overs between a and c would have to be 2.1.

The most decisive way of assigning the order of linked genes, however, is through analysis of double crossing-overs. The results of crosses employing three or more linked markers (so-called three-point test crosses) have shown that in addition to single crossing-overs, double or even multiple crossing-overs may occur (Fig. 100). Their probability is far less than that of single crossing-overs, being theoretically the product of the probability of independent single crossing-overs (in our example—a→b: 0.076, b→c: 0.097—double crossing-overs in the a→c region should be 0.076 × 0.097 or 0.007%, yielding the classes a b c and + + +). Actually, however, the frequencies of double crossing-overs are usually found to be less than expected on the basis of single crossing-overs, a phenomenon that is known as *positive interference*. This term expresses the fact that the occurrence of one crossing-over decreases the likelihood of the occurrence of another one involving an adjacent region within the same chromosome.

Note that the double cross-over class is always the smallest class and that a double crossing-over has the effect of changing, in a three-point test cross, the associations of the two members of the allelic pair that are

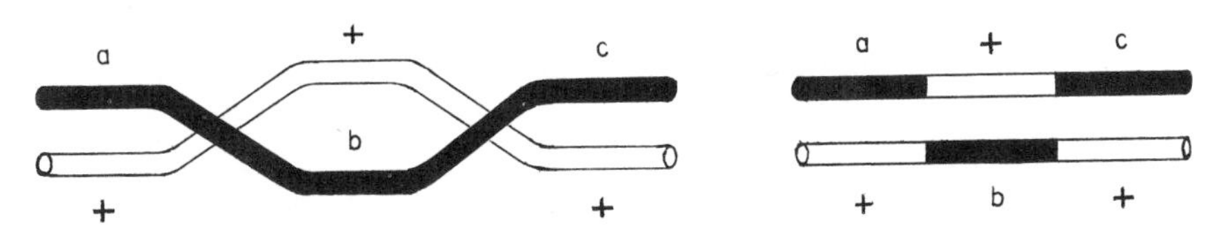

FIGURE 100. Double crossing-over in higher organisms.

between the two distant genes (e.g., double cross-overs from $\frac{a\ b\ c}{+\ +\ +}$ are a + c and + b +; from $\frac{b\ c\ a}{+\ +\ +}$ they would be b + a and + c +). This permits the assignment of the proper relative order of genes in the chromosome on the basis of results from three-point test crosses.

SOME DISTINCTIVE FEATURES OF RECOMBINATION IN HIGHER ORGANISMS

For subsequent comparisons with recombination events in bacteria, we now should note several distinctive features of recombination in higher organisms. First, note that for each cross-over class (e.g., a b +) there exists a reciprocal class (e.g., + + c) containing a comparable number of individuals. This is due to the occurrence of a reciprocal exchange of chromosome sections, as illustrated in Figure 99. We shall see later that such *reciprocal recombinant classes* do not occur in bacterial recombination; they may also be absent in certain cases of recombination in higher organisms.

Second, we have already referred to the phenomenon of *positive interference*, which is the reduced likelihood of an occurrence of multiple crossing-overs between genes more than one cross-over unit apart. This phenomenon contrasts with *negative interference*, which can occur between closely linked markers and is very frequently encountered in recombinational events among microorganisms. Negative interference (an awkward term!) expresses the fact that recombinations may occur more frequently than anticipated, or in other words, that the occurrence of one exchange can increase the probability of an occurrence of another exchange in a neighboring chromosomal region.* Finally, the mapping of linked genes in higher organisms has resulted in *linear linkage maps* which correspond with the linear configuration of the chromosomes. In contrast, linkage maps in bacteria, at least among those so far analyzed in sufficient detail, are circular (see p. 307) and this agrees with the cytological evidence for the DNA-rich structures in *E. coli* (Fig. 11) and in phages.

MECHANISMS OF RECOMBINATION

The actual mechanisms responsible for recombination are not yet fully understood, either in diploid, sexually reproducing, higher organisms in which recombination occurs during meiosis, or in the haploid bacteria in which recombination occurs prior to mitosis in merozygotes. The occurrence of *breakage and fusion* between parts of homologous chromosomes (or, more accurately, between non-sister chromatids) giving rise to reciprocal exchanges, as pictured in Figure 99, has been confirmed by direct observations of the chromosomes in higher organisms, and its occurrence

*In general, it has become increasingly clear that cross-overs may not occur with equal probability in all regions of the chromosome, or of its equivalent in bacteria. There appear to be certain regions which for structural reasons, or perhaps because certain nucleotide sequences are more easily broken, participate in crossing-over events more frequently than other regions.

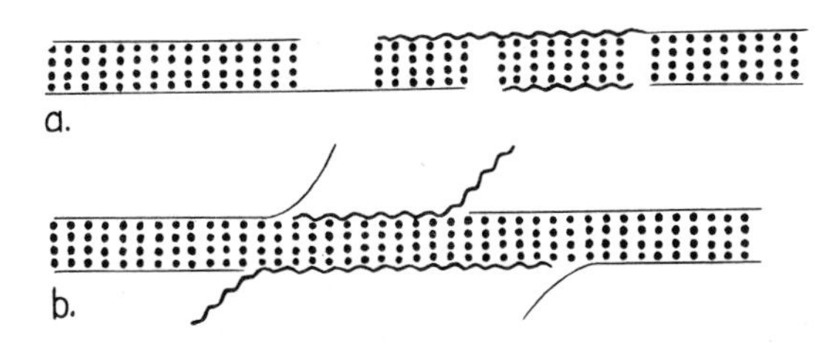

FIGURE 101. Two of several possibilities for structural exchanges between two double-stranded DNA strands involving breaks at different places in each strand. Only the possible configuration of one double-stranded DNA structure, after the exchange has occurred, is shown. a, Non-matching regions are subsequently "filled" by new synthesis of the missing nucleotides. b, Non-matching single-strand regions "stick out" from the new double-strand and are destroyed by enzymatic action. (After a suggestion of S. Brenner.)

in microorganisms has been suggested by the results of studies with radioactively labeled DNA (Meselson and Weigle, 1961; Siddiqi, 1963). Although it is not easy to understand how corresponding breaks may occur in four different places in the two double-nucleotide strands that are involved in the crossing-over between DNA molecules, a number of possibilities, such as those indicated in Figure 101, have been considered.

In addition to structural exchanges, another (not necessarily alternative) mechanism for recombination has been proposed, namely, that of *copy choice*. In this mechanism there is no structural exchange between chromatids of the chromosomes of higher organisms or between the double-stranded DNA piece of a donor bacterium and the corresponding double-stranded DNA region of the recipient. Rather, it is assumed that during the replication of DNA one strand of the recipient's DNA and one strand of the donor's DNA serve as alternate templates for the synthesis of the new DNA strand, as illustrated in Figure 102. As the result of such template switching no reciprocal classes of recombinants would occur (no reciprocal exchange being involved); this is indeed the case when the recombinational events involve very small regions of the chromosome in higher organisms, and this is also the case in recombinations observed among bacteria and phages. (However, in bacteria the lack of reciprocal classes of recombinants is undoubtedly due to the fact that one of the two members of any DNA exchange phenomenon, namely, the donor DNA piece, cannot generate its own progeny, being only a fragment of the total cellular genome.) To account for the possible occurrence of both breakage-fusion and copy-choice mechanisms in all living organisms, it has been suggested that breakage-fusion events may occur in the hypothetical "protein links" of the DNA model, as shown in Figure 19, whereas copy-choice events may occur within the DNA molecules themselves (see Lissouba *et al.*, 1962).

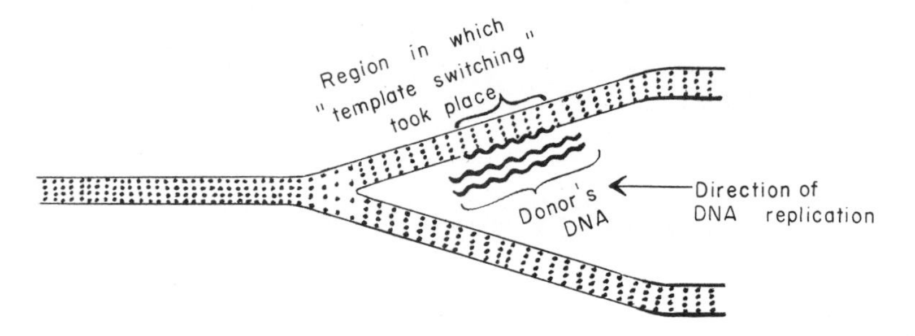

FIGURE 102. A possible copy-choice mechanism resulting in the replacement of some of the recipient's nucleotide sequence by some of the donor's nucleotide sequence.

Still a third mode of recombination, involving neither breaks nor copy choice has been suggested in a "partial replica" model proposed by Bresch (1962) for bacteriophage replication and recombination. He speculates, on the basis of limited experimental data, that the sugar-phosphate backbone of DNA has "gaps" which leave a 5′-phosphomonoester on one side and a 3′-deoxyribosehydroxyl on the other:

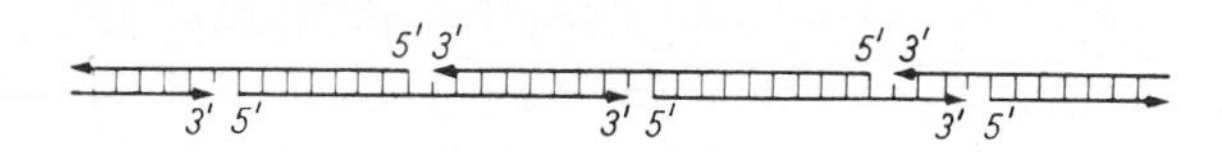

Replication of such a structure would always start from the 3′-OH end; as a result, replication of a genome-containing gaps would lead to a disintegration of the structure:

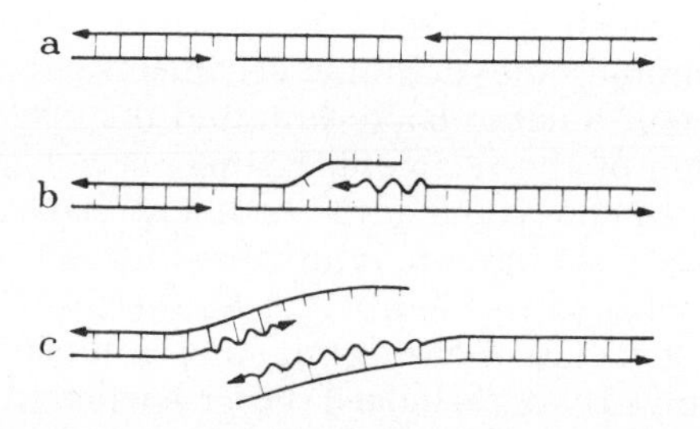

The resulting fragments (double-stranded partial genomes) are assumed (1) to multiply in a series of fairly complex events and (2) to be integrated subsequently into a complete genome. Obviously, such a model could account for a dispersion of parental DNA into offspring DNA without any breaks having occurred in the ordinary sense of the word, and without any requirement for a switching of templates as proposed in the copy-choice concept. However, even if some aspects of this model can be validated for phages, it would appear unlikely that such a disorderly process as fragmentation and reintegration could play a role in recombinations in bacteria and higher organisms. However, we have cited this concept of a still different mode of recombination to illustrate our current relative ignorance regarding the molecular basis of recombination.

INTERGENIC AND INTRAGENIC RECOMBINATION

In all of the older genetic studies, the gene—as the determinant of a given chracteristic—was regarded as the ultimate indivisible subunit of the chromosome, and consequently, it was postulated that crossing-over could occur only between genes and not within the then indivisible gene. However, we now know that the functional gene is actually a series of nucleotides that spell out the information for the corresponding sequence of amino acids in a specific polypeptide (see pp. 322 and 343). Let us, for the sake of illustration, assume that the "sense" nucleotide message for the specification of one polypeptide reads *baggage*, each letter in this word being identical either to a nucleotide or to a coding unit. A change (mutation) in one of the units would result in a "nonsense" message, i.e., a non-functioning enzyme e.g., *bargage*. But "nonsense" also would be produced by a change in another unit, e.g., *baggale*. Now assume the occurrence of a recombinational event between the two "nonsense" messages as follows:

This would result in the formation of the original sense message *baggage* in one of the two recombinant molecules. Thus, from the standpoint of mutation and recombination, we could subdivide our message (=functional gene, *cistron*) into seven subunits (*mutons* and *recons*, in the terminology proposed by S. Benzer), each of which could potentially participate in mutational and recombinational events *within the old-fashioned gene.**

In view of our present knowledge it is, therefore, not at all surprising to find that recombination does occur within genes. To the geneticist of the 1950's, however, it was a surprise to discover that two apparently identical mutants of independent origin, let us call them *s*, when crossed to each other could in fact be separated by rare crossing-overs which yielded normal (+) recombinants. To explain this, it had to be assumed that two different alleles (originally referred to as pseudoalleles) of *s* existed as s' and s'' and that the events involved a crossing over between them:

$$\frac{s'\ +}{+\ s''} \rightarrow +\ + \text{ and } s'\ s''$$

Wild-type progenies (recombinants) were subsequently recovered quite frequently from genetic transfers between mutants with identical pheno-

*Actually, not even the cistron is equal to the old-fashioned gene, because, as we shall see later, the cistron can be equated to one polypeptide, and many proteins consist of more than one polypeptide.

types that had undergone genetic alterations within the same locus (a locus = a cistron = a series of genetic sites = a potentially functional sequence of nucleotides). It became particularly easy in studies with microorganisms to recover the wild-type progeny from crosses between two allelic mutants, because even though the frequency of intragenic recombinations is extremely low, the availability of simple selection procedures in work with microorganisms permits the relatively easy recovery of such recombinants, even when their frequency is less than 1 in 10^9 (see p. 000). Consider, for example, genetic transfers between two independently isolated, histidine-requiring, bacterial mutants, his_1 and his_2 (both due to nucleotide changes in the same cistron). Neither *his* mutant can grow on histidine-free media, but a histidine-independent recombinant (++) resulting from a recombination involving $\frac{his_1+}{+his_2}$, can be easily spotted by its ability to develop into a colony on histidine-free media, thus revealing intragenic recombination.

ADDITIONS TO THE GENOME BY TRANSFERS OF GENETIC MATERIAL

In bacteria, as in higher organisms, most transfers of genetic material result in the long-term maintenance of a relatively *constant* amount of total genetic information, despite the initial *addition* of genetic information. As we pointed out before, transformation, transduction by phage and most cases of conjugation involve the transfer of genetic material that, following recombination with the corresponding region of the DNA of the recipient cell, will not be passed on as a replicating entity to daughter cells.* Several types of genetic transfers, however, can *add* small amounts of information to the recipient and such information can be maintained in the progeny of the merozygote for long periods of time. Thus, as we will discuss in Chapters 14 and 15, such extra-chromosomal elements as prophages, colicinogenic agents and the sex factor F may carry into recipient cells the information required for their own maintenance, as well as a few chromosomal genes they may have acquired by recombination. The *added* information carried by these replicons (F factor, colicinogenic agent), or by prophages, will subsequently manifest itself not only in the infected cell but also in all of the progeny of this cell, because these episomes and the information carried by them can multiply either in direct association with, or independent of, the recipient's chromosome. If this last statement seems hard to comprehend at this point, don't worry about it. The somewhat complex relationships between the original information of the recipient cell, on the one hand, and the information supplied by the related donor cell, on the other hand, will become much clearer as we now proceed to a discussion of the various known modes of transfer of genetic information in bacteria.

*See Figure 116 for an illustration of the maintenance of a *non-replicating* piece of added DNA in a few cells of the clone that develops from a merozygote.

[13]

GENETIC TRANSFERS II: TRANSFORMATION

Transformation is a process of intercellular transfer of information in which a fraction of a donor cell's total DNA, obtained by chemical extraction or natural cell lysis, can penetrate into a related bacterial cell and replace there, through a process of recombination, a specific nucleotide sequence of the recipient's genome (see Fig. 3). If the newly integrated nucleotide sequence derived from the donor differs in part from the replaced nucleotide sequence of the recipient, new information for the characters controlled by this DNA region will be provided for the "transformed" cell and its progeny.

The amount of DNA participating in any one transformation event is quite small compared to the total DNA of donor and recipient cells—representing usually only 5 per cent or less of the total genome. Even under conditions in which all cells of a transformable strain are theoretically competent to be transformed, the percentage of cells permanently transformed rarely exceeds for a given marker (e.g., streptomycin resistance), 1 per cent of the DNA-exposed population. Transformation differs from conjugation by virtue of a lack of requirement for direct contact between the donor and recipient cells, and it differs from both conjugation and transduction by the sensitivity of the transforming agent to DNAase; the protected DNA involved in transduction and conjugation is inaccessible to DNAase.

The term "transformation" dates back to the early years of studies on this phenomenon (1928-1944) when, without an understanding of the underlying causes, it was observed that certain strains of bacteria grown in the presence of killed cells, or in culture filtrates and extracts from other related strains, could acquire and manifest in subsequent generations certain properties of the related strain; in other words, these bacteria were being "transformed." The demonstration, in 1944, by Avery, MacLeod and McCarty that the genetically active material directing such heritable changes was DNA represents an important milestone in the history of biological research. Although indirect evidence had earlier suggested that nuclear determinants of hereditary characteristics in higher organisms may contain deoxyribose nucleic acid, the demonstration that the transforming principle (TP) was DNA in nature provided the first *direct* evidence for the genetic role of DNA.

Table 18. *Bacterial species in which transformation has been observed**

Diplococcus pneumoniae (or *Streptococcus pneumoniae*)	*Agrobacterium tumefaciens*
Streptococcus viridans	*Agrobacterium radiobacter*
Streptococcus sbe	*Agrobacterium rubi*
Streptococcus, serological group H, hemolytic strain *Challis*	*Xanthomonas phaseoli*
Hemophilus influenzae	*Bacillus subtilis*
Hemophilus parainfluenzae	*Bacillus licheniformis*
Hemophilus suis	*Rhizobium* sp.
Neisseria meningitidis	*Staphylococcus aureus*
Neisseria sicca	*Shigella paradysenteriae*†
Escherichia coli, K-12	*Salmonella typhimurium*†
	Salmonella sp.†

*From Ravin, 1961, where specific references may be found.
†Reported to occur, but reproducible conditions were not found.

All of the early transformation studies, including those that led to the identification of the role of DNA in TP, utilized strains of pneumococci in which changes in the characteristics of the cell surface (i.e., capsular type specificity) were being observed. Since then, transformation has been demonstrated in a number of bacterial species (Table 18), and a very large variety of characteristics have been utilized in the study of transformation (Table 19).*

Early Studies on the Transformation of Pneumococcal Capsular Types

Transformation was observed first with *Diplococcus pneumoniae* (*Streptococcus pneumoniae* in the current English system of classification) in which the encapsulated, so-called smooth (S) type is virulent and possesses a capsule composed essentially of polysaccharides.† In Chapter 9 we discussed the fact that the chemical composition of capsular poly-

*For reviews of transformation studies, see Austrian, 1952; Ephrussi-Taylor, 1955, 1960; Hotchkiss, 1955; Ravin, 1961; and Schaeffer, 1964.

†The smooth-rough terminology introduced by Griffith for pneumococcal variants differing in antigenicity and colonial morphology does not correspond to similar terms applied to analogous variants in most other bacterial species. Thus, the Griffith S corresponds to variants that are commonly designated as mucoid (M) in other species; unencapsulated rough (R) pneumococci correspond to variants which are usually designated as S; "extremely rough" (ER) pneumococcal variants (Taylor, 1949) correspond to types designated as R in most other species, and the intermediate (I) variants of pneumococci appear comparable to "weakly M" types of other species. The Griffith terminology has been retained by most investigators interested in the study of pneumococcus who discouraged appropriate changes in terminology in order to avoid added confusion. More recently, however, some laudable efforts have been initiated to designate the encapsulated types as S^+ and the unencapsulated types as S^-. The problem of terminology has become even more complex because of the finding that both S and R types of pneumococci can occur in two morphological forms, either filamentous (S, fil^+ or R, fil^+) or non-filamentous (S, fil^- or R, fil^-), each of these properties being separately transformable (Austrian, 1953).

TABLE 19. *Various hereditary bacterial characters that have been found to be transformable**

CHARACTER TRANSFORMED	SPECIES
I. Capsular polysaccharide synthesis	
	D. pneumoniae
	H. influenzae
	N. meningitidis
	E. coli
	X. phaseoli
II. Filamentous type of growth	*D. pneumoniae*
III. Specific protein antigens	
M protein	*D. pneumoniae*
IV. Drug and antibiotic resistance	
Penicillin: 3 levels	*D. pneumoniae*
Streptomycin: several levels	*D. pneumoniae*
Streptomycin: high level	*Strep. viridans*
Streptomycin: high level	*H. influenzae*
Streptomycin: high level	*N. meningitidis*
Streptomycin: high level	*X. phaseoli*
Streptomycin	*Rhizobium* sp.
Sulfanilamide: several levels	*D. pneumoniae*
Optochin	*D. pneumoniae*
Erythromycin: several levels	*D. pneumoniae*
Erythromycin	*N. meningitidis*
Bryamycin	*D. pneumoniae*
Canavanine	*D. pneumoniae*
Amethopterin	*D. pneumoniae*
Aminopterin	*D. pneumoniae*
8-Azaguanine	*D. pneumoniae*
Cathomycin	*H. influenzae*
V. Antibiotic dependence	
Streptomycin	*N. meningitidis*
VI. Synthesis of specific enzymes	
Mannitol dehydrogenase	*D. pneumoniae*
Salicin fermentation enzyme	*D. pneumoniae*
Maltase	*D. pneumoniae*
Lactic acid oxidase	*D. pneumoniae*
Sucrase	*B. subtilis*
β-Galactosidase	*B. subtilis*
Enzyme necessary for synthesis of cysteine	*Rhizobium* sp.
Enzymes necessary for synthesis of tryptophan	*B. subtilis*
Enzyme necessary for synthesis of nicotinic acid	*B. subtilis*
Various auxotrophs	*B. licheniformis*
VII. Sporulation	*B. subtilis*
VIII. Other characters	
Ability to infect plants	*Agrobacterium* sp.
	Rhizobium sp.

*From Ravin, 1961, where specific references may be found.

saccharides determines their immunological properties and that there are specific differences in these properties among different strains.

Almost 85 different serological types have been detected among encapsulated smooth pneumococci. This serological type specificity is a hereditary property and is maintained during prolonged cultivation as long as the cells remain encapsulated. Spontaneous mutation from one type-specific S type to another capsular type has never been observed. However, in a fashion similar to the spontaneous changes in antigenicity and colonial morphology described for other bacterial species (Chapter 9), S strains may undergo population changes involving the establishment of spontaneous unencapsulated R mutants. The R type cells are non-encapsulated, lack the serological type specificity of their S parent cells, and give rise to colonies that are more granular than those formed by S cells. Many of the so-called R types actually seem to be poorly encapsulated types; that is, the quantity of type-specific capsular polysaccharide secreted at the cell surface is very meager. Such types are more properly designated as intermediate (I) types and they may undergo spontaneous reversions to a fully encapsulated S type. Type specificity is always retained in such spontaneous reversions. Thus:

$$\text{S } II \rightarrow \text{I} \rightarrow \text{S } II$$
$$\text{S } III \rightarrow \text{I} \rightarrow \text{S } III$$

In 1928 Griffith discovered that it was possible to transform a non-encapsulated R variant derived from one specific type into encapsulated S cells of a heterologous type by *in vivo* passage in the presence of heat-killed heterologous S cells. He injected a small number of live R cells into mice simultaneously with a large number of heat-killed S cells with serological specificity different from that of the S strain from which the R cells had been derived. Many of these mice died subsequently and pneumococci isolated from them were found to be virulent, living S cells displaying the same type specificity as that of the killed S cells inoculated. Thus:

$$\text{S } II \rightarrow \text{R} \xrightarrow[\text{+ heat-killed S } III]{\text{into mice}} \text{S } III$$

Several investigators successfully repeated this experiment and eliminated the possibility that the results may have been due to contamination of the inoculum with a few live S *III* cells. In much later work the possibility of accidental contamination was ruled out even more conclusively by employing R cells "labeled" with a specific somatic protein antigen or with drug-resistance properties which vary independently of capsular polysaccharide (Langvad-Nielsen, 1944; Austrian and MacLeod, 1949). Thus:

$$\underset{\substack{\uparrow \\ \text{(specific M protein)}}}{\text{S } II \text{ (M2}')} \rightarrow \text{R (M2}') \xrightarrow[\text{+ heat-killed S } III]{\text{into mice}} \text{S } III \text{ (M2}')$$

In 1931 Dawson and Sia obtained similar transformations *in vitro* by growing an R strain in broth containing anti-R serum and heat-killed S cells. Subsequently, Alloway (1932, 1933) succeeded in obtaining specific *in vitro* transformations in the presence of cell-free extracts obtained from S cells. This opened the way for the brilliant investigations of Avery, MacLeod and McCarty (1944), who succeeded in isolating the active transforming principle (TP) in the form of deoxyribonucleic acid (DNA). Crude transforming extracts obtained from heat-killed encapsulated Type *III* cells proved to contain many inactive components, including protein, lipids, ribonucleic acid, and polysaccharides. When these were removed by chloroform extraction, enzymatic hydrolysis and alcohol fractionation, a final product was obtained which possessed practically all the activity of the crude extract. By a variety of means, including inactivation by purified deoxyribonuclease, chemical analysis, and ultraviolet absorption curves, the DNA nature of the TP was proven (McCarty and Avery, 1946). Additional studies gave convincing proof that the active fraction owed its activity merely to highly polymerized DNA; there was no reason to believe that it was contaminated with traces of possibly active protein, and it was free of polysaccharide (Hotchkiss, 1948). The purified DNA was highly active: as little as 1 part in 600,000,000 was capable of causing specific transformation of competent R cells in appropriate media (Fig. 103). Thus:

$$\text{S } II \rightarrow \text{R} + (\text{DNA from S } III) \rightarrow \text{S } III$$

Not only did the induced change persist in the progeny, but active DNA capable of inducing similar specific transformations to Type *III* could now be isolated from the transformed encapsulated cells and their

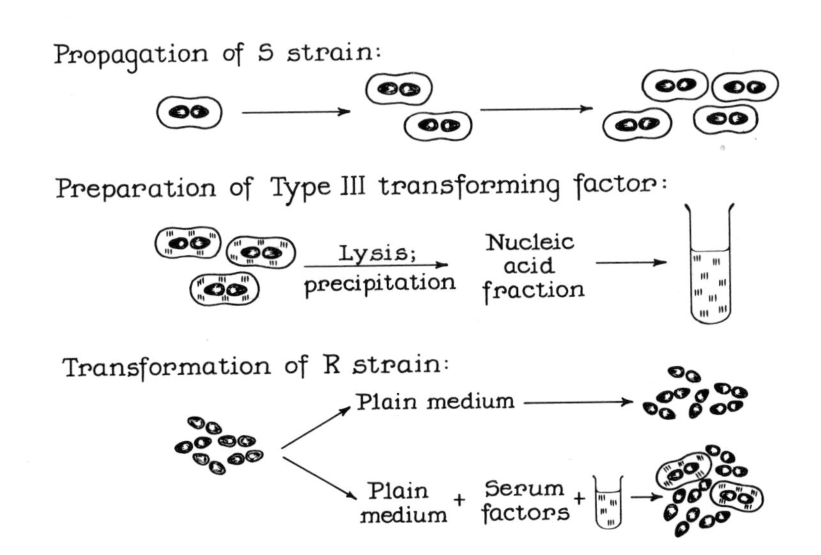

FIGURE 103. Transformation of capsular type in pneumococcus. (R. Hotchkiss.)

progeny in amounts far greater than that originally required to induce the change. This fact indicated that the specific DNA used in the process of transformation initiated the reproduction of similar DNA in the progeny of the transformed cells.

The specificity of the transforming preparation of DNA was proven by the fact that DNA from Type *II* cells caused transformation to Type *II*, DNA from Type *VI* cells induced changes to Type *VI*, etc. For example:

$$\text{S } \mathit{II} \rightarrow \text{R} + (\text{DNA from S } \mathit{VI}) \rightarrow \text{S } \mathit{VI} \rightarrow \text{R} + (\text{DNA from S } \mathit{II}) \rightarrow \text{S } \mathit{II}$$

Furthermore, the reciprocity of such transformation reactions was demonstrated (Taylor, 1949; Ravin, 1959). For example, using DNA from an intermediate type designated S *III*i:

$$\text{S } \mathit{III} + (\text{DNA from S } \mathit{III}\text{i}) \rightarrow \text{S } \mathit{III}\text{i} + (\text{DNA from S } \mathit{III}) \rightarrow \text{S } \mathit{III}$$

The transformed types were recovered at a frequency significantly greater than that of spontaneous mutations.

These results indicated (1) the existence of specific nucleic acids, each capable of evoking the production of a specific polysaccharide, and (2) the replacement of a bit of information (specific DNA) existing in the recipient cell by a different bit of information (specific DNA) furnished by the donor of the TP. It should be noted that this discovery of enormous importance also furnished an intriguing puzzle in the 1940's, since at that time no real clue existed as to the chemical nature of the apparently specific differences in DNA.

It was also recognized fairly early that the specificity associated with different transforming DNA preparations must reside in only a small portion of the total DNA isolated. Two observations supported this conclusion: (1) a DNA fraction could also be obtained from unencapsulated R pneumococci by methods identical to those employed in the isolation of active DNA from S cells, but this DNA from R cells was (as one would readily expect on the basis of today's more sophisticated knowledge) entirely inactive in capsular transformation of R recipients; (2) when the DNA donor cells differed from the cells to be transformed in more than one distinct property [e.g., polysaccharide capsule *and* "somatic protein" (Austrian and MacLeod, 1949), or different types of antibiotic resistance and sugar utilization (Hotchkiss, 1951; 1952; 1954)], a given DNA preparation was found to contain more than one transforming activity. For example, when rough penicillin-sensitive (*ps*) pneumococci were exposed to DNA from smooth penicillin-resistant (*pr*) donor cells, both rough penicillin-resistant and smooth penicillin-sensitive transformants could be isolated (we shall ignore the additional rare isolation of S *pr* cells until later):

$$\text{R } \mathit{ps} + (\text{DNA from S } \mathit{III}\ \mathit{pr}) \begin{array}{l} \nearrow \text{R } \mathit{pr} \\ \rightarrow \text{S } \mathit{III}\ \mathit{ps} \\ \searrow \text{S } \mathit{III}\ \mathit{pr} \end{array}$$

Today, of course, we realize that these different specificities associated with a single DNA preparation are due to the specificity of different and distinct nucleotide sequences, all residing within one long DNA molecule. Such separate nucleotide sequences, if closely linked on the DNA molecule, have their own probability of participating together or apart in recombination (see below); if not closely linked, i.e., if they are quite far apart on the bacterial chromosome, they are likely to become physically separated during the process of extraction of the DNA from the donor cells. Over the years it has become quite clear that a non-random fractionation of the bacterial chromosome into pieces of much smaller size occurs in the extraction of DNA. If the resulting polynucleotide pieces are of sufficient size (approximately 1×10^6 to 1×10^7 MW),* they can penetrate into competent recipient cells, where, in a series of events to be described later, part of these molecules may eventually participate in recombinations with corresponding regions of the recipient's chromosome. According to whether or not the information for two different detectable characteristics is closely linked in the bacterial chromosome (i.e., is determined by neighboring or nearby nucleotide sequences), we should expect two types of results in transformations involving DNA from a donor that differs from its related recipient by two distinct properties, A and B: If the information for A and B is linked, the likelihood of its being in one transforming DNA piece would be high and double transformations (AB) would be frequent; alternately, if the information is not linked, information for A and information for B would be likely to end up in two different DNA fragments of the transforming preparation and the probability of a double transformation (AB) would be quite low, namely, the product of the probabilities for single (A or B) transformations. The results obtained in many transformation studies, including early studies with pneumococci in which capsular type specificity was one of the two markers, confirmed these expectations.

More Recent Studies on Capsular Transformations

We shall later discuss additional specific examples of linked and non-linked determinants in transformation, but at this point let us fill in a few more details regarding pneumococcal capsular type transformations. Fairly recent biochemical studies on the synthesis of pneumococcal capsular polysaccharides (see p. 165) have shed considerable light on the nature of the biosynthetic events that are affected by transformation reactions which alter type specificity (Austrian *et al.*, 1959; Mills *et al.*, 1961; Mills and Smith, 1962). Thus, the failure of production of Type *III* capsular polysaccharide appears usually to involve a deficiency in the enzyme UDPG dehydrogenase. Transformations of the type: R + (DNA from S *III*) → S *III* therefore bring about a restoration of the information required for the production of this enzyme and the consequent formation of uridine diphosphate glucuronic acid (UDPGA). In the case of transformations involving the formation of Type *I* capsules, transfer of information affecting the formation of either of two different enzymes – UDPG dehydro-

*Pieces smaller than this do not get into cells.

genase or UDPGA 4-epimerase—can play a role. A lack of activity or production of either of these two enzymes has been found in different R mutants derived from S *I*. It has been possible to produce by transformation fully encapsulated Type *I* cells from the two types of R mutants (i.e., using DNA from the UDPG dehydrogenase-negative R strain, it was possible to transform UDPGA 4-epimerase-negative R cells into fully encapsulated cells). In this case, the recombination events following the penetration of the DNA into the competent recipient must have involved at least two cistrons, each determining the specificity of one enzyme.

As a result of the recognition of specific sites of biosynthetic lesions caused by the mutation of S pneumococci to the non-encapsulated R type, it has also become possible to elucidate the cause of some rather odd binary encapsulated types which may result, for example, from the following transformation:

$$\text{S } III \rightarrow \text{R (+ DNA from S } I) \begin{cases} \nearrow \text{S } I \text{ (many)} \\ \searrow \text{S } I\text{-}III \text{ (few)} \end{cases}$$

It has turned out that the binary encapsulated cells, which produce a normal amount of Type *III* capsular polysaccharide and a small amount of Type *I* capsular polysaccharide, result from interactions at the metabolic level rather than at the genetic level. Figure 104 shows the metabolic pathways which presumably exist in cells in which the genetic deficiency of S *III* and the S *I* genome coexist. It may be noted that under these conditions the Type *III* synthetic pathway utilizes UDPGA from the functioning Type *I* pathway and converts it into the glucuronic acid and glucose-containing Type *III* polysaccharide, as illustrated in Figure 75.

In addition to transformations involving *qualitative* changes in capsular polysaccharides, i.e., altered type specificity, many studies with transformable pneumococci have been concerned with *quantitative* alterations in capsule production. We have previously mentioned the particular mutants involved, the so-called intermediate mutants (p. 244). They differ from the encapsulated S type in the quantity of capsular polysaccharide secreted at the cell surface, but the chemical nature of their polysaccharide does not differ from that of the parental S type. The nucleotide regions of the bacterial chromosome affecting the quantitative control of polysaccharide formation are now known to be closely linked with those controlling the specificity of the enzymes concerned with capsular polysaccharide synthesis (see p. 166).* To illustrate the sort of analyses carried out with the intermediate forms, let us cite the following: Among many different stable I mutants, one, designated as S *III*-1, synthesizes very little Type *III* capsular polysaccharide; another, S *III*-2, consistently secretes a larger amount of Type *III* polysaccharide on the

*The precise arrangement of the genetic factors controlling the production of type-specific polysaccharides in pneumococci is still uncertain. One region involving a closely linked series of separate genes controlling a variety of different biosynthetic reactions must be involved since in transformation experiments this whole region is usually transferred as a single unit (Austrian *et al.*, 1959; Beale and Wilkenson, 1961).

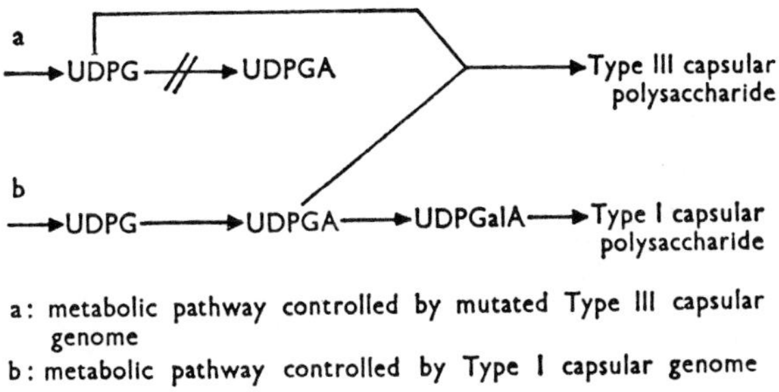

a
→UDPG –//→ UDPGA → Type III capsular polysaccharide

b
→UDPG → UDPGA → UDPGalA → Type I capsular polysaccharide

a: metabolic pathway controlled by mutated Type III capsular genome
b: metabolic pathway controlled by Type I capsular genome

FIGURE 104. Metabolic pathways in binary encapsulated *I-III* cells of *D. pneumoniae*. (From Mills and Smith, 1962.)

cell surface; and a third type, S *III*-N, represents the normal, fully encapsulated S type (MacLeod and Kraus, 1947; Taylor, 1949). DNA isolated from each of these three types will transform competent R cells to the condition corresponding to the type from which the TP was prepared:

R + (DNA from S *III*-1)→S *III*-1
R + (DNA from S *III*-2)→S *III*-2
R + (DNA from S *III*-N)→S *III*-N

Furthermore, R cells derived spontaneously from either of the intermediate mutants could be transformed to normal S cells by TP from S *III*-N. For example:

S *III*-1→R + (DNA from S *III*-N)→S *III*-N

a finding which again indicated that each I type contained only its particular DNA, having lost or altered its original information (nucleotide sequence) as the result of the S→I mutation that led to altered quantitative polysaccharide production.

One of the most interesting aspects of the studies with intermediate types of pneumococci has been the demonstration that complex interactions can occur between the transforming DNA and the recipient's genome (Ephrussi-Taylor, 1951a, b; Ravin, 1960). It was observed that two types of encapsulated cells resulted when S *III*-1 cells were exposed to the TP from S *III*-2:

S *III*-1 + (DNA from S *III*-2)→S *III*-2 (many)
↘S *III*-N (few)

The resulting S *III*-2 cells correspond phenotypically to the cells from which the TP was obtained, the S *III*-N cells found represent an entirely different type that does not correspond to the TP employed. Ephrussi-Taylor has designated the latter type of transforming activity as "allogenic," the former as "autogenic,"and she and Ravin furnished a number of examples of allogenic transformations of Type *III* cells, which led to the conclusion that the new type represents the result of recombinational events of the following kind:

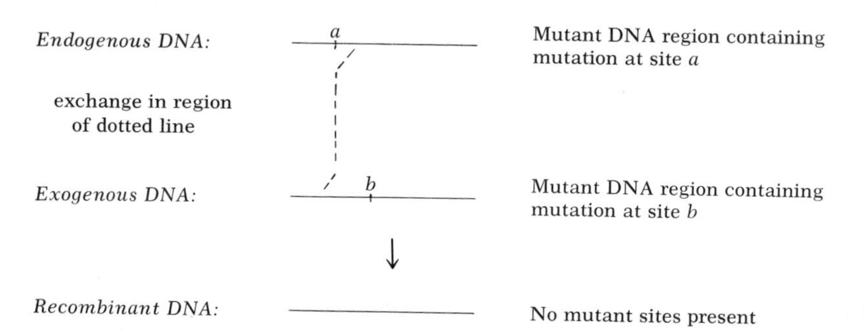

By determining the type and frequency of different recombinants that arose in transformations of Type *III* derivatives, a model could be constructed of the presumed location of altered regions in the DNA molecule responsible for the various Type *III* transformations (Fig. 105). This model reflects the fact that S *III*-N recombinants were never obtained from transformations among R I, S *III*-2 and R II, the reason for this being that all of these presumably have mutated sites in the very same region. Similarly, transformations between R 36H and R 36R never yielded S *III*-N types, whereas transformations between R 36R and R I did.

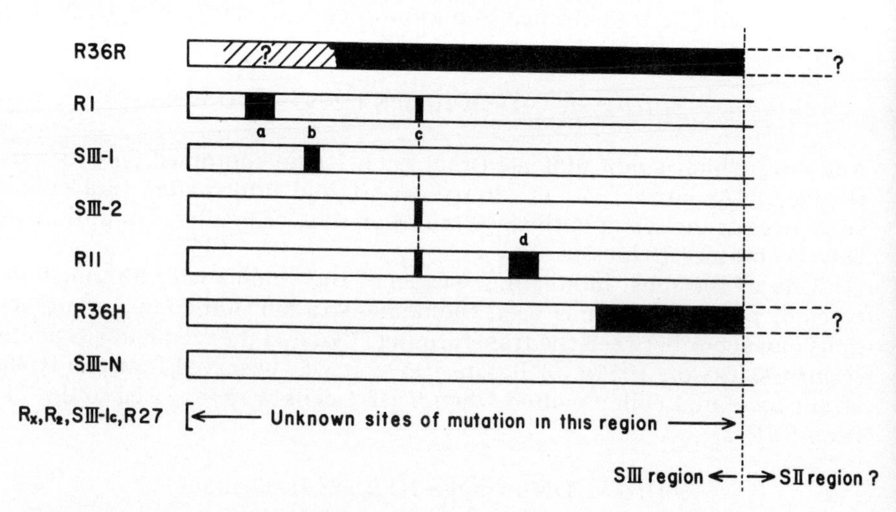

FIGURE 105. Diagrammatic representation of sites, within a small portion of pneumococcal DNA (S *III* region), which are capable of undergoing mutation resulting in impaired synthesis of Type *III* capsular polysaccharide. The designations for the mutant strains are shown on the left. (From Ravin, 1961.)

While these events involve recombinations that are made possible by the participation of a single transforming DNA molecule, it is not certain whether they involve recombinations within a single cistron or among several cistrons, because too little is known about the chemical and genetic basis of regulation of the amount of capsular polysaccharide produced. However, analyses of the enzymatic steps in S *III* synthesis have revealed that most mutations affecting the synthesis of Type *III* polysaccharides are found in the cistron controlling the formation of UDPGA. Accordingly, the two types of transformations observed in the scheme shown on page 000 are likely to reflect (1) an exchange of at least the cistron controlling UDPG dehydrogenase, and (2) recombination within this cistron (Austrian *et al.*, 1959). More decisive examples of recombinations between different genes and within single genes became available when characters other than capsulation were employed in transformation studies (see p. 251).

Transformation Reactions Involving Antibiotic Resistance and Growth Factor Requirements – the Phenomenon of Linkage

Transformation studies using capsulation as a marker have two disadvantages: (1) as just mentioned, too little is known regarding the degree of complexity of the chemical reactions and genetic sites involved in capsule formation, and (2) it is difficult to use capsule characteristics for a study of the different stages and kinetics involved in transformation. In capsular transformations it is always difficult to recognize the first transformed cells, whereas in transformation involving growth requirements and antibiotic resistance it is possible to eliminate the original recipient cell type (e.g., penicillin-sensitive or histidine-requiring recipients) while permitting the growth of the transformed cell type (e.g., penicillin-resistant transformants growing on penicillin-containing media, or histidine-independent transformants growing on minimal media).

Antibiotic resistance was exploited as a marker in transformation quite early; a utilization of nutritional mutants in transformation studies became possible when defined minimal media were developed for such transformable species as pneumococci (Rappaport and Guild, 1959) and *Hemophilus* (Talmadge and Herriott, 1960), and also when transformation reactions were demonstrated with *Bacillus subtilis* (Spizizen, 1958), an organism that grows easily in defined minimal media.

With the availability of additional markers such as antibiotic resistance and nutritional requirements, it became feasible to explore the problem of multiple transformations more thoroughly. It then became obvious that one had to distinguish between two major types of double transformations: (1) those due to *two independent,* but almost simultaneous, events involving non-linked markers, and (2) those due to *one* event in which linked markers participate. Double transformations involving *non-linked markers* were demonstrated in many different transformation reactions. The salient feature of these events was (and is) the fact that in a system in which two non-linked markers (A and B) are employed, the frequency of doubly transformed cells (AB) is equal to, or usually less than, the product of the frequency of single transformants (A cells and B cells). In other words, each transformation is an independent event (penetration of a particular transforming DNA molecule and subsequent integration, by recombination, of part of it), and the likelihood of two such independent events occurring simultaneously, as far as one competent recipient cell is concerned, is merely a matter of statistical chance.

We can illustrate this by completing the full story of what happened when rough penicillin-sensitive (R *ps*) pneumococci were exposed to DNA from smooth penicillin-resistant (S *pr*) donor cells (see p. 244). We stated previously that two types of transformants, namely, R *pr* and S *ps*, were recovered. Actually, however, a rare third type, S *pr*, was also recovered. The complete reaction may be written as follows:

S *II ps* → R *ps* + (DNA from S *III pr*) ↗ R *pr*
→ S *III ps*
↘ S *III pr* (a double transformation involving two independent reactions)

The recovery of *pr* cells in this reaction was 10,000 times greater than following spontaneous mutations in the absence of DNA from *pr* cells.* The recovery of the double transformant S III *pr*, however, was an extremely rare event, yet it occurred more frequently than one would expect for two simultaneous, but independent, mutational events.

In the case of *linked markers*, the frequency of joint transformations is significantly higher than would be expected on the basis of the probability for two separate events. For example, resistance to streptomycin (*sr*) and the ability to utilize mannitol as an energy source ($mann^+$) are being transferred and integrated into the recipients' genomes at a frequency 15 times greater than expected on the basis of two separate simultaneous or successive transformations (Hotchkiss and Marmur, 1954). This finding was interpreted as having been due to a coexistence of the information for the two markers on the same molecule of transforming DNA. Thus:

(1) *ss*, $mann^-$ + (DNA from *sr*, $mann^+$) ↗ *ss*, $mann^+$ (many)
→ *sr*, $mann^-$ (many)
↘ *sr*, $mann^+$ (15 per cent of single transformants)

This interpretation was supported by the finding that a mixture of DNA's from *sr*, $mann^-$ and *ss*, $mann^+$ added to an *ss*, $mann^-$ population yielded

*A noteworthy feature of transformation to penicillin resistance is the fact that, as in the case of spontaneous mutation to penicillin resistance, the increase in the degree of resistance occurs stepwise. Thus, DNA obtained from *pr* cells 30 times more resistant than the susceptible recipient cells causes transformations to cells with only a fivefold resistance. Exposure of these resistant cells to the same DNA preparation thereupon yields transformed cells showing twelvefold resistance to penicillin, etc., reflecting a similarity with the steps that had occurred in the original mutation series.

sr, mann$^+$ transformants only in small numbers, i.e., at a frequency that was the product of the frequency of the single transformation. Further confirmation of the linkage between mannitol utilization and streptomycin resistance was obtained also by the demonstration that many of the *mann*$^+$ cells selected from an experiment

(2) *sr, mann*$^-$ + (DNA from *ss, mann*$^+$)

proved to be streptomycin-sensitive. Similarly, when *sr* cells were selected from an experiment

(3) *ss, mann*$^+$ + (DNA from *sr, mann*$^-$)

a large proportion of the *sr* cells proved to be *mann*$^-$.

In the latter two examples the frequency of double transformations [*ss, mann*$^+$ in (2), *sr, mann*$^-$ in (3)] was identical with those (*sr, mann*$^+$) observed in experiment (1). This observation showed that the degree of linkage was identical in all experiments, as far as the polynucleotide regions concerned with susceptibility to streptomycin and utilization of mannitol are concerned. Additional tests have suggested that these two separate bits of information tend to end up on one fragment of the fractionated DNA that is commonly the end product in the extraction of transforming DNA. Separation of the two regions of information *after* their joint penetration into a competent recipient cell, therefore, must involve recombinational events, i.e., either a breakage of the molecule prior to its incorporation (= prior to its replacing a corresponding polynucleotide region of the recipient's genome), or a copying of only part of this molecule, if copy-choice is the mechanism responsible for recombination.

A number of additional cases of linkage between determinants of different characteristics have been detected in transformation studies. The relative degree of linkage between such determinants can be estimated by calculating the proportion of double transformants to single transformants identified in tests involving DNA from multiple marked donors. Thus, in pneumococci, resistance to sulfanilamide is linked to streptomycin resistance, but the degree of linkage between the two polynucleotide regions determining these resistances is less than between *sr* and *mann*$^+$. Resistances to cathomycin and to streptomycin have been found to be linked in *Hemophilus* (Goodgal and Herriott, 1957). In *B. subtilis*, linkage has been reported (a) for the determinants of an enzyme involved in the formation of indole and an enzyme concerned with the synthesis of sucrose (Spizizen, 1959), (b) for an enzyme involved in the formation of indole glycerol phosphate and an enzyme active in histidine biosynthesis (Nester and Lederberg, 1961), (c) for streptomycin resistance and spore formation, and (d) for methionine and isoleucine syntheses (Yoshikawa and Sueoka, 1963).

It should be realized that "linkage" in transformation has a very special connotation; it merely reflects a *close* linkage which leads to the probability of two "linked" determinants ending up in the same DNA molecule after DNA extraction. *In vivo*, all of the determinants in pneumococci, *B. subtilis, Hemophilus* and most other transformable bacterial species

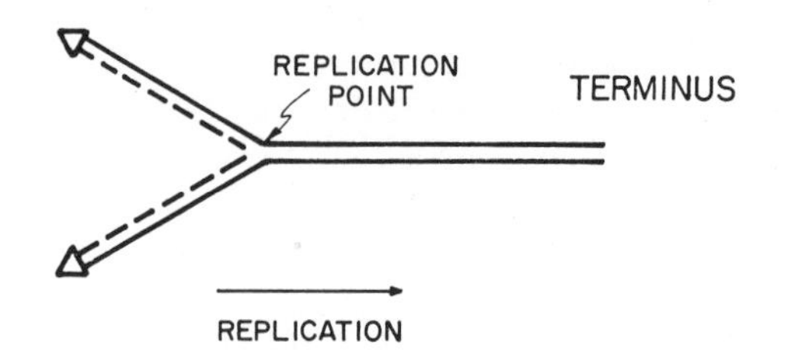

FIGURE 106. A replication model of the bacterial chromosome. Both strands are copied, starting from one end (origin) and proceeding toward the other end (terminus). The solid line represents the old strands, and the broken lines the newly synthesized strands. (From Yoshikawa and Sueoka, 1963.)

are probably linked in the usual genetic sense, which means that they are all located on the same bacterial chromosome. However, the degree of such true genetic linkage is impossible to estimate directly in the usual transformation experiment in which, as we have now stressed repeatedly, the donor's bacterial chromosome appears to be fragmented, probably in a non-random manner, during extraction.* Nevertheless, an ingenious indirect approach to the mapping of the linked determinants of *B. subtilis* was developed by Yoshikawa and Sueoka (1963). They calculated that if the chromosome of *B. subtilis* replicates in a sequential fashion, starting from one point of origin (Fig. 106), then, in an exponentially growing, non-synchronized, bacterial population, the frequency of chromosomes that have just started to replicate must be nearly twice as high as that of chromosomes which are about to complete their replication. This also means that the amount of any genetic marker located near the origin of replication should, in comparison to that in non-replicating stationary populations, be twice as high as the amount of a marker located near the terminus of replication. In other words, as replication proceeds, markers near the origin of replication (let us call them O markers) would be present in more copies than markers near the terminus (T markers); consequently, transforming DNA donated by O markers should be more frequent than that donated by T markers.

By measuring the frequency of transformation for different markers with DNA isolated from *B. subtilis* at different population stages of exponential growth and by comparing this frequency to a base value obtained with DNA from stationary cultures, it was shown that at different stages

*The non-random fragmentation of the bacterial chromosome during extraction of transforming DNA is indicated by the consistent heterogeneity in density of the pieces of DNA (= DNA molecules) present in the transforming DNA suspension. Such heterogeneity has made it possible to achieve a relative enrichment of transforming activity for a given marker in one layer of a CsCl density gradient centrifugation, and for another marker (presumably associated with a piece of different density) in a different layer of such a gradient (Rolfe and Ephrussi-Taylor, 1961, Guild, 1963). A similar separation of markers has been achieved by assays of coprecipitates of transforming DNA which sediment at different times after exposure to antisera (Braun *et al.*, 1962); this finding again appears to reflect a consistent difference in size or composition of DNA pieces with which different determinants are associated (see also p. 263).

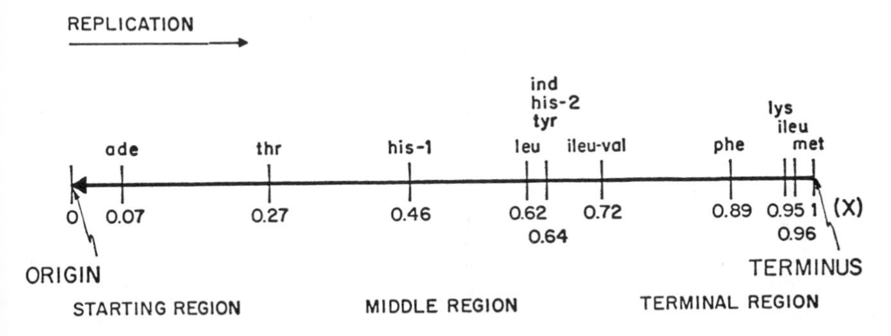

FIGURE 107. A genetic map of *B. subtilis* based on results obtained by marker frequency analysis, as described in the text. (Courtesy of H. Yoshikawa, M. N. Hayashi, and N. Sueoka.)

of cultural growth there are indeed significant differences between the frequencies with which different markers are donated by transforming DNA. For example, with DNA isolated from cells of early exponential growth, the relative frequency of transformation for the *ade* marker (adenine-requirement) was 1.96, for *thr* (threonine-requirement) 1.74, and for *leu* (leucine-requirement) 1.37, all expressed in relation to the frequency of transformation for DNA from the stationary phase, with the rate for the *met* (methionine-requirement) marker taken as unity. Such comparisons of transformation frequencies for different markers with DNA isolated during exponential growth of the donor cells then permitted the construction of a genetic map of *B. subtilis*, in which the location of each marker is a reflection of its frequency in the tests just described (Fig. 107). The sequential replication of the *B. subtilis* chromosome, which was suggested by these results, subsequently was confirmed by direct measurement of the replication of different markers, using isotopically labeled DNA as an indicator. In these tests the cells donating the transforming DNA were first grown in an N^{15}-containing medium and then transferred into an N^{14}-containing medium; the rate of conversion of various markers from heavy (parental) into intermediate (hybrid) DNA molecules was then measured and found to follow the sequence established by the prior transformation tests (Yoshikawa and Sueoka, 1963).

Cellular Competence and Environmental Conditions Required for Transformation

Even in species in which transformation has been demonstrated, different strains differ in their ability to be transformed. Furthermore, cells belonging to a transformable strain can be more easily transformed in certain media than in others, and within a given medium, they will attain an optimum physiological state suitable for transformation (so-called *competence*) for only relatively brief periods. Thus, the ability to be transformed depends on both genetic and environmental factors, many of which are only poorly understood so far (cf. Ravin, 1961). Among the more obvious inherent properties that can interfere with transformability are the secretion of DNAase, which would inactivate transforming DNA, and unusual cell surface barriers, such as dense mucoid capsular materials which could interfere with the penetration of DNA into the cell. Thus, it was demonstrated that among smooth pneumococcal strains that secrete different amounts of capsular polysaccharide, there is an inverse correlation between transformability and the amount of capsular material secreted (Ravin, 1957). Genetic control of transformability is also illustrated by the fact that the introduction of certain determinants, such as those leading to erythromycin-resistance of pneumococci, can lead to a marked decrease or complete loss of competence in originally highly transformable recipient strains (Sirotnak *et al.*, 1963). In this example, the loss of transformability was directly correlated with a decreased capacity of the cells to take up P^{32}-labeled DNA.

The actual process of transformation can be divided into several stages, of which adsorption and penetration of DNA into the cell are the early steps, and the integration, by recombination, of part of this DNA into the recipient's genome is the final step. The differences in competence of the cells of a transformable strain during different stages of growth has been assumed to involve primarily alterations in the first step. From studies with radioactively labeled DNA we do know that the transforming DNA gets into competent cells (Lerman and Tolmach, 1957; Goodgal and Herriott, 1957; Fox, 1960; Young and Spizizen, 1963). Although we do not know exactly how it gets in (see also p. 257), there is a general belief that uptake of DNA is dependent on the surface components of the cell and that changes in competence may reflect generalized and localized alterations of these components. Some investigators have favored the "localized protoplast" hypothesis, which assumes that the attainment of competence is associated with the development of holes in the cell wall, or of otherwise partially naked surface sites, during certain stages of cellular growth (Ravin, 1961). This view is supported by the finding of distinct peaks of competence for transformation at specific stages of a culture's growth and by the demonstration that synchronized growth of cells, induced by temporary chilling, favors the attainment of optimum competence of a population (Hotchkiss, 1954). This, however, cannot be the whole story because it has been shown that entire protoplasts are unable to take up DNA (Miller and Landman, 1963), and evidence also has been provided that the attainment of competence, at least by pneumococci, can be dependent upon protein synthesis (Fox and Hotchkiss, 1957). This observation has led to the suggestion that competence may involve the formation of specific surface sites capable of binding DNA.

In transformation of pneumococci and *Hemophilus* it has been possible to achieve conditions under which most cells of the DNA-exposed population are competent as judged by DNA uptake (Fox and Hotchkiss, 1957; Schaeffer, 1957; Goodgal and Herriott, 1961), but nevertheless, the frequency of single transformants does not exceed 5 per cent under these optimum conditions and in the presence of excess DNA. This finding means that even when an encounter between transforming DNA and a competent cell is assured, the DNA taken up by the majority of the cells may not carry the marker under scrutiny in the test, and also, subsequent events may interfere with the development of transformed progeny despite the fact that the appropriate DNA has entered the competent recipient cell.

In *B. subtilis* considerable heterogeneity in competence within a population has been observed and it has been calculated that less than 10 per cent of a population brought to the peak of competence is capable of undergoing transformation (Nester and Stocker, 1963).* Competent cells of *B. subtilis* are more resistant to penicillin than their non-transformable sister cells (a possible reflection of temporary metabolic sluggishness in competent cells), and it has been possible to increase transformation frequencies five- to tenfold by adding penicillin to a "competent" culture prior to exposure to DNA (Nester and Stocker, 1963).

In many strains, competence, once achieved by growth of appropriately synchronized cells in the proper medium, can be preserved for some time by storage at −20° C in the presence of 10 per cent glycerol (Fox and Hotchkiss, 1957).

In the early transformation studies, which dealt principally with pneumococci, complex media were required. For example, to obtain capsular transformations (R→S) *in vitro*, it was customary to add (1) agglutinating R antibodies, (2) a dialyzable serum factor which was replaceable by pyrophosphate, and (3) an additional serum factor which could be supplied by adding a serum albumin fraction (McCarty *et al.*, 1946; Hotchkiss and Ephrussi-Taylor, 1951). In the light of more recent knowledge it is likely that the antibody, or some other conditions that prevented the dispersion of the R recipient cells, served to create a selective environment that favored the transformed S cells. The role of albumin is not clear, but it is possible that the albumin aided in stabilizing transforming DNA or contained, complexed reversibly to it, trace amounts of substances that stimulate competence (Ravin, 1961). Pyrophosphate may have served to chelate ions that may interfere with the contact between transforming DNA and the recipient cell, or it might have had an influence on DNAase levels or on DNA synthesis which, when accelerated, may increase the likelihood of integration of transforming DNA. A role of DNAase in supporting pneumococcal capsular transformations was recognized by Kohoutová (1962), who showed that low levels are necessary, but that high levels inactivate. More recent transformation studies with pneumococci have employed less complex media, supplemented only with serum albumin, or a defined medium consisting of salts, amino acids, vitamins, glucose and sodium pyruvate (Rappaport and Guild, 1959); however, the efficiency of transformation is reduced in the defined medium which supports only slow growth of the organisms.

The requirements for transformation of *Hemophilus* are somewhat simpler than those for pneumococci; fairly high frequencies of transformation are obtainable in media ordinarily used for the growth of *Hemophilus* (Alexander and Leidy, 1951), and in a relatively simple defined medium (Talmadge and Herriott, 1960). Transformable strains of *B. subtilis* also transform well in a relatively simple defined medium (Spizi-

*The typical percentage of transformation for single markers in this organism is 0.1 to 0.5 at saturating levels of DNA.

zen, 1958) in which optimal conditions for competence are further dependent on temperature, pH, aeration and the presence of certain divalent cations (Young and Spizizen, 1963).

Stages in the Transformation Reaction

The different stages in transformation reactions so far recognized or postulated can be grouped roughly as follows:

Stage	*Characteristics*
1. Binding of DNA to cell	Reversible.
2. Uptake (also referred to as penetration, incorporation, or fixation) of DNA	Irreversible. Loss of DNAase-sensitivity of transformation reaction. Temporary loss of recovery of biologically active transforming DNA. Not affected by chloramphenicol exposure.
3. Association ("pairing," synapsis) of transforming DNA with corresponding segment of recipient's chromosome	Biologically active DNA can be recovered. Subsequent events can be inhibited by chloramphenicol.
4. Integration, by recombination, of part of the transforming (exogenous) DNA molecule into recipient's (endogenous) chromosomal DNA	Biologically active DNA can be recovered. The introduced marker is replicated (copied) during the next replication of the recipient's chromosomal DNA.
5. Replication of the integrated new information	Development of a transformed clone.

While the initial stages require uninhibited growth, it has been claimed that stages 3 and 4 can occur in the absence of significant growth, and also when 5-fluorodeoxyuridine has at least partially inhibited growth and DNA synthesis (Fox, 1960). Naturally, uninhibited DNA synthesis is a prerequisite for stage 5.

In order to be taken up, DNA must have a minimum *molecular size*, which appears to be a molecular weight of approximately 10^5. The MW of DNA in a good transforming preparation is about 10^7; transforming activity decreases very rapidly when the MW of the DNA molecule is reduced, without a separation of the complementary strands, through shearing by high pressure spraying or by ultrasonic oscillations (Litt *et al.*, 1958; Rosenberg *et al.*, 1959). Single-stranded (heated) DNA is much less readily incorporated than undenatured, double-stranded DNA (Roger and Hotchkiss, 1961; Guild, 1961; Young and Spizizen, 1961).

There is experimental evidence, however, obtained in studies with P^{32}-labeled DNA, that in the process of entry into the cell, the double-stranded DNA may be converted into single-stranded DNA, at least in pneumococcal transformations (Lacks, 1962). In fact, Lacks has speculated that the process of uptake of DNA may involve the penetration of one end of an extracellular DNA molecule through the cell membrane and the intracellular attachment of DNAase to one of the strands. While the enzyme then alternately attaches to and splits linkages along one strand (being inactive for the other strand on account of its opposite polarity), it will drag the other, unaffected strand into the cell. While this speculation remains subject to experimental confirmation, the available data indicate that, at least in pneumococci, transforming DNA immediately after uptake is in a single-stranded form, and participates as such in the subsequent recombination event. It is probable that such single-strandedness may explain the absence of recoverable biologically active DNA from stage 2, as cited above.

It has been calculated that competent bacteria possess 30 to 75 *adsorption sites* for DNA (Fox and Hotchkiss, 1957). As indicated by studies on competition between transforming DNA and other (homologous or heterologous) DNA in transformation reactions (Hotchkiss, 1957), these sites can be occupied by any DNA of sufficient molecular size. Sufficiently large quantities of non-transforming homologous or heterologous DNA, even DNA from calf thymus, can, therefore, compete with DNA carrying the marker under study and decrease or abolish its effects.

DNA from different species, even though not giving rise to transformants, can get into competent cells with about the same facility as DNA from fairly closely related species, as indicated by studies with P^{32} labeled DNA (Schaeffer, 1958). In general, however, entrance into the cell of one appropriate transforming molecule appears to suffice to set off the events that can give rise to transformed progeny.

In a number of studies, irreversible uptake of P^{32} labeled DNA and transformation were found to be directly correlated (Lerman and Tolmach, 1957; Goodgal and Herriott, 1957), but more recent evidence shows that such a correlation does not always occur (Young and Spizizen, 1963).

The time required for effective initial contact between DNA and the competent cell can be extremely brief. Thus, transformation can ensue when DNAase is added ten seconds after exposure of competent pneumococci to transforming DNA (Hotchkiss, 1954). Similarly, in *H. influenzae* the changes that allow some cells in an R population to form colonies of type-specific S organisms, following the exposure to TP from type-specific cells, are initiated within three minutes (Alexander and Leidy, 1951). This means that after this period the addition of DNAase to the TP-containing environment will not affect the occurrence of transformation.

Once the DNA is in the cell, the time required for integration of part of the information carried by the exogenous DNA into the DNA of the recipient cell (more precisely, the recombinational events involving the transforming DNA and the endogenous DNA) seems to be quite brief in many, but not all, instances. Integration may occur within 10 to 30 minutes after uptake (Fox, 1960; Fox and Hotchkiss, 1960; Voll and Goodgal, 1961; Nester and Stocker, 1963) as judged, for example, by the re-extraction after this period, of transforming recombinant *try*$^+$ *his*$^+$ DNA from *try*$^-$ *his*$^+$ *B. subtilis* cells that had been exposed to *try*$^+$ *his*$^-$ DNA. Also, it has been reported that the information for synthesis of amylomaltase (an enzyme controlling maltose fermentation) may express itself, and thus presumably is already integrated in the recipient's genome* as rapidly as

*See page 259 for the requirement for integration prior to phenotypic manifestations in transformed cells.

ten minutes after DNA uptake of transformable pneumococci (Lacks and Hotchkiss, 1960).

Other observations, however, have suggested that the time of integration may vary and may be delayed for as long as several generations. In the case of transformation of pneumococci to streptomycin resistance, for example, integration (as evidenced by subsequent replication of the marker) seems to be delayed for several hours, sometimes not occurring in the pneumococcal cell exposed to DNA, but in its progeny (Hotchkiss, 1956; Ephrussi-Taylor, 1960; Ravin, 1961). It remains unclear, however, whether all such delays are real or whether some of them may not be attributable to a lag that delays an increase in number of transformants *after* integration has occurred (Nester and Stocker, 1963). To summarize then: Replication of the newly introduced information, accompanied by the phenotypic manifestation of the new trait, may be rapid in some cases and greatly delayed in others, and this fact may be regarded as an indication that the prerequisite integration of the exogenous DNA can be correspondingly rapid or delayed.

The probability of integration is greater when small segments of the transforming DNA are introduced into the recipient cell instead of large segments. For example, when the transforming molecule contains information for three linked markers, transformants possessing one of these markers will be isolated more frequently than transformants showing two of these markers; transformants displaying all three linked markers are least frequently isolated (Hotchkiss, 1957; Ravin and Iyer, 1961). As we shall see, integration also appears to be dependent on the nature of the nucleotides located adjacent to the marker under study (p. 261).

Schaeffer (1964) has cited some good reasons why the pairing between exogenous and endogenous DNA, prior to integration of a piece of the exogenous DNA, probably does not occur between a single-stranded exogenous DNA strand and a *single*-stranded endogenous DNA strand. He argues that structural considerations indicate that such pairing between two complementary single strands would result in a lethal fragmentation of the DNA structure during breakage and reunion. However, pairing between a single-stranded exogenous DNA and a *double*-stranded endogenous DNA segment, leading to a temporary triple-helix structure, would permit breakage and reunion without fragmentation of the genome.

Following the occurrence of recombinational events, the portion of the transforming DNA that has not participated in recombination is lost from the cell. Thus, if we picture the constitution of part of a transforming (exogenous) DNA molecule as

. . .abcdefgh. . .

and the corresponding polynucleotide region of the recipient cell (endogenous DNA) as

. . .ABCDEFGH. . .

then, following recombination (integration) involving

cdef

(giving rise to a recombinant DNA

...ABcdefGH...)

the "unused" donor DNA portions

...ab gh...

are lost, possibly through destruction by intracellular DNAase. Once integrated, the new information, i.e., the new polynucleotide sequences, will replicate in concert with the recipient's DNA.

Phenotypic Effects of Transforming DNA

Available evidence suggests that transforming DNA cannot produce a phenotypic effect prior to its integration into the recipient cell's chromosome. In other words, transcription from DNA to RNA, and all subsequent events, cannot occur until the donor DNA has become integrated into the recipient's DNA. This is in striking contrast to the behavior of DNA introduced into a bacterial cell by phage, i.e., in transduction. It is known from viral conversion (p. 161) and abortive transduction (p. 274) that DNA injected into a cell by phage can exert an immediate phenotypic effect; i.e., the information can be transcribed. The reasons for the differences between transforming DNA and transduced DNA, in regard to their respective capacities to be transcribed, are still somewhat obscure. It might be that the chemical extraction of transforming DNA removes material necessary for transcription, but it is more likely that the single-stranded state of the exogenous DNA, after its penetration into the recipient cell and prior to its integration into the recipient's genome, does not allow transcription.

The requirement for transcription of the new DNA information from (integrated) DNA to messenger RNA prior to phenotypic manifestation of the new trait is supported by the demonstration that transforming DNA (carrying the marker for sulfonamide resistance) can be used for the *in vitro* synthesis of RNA (see p. 325), which in turn, can cause a temporary *phenotypic* transformation of pneumococci after uptake of such RNA (Hurwitz *et al.*, 1963).

Natural Occurrence of Transformation

Since the vast majority of studies on transformation have employed DNA extracted by chemical means, one might ask whether transformation ever occurs under natural conditions. So far this question lacks a decisive answer. While it has been possible to transform pneumococci *in vivo* following subcutaneous or intraperitoneal injection of dead donor strains and live recipient cells, or of live donors and recipients, into a variety of mammals, transformation has not been observed in the natural habitat of pneumococci, i.e., in the respiratory tract (Austrian, 1952; Ottolenghi and MacLeod, 1963). On the other hand, it has been demonstrated that transforming DNA can accumulate in the liquid medium of growing pneumococcal cultures and can transform other appropriately labeled pneumococci present in the same culture (Ottolenghi and Hotchkiss, 1960). It has not been established whether this extracellular transforming DNA accumulates as the result of active excretion or lysis of some cells. However, it has been shown that there is a striking, but perhaps accidental, correlation between the time of extracellular recovery of transforming activity and the development of competence for transformation. DNA is also known to accumulate in the culture fluid of many other bacteria, but except for the case of *Neisseria meningitidis* (Catlin, 1960), it has not been determined whether such DNA possesses transforming activity. Aside from natural extracellular accumulation, transforming DNA also has been released from cells by lysis with penicillin or streptomycin (Hotchkiss, 1951). Thus, at least under certain natural as well as certain adverse environmental conditions, transformation may serve to create new, and perhaps sometimes better adapted, genotypes.

Interspecific Transformations

In most studies of transformation both DNA donor and recipient strains belonged to the same species. In a number of instances, however, transformation has been found to be possible between members of different but related species. For example, genetic traits have been transferred by chemically extracted DNA among a number of species of *Hemophilus* (Schaeffer, 1958; Leidy *et al.*, 1959), among *Neisseria* species (Catlin and Cunningham, 1961), among Bacillaceae (Marmur *et al.*, 1963), between *Streptococcus* and *D. pneumoniae* (Bracco *et al.*, 1957) and apparently also among *Salmonella* and *Shigella* species (Romantsova, 1963). Similarity of base composition (guanine plus cytosine content of DNA), which is believed to reflect homologies in base sequences, is a minimum requirement for heterospecific transformations (Marmur *et al.*, 1963). Thus, *B. subtilis*, with 43 per cent G + C, can be transformed by DNA from *B. natto*, *B. niger* and *B. polymyxa*—all of which have a similar percentage of G + C—but is not transformed by *B. cereus* (33 per cent G + C), *B. licheniformis* (46 per cent G + C), or *B. megaterium* (36 per cent G + C). Such requirements for a microhomology of DNA structure among intertransformable strains belonging to different species are paralleled regularly by a similar requirement for the formation of DNA hybrid molecules *in vitro* (Marmur, 1963) (see p. 63).

The frequency of transformation of a given marker in interspecific transformations (using *heterologous* DNA) is often much less than the transformation frequencies for the same marker between strains belonging to the same species (using *homologous* DNA). Two possible causes for such low frequencies have been advanced: (1) the occasionally poor ability of recipient cells to take up transforming DNA from a different species (Lerman and Tolmach, 1957), and (2) the reduced efficiency for pairing between the endogenous (recipient) DNA and the exogenous (transforming) DNA (Schaeffer, 1958), an event that must precede the integration of part of the exogenous DNA. In the latter case, reduced uptake of the heterospecific DNA has been excluded as a contributory influence by direct

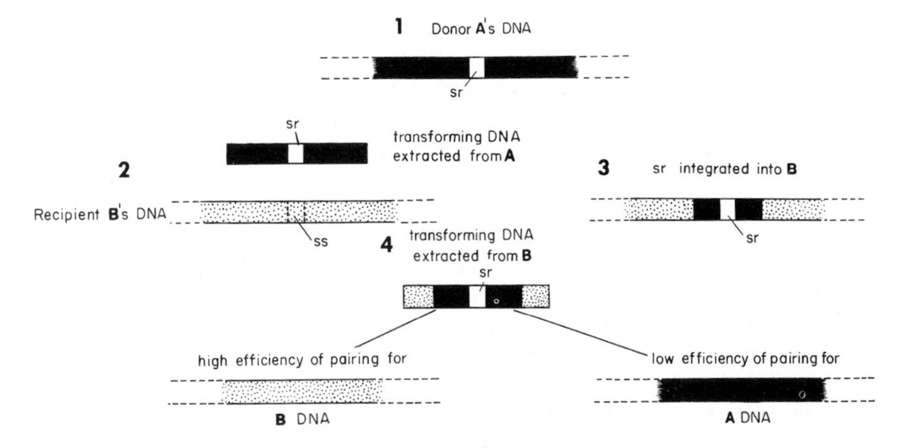

FIGURE 108. A possible mechanism for the shift from low frequency to high frequency of interspecific transformation of streptomycin resistance (*sr*) from *H. parainfluenzae* to *H. influenzae,* when the same marker (nucleotide sequence), recovered after integration into *H. influenzae,* is employed for transforming *H. influenzae.* (After P. Schaeffer.)

observations with P^{32}-labeled DNA, while a series of interesting observations has pointed to a decreased efficiency of pairing and integration as the cause for the lowered frequency of interspecific transformations. These observations were as follows: When DNA was isolated from a streptomycin-resistant *Hemophilus parainfluenzae* donor (A *sr*), it produced many transformants among streptomycin-sensitive *H. parainfluenzae* recipients, but only a small number when used on sensitive recipients of a different species, namely, *H. influenzae* (which we shall label B). However, DNA reisolated from B (B *sr*) now transformed B cells at high frequencies, while transforming A cells at low frequencies.

These findings suggest that integration into the B genome must have freed the A *sr* DNA of factors that contributed to the low frequency of transformation of B cells by A DNA. Schaeffer has suggested that what is lost may be poorly matching (presumably adjacent) pieces of the exogenous DNA (A *sr*, in our example) which by their lack of complete homology with corresponding regions of the endogenous DNA may prevent a high efficiency of pairing. As illustrated in Figure 108, after integration and subsequent extraction of transforming DNA (B *sr*, in our example) the adjacent regions of the DNA piece now would match the B genome and facilitate pairing with B recipients, while complicating pairing with A recipients (from which the *sr* marker was originally obtained).

A third, and currently most favored, explanation for the low efficiency of interspecific transformation has been suggested, namely, a host-induced "stamping" of the DNA, which for unknown reasons may subsequently make it more susceptible to degradation, prior to integration, in a foreign environment (cf. Schaeffer, 1964). The "stamp of origin" process might be in the nature of an attachment of some compound that is recognized as "foreign" by cells of other species.* This sort of host-induced specificity of DNA, leading to the phenomenon of *restriction*, was first recognized in studies with bacteriophages (Arber and Dussoix, 1962) and also has been observed more recently in studies on transduction and conjugation between certain bacterial strains (Arber, 1964; Boyer, 1964; Arber and Morse, 1965).

Altered capacities for integration have been observed not only in interspecific transformations, but also in intraspecific transformations. Thus, studies with pneumococci revealed that a certain strain permitted the ready integration of the marker under scrutiny (*sr*), while another strain failed to do so. The factor responsible for such differences was found to be closely linked to the *sr* marker studied (Green, 1959). Ravin (1961) has suggested that factors of this sort may represent an initial step in the evolution of isolating mechanisms that give rise to genetic discontinuity among formerly closely related, and thus "interbreeding," groups of organisms.

Transformation as a Tool for Physico-chemical Studies on DNA

Because in transformation chemically purified DNA has proved to be the agent responsible for genetic transfers, biochemists and biophysicists adopted this phenomenon as a favorite tool for the analysis of the physico-chemical nature of genetically active DNA. Their interest has been centered principally on relationships between molecular size, structural configuration and biological activity, as well as on an analysis of the effects of mutagenic agents on activity and structure. We already have referred to a number of these studies (pp. 96, 98 and 105). In listing some others here we must first voice this word of caution: Many types of treatment of transforming DNA have led to a loss of biological activity of the DNA which was then regarded as reflecting a causal relationship between *genetic activity* and the chemical or physical alteration suffered by the treated DNA. In some instances, however, it has turned out that the changes merely interfered with the uptake of the treated DNA by recipient cells, rather than altering the ability of such DNA to be transcribed. The most prominent example of this sort is the relationship between molecular size and transforming activity of DNA, to which we have already referred (p. 256). Therefore, unless accompanied by studies that measure DNA uptake, deductions based on studies with treated DNA must be made with caution as far as conclusions regarding altered genetic activity (transcription, replication) are concerned.

The transforming activity of DNA is abolished or reduced by exposure to DNAase; x-radiation; UV-radiation; bombardment by electrons, protons, or deuterons; nitrogen mustard; decay of incorporated P^{32}; molecular shearing; and deamination by formaldehyde or nitrous acid (reviewed by Ravin, 1961). Deamination not only inactivates, but is also capable of inducing mutations of transforming pneumococcal DNA *in vitro*,

*A host-specific methylation of DNA is now suspected of playing a role.

the susceptibility of different genetic markers being distinctly different as far as such mutagenic effects of nitrous acid are concerned (Litman, 1961; Stuy, 1962). Other well-known mutagens, such as UV, formaldehyde and nitrogen mustard, have not yet been reported to produce mutations when employed for treatment of transforming DNA *in vitro*.

Heating above approximately 90° C has been shown to reduce the transforming activity of treated DNA, but never completely. As discussed in Chapter 4, such effects are due to a melting of DNA into single strands (denaturation) by heat, and it is now known that single-stranded DNA penetrates poorly into competent cells (Lerman and Tolmach, 1959). Inactivation of transforming activity can also occur following heat treatment at temperatures below the melting point (Roger and Hotchkiss, 1961). In this case the treated DNA can penetrate into recipient cells but it lacks transforming activity, presumably as the result of depurination (p. 98). Markers of different sizes seem to have different susceptibilities to this depurination effect.

You will recall that complementary strands of heat-denatured DNA can be rejoined (renatured) under appropriate conditions of cooling (p. 63). Taking advantage of such renaturation, Herriott (1961) demonstrated that it is possible to create *hybrid transforming DNA in vitro*. He used two mutations known to be linked when present together in *H. influenzae*, namely, resistance to cathomycin (*cr*) and resistance to streptomycin (*sr*).* He then mixed *sr* DNA with *cr* DNA *in vitro*, heated the mixture, and cooled it slowly (which promoted renaturation). Following this treatment, transforming DNA capable of transferring both *cr* and *sr* to competent recipient cells was obtained. In contrast, unheated mixtures of these two preparations of DNA very rarely yielded double transformants (*cr sr*) (they occurred with a frequency that was the square root of the frequencies for single transformations).

UV-damaged transforming DNA can be reactivated *in vitro* by visible light (photoreactivated), a process which presumably involves the enzymatic splitting of thymine dimers formed as a result of irradiation (see p. 102). In order for such photoreactivation to occur in DNA of *Hemophilus*, which has been studied most extensively (Rupert, 1960), the UV-treated DNA must be exposed to a cell-free extract from *E. coli* and to light. It appears that photoreactivation requires an enzyme that is lacking in *Hemophilus*, but which can be supplied by other microorganisms such as *E. coli*.

A method permitting the production of specific antisera to DNA and synthetic polydeoxyribonucleotides was developed recently; it employs complexes of the nucleic acids with methylated bovine serum albumin for immunization (Plescia *et al.*, 1964). Antisera against calf-thymus DNA prepared by this procedure cross-react with single-stranded DNA from many different sources (as revealed by complement fixation tests) and inactivate transforming DNA of *B. subtilis* and pneumococci; preliminary studies have indicated that antisera against synthetic poly-dAT not only inactivate but produce a differential inactivation of different markers (Braun *et al.*, 1965). This finding, if confirmed, may lead to future assays on differences in nucleotide content of individual cistrons.

*Remember, such linked markers are carried on the same molecule of transforming DNA when obtained from an *sr cr* donor.

Finally, attempts have been made to fractionate preparations of transforming DNA in such a manner that specific markers would be recovered from different fractions. From what we know about linkage and minimum requirements of molecular size for DNA uptake, it could be predicted that fractionation of linked genetic markers (and, ultimately, the recovery of transforming DNA carrying only the information of one cistron) would be very difficult, if not impossible. In contrast, it is possible to assume that during DNA extraction the breakage of the chromosome into pieces of transforming DNA may be non-random and that, therefore, marker *a* may tend to be associated with a piece of DNA with a slightly different density and size than markers *b* or *c*. The validity of this is supported by the observations we have already cited on page 252, namely, the ability of CsCl density gradient centrifugation to separate pneumococcal DNA fractions that differ slightly, but significantly, in their ability to cause transformation for a given marker (Rolfe and Ephrussi-Taylor, 1961; Guild, 1963). We have also mentioned previously that transforming DNA of penumococci labeled with a series of unlinked markers, when co-precipitated by antisera against DNA-associated antigens, will yield in the early precipitates more transforming activity for certain markers, while later precipitates will yield more activity for other markers (Braun *et al.*, 1961). Despite such partial fractionation of genetically active DNA, the day when DNA fragments equivalent to one cistron may be isolated still seems quite far off. Transformation would seem to be the proper tool for eventually accomplishing such a feat. Even if one were successful in isolating individual cistrons, however, the difficulties of getting the resulting small pieces of DNA into competent cells, having them pair there with homologous regions of the recipient's DNA, and assuring their subsequent integration into the recipient's genome may be too great to permit this ultimate achievement of experimental genetic manipulation.

[14]

GENETIC TRANSFERS III: TRANSDUCTION

In transduction, information in the form of DNA is transferred via phage from one bacterial cell to a related, phage-susceptible cell (for general reviews, see Hartman, 1947; Hartman and Goodgal, 1959; Clowes, 1960; Jacob and Wollman, 1961; and Campbell, 1964). The transducing phage acts as a kind of trolley car, carrying inside its protein coat a fraction of DNA from its previous bacterial host,* and injects such DNA, in the same manner as phage DNA, into its next susceptible bacterial host cell. Transducing phages represent a very small fraction ($1/10^5$ to $1/10^8$) of the phage population released either (1) through lysis of sensitive bacterial host cells by virulent phages, or (2) through the induction of prophage-carrying, i.e., lysogenic bacteria. In respect to (2), it will be recalled that so-called temperate phages can lysogenize phage-susceptible bacteria, and that in lysogeny the phage DNA, in the form of so-called "prophage," enters into direct association with the bacterial DNA, presumably in the manner shown in Figure 109.† The major features of all transduction processes is

*The DNA content of a phage is less than $1/100$ of the DNA of a bacterial cell.

†*A note on lysogeny:* Following the infection of a susceptible bacterial cell, the genome of a virulent (or intemperate) phage initiates a series of events that are characterized by the sequential activation of a series of enzymatic reactions, which lead to "vegetative multiplication" of the phage genome, the production of phage-coat proteins, the maturation of phage particles and the setting free of such mature phage particles as a result of the formation and action of bacteriolytic enzymes (Luria, 1960). In vegetative multiplication the phage DNA replicates at a rate completely independent of the rate of replication of the host genome; in fact, the replication of the host genome is suppressed as the result of new enzyme activities which appear within minutes after infection.

In the case of temperate phages the phage genome persists in the infected (lysogenized) bacterium, in association with the bacterial chromosome, as a prophage (Bertani, 1958). In this state the phage genome replicates in tune with the bacterial genome. At the same time it produces specific immunity- or repressor-substances that prevent the vegetative multiplication and the maturation of the phage, as well as the superinfection of lysogenic cells by similar phages. Vegetative multiplication and subsequent phage maturation can occur spontaneously in a very small proportion (about $1/10^6$) of lysogenic cells, or it can be induced in a large proportion of lysogenic cells by such agents as UV or nitrogen mustard (Lwoff, 1953). The initial step in such inductions of vegetative multiplication from the prophage state is probably the destruction of the repressor substance. Lysogenization is found only when the phage and the host bacterium have DNA's of similar GC content (Lanni, 1960; Luria, 1963). It is likely that a prophage and the region of the bacterial chromosome with which it associates itself are complementary, but not homologous, structures (Jacob and Wollman, 1961). It may be that a small portion of the prophage DNA matches, either by nucleotide sequences or by the presence of unusual bases, certain regions of the bacterial chromosome.

the ability of a few of the subsequently maturing phages (which may mature either spontaneously or as a result of induction) to pick up a limited portion of the host genome (one determinant or a set of linked determinants) and to transfer it into a related phage-susceptible cell.

Two principal types of transduction, namely, (1) general, nonspecific transduction, and (2) restricted, specialized (or special) transduction, can be distinguished. The first is mediated by phage types that develop from prophages (DNA) which can associate themselves with *any* site on the bacterial genome; the second is mediated by phages with a "homing instinct," whose DNA associates itself only with *one* site on the bacterial genome.

In so-called *general or nonspecific transduction* the details of the occasional "picking up" of bacterial DNA in the process of phage maturation are not entirely clear. It is possible that in the mature transducing phages of this type, the bacterial DNA piece and the phage DNA may exist as unconnected, separate entities, or they may be temporarily associated as they are in specialized transduction (see below). In any event, the piece of bacterial DNA, after having been injected by the phage into the recipient bacterium, can pair with a homologous region of the new host bacterium's DNA. Either one of two events can occur next: (1) the exogenous DNA participates in recombinational events with the endogenous DNA, leading to an integration into the host genome of part of the exogenous DNA (*complete transduction*), or (2) the exogenous bacterial DNA persists without integration and replication in the recipient cell and in only one cell of its progeny (*abortive transduction*). When integration of part of the bacterial DNA occurs in complete transduction, the final steps of this process ["transduction by integration," (Luria *et al.*, 1960)] probably are very similar to those we discussed in the last chapter for the late stages of transformation.

In *restricted or specialized* transduction only the bacterial determinants located directly adjacent to the specific site of association of the prophage DNA and the bacterial DNA in the donor cell can be transduced. We know a fair amount about the manner in which bacterial DNA can become associated with phage DNA in this case. As indicated in Figure 109, while detaching itself from its former site of residence in the bacterial chromosome, the phage DNA may attach to itself a bit of bacterial DNA. As a consequence of this association, the maturing phage will be defective in phage DNA, but will now be able to carry a bacterial determinant to the usual specific site of the phage DNA's association with the bacterial chromosome in the next host cell. In this restricted transduction no replacement of a bit of host DNA by a bit of corresponding phage-carried bacterial DNA takes place; rather, at the site of association (Fig. 110) there now exists an extra bit of informative bacterial DNA ("transduction by lysogenization"). It has become customary to refer to the extra piece of bacterial information introduced into a recipient cell by genetic transfer as the *exogenote*, in contrast to the recipient cell's own complement of information which is termed the *endogenote*. A cell containing its own set of informative DNA plus an extra piece of slightly different exogenous DNA, as it may occur, for example, in restricted transduction, is called a *heterogenote* (i.e., it is heterozygous for the transduced fragment).

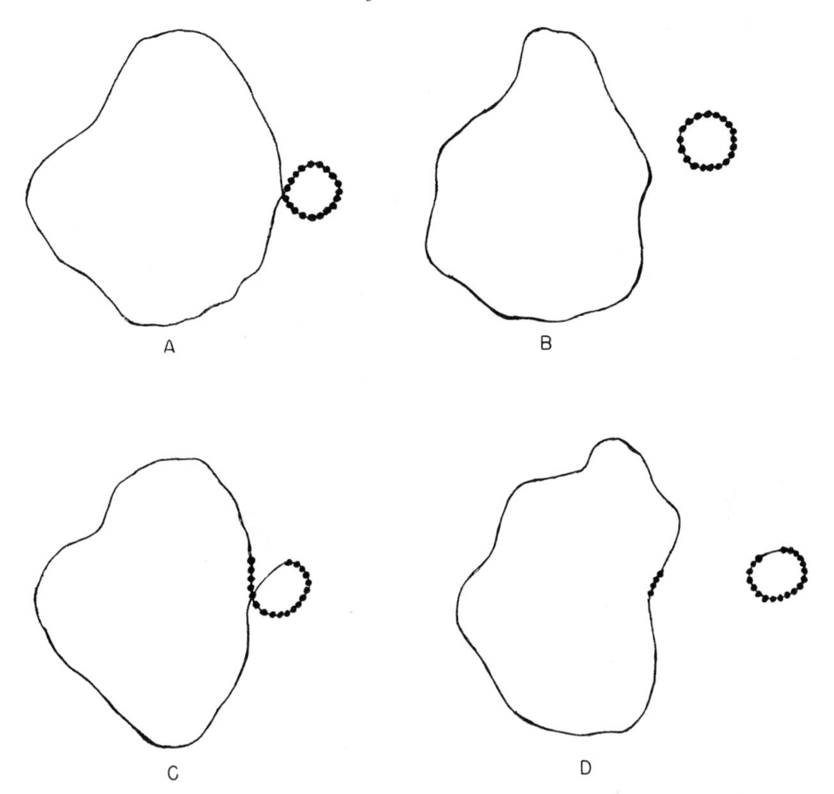

FIGURE 109. A and B: normal separation of prophage DNA from its association with the chromosomal replicon; C and D: aberrant separation resulting in the incorporation of a piece of chromosomal DNA into the phage DNA, and vice versa.

The noticeable end result of transductions can be an alteration in the bacterial phenotype if the transduced piece of bacterial DNA introduces new information. We have previously discussed another phage-elicited phenomenon that can result in an alteration of the bacterial phenotype, namely, so-called viral conversion (p. 161). It is quite important to differentiate clearly between transduction and viral conversion. In viral conversion all phage-infected bacteria alter their phenotype by virtue of the presence of new information brought into the bacterial cell by the phage, either in the form of phage (viral) DNA or a bit of bacterial DNA permanently associated with the phage DNA. In transduction, be it by lysogenization, by integration, or abortive, only a very small proportion of the phage-infected cells will show changes. These changes are due to the introduction of bacterial DNA which had been present in only a very few particles of the entire infecting phage population.

In viral conversion, the change in the bacterial phenotype will persist only as long as the prophage or phage is present in the cell; in transduction by integration, the new information can persist even when the descendants

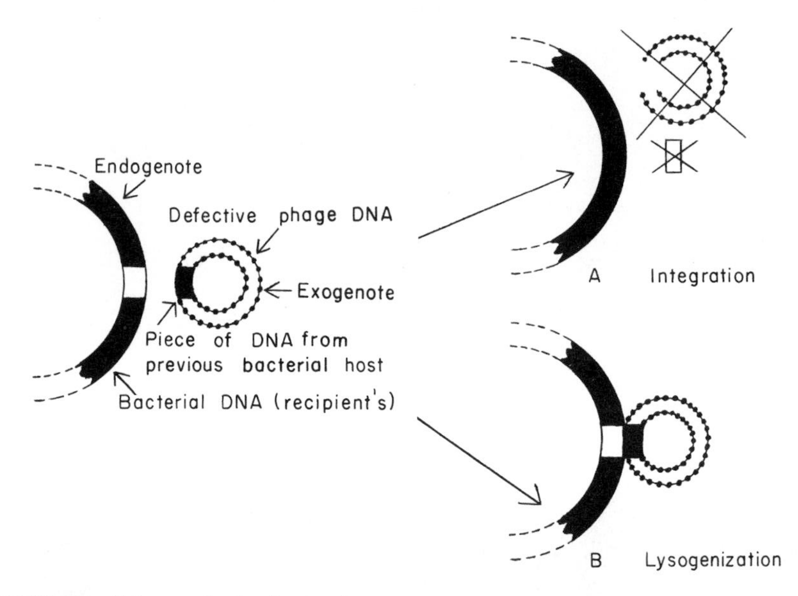

FIGURE 110. Scheme of transduction by integration or lysogenization. In A, the exchanged piece of the recipient's DNA does not replicate and is lost; in B, no exchange takes place.

of the transduced bacterium are freed of prophage. However, it should be noted that viral conversion and transduction may occasionally occur simultaneously; the likelihood of such an event depends on the degree of defectiveness of the phage DNA in the transducing phage as the result of the presence of bacterial DNA (Luria *et al.*, 1960).

The Discovery of Transduction

The discovery of generalized transduction preceded the recognition of restricted transduction and dates back to the early 1950's when, subsequent to the discovery of recombination in *E. coli* (see Chapter 15), Zinder, then a student in Lederberg's laboratory, tried to determine whether recombinations might also occur among strains of *Salmonella typhimurium*. In these efforts he tested 20 different auxotrophic mutant strains [obtained by the penicillin screening procedure (p. 129) from different *S. typhimurium* strains] for their ability to yield prototrophs following mixed cultivation. In 9 combinations of the 79 tested, prototrophs were obtained in large numbers and at frequencies significantly higher than those observed when the parent strains were tested separately (Zinder and Lederberg, 1952). When such strains were maintained physically separated from each other in a U-tube with an ultrafine fritted-glass filter at the base, prototrophs could still be recovered in large numbers from one arm of the U-tube culture. This immediately indicated that the phenomenon under observation was fundamentally different from the earlier discovered phenomenon of recombination in *E. coli* which was known to be dependent on direct cellular contact between the parental cells.

Figure 111 illustrates a typical **U**-tube experiment with *S. typhimurium* in which a histidine-requiring strain (2A) and a tryptophan-requiring strain (22A) were employed. When 10^8 cells of either strain were inoculated alone into such a **U**-tube, no prototrophs were recovered, but when 10^8 cells of strain 22A were inoculated on one side and 10^8 cells of 2A were inoculated on the other side, about ten prototrophs per million cells were recovered from the side inoculated with 22A cells. No prototrophs were recovered from the side inoculated with 2A cells.

It was found that strain 22A carried a phage (P22 or PLT22) capable of lysing strain 2A cells and that this phage, after traversing the fritted-glass filter and lysing the 2A cells, released a filtrable agent (FA) which, in turn, passed the glass filter. Under the influence of this FA, certain cells of 22A then acquired specific heritable properties typical of the FA-donor strain. In the case illustrated, this property was the ability to grow without tryptophan, but it was soon shown that many other traits, including fermentation characteristics, antibiotic resistance and antigenic properties, could be similarly transduced. It was then ascertained that the activity of the filtrable agent was not destroyed by deoxyribonuclease, and that its properties (e.g., its size as determined by filtration and sedimentation, the kinetics of its inactivation by antiserum, and its sensitivity to heat) were identical with those of phage PLT22 (Zinder, 1955). Furthermore, a direct correlation was established between the multiplicity of infecting (lysogenizing) phage PLT22 and the frequency of transduction.

It was also shown by infecting phage-sensitive cells simultaneously with a very low multiplicity (<1) of virulent phage and a high multiplicity of non-transducing, lysogenizing phage (which permits the survival of over 90 per cent of the infected bacteria) that even virulent phage could transduce. This observation was confirmed later by transductions that were obtained with UV-irradiated virulent phages (Goldschmidt and

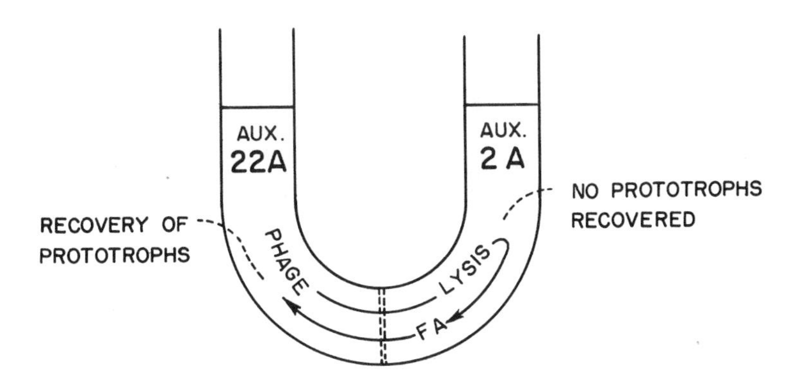

FIGURE 111. Diagram of a transduction experiment with *Salmonella typhimurium* employing a **U**-tube with a fritted glass filter plate in the cross-limb.

Landman, 1962). The actual frequency of transductions per phage particle (usually ranging from 1×10^{-8} to 1×10^{-5}) was shown to depend on the marker, on the physiologic state of the donor and recipient cells, and on the number of infecting phage particles per cell. Even in the early studies it was noted that many of the transduced cells and their progeny were not lysogenic, which furnished the first clue to a defectiveness of the phage DNA in the bacterial DNA-carrying, transducing phage.

Early studies also demonstrated that, in what is now known as complete and generalized transduction, the fragment of bacterial information introduced via phage can replace, rather than add to, the preexisting information in the transductants (Lederberg and Edwards, 1953). In other words, recombination events were shown to occur that resulted in the exchange of informative DNA between a portion (or all) of the exogenote and the homologous region of the endogenote. This was shown, for example,

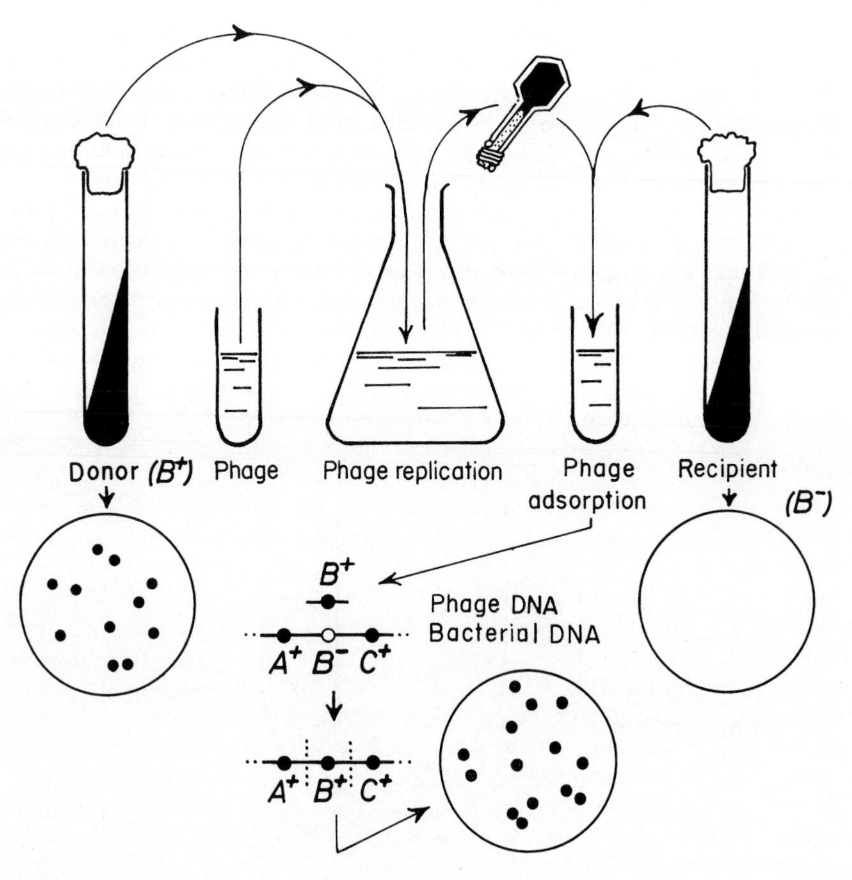

FIGURE 112. Diagram of a transduction experiment employing a prototrophic donor and an auxotrophic recipient. (From Kaudewitz, 1960.)

by the fact that in transductions of flagellar antigens the new H antigen replaced the prior H antigen in the progeny of the transduced cell, and the previous homologue (i.e., the determinant for the prior H antigen) never reappeared in the transduced clone.

Like transformation, transduction proved to involve the transfer of only small fragments of the donor cell's total genome. Thus, only determinants of single characteristics or closely linked determinants of several characteristics were found to be involved in single transductional events. Figure 112 shows the general technique of transduction tests.

General Transduction

The *Salmonella* phage P22 just discussed can transduce any one of a very large number (possibly all) of the single or linked determinants of nutritional (Demerec and Hartman, 1959), serological (Kauffmann, 1953), fermentative (Englesberg and Baron, 1959), antibiotic resistance (Watanabe and Watanabe, 1959), virulence (Furness and Rowley, 1956), and flagellar (Stocker *et al.*, 1953) characteristics. The detection of a few nontransducible markers may be attributed to the control of these markers by more than one determinant (polygenic systems) or by a chromosomal aberration such as an inversion (Fig. 47) (cf. Hartman and Goodgal, 1959). In addition to P22, other *Salmonella* phages, such as the Vi phage (Baron *et al.*, 1953) and some undefined, naturally occurring phages (Bailey, 1956), have been shown to transduce determinants among salmonellae that are susceptible to infection by these phages. Phage ϵ-15, famous for its ability to induce the formation of antigen 15 in lysogenic *Salmonella* strains (p. 169), also can participate in general transduction (Iseki and Sakai, 1954). Several other converting phages also can participate in general transduction (cf. Hartman and Goodgal, 1959), which means that besides contributing new information by their presence in the bacterial cell, these phages occasionally may also carry additional DNA from their prior bacterial host and permit such DNA to recombine with the recipient's DNA.

Phage P1 (Lennox, 1955) and a closely related phage (Jacob, 1955) can participate in general transduction among *E. coli* strains; P1 also has been used extensively to transduce determinants, such as the ability to utilize lactose (lac^+), between strains of *E. coli* and *Shigella dysenteriae* (Franklin and Luria, 1961). General transduction by specific phages also has been reported for staphylococci (Morse, 1959; Morse and LaBelle, 1962; Korman and Berman, 1962), for *Vibrio* (Bhaskaran, 1958), for *Pseudomonas aeruginosa* (Loutit, 1958; Holloway and Monk, 1959), for *Proteus mirabilis* (Coetzee and Sacks, 1960), for *Bacillus licheniformis* (Taylor and Thorne, 1963) and for *Mycobacterium phlei* (Hubacek, 1960).

Using phage P1 and transduction of lac^+ and lac^- recipient bacteria, Luria and his associates (Luria *et al.*, 1955; Franklin and Luria, 1961) confirmed that in general transduction the *transducing phage tends to be defective, as far as phage determinants are concerned.* The defective phage particles (P1 *dl* = "defective lactose"), resulting after induction of the prophage, can differ in the extent to which the P1 phage genome has become defective by virtue of the presence of various amounts of bacterial lac^+-determining DNA. This defectiveness can be detected by testing for specific properties of the phage particles, which in their non-defective forms carried markers such as host range, plaque morphology and the ability to overcome the immunity of lysogenic bacteria.

These studies also demonstrated that intraspecific transductions (*E. coli* strains being both donors and recipients) yielded stable lac^+ transductants that represented transductions by integration. In contrast, interspecific transductions (from *E. coli* lac^+ donors to *Shigella* lac^- recipients) yielded transductants that were very unstable and segregated in their progeny into lac^+ and lac^- cells; this must be regarded as transduction by lysogenization in which the lac^+ determinants remain associated with the P1 *dl* exogenote and do not integrate (as in the case of intraspecific transductions) into the endogenote. The general conclusion from such tests was that a high degree of genetic homology between the donor and the recipient favors integration, whereas a low degree of genetic homology interferes with integration and gives rise to transductants that carry the transducing element as a prophage (see Fig. 110).

The presence of bacterial DNA in transducing phages has also been demonstrated more directly in tests involving a transducing phage (SP10) of *B. subtilis* (Okubo *et al.*, 1963). DNA from these transducing phages, which had been obtained from the lysis of ind^+ (indole-independent) *B. subtilis* was found to be effective in transforming competent ind^- (indole-requiring) cells of *B. subtilis*. Further, it was determined that the DNA of this phage differs from its host's bacterial DNA by virtue of some as yet unidentified abnormal components and, as a result, SP10 DNA has a lower thermal denaturation temperature and a higher density in a Cs_2SO_4 gradient than the DNA of *B. subtilis*. These properties then permitted the demonstration that (a) the transforming activity for ind^- *B. subtilis* recipients can be separated from the bulk of SP10 DNA by centrifugation in a Cs_2SO_4 gradient where it bands with bacterial rather than phage DNA, and that (b) the transforming activity present in SP10 DNA preparations denatures at a temperature characteristic of *B. subtilis* DNA rather than phage DNA.

Restricted Transduction

The type of transduction which is restricted to the transfer of certain specific determinants of the donor, and which, as we discussed before, occurs in the case of bacteriophages that associate themselves with only one specific site on the bacterial chromosome, was first discovered in studies with the phage lambda (λ) of the lysogenic K-12 strain of *E. coli* (Morse *et al.*, 1956). Prophage λ is closely linked to a series of DNA sites that determine the formation and activity of the enzymes galactokinase and galactose transferase, which control the fermentation of galactose.

Morse and the Lederbergs found that following induction of lysogenic K-12 Gal^+ $(\lambda)^+$ bacteria by UV, about 1 in 10^6 of the released bacteriophages could transfer the Gal^+ property to Gal^--recipient bacteria (Fig. 113). However, these transductants proved to be unstable, segregating stable, non-lysogenic Gal^- progeny (Fig. 114). This indicated that they were heterogenotes (p. 266) containing both Gal^- and Gal^+ determinants (Fig. 110B) and not recombinants. Induction of these heterogenotes yielded

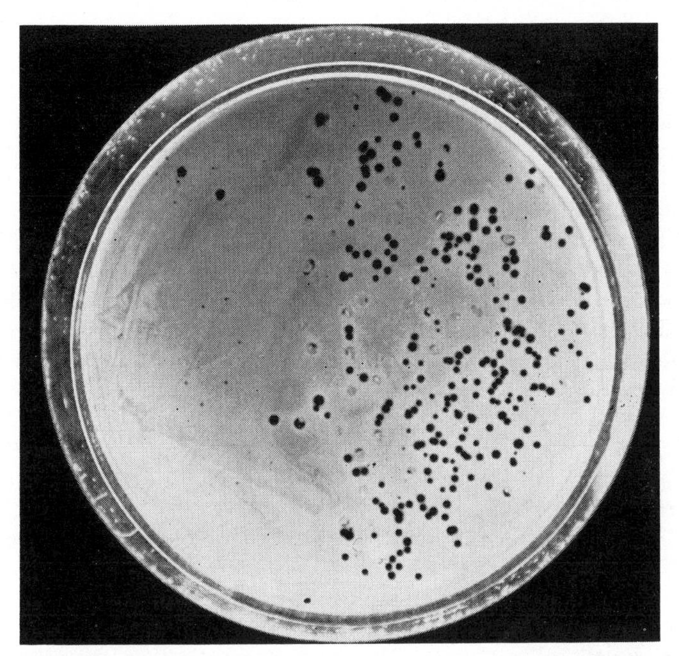

FIGURE 113. *Gal*$^+$ papillae growing on a background of *Gal*$^-$ cells of *E. coli*, K-12 cells that had been exposed to a lysate, containing lambda phage, from a *Gal*$^+$ culture (right side of plate; left side represents the lysate-free control). Some of the papillae have been picked with a needle. The medium is EMB galactose agar. (From Morse *et al.*, 1956.)

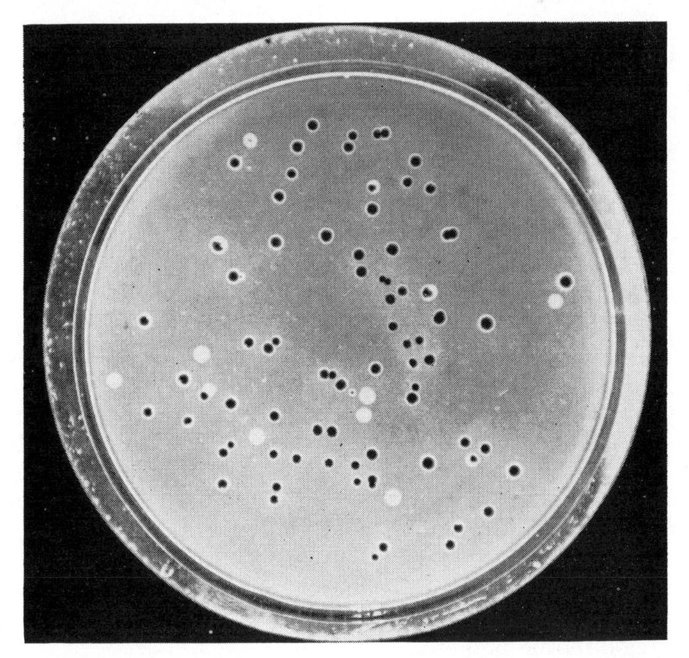

FIGURE 114. EMB galactose agar plate inoculated with cells from a culture of a heterogenote. Note the presence of *Gal*$^+$, *Gal*$^-$ and sectored colonies. (From Morse *et al.*, 1956.)

a very high proportion of λ phages capable of transducing the Gal^+ determinant, which showed that a true association had been established between λ and the Gal^+-determining DNA, an association that was maintained during the vegetative multiplication that followed induction of the transduced Gal^+/Gal^- heterogenote. The Gal^+-carrying, transducing λ particles are defective (λ *dg*); they can cause immunity of the recipient bacteria to superinfection with normal λ, but they cannot liberate infectious λ phage, either after induction or spontaneously (Campbell, 1957). However, transducing phage can be released when the Gal^+/Gal^- heterogenotes are induced and then infected with normal λ phage. These and other studies have indicated that in λ *dg*, part of the viral information has been replaced by bacterial information. It has been calculated that the displaced segment of λ *dg* can be as large as one-fourth of the linkage group of normal λ (Arbor, 1960; Jacob and Wollman, 1961). The replacement of phage DNA by bacterial DNA in transducing λ *dg* is sufficient to permit a separation of the two DNA's by centrifugation in a density gradient (Weigle *et al.*, 1959).

The bacterial determinants controlling galactose utilization (Gal^+), which are located near the point of λ's association with the host chromosome, are genetically distinguishable. The Gal^- property can be affected by any one of a series of changes at different, closely linked sites in the DNA region controlling Gal^+. This was borne out in the transduction studies with λ. Thus λ grown on Gal_1^- mutants produced galactose-positive cells following the transduction of Gal_2^- cells. This was interpreted as representing a transduction of galactose-negative Gal_1^+ Gal_2^- cells by phage released from galactose-negative Gal_1^- Gal_2^+ cells, yielding galactose-positive Gal_1^+ Gal_2^+ heterogenotes (more correctly written: Gal_1^+ Gal_2^-/Gal_1^- Gal_2^+). As already noted, such heterogenotes tend to segregate (about $1/10^3$), giving rise to galactose-negative Gal_1^+ Gal_2^- cells. But occasionally a new type, Gal_1^- Gal_2^-, can be found among such segregants, indicating that exchanges between the exogenote and the endogenote, though rare, can take place (Morse *et al.*, 1956).

Other phages capable of transducing the bacterial *Gal* region have been observed (Jacob and Wollman, 1961). Also phage Ø 80 of *E. coli*, which in its prophage state has a location close to bacterial genes governing tryptophan synthesis, can transduce these genes (Matsushiro, 1961).

Abortive Transduction

In abortive transduction the bacterial DNA fragment carried by the phage is injected into the recipient bacterium and functions there, but does not replicate and is not integrated into the bacterial genome. The ratio of abortive to complete transduction is about 10 to 1. Abortive transduction was first noted in studies of the transduction of motility in *Salmonella typhimurium* (Stocker *et al.*, 1953; Stocker, 1956; Lederberg, 1956) in which, following the transduction of non-motile strains by PLT22 phage-lysates from motile strains, some of the transduced motile bacteria gave rise to non-motile progeny.

On semisolid media on which non-transduced, non-motile cells produced surface growth confined to one area, and where stable motile trans-

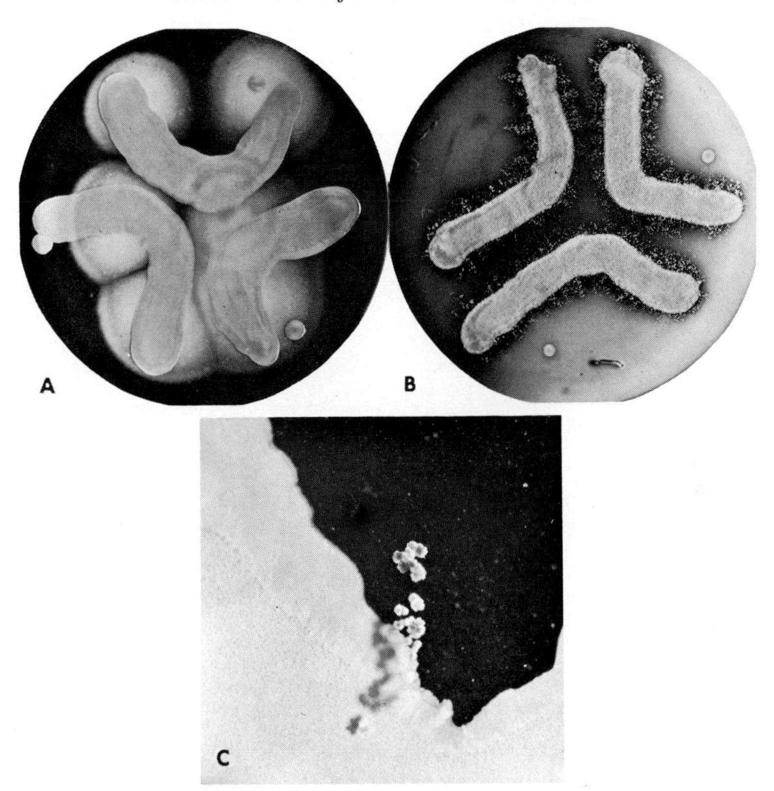

FIGURE 115. Transduction of motility in *Salmonella,* tested by the appearance of swarms (complete transduction) or trails (abortive transduction) on semisolid agar inoculated with cells of a non-motile mutant strain exposed to a phage lysate from a motile strain. A, Discrete swarms consisting of growth of stably transduced motile organisms which have moved away from the dense growth area of non-motile organisms. B, Trails formed by abortively transduced motile organisms. C, Enlargement (× 5) of a single trail. (From Stocker *et al.*, 1953.)

ductants produced spreading swarms, the abortively transduced cells produced trails of microcolonies in the depth of the medium (Fig. 115). Micromanipulation indicated that these trails were due to the non-replication of the motility-controlling, abortively transduced DNA, which, although initiating motility in the cell that carried this DNA, transferred this information to only one of its two daughter cells.* Consequently, at any given time only one cell of the entire clone carries this DNA fragment.

*Note that in transduction, in contrast to transformation (p. 259), the transduced fragment, even though not integrated in the recipient's genome, can manifest its information phenotypically.

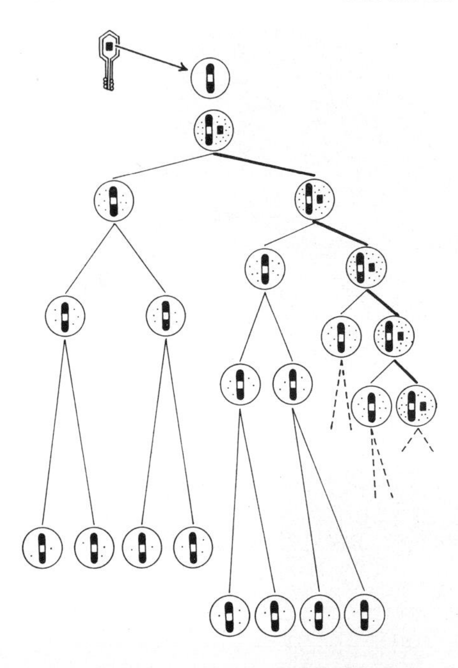

FIGURE 116. Diagram of a clone following abortive transduction. Heavy lines show linear inheritance. The number of dots indicates the relative amount of an enzyme that is lacking in the auxotrophic recipient but for which determinants are present in the DNA piece contributed by the donor. The distance of the cell generations on the ordinate reflects the generation time on minimal medium. (After Kaudewitz, 1960.)

This results in a phenomenon that has been termed *linear inheritance* in which, as indicated by the heavy line on the right hand side of Figure 116, only a very small proportion of the descendants of an abortively transduced cell (a proportion that gets smaller as the size of the clones increases) will display the transduced trait.*

A similar phenomenon occurs in the abortive transduction of auxotrophs (Ozeki, 1956; Demerec and Ozeki, 1959; Hartman *et al.*, 1960). When an auxotroph such as *his*$^-$ (histidine-requiring), for example, is exposed to a transducing phage population harvested from wild-type *his*$^+$ bacteria and then spread on a minimal agar medium (on which *his*$^-$ cannot grow), a number of minute colonies, in addition to a few very large colonies (the progeny of completely transduced bacteria), are observed (Fig. 117). These minute colonies proved to contain (a) one cell that carried the *his*$^+$ gene introduced by the phage, (b) *his*$^-$ cells that could grow temporarily, presumably by virtue of a carry-over of histidine found in the *his*$^+$-containing cell and (c) the final progeny of such cells, which could no longer divide on a histidine-free medium (see Fig. 116). Since minute colonies appear only when the donor possesses the wild-type allele of the mutant gene present in the recipient and do not appear when the identical mutant gene is present in the donor, it was soon recognized that abortive transduction could provide an excellent tool for the analysis of the genic identity or non-identity of independently isolated mutants with similar phenotypes (Demerec and Ozeki, 1959). The manner in which this was

*Experimental data indicate that the story actually is a bit more complicated, since the very presence of the motility gene can initiate the formation of a limited number of motility-conferring particles which, in turn, can be distributed to a limited number of descendants.

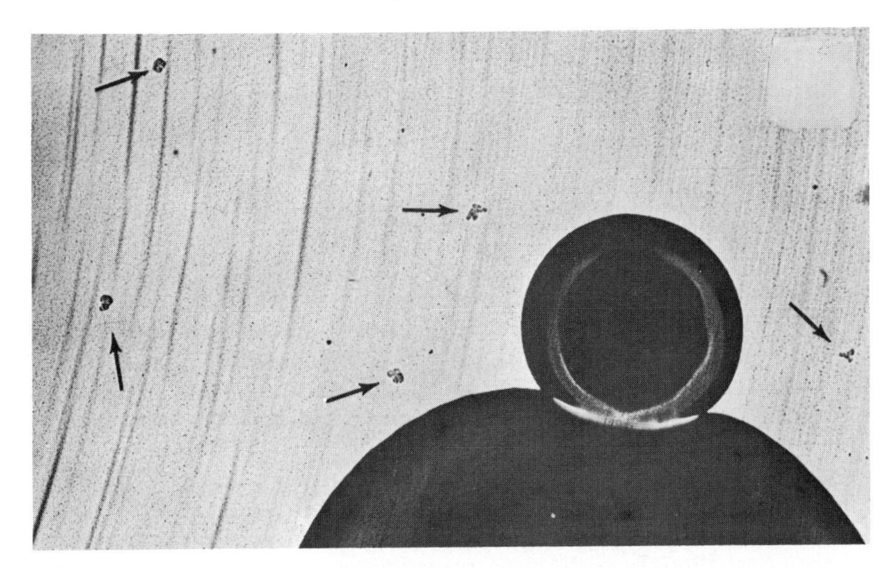

FIGURE 117. Portion of a Petri dish containing minimal medium showing growth following infection of *S. typhimurium* mutant *his*⁻-11 with phage grown on mutant *his*⁻-56. Incubation period was 72 hours at 37° C. The part of the large colony shown on the left developed from a wild-type recombinant; a *his*⁻-56 type small colony is seen adjacent to it. Arrows indicate the location of minute colonies resulting from abortive transductions. (Magnification: × 25.) (From Hartman *et al.*, 1960.)

carried out and how this aided in the recognition of the fine structure of the "gene" will be detailed in the section that follows.

GENETIC FINE STRUCTURE AS REVEALED BY TRANSDUCTION

Transduction has aided substantially in the analysis of the complex nature of the DNA regions that customarily had been referred to as a "gene," i.e., individual regions that control one trait (or better—the formation of one enzyme). Transduction tests offer two great advantages for such genetic analyses: (1) A recombinational event involving two non-identical auxotrophs, for example, can be detected even when it occurs very rarely (e.g., $1/10^{11}$), because the recombinant prototroph resulting from complete transduction is the only one that can grow into a large colony on minimal medium (and there is no problem in plating 1×10^{11} cells on a single plate), (2) In abortive transduction a situation comparable to that in heterozygotes of higher organisms is created; i.e., unlike changes in identical genes may coexist. By scoring for the absence or presence of minute colonies in tests with pairs of similar but independently isolated auxotrophs, one can, therefore, determine whether or not, in heterogenotes resulting from transduction, two genes can function together (complement each other) to yield a final product that cannot be produced by either genetic region alone.

SOME "WORD GAMES"

To understand such analyses better, let us assume that the message in the DNA region concerned with the production of one specific end product, e.g., histidine, reads as follows:

"This region oversees formation of histidine."

Each word [= a *locus* (Demerec and Ozeki, 1959)] in this message is supposed to represent the information required for the formation of one enzyme in the biosynthetic pathway leading to histidine, and each letter in each word represents the smallest unit subject to mutation—in all likelihood a single base (a *site*). In accepting this simile, our curiosity must be aroused immediately by the implication that all the information for the several enzymatically controlled, biosynthetic steps in histidine synthesis (see Fig. 121) are located in one particular chromosomal region, rather than being scattered over various areas of the chromosome. Such an adjacency of loci controlling related reactions is indeed a common feature in bacteria and was first brought to light in transduction studies with *Salmonella*. Furthermore, these loci are not only adjacent but tend to be arranged in the same order as the separate biosynthetic steps (...C → D → E → F → G → H).

Next, we should note a change (mutation) in any one of the letters, e.g., farmation (= single site mutation), or in several letters, e.g., faniation (= multisite mutation), could abolish the sense of the affected word (= create a wrong message, which results in the failure of production of a functional enzyme). Such changes would ruin the reading, or the sense message, of the entire sentence. However, the faulty message could be repaired in any one of several ways: (1) The properly spelled word (from a "wild-type" cell) may be brought into the mutant cell and may repair the faulty message by recombination (*in transduction by integration*) in either one of two ways—
(a) by replacing the whole word:

	Exogenote:	*formation*
(1a)	Endogenote:	*...oversees farmation of...*
	Recombinant:	*...oversees formation of...*

or (b) by replacing the faulty letter (or letters):

	Exogenote:	*formation*
(1b)	Endogenote:	*...farmation...*
	Recombinant:	*...formation...*

Example 1a represents *inter*genic recombination; example 1b represents *intra*genic recombination.

(2) The proper letter may be furnished not only by the properly spelled word (from a wild-type donor) but also by a mutant donor that has a different misspelling (= mutation at a different site). An example of this variation on 1b, again involving transduction by integration, would be:

	Exogenote:	*formagion*
(2a)	Endogenote:	*...farmation...*
	Recombinant:	*...formation...*

Note that in this last case any exogenotic misspelled word (= allelic mutant) which has not suffered a change in the same letter as the endogenote (= mutation at the identical site) can repair the word sense (= proper information for enzyme structure) by recombination. However, the situation is quite different when several sequential letters in the word are misspelled, i.e., in the case of multisite mutations. In that case some but not all of the exogenotic words (= DNA introduced by transduction) can furnish the appropriate letters for recombination. For example,

	Exogenote:	*formagion*
(2b)	Endogenote:	*...faniation...*
	Recombinant:	*...formation...*

will repair the message, whereas neither farmation, fokmation, nor forpation could serve as donor-derived messages that could lead to sense repair by recombination.

(3) The proper message may also be produced in *abortive transduction* as long as the properly spelled information is present in the cell, even though it is not integrated into the full (yet defective) sentence of the recipient's DNA. For example, the combined presence in one cell of:

(3)	Exogenote:	*formation*
	Endogenote:	*...oversees farmation of...*

can produce the proper information in this heterogenotic cell. In contrast, in abortive transduction the introduction of a corresponding word misspelled in any one of its letters (= DNA from a mutant with a change in the same gene locus) will not produce a sense message. For example,

(4)	Exogenote:	*formatoon*
	Endogenote:	*...oversees farmation of...*

is still a defective message.

A somewhat different situation from examples 3 and 4 may occur when a compound word (= a nucleotide sequence specifying the information for an enzyme that is subdivisible into two or more major component parts) is involved. Thus, in our example, two distinct misspellings (= mutations) affecting the word *oversees* could complement each other to give a sense message:

(5)
Exogenote: *over/se***ks**
Endogenote: *...o***g***er/sees...*

in which the exogenote contributes the information for *over* and the endogenote contributes the information for *sees.* In this case of *complementation* then, the word *oversees* actually consists of two functional units (cistrons)—one being *over*, the other being *sees.* If we have two different mutations in one functional unit (e.g., in "over"), their presence in the same reading sequence (= in the same nucleotide sequence = *cis position)* will still permit the development of a sense message (functional enzyme) *in the presence of another reading sequence supplying the proper information:*

(6)
Exogenote: *over/sees*
Endogenote: *...o***gb***r/sees...*

However, if the two mutations are in different nucleotide sequences (= *trans position*), e.g.,

(7)
Exogenote: *o***vb***r/sees*
Endogenote: *...o***g***er/sees...*

neither can substitute for the other (in the absence of recombination) and no sense message can be developed. This is further illustrated in Figure 118.

At this point we should be able to state something we have already hinted at previously, namely, that events such as those shown in (5) and (6) are possible only if the functional enzyme consists of two or more polypeptide subunits, each of which is specified by separate polynucleotide regions capable of complementing each other. To put it differently, two different assembly lines, each slightly defective and therefore incapable of furnishing a complete product, still could furnish non-defective parts which, if the defect in each of the two assembly lines is different, may be assembled subsequently into a properly finished product. Recent studies (cf. Catcheside, 1960; Levinthal and Davison, 1961; Schlesinger and Levinthal, 1963; and Garen and Garen, 1963) have furnished experimental support for this concept of complementation by indicating that an assembly of separate polypeptide units, each under the control of one cistron, can indeed result in the formation of a functional enzyme.

Fine Structure Analysis by Complete Transduction

The actual occurrence of the types of recombinational events that we have tried to illustrate above with our "word game" have been amply demonstrated in tests with *Salmonella* auxotrophs using complete transduction as the analytical tool (cf. Demerec and Hartman, 1959; Hartman *et al.*, 1960; Ames and Hartman, 1962; and Clowes, 1960). These tests re-

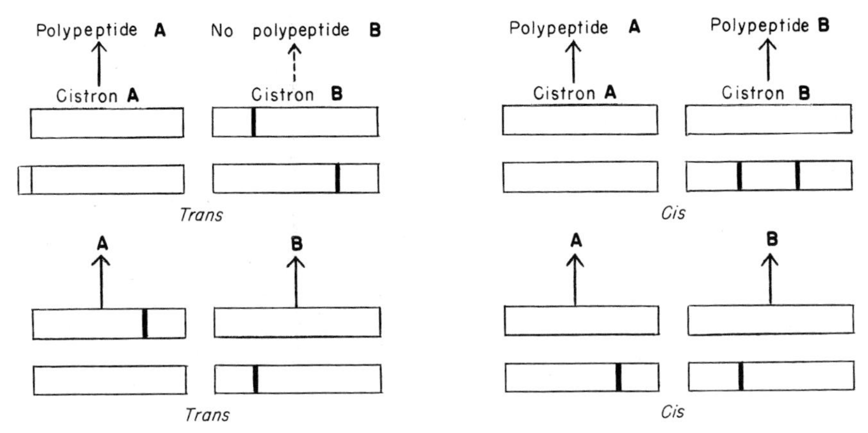

FIGURE 118. Diagram illustrating the manner in which the *cis-trans* test conducted with heterogenotes can indicate whether or not two mutations have affected information within *one* functional unit (cistron) or within two adjoining separate functional units. Solid arrows indicate availability of proper information; broken arrow indicates lack of proper information.

vealed the existence of a complex genetic fine structure quite some time prior to the experimental demonstration and intellectual understanding of the coding functions of polynucleotides (see p. 337). The general conclusions derived from the *Salmonella* studies paralleled those obtained in comparable studies with bacteriophages (Benzer, 1957), with *E. coli* (cf. Levinthal, 1959; Yanofsky, 1963) and with the fungus *Neurospora crassa* (cf. Bonner and DeMoss, 1960; Bonner, 1961; and Fincham, 1962).

The basic technique for all these studies, which revealed that a given chromosomal region controlling one enzyme can be subdivided into a considerable number of mutable and recombinable subunits, is quite simple. It consists of tests for the occurrence or non-occurrence of recombinational events among a series of independently derived mutants affecting the same phenotype. Let us choose as an example mutants of the *his D* locus, which have a requirement for histidine owing to the lack of formation of the enzyme histidinal dehydrogenase. If these auxotrophic mutants, unable to grow without histidine, are the result of a change at the same site of the *his D* locus (due to a change affecting the same nucleotide pair) no dehydrogenase-forming, wild-type recombinants capable of growing without histidine should be obtainable. Thus, writing the functional locus as *abcdefgh* and the mutated site as *x*:

donor: *abcdxfgh*
→ no functional recombinants can be produced.
recipient: *abcdxfgh*

On the other hand, functional recombinants can be obtained if the mutation has affected a different site (different nucleotide pair) of the same locus* in donor and recipient:

donor:	*abcdxfgh*	⟶ *abcdefgh*	a functional recombinant can be produced.
recipient:	*axcdefgh*		

In this manner, hundreds of spontaneous and induced auxotrophic mutants of the same phenotype were tested by transduction to see whether, following the exposure of auxotroph *A* to transducing phages harvested from a phenotypically similar auxotroph *B*, recombinants capable of growing on minimal medium could be obtained. If such mutants yield wild-type recombinants with any other non-identical mutant deficient in its ability to form the same polypeptide, the conclusion can be drawn that they are single site mutants of the same locus or polynucleotide region. If, however, such a mutant can be transduced to "wild" type only by some, but not by all, of the other allelic mutants of the same locus, then a multisite mutation, including *deficiencies* and *inversions*, must be involved.† The extent of the polynucleotide region affected by a multisite mutation can be judged on the basis of which members of a series of allelic mutants (and also mutants of neighboring loci) can yield wild-type recombinants in transduction tests with the multisite-mutant recipient (Fig. 119).

LINKAGE

The transduced piece of DNA is large enough to permit the simultaneous transduction of several adjoining gene loci, thus revealing *linkage* through the occurrence of simultaneous transduction for more than just one function, e.g., for the formation of two, three, or occasionally more, different enzymes. Since transduction between two non-identical mutants of the same locus produces a considerably smaller number of prototroph recombinants than do two mutants belonging to two different, closely linked loci, it is possible to group a number of independent mutants by transduction tests, as shown in Table 20 for a series of tryptophan-requiring mutants.

These data indicate that mutants labeled *try*-1, -6, -7, -9, -10 and -11 belong in one group; *try*-2 and -4 in another group; *try*-3 in a third group; and *try*-8 in still a fourth group. Biochemical studies have established that these mutants can also be divided into four groups according to the particular enzymatic step that is blocked in the biosynthesis of tryptophan (Brenner, 1955):

	⟶ anthranilic acid	⟶ indole glycerol phosphate	⟶ indole	⟶ tryptophan
Group:	A	B	C	D
Mutant:	*try*-8	-2,-4	-3	-1,-6,-7,-9,-10,-11

*Giving rise to the "pseudoalleles" of classic genetics.

†Incidentally, the presence of a multisite mutation is also indicated by the fact that such mutants, in contrast to single site mutants, are not observed to revert spontaneously to the wild-type.

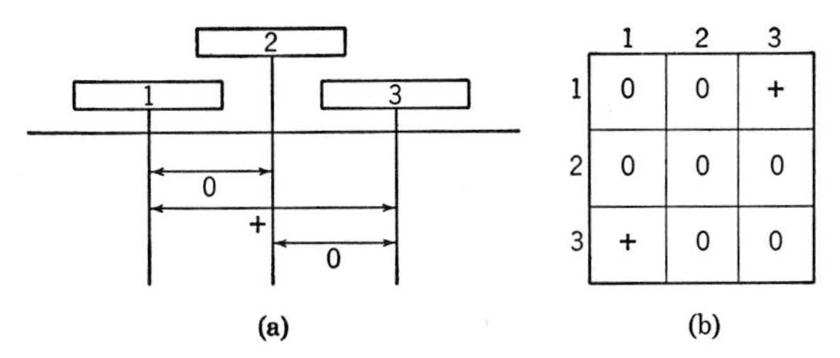

FIGURE 119. Mapping of deletions. (a) Three mutants are shown, each differing from wild-type in the deletion of a portion of the DNA polymer. Mutants 1 and 3 can recombine with each other to produce the wild-type (+), but neither of them can produce wild recombinants with mutant 2. (b) A matrix showing the results obtained in recombination tests with the three mutants in terms of lack of recovery (O) or recovery (+) of wild-type recombinants. The results are indicative of the order of mutations as shown in (a). (From Benzer, 1957.)

We now can see that the transduction tests reveal that four separate but linked loci control these four separate biosynthetic steps.

Similar tests using complete transduction have established that many neighboring loci can carry information for the formation of different enzymes that have one important common feature, namely, the enzymes under the control of such groups of loci are concerned with catalyzing (usually sequential) steps in one given biosynthetic pathway. Thus, for example, the nucleotide regions controlling the formation of the enzymes concerned with sequential steps in the synthesis of histidine are adjacent to each other (linked); so are those for threonine, for proline, and

TABLE 20. *Transduction experiments with* try *markers**†

RECIPIENT	DONOR										
	try-1	-6	-7	-9	-10	-11	-3	-2	-4	-8	+
try-1.....	0	66	203	104	219	208	291	706	458	418	1264
-6.....	141	0	11	60	21	182	188	179	234	100	1617
-7.....	21	2	0	10	19	22	444	537	435	107	717
-9.....	26	8	41	0	101	66	310	361	247	437	1456
-10	4	2	7	12	0	0	270	628	602	206	1822
-11....	22	1	23	22	0	0	280	240	315	497	1406
-3.....	166	50	30	75	88	107	0	139	111	123	336
-2.....	542	375	126	320	295	440	344	0	18	66	3074
-4.....	173	120	44	213	145	235	163	20	0	85	2257
-8.....	144	123	138	560	345	111	133	125	44	0	3264

*From Demerec, 1956.

†Figures indicate the numbers of colonies that developed from transduced cells on enriched minimal agar plated with approximately 2×10^7 phage-infected bacteria per plate. Multiplicity of infection, 5; adsorption of phage, 5 to 15 minutes at 37° C.

also for enzymes involved in the sequential breakdown of a sugar such as L-arabinose (Lee and Englesberg, 1962).

THE ORDER OF LINKED SITES AND LOCI

The order of linked sites and loci within a chromosome region can be determined from reciprocal transduction experiments involving three linked markers. For example, loci controlling tryptophan synthesis (*try* A—G) and a locus controlling one of the steps in cysteine biosynthesis (*cys* B) are linked (cf. Demerec *et al.*, 1958). It could be assumed that the arrangement of two of the *try* markers (*try* A, *try* B)* and *cys* B could be either *try* A · *try* B · *cys* B, or *try* B · *try* A · *cys* B. Transduction tests in which the double auxotroph *try* A, *cys* B served as the recipient in one case, and as the donor in the other case (Fig. 120) established that the order must be *try* B · *try* A · *cys* B for the following reasons: In cross *a* the numbers of try A · + · + recombinants was found to be similar to the number of + · + · + recombinants. However, in cross *b* the number of + · + · *cys* B recombinants was only about $1/20$ of either + · + · +, + · *try* A · +, or + · *try* A · *cys* B clones. Since a double cross-over occurs less frequently than a single cross-over, the data would not fit order A since in cross *a try* A · + · + would require one cross-over (in regions III and IV), and + · + · + would require two cross-overs (in regions I, II, III and IV) and yet the two recombinant classes occurred with equal frequency. However, order B would fit the data in both crosses *a* and *b*.

The relative distance of the mutant sites from each other can be deduced from "three-point tests" by the frequency with which different recombinant classes are recovered (see p. 232). On this basis, linkage maps such as the one shown in Figure 121 can be constructed.

RECOMBINATION WITHIN CODING UNITS

It also has become possible to demonstrate the occurrence of recombination within coding units in transductional studies with *E. coli*† (Yanofsky, 1963). This remarkable feat was accomplished through an understanding of the nucleic acid code controlling the incorporation of specific amino acids into polypeptides (see p. 337). All the mutants studied had undergone different amino acid replacements at one particular site in the well-analyzed A-protein of the enzyme tryptophan synthetase. The functional wild-type protein has glycine (RNA code: GGA or GGU) at a site that when replaced by serine (AGU), as a result of mutation, still yields a functional enzyme, but when replaced by arginine (AGA) or valine (GUA) yields inactive or poorly functioning enzymes. In transduction involving the arginine and valine mutants, recombinants with fully functioning tryptophan synthetase (i.e., capable of growing in the absence of added tryptophan) were recovered and an analysis of their protein by "fingerprinting"‡

*These are phenotypically distinguishable from each other.

†A coding unit, as we shall discuss in Chapter 16, is a triplet of neighboring nucleotides.

‡In "fingerprinting" the proteins are subjected to enzymatic hydrolysis, and the resulting peptides are separated on paper by chromatography in one direction and electrophoresis in the other direction. Ninhydrin treatment shows the location of the fragments on the paper, and these can then be analyzed for amino acid content by elution and further degradation.

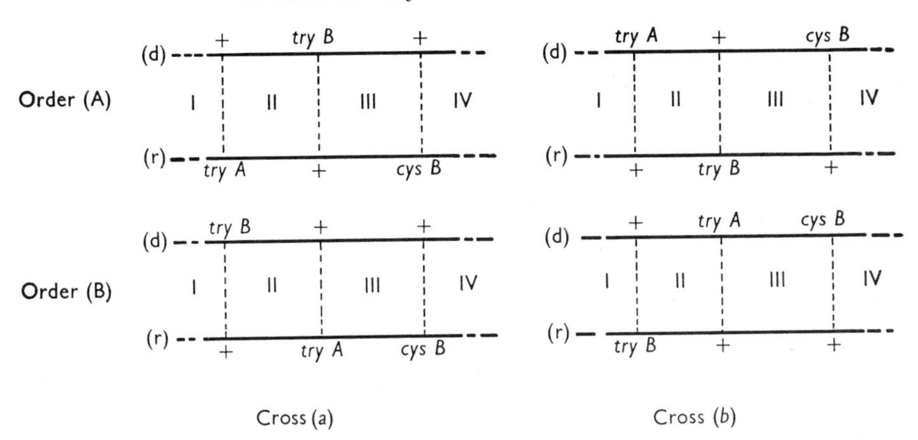

FIGURE 120. Cross (*a*) is a diagrammatic representation of the paired chromosomal regions in transduction of *try* A *cys* B (recipient) by phage propagated on *try* B (donor). Orders (A) and (B) show alternative arrangements of *try* in donor and recipient. Cross (*b*) is a similar representation of the reciprocal cross, in which *try* B is the recipient and *try* A *cys* B the donor. (From Clowes, 1960.)

(cf. Anfinsen, 1959; Ingram, 1961) revealed that half of these recombinants contained glycine and the other half serine at the critical site, as expected from the following consideration:

Donor:	*Arginine*	*AGA*	$\rightarrow$ recombinants GGA (glycine) and AGU (serine)
Recipient:	*Valine*	*GUU*	

Comparable *intra-codon* recombinations were observed in transductions between the arginine-containing mutant and a mutant in which glutamic acid (GAA) had replaced the normally present glycine. From these transductions (GAA × UGA) normal glycine-containing (GGA) recombinants were isolated.

SUPPRESSOR MUTATIONS

Complete transduction tests also have helped in the elucidation of at least one mechanism by which *suppressor mutations* may act (Yanofsky, 1963). Suppressors can restore partially or fully the normal phenotype in the continued presence of a mutant gene and are, more often than not, due to a mutation at a distant, unlinked locus in the chromosome (cf. Demerec and Hartman, 1959). They can be very specific in their activity; thus, a specific suppressor mutation may restore the enzymatic deficiency caused by a mutation at one site of a locus, while the effects of a mutation at a neighboring site are not influenced at all (cf. Suskind and Yanofsky, 1961.)

Some suppressors apparently act by reducing the concentration of an inhibitor of an abnormally sensitive mutant enzyme. Other suppressors have been found not only to restore the formation of the wild-type enzyme (in the continued presence of the mutation causing enzyme inactivity

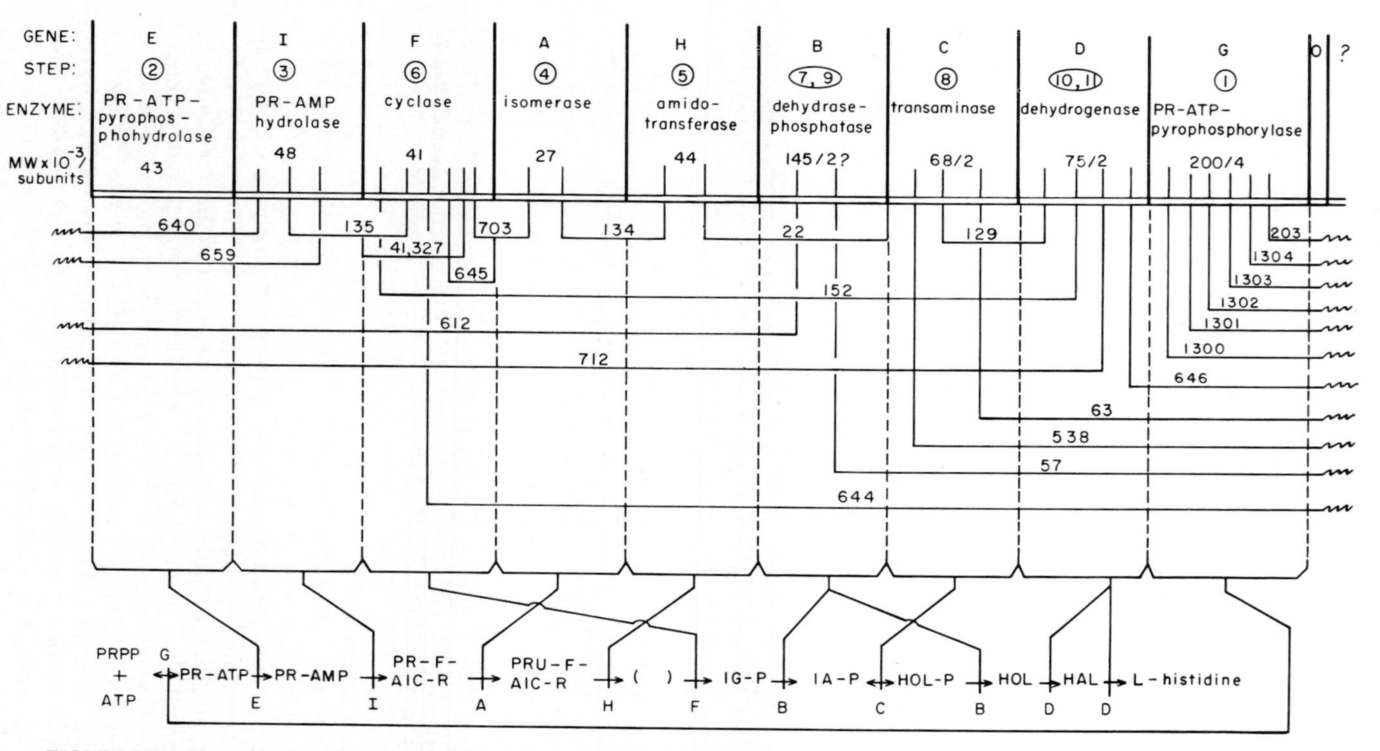

FIGURE 121. Map of the histidine operon of *S. typhimurium*, showing the order of the genetic sites involved in the formation of specific enzymes of the biosynthetic pathway shown at the bottom. Multisite (deletion) mutants and their numerical designations are represented by lines below the bar representing the chromosome. Single site mutants are not shown. Deletion mutants like 203, 63, 538, 57 and 644 produce no detectable histidine enzymes. PRPP = phosphoribosyl pyrophosphate; PR-ATP = phosphoribosyl ATP; PR-F-AIC-R = phosphoribosyl formimino aminoimidazole carboxamide ribotide; PRU = phosphoribulosyl; IGP = imidazole glycerol phosphate; IAP = imidazole acetol phosphate; HOL-P = L-histidinol phosphate; HAL = L-histidinal. (From Loper *et al.*, 1964, based on the work of Hartman, Ames and co-workers.)

in the absence of the suppressor mutation), but in addition, to affect the amino acid composition of other proteins. This suggests that such suppressor genes alter the specificity of amino acid incorporation into proteins, apparently by changing transfer RNA molecules (see p. 330) in such a manner that they occasionally accept the wrong amino acid (Yanofsky, 1963). This represents a truly exciting group of mutations since, instead of affecting the information for the formation or activity of a particular enzyme, they alter the entire mechanism of information translation.

Abortive Transduction and the Problem of Complementation

On page 277 we mentioned the usefulness of abortive transduction in the analysis of functional genetic units, and explained then that this is because of the fact that in abortive transduction temporary heterogenotes containing the genomes of two strains, which are mutants for the same phenotype, can be created. This permits an assessment of whether the mutation has affected the same unit required for enzymatic activity, in which case no complementation can occur, or whether two different functional units have been affected, in which case functional enzymes are formed as a result of complementation (see Fig. 118).

Hundreds of phenotypically similar auxotrophic mutants of *Salmonella* have been analyzed by abortive transduction, the occurrence of complementation being identified by the appearance of minute colonies, and the absence of complementation by a lack of such minute colonies (Demerec and Ozeki, 1959; Hartman *et al.*, 1960). These tests revealed not only that mutations in different linked loci, such as *his* B, *his* C, and *his* D, could complement each other, but that subgroups of from two to four complementary units could be detected even within a given locus such as *his* B or *his* D (see Fig. 121). Initially, such intragenic complementation was regarded as an indication that a locus determining the formation of one particular enzyme may be subdivided into several cistrons, each determining the formation of one polypeptide unit of the protein involved. However, as we shall discuss shortly, it has become increasingly clear that in addition to *intercistron* ("intergenic") complementation, *intracistron* ("intragenic") complementation (see p. 278) leading to complementation involving identical monomers of the protein polymer also may occur (Schlesinger and Levinthal, 1963).

The original concept of a cistron as the smallest functional unit, based on the results of the *cis-trans test*, was pioneered by S. Benzer (1957), who contributed brilliantly to the utilization of this test through his studies with bacteriophages. He coined the term *cistron* for the unit in which all of the mutations show a *cis-trans* effect in pairwise tests (see Fig. 118 and p. 280). This means that two mutations are classified as being in the same cistron if the *trans* arrangement shows no activity (or reduced activity) compared to the activity displayed by the *cis* arrangement. In general, this distinction still holds true if it is restricted to the situation in which *all* mutants complement each other, which is the case for intercistron complementations, in which each cistron determines the formation of a polypeptide. But, in addition, studies with bacteria (Levinthal and Davison, 1961;

Schlesinger and Levinthal, 1963; Garen and Garen, 1963) and fungi (Giles *et al.*, 1957; Catcheside, 1960; Fincham, 1962) have shown that *some* mutants belonging to the same cistron can lead to complementation, but the amount of active enzyme found is dependent on the particular pair of mutants used and is usually much lower than is the case with intercistron complementation (Schlesinger and Levinthal, 1963).

In the case of intracistron complementation, the production of a functional hybrid polypeptide is due to the supply of differently "damaged" monomer units by each of the genomes in the *trans* arrangements, as illustrated in our "word game" on page 280. This concept of hybrid protein formation in intracistron complementation is supported by the demonstration that enzymatically active alkaline phosphatase can be formed by mixing, *in vitro*, monomer subunits derived from inactive proteins isolated from different phosphatase-negative mutants of *E. coli* (Schlesinger and Levinthal, 1963). The normal alkaline phosphatase protein was shown to consist of two identical subunits that can be separated *in vitro* by mild acid treatment. Both units of this protein dimer are determined by one single functioning genetic unit, i.e., by one cistron. Thus, in view of the existence of intracistron complementation, the mere occurrence of complementation, without precise knowledge of the structure of the polypeptide produced, can no longer be used as a definitive indicator of the participation of two separate cistrons. But the very fact that it has become possible to detect such complexities testifies to the enormous resolving power of analyses employing genetic transfers, including transduction, for the elucidation of gene-enzyme relationships.

[15]

GENETIC TRANSFERS IV: CONJUGATION

Transfer of information by conjugation involves direct cellular contact between a donor (male) bacterium and a recipient (female) bacterium. Following such contact and the formation of a connecting cellular bridge (Fig. 122), a considerable segment (sometimes even all) of the male's "chromosome" may be transferred into the female, and may then undergo recombination with a corresponding (homologous) "chromosomal" segment of the recipient.*

Conjugation itself, i.e., the process of cellular connection between two sexually differentiated bacterial cells, can occur without a transfer of chromosomal material, and transfer of chromosomal material also may take place without subsequent recombination. When chromosomal material is transferred, the transfer is usually partial because the polynucleotide chain tends to break prior to complete transfer from male to female. Owing to such breakage, the resulting, temporarily diploid, zygote is almost always a partial zygote, or *merozygote* (Jacob and Wollman, 1961). As a rule, the transferred piece does not replicate itself; only those portions of it that by recombination become part of the recipient's genome will participate in the subsequent replication of the genome. Thus, except for certain unique cases in which stable, partially diploid heterozygotes are produced (Lederberg, 1949; Zelle and Lederberg, 1951), the partially diploid condition of many exconjugants is rapidly reduced (with or without recombination) to the typical haploid condition. The genetic material transferred from the male to the female does not deplete the donor's storehouse of innate information; rather it represents a newly replicated *copy* of the donor's chromosome.

The entire process of conjugation and recombination can be separated into several distinct and successive stages (Clark and Adelberg, 1962): (1) The formation of specific "mating" pairs following random collisions of cells of opposite mating type; (2) the provision of energy sources for the formation of a conjugation bridge and for the transfer of genetic material; (3) the transfer of genetic material; (4) the integration of some (or all) of

*For general reviews, see Hartman, 1957; Hartman and Goodgal, 1959; Jacob and Wollman, 1961; Clark and Adelberg, 1962; Hayes, 1962; Gross, 1964; Hayes, 1964.

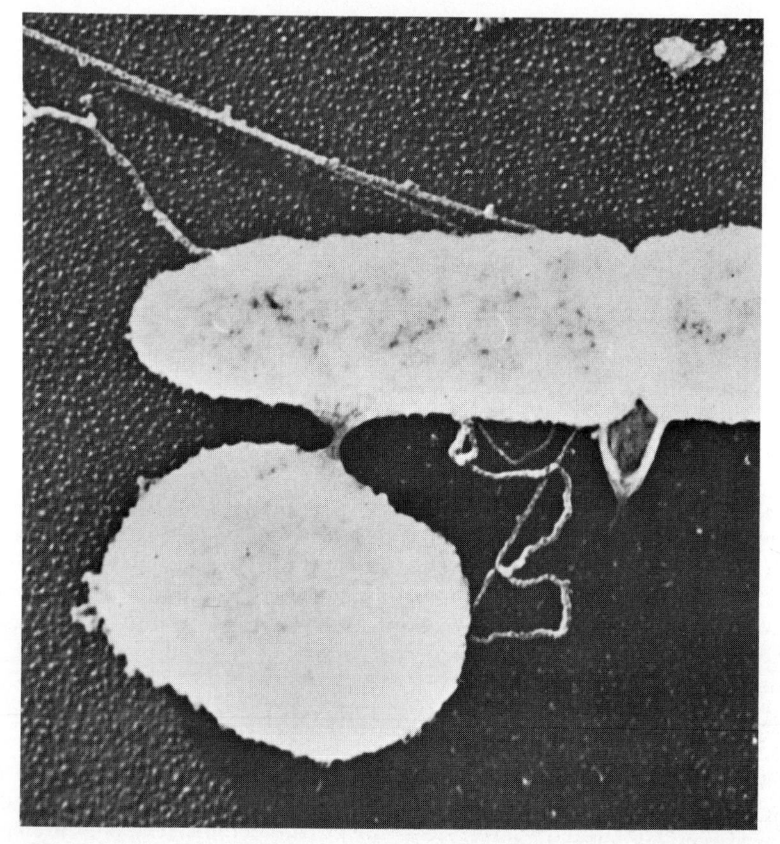

FIGURE 122. Electron micrograph of conjugating *E. coli*. The mating was between Hfr K-12 (elongated cell in the process of division) and F^- bacteria from strain C (plump cell). The long thin structures attached to the K-12 bacterium are flagella. (From Anderson *et al.*, 1957.)

the transferred material into the recipient's chromosome; and (5) the segregation of the resulting recombinant chromosome.

Specialized genetic elements, which Luria (1963) has christened "conjugons," are required for the establishment of the cell-to-cell contact, which is a prerequisite for the subsequent occurrence of DNA transfer and "sexual recombination." Three types of conjugons have so far been recognized: the *F* (fertility) factors, the *Cf* (colicinogenic) factors and the *RTF* (resistance transfer) factor. In the presence of any of these factors in a donor cell, conjugation can take place with a related cell, usually with one lacking such a factor. During conjugation, the conjugon is usually (but not always) transferred from the male to the female cell. In the course of such a transfer the conjugon may, in some instances, also transport, from the donor cell to the recipient cell, male chromosomal material that has become temporarily associated with the conjugon (see p. 299 for details). Thus, whereas phage protein serves as a "trolley car" in transduction, the conjugon appears to serve as a kind of "truck cab" that permits (probably by pushing rather than pulling) the transfer of a "trailer load" of chromosomal material from a male to a female cell. Conjugons are DNA-containing elements. According to some current concepts, they exist in male cells of conjugating strains as separate structures which are quite distinct from the bacterial chromosome, but like the chromosome they are probably circular, able to replicate themselves and probably attached to the cell membrane (see Fig. 21). Like the genetic material of temperate bacteriophages (see p. 161), the extra-chromosomal conjugons may be regarded as accessory genetic elements that can either multiply autonomously in the bacterial cell or associate themselves with the bacterial chromosome in a manner that we shall describe later. In 1958, Jacob and Wollman proposed the term *episomes* for such accessory extra-chromosomal genetic elements which can exist either autonomously or integrated with the chromosome. More recently, when evidence accumulated indicating that genetic elements like the *F* and *Cf* conjugons probably are chromosome-like, separate, replicating structures (as indicated for *F* in Figure 21), which differ from the DNA structure called "chromosome" only in size and rate of replication, the term *replicon* was proposed as a common designator for the bacterial chromosome and the conjugons (Jacob *et al.*, 1963).

Thus both terminology and concepts have undergone fairly drastic changes since sexual recombination was first described by Lederberg and Tatum in 1946. In the present chapter we shall try to sketch the evolution of our current concepts of conjugation, a phenomenon which has been found to occur in strains of *Salmonella, Shigella, Pseudomonas, Vibrio, Streptomyces* and *E. coli*, but has been subjected to extensive analysis only in *E. coli*.

Early Studies on Recombination in *E. coli*, K-12

Some very early attempts to detect recombination of characteristics following mixed cultivation of mutant strains of *E. coli, Aerobacter aerogenes* and *Phytomonas stewartii* yielded only negative results (Sherman and Wing, 1937; Gowen and Lincoln, 1942). The first conclusive positive results were obtained by Lederberg and Tatum in studies with mutant strains of *E. coli*, K-12 (Lederberg and Tatum, 1946; Tatum and Lederberg, 1947). These investigators used auxotrophic parent strains which were unable to grow on minimal medium and they recognized the occurrence of recombination by isolating, following mixed cultivation of these strains, cells that were able to grow on minimal medium and displayed characteristics of both parent types (Fig. 123). Thus one parent strain (58-161) required biotin (B^-) and methionine (M^-) for growth, the other parent strain (W-1177) required threonine (T^-), leucine (L^-) and thiamine (B_1^-).* In addition, the latter strain carried the following markers: Lac^- Mal^-

*Throughout this section the mutant symbols will be cited as they were given in the original publications, but it should be kept in mind that in this instance the use of capital letters does not necessarily reflect the dominance of the genes involved.

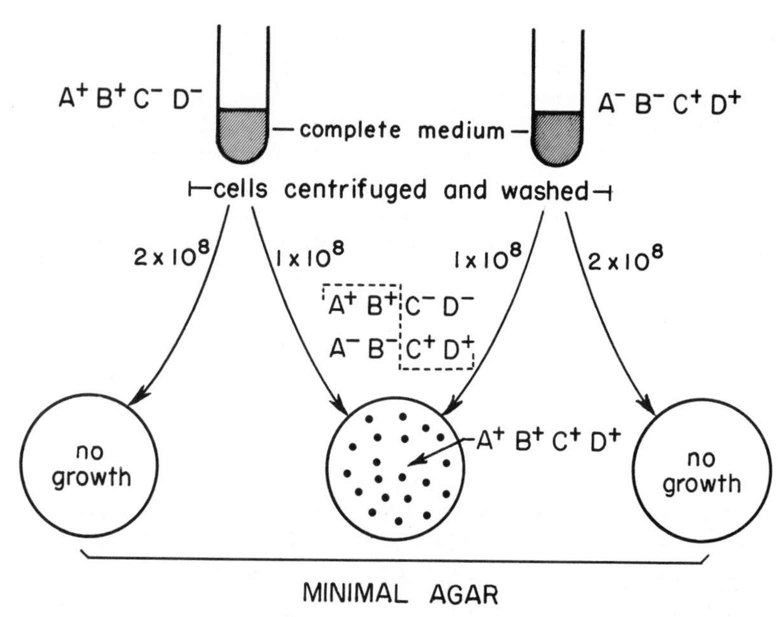

FIGURE 123. Occurrence of recombination following mixed cultivation of two auxotrophic strains of *E. coli*, K-12, on minimal agar.

Mtl^- Xyl^- Gal^- Ara^- (non-fermenter of lactose, maltose, mannitol, xylose, galactose and arabinose), as well as phage-resistance (T_1^r) and streptomycin-resistance (S^r). These strains had been derived by a series of individual mutational steps from the original K-12 parent culture. Spontaneous reversion of either auxotroph strain to the prototrophic condition (ability to grow on minimal medium) was never observed. Since such reversions would require simultaneous mutation of two genes in the case of the 58-161 strain, namely B^- and M^-, and simultaneous mutation of three genes in the case of the W-1177 strain, namely T^-, L^- and B_1^-, such spontaneous changes would not be likely to occur. It should be remembered that spontaneous mutations from a specific auxotrophic type to the prototrophic condition, e.g., B^- to B^+, generally occur at rates of 1×10^{-7}, a simultaneous reversion of a double auxotroph to prototrophy, e.g., $B^- M^-$ to $B^+ M^+$, would only be likely to occur at rates as low as 1×10^{-14}. However, when the parent strains were plated in mixture on a minimal medium, prototroph colonies developed at the rate of approximately 1 for every 10^7 cells plated. Thus the auxotroph mixture:

$$B^-M^-T^+L^+B_1^+ \times B^+M^+T^-L^-B_1^-$$

yielded a very small number of stable prototroph cells of the genotype $B^+M^+T^+L^+B_1^+$.

This result was explained most easily on the assumption that sexual fusion of certain parent cells and subsequent segregation of genes in new combinations may occur. In other words, it was assumed that two cells, one from parent strain *A*, the other from parent strain *B*, may mate, forming a zygote in which recombination could occur. Subsequent studies supported this assumption. Thus, it was demonstrated that all conceivable combinations of the characteristics of both parents could be detected among the recombinants. For example, if mixed platings were made on a minimal medium enriched with thiamine, $B^+M^+T^+L^+B_1^-$ cells could develop into colonies and were found to occur in addition to the $B^+M^+T^+L^+B_1^+$ prototrophs after mixed plating of the parent strains. However, the proportion of these B_1^- recombinants recoverable from mixed platings of a given number of parent cells was always greater than the proportion of recoverable $B^+M^+T^+L^+B_1^+$ prototrophs. This indicated that recombination did not take place arbitrarily, but that certain forces controlled the likelihood of genes introduced with one of the parents to separate from their original combination, recombine and segregate with the genic complement introduced by the other parent. Linkage groups similar to those discovered in studies with higher organisms appeared to exist.

Thus if the genes for the tested characteristics were arranged in one chromosome as follows:

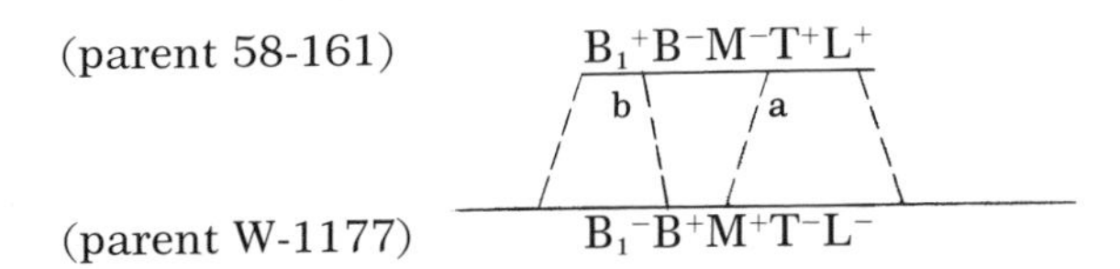

a single exchange (at site *a*) may occur relatively frequently after sexual fusion, yielding $B_1^-B^+M^+T^+L^+$ recombinants, whereas a recombinant cell of the type $B_1^+B^+M^+T^+L^+$ would require the occurrence of two exchanges (at sites *a* and *b*), an event which is less likely to occur than a single exchange.* In this manner the linkage relationships of various genes were tested by inspection of the frequency with which various recombinations occurred. The results were in general agreement with the idea that the tested genes of *E. coli* K-12, are arranged linearly at definite distances from each other in one linkage group (chromosome) and that the observed recombinations occurred by sexual fusion and recombination between haploid parent cells (Lederberg, 1947; Lederberg *et al.*, 1951; Rothfels, 1952).

These conclusions were strengthened by studies on the "unselected" markers such as fermentation characteristics and phage- or antibiotic-resistance. The latter characteristics are termed "unselected" markers because they may show arbitrary, non-selected recombinations in the pro-

*For the sake of easier comprehension we have sketched the foregoing example of chromosomal exchanges in a manner that reflects the present knowledge of sexual differentiation in conjugation, i.e., a donor (parent 58-161) and a recipient (W-1177). This knowledge did not exist at the time of the original studies; at that time recombinations giving rise to two viable recombinant clones (one being essentially 58-161, the other essentially W-1177) were assumed to occur. We know now that parent 58-161 usually contributes only part of its chromosome and that the recombinants are derived from an exchange between this part and a section of the chromosome of the W-1177 recipient cell, the latter being the only parent of the recombinant clone that may result.

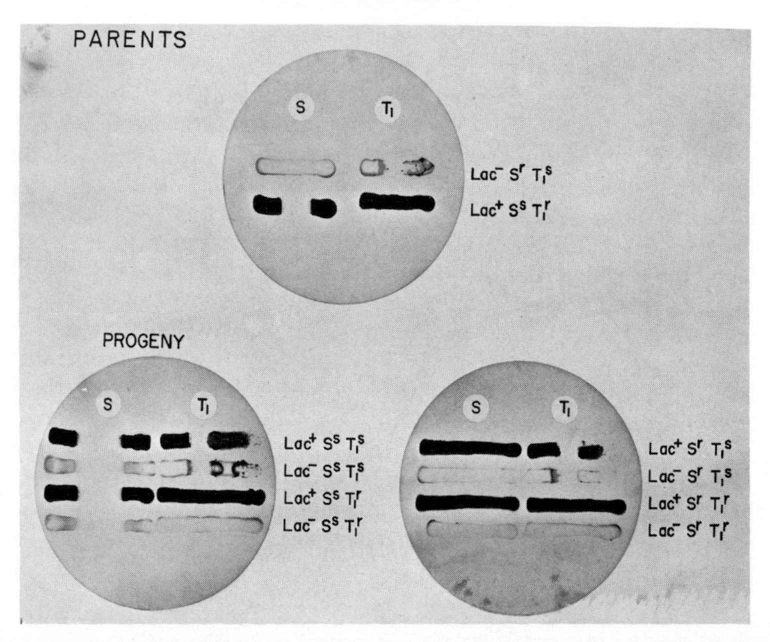

FIGURE 124. Recombination among unselected markers in an experiment with strains derived from *E. coli*, K-12. Samples from the auxotrophic parent strains and from recombinant prototrophic colonies have been streaked on EMB-lactose agar to detect capacity for lactose fermentation; they also were cross-streaked with a solution of streptomycin (S) and a suspension of phage (T_1) to determine streptomycin- and phage-resistance. A break in the streak in the area of cross-streaking is indicative of susceptibility to phage or streptomycin, respectively. (Courtesy of H. B. Newcombe.)

totroph cells isolated following crosses made between multiple auxotroph parents on minimal media, where the growth requirements serve as "selected" markers permitting the rapid identification of recombinants which are represented by all those cells capable of developing into colonies on minimal media (Fig. 124). Thus mixed plating on minimal media of

	selected markers	unselected markers
(parent 58-161)	B_1^+ B^- M^- T^+ L^+	Lac^+ Mal^+ Mtl^+ Xyl^+ Gal^+ Ara^+ T_1^s S^s
(parent W-1177)	B_1^- B^+ M^+ T^- L^-	Lac^- Mal^- Mtl^- Xyl^- Gal^- Ara^- T_1^r S^r

can give rise to all of the 2^8 possible combinations (256) among the unselected markers if a sufficient number of recombinant colonies are examined. For example:

B_1^+ B^+ M^+ T^+ L^+	Lac^+ Mal^- Mtl^- Xyl^+ Gal^+ Ara^+ T_1^s S^s
B_1^+ B^+ M^+ T^+ L^+	Lac^- Mal^+ Mtl^+ Xyl^- Gal^- Ara^+ T_1^r S^r
B_1^+ B^+ M^+ T^+ L^+	Lac^- Mal^- Mtl^+ Xyl^+ Gal^- Ara^+ T_1^r S^s
B_1^+ B^+ M^+ T^+ L^+	Lac^+ Mal^+ Mtl^- Xyl^- Gal^+ Ara^+ T_1^s S^r
	etc.

Again, certain recombinations occur more frequently than others, indicating different degrees of linkage, i.e., distance between different genes on one chromosome, in this case between genes controlling fermentation and resistance characteristics.

In these early studies Lederberg (1950) also demonstrated that growth inhibitors can be used efficiently for selective markers in recombination experiments. Thus mixed platings of a streptomycin-resistant (*sr*) strain of *E. coli*, K-12, with an azide resistant (*azr*) K-12 strain on media containing both streptomycin and azide yielded *sr azr* recombinants capable of growth into colonies, whereas either parent strain proved incapable of growing on such a medium, except for the rare occurrence of *sr* mutants among *azr* cells, or of *azr* mutants among *sr* cells. The rate of such spontaneous mutants was found to be 1 per 7×10^9 cells and 7 per 1×10^9 cells, respectively; however, mixed *azr* and *sr* cultures yielded an average of 250 dually resistant cells per 10^9 cells plated. The presence of unselected markers (fermentation characteristics) in the parent strains confirmed that 93 per cent of dually resistant cells recovered from plating *azr* and *sr* cells on an azide-streptomycin-containing medium represented recombinants.

Since the isolation of mutants resistant to growth-inhibitors is usually far simpler than the isolation of nutritional mutants, the use of resistance characteristics as selective markers proved of value in searching for the occurrence of recombination among other bacterial strains. All the early results described so far were obtained in studies with *E. coli*, K-12, a typical coliform bacterium originally isolated from human feces. Subsequent attempts to detect similar phenomena in other widely used laboratory strains of *E. coli*, such as strain B, met with failure except for the discovery of one additional strain in England that could be crossed with K-12 (Cavalli and Heslot, 1949). In view of this apparent rarity of "fertile" strains Lederberg (1951) tested a large number of cultures isolated from human urine and chicken cecal flora for their ability to cross with K-12, using antibiotic resistance and prototrophy as selective markers. Among 100 human isolates he found 8 that participated in recombination with the same facility as K-12. One of the 40 chicken isolates examined also showed recombinations with K-12. This finding removed strain K-12 from the position of being unique as far as recombination is concerned; more recently about 30 per cent of 199 other *E. coli* strains tested were found to be fertile in recombination tests (Ørskov and Ørskov, 1961).

The early investigators of these recombination events realized that in view of the then quite well-analyzed phenomenon of transformation in pneumococci (p. 240) it was necessary to rule out the involvement of diffusible transforming substances. Lederberg (1947) provided a number of experiments that made the participation of diffusible substances most unlikely. For example, neither culture filtrates nor cell autolysates prepared from one of the parent strains were capable of producing the described genetic changes in the other parent strain. In addition, the linkage relationships and the fact that whole groups of marker-genes appear recombined in the progeny argued against the involvement of transforming substances.

The most substantial proof against the role of diffusible transforming substances in the recombination phenomenon, however, was provided in an experiment described by Davis (1950). He employed a **U**-tube containing an ultrafine fritted-glass filter at the base, like the one shown in Figure 111. In such a tube bacteria growing on either side of the filter are prevented from physical contact, yet diffusible substances can pass freely from one side of the tube to the other. When cells of strain 58-161 were inoculated into one arm of the tube, filled with complete broth, and cells of strain W-1177 were inoculated into the other arm, subsequent plating into minimal medium failed to uncover any recombinants. In contrast, when both parent strains were inoculated into the same arm, thus permitting direct contact between the cells, the expected number of recombinants could be recovered.

Although the early studies provided substantial indirect evidence for cellular contact as a requirement for recombination in *E. coli*, K-12, and other strains, direct microscopic evidence for the formation of conjugal pairs in mixed cultures of recombining strains was not provided until several years later (Lederberg, 1956; Anderson *et al.*, 1957). The early studies also assumed that bacteria participating in conjugation showed no evident sexual differentiation, i.e., were *homothallic*, whereas it developed subsequently that there was a polarity in bacterial matings, one member of each conjugal pair serving as donor or male, the other as recipient or female; in other words, the participants in conjugation were *heterothallic*. Finally, the early studies assumed that the contributions to the zygote resulting from the mating event were equal as far as the two parents are concerned, whereas the later studies revealed that in the unidirectional transfer of chromosomal material from the male to the

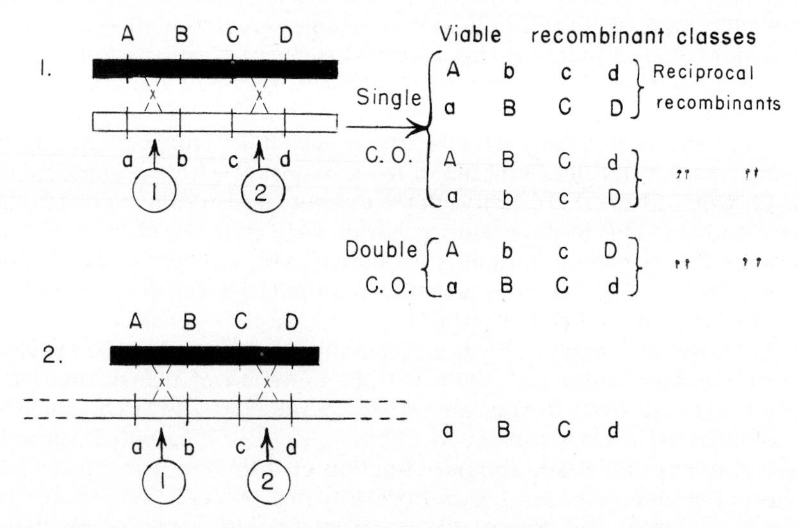

FIGURE 125. Comparison of viable recombinant classes that may be expected in a case (1) in which recombination takes place between two entire and equivalent chromosomal structures, each of which can give rise to progeny, and (2) between an entire chromosomal structure of a recipient cell and a partial (non-reproducing) chromosomal piece transferred from a donor cell.

female bacterium, only a fraction of the male chromosome usually enters the female cell.

Both the occurrence of partial transfer and the sexual differentiation of the mating cells, which we shall discuss in the next section, actually were foreshadowed, but not comprehended, on the basis of several unexpected anomalies that became apparent in early recombination studies with *E. coli*, K-12: Some of the expected recombination classes were always absent in the progeny of zygotes; in particular, the reciprocal recombinant classes that would be expected from crossing-overs between equal contributors (Fig. 125) were lacking—some of the markers present in one of the parents rarely, if ever, showed up in the recombinant progeny. Also, linkage relationships among some of the markers were very difficult to define; striking differences were sometimes obtained when the results of crosses between different strains, involving similar markers, were compared and, in addition, reciprocal crosses (e.g., Ay × Bz vs. Az × By) yielded quite different results (cf. Lederberg *et al.*, 1951; Hayes, 1953).

Mating Types: Recognition of the *F* Factor

The analysis of the mechanism of conjugation was greatly aided by the discovery of certain strains, labeled *Hfr* (= high frequency of recombination), which when mated with a strain like W-1177 yielded 1000 times more recombinants than a strain such as 58-161. The first Hfr strain was derived more or less by accident from strain 58-161 (Cavalli-Sforza, 1950). Next, the existence of a fertility factor (*F*), apparently (but, as we shall see later, not really) distinct from Hfr, became obvious when it was discovered that recombinations could occur between certain strains, such as *A* and *B*, or *A* and *C*, but not between *B* and *C* (Lederberg, *et al.*, 1952).

Such sexual differentiation was even more clearly indicated by Hayes' observation that recombinants were still recoverable in matings between two competent strains when one of the parents (namely, the male) was exposed to a bactericidal concentration of streptomycin, whereas recombination was prevented when the other parent (the female) was exposed to the antibiotic (Hayes, 1952, 1953). These experiments demonstrated that the role of the two parental types were not identical; the survival of one is required for the formation of recombinants, but the other contributor does not have to survive. This then furnished the basis for distinguishing two sexual types: F^+ (donor or male) strains and F^- (F-deficient recipient or female) strains. Strain 58-161, used in the early studies, was now recognized as an F^+ strain and W-1177 as an F^- strain.

It was then established that mixtures of cultures containing F^+ males and F^- females yield recombinants at low frequencies (usually $1/10^5$), $F^+ \times F^+$ yield recombinants at extremely low frequencies, and $F^- \times F^-$ are sterile. As already stated, Hfr × F^- crosses yield recombinants at very high frequencies ($1/10^2$ or higher).

Recombinants derived from an $F^+ \times F^-$ cross are always F^+. In fact, within less than one hour after exposure to F^+ cells, most or all F^- cells in a culture attain the F^+ property. This infective transfer of F^+ into F^- cells requires cellular contact (conjugation) and, since only 1 out of 10^5 cells yields recombinants, can occur without transfer of chromosomal markers.*

How many *F* elements† are there in an F^+ cell? It was found that when a small number of F^+ (male, donor) cells was mixed with a large number of F^- (female, recipient) cells, the F^+ property spread very rapidly through the entire F^- cell population, and this gave rise to the early concept that F^+ cells may possess many *F* "episomes" (Cavalli-Sforza *et al.*, 1953). However, more recent studies indicate that this rapid spread of *F* through an F^- population is due to *F's* rapid rate of replication and that there is in all probability only one *F* element per nucleus of an F^+ cell (cf. Jacob *et al.*, 1964). The sex factor *F* thus behaves as a genetic determinant which, in F^+ cells, is structurally independent of the bacterial chromosome and replicates autonomously. It may be *lost* spontaneously, or can be removed by treatment of F^+ cells with acridine orange (Hirota, 1960), but *F* can never be *acquired* by spontaneous mutation – only by transfer following conjugation.

Under certain environmental conditions F^+ cells can behave temporarily as F^- cells; such F^- phenocopies are frequent in aerated older cultures (Lederberg *et al.*, 1952), and their occasional presence in young F^+ cultures probably explains the occasional matings in $F^+ \times F^+$ crosses (Hayes, 1953). F^- phenocopies also can be produced by periodate treatment (Sneath and Lederberg, 1961).

The *F* element, according to data collected with radioactive tracers and mitomycin C, an inhibitor of DNA synthesis, appears to be DNA in nature (Driskell and Adelberg, 1961). It can be inactivated by P^{32} decay and the rate of such inactivation suggests that it contains about 3×10^5 base pairs; i.e., its DNA content is similar to that of a bacteriophage and about 1 per cent of the *E. coli* chromosome (Driskell and Adelberg, 1961).

The presence of *F* in *E. coli* cells leads to the formation of specific surface properties. These properties express themselves in several ways: (1) the presence of a specific antigen (Ørskov and Ørskov, 1960) which may be identical to a periodate-labile carbohydrate found in F^+ and Hfr cells (Sneath and Lederberg, 1961); (2) differences in surface charge properties (Maccacaro and Comolli, 1956); and (3) the possession of adsorption sites for specific RNA bacteriophages (Loeb and Zinder, 1961). In all probability all of these properties are the expression of the formation of a particular polysaccharide in the cell wall of F^+ (and also Hfr) cells, which, in turn, is important for the effective contact with F^- cells, which lack such surface properties.‡ The initial contact leading to a pairing of F^+ and F^- cells (also, as we shall see, of Hfr and F^- cells) appears to be the result of random collisions. The subsequent formation of the conjugation bridge and the still later transfer of *F*, or of *F*-associated chromosomal material,

*This lack of linkage between *F* and the chromosome-associated determinants first gave rise to the concept that *F* is an episome, i.e., an element that can exist independent of the chromosome.

†It has been customary to talk about *F* factors and about F^+ cells carrying such factors. In view of the likelihood that the *F* factor is part of a separate *F* replicon, we shall refer to this replicon as an *F* element.

‡C. C. Brinton has recently presented some evidence suggesting that special pili (see p. 144), *F pili*, present on F^+ cells, may serve to transfer DNA from male to female cells.

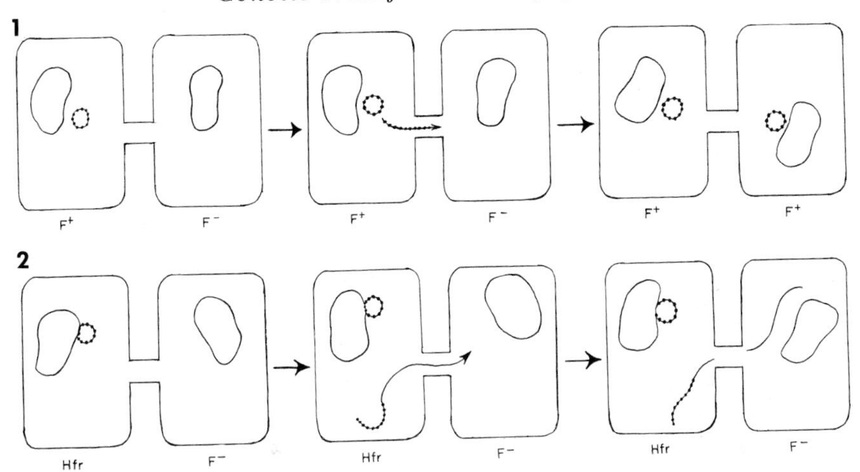

FIGURE 126. Diagram of presumed events in $F^+ \times F^-$ matings (1), and in Hfr $\times F^-$ matings (2). —— represents chromosomal DNA, ⋯⋯ represents *F*, and ⋯⋯› replicated *F*. Both chromosomal and *F* elements are shown as circular structures (except when in the process of transfer); this is in conformance with conclusions that were reached only many years after the recognition of the basic features of the F and Hfr states.

are energy-requiring processes (cf. Clark and Adelberg, 1962 for references).

As already indicated, Hfr cells possess the same conjugation-promoting surface properties as F^+ cells. However, Hfr cells differ from F^+ cells in at least two striking aspects: (1) They donate chromosomal markers to the female recipient cell 1000 times more frequently than F^+ cells do, and (2) the recombinants derived from Hfr $\times F^-$ crosses are usually, but not always, F^- (a few recombinants are Hfr). Furthermore, acridine orange, which "cures" F^+ cells of their *F* element and thus converts them into female F^- cells, does not change the "super-male" state of the Hfr cells.

What then might be the relationship between the two male types Hfr and F^+? We owe our present knowledge regarding their probable relationship largely to the intellectual and experimental efforts of Jacob and Wollman. Their studies led to the suggestion that the independent *F* element, which, as we have seen, is routinely transferred from F^+ to F^- cells following conjugation, may occasionally associate itself with the bacterial chromosome and help to transfer all or some part of the chromosome (Fig. 126). This would represent the occasional transfer of chromosomal markers in $F^+ \times F^-$ matings.* In the case of Hfr $\times F^-$ matings, the *F* element

*The fact that recombinants from $F^+ \times F^-$ matings are F^+ might reflect an occurrence of more than one mating of the F^-; one with Hfr, which results in a transfer of chromosomal material, and the other with F^+, which would result in a transfer of *F* (D. Bacon, personal communication).

would remain associated with the chromosome in such a fashion that it would sit at the tail end of the migrating chromosome (Fig. 126). This would account for the rare transfer of the Hfr property to female cells, since other studies have shown that owing to apparent random breakage of the migrating chromosome in the course of its journey from the male to the female cell, the tail end of the bacterial chromosome only rarely enters the female recipient.

As already stated, according to this concept the occasional transfer of chromosomal determinants in $F^+ \times F^-$ matings would be due to the rare occurrence of the Hfr-like state (i.e., the chromosome-associated *F* element) in some of the cells of the F^+ population (except that Hfr's of this type, in contrast to the typical Hfr, appear to yield F^+ recombinants). This was supported by two types of experimental evidence: (1) The fluctuation test (p. 69) revealed that chromosome donors arose in independent F^+ cultures spontaneously, the variance of the total number of recombinants recoverable from matings involving independent cultures of an F^+ strain being significantly greater than that found for different samples of the same culture. (2) When a lawn of F^- was imprinted, by velveteen (see replica plating, p. 72), with F^+ cells, it became possible to recover Hfr clones from many of the sites on the F^+ "master plate" that corresponded to sites of recombinant production on the "F^- plus F^+" test plates (Jacob and Wollman, 1956). (The test plates just cited contained a selective medium on which only recombinants could grow.)

One additional important difference, aside from frequency of recombinant formation, became apparent when the results of Hfr $\times$ F^- and $F^+ \times F^-$ matings were compared. This difference is in the frequency of appearance of different donor markers in the recombinant progeny. Although recombinants are rare in $F^+ \times F^-$ matings, any one of the donor's markers has a similar probability of appearing in the total recombinant population. This must mean that in F^+ populations the chromosome donor can transfer any one of their chromosomal segments. In terms of the association between the *F* element and the chromosome, which, as we discussed previously, appears to be a prerequisite to chromosome transfer, this means that in F^+ cultures *F* can associate itself with *any* site of the donor's chromosome (Fig. 127A).

In contrast, in Hfr $\times$ F^- matings, certain markers of the donor always appear with very high frequency among the recombinants; other markers appear only rarely among the recombinants, or not at all. The kinds of markers that do appear frequently depend on the particular Hfr strain. Thus, if we have markers A, B, C, D. . .M, N, O, P. . .W, X, Y, Z in the donors (and the corresponding alleles a, b, c, d. . . in the recipients), those of Hfr-*1* strain may yield recombinants showing mostly markers M, N, O, P, and those of Hfr-2 strain may yield recombinants showing mostly markers A, B, C, D, etc. This, besides being a reflection of a partial transfer of donor determinants, indicates that each Hfr strain tends to transfer a particular segment of the donor chromosome with high frequency. In terms of the association between the *F* element and the chromosome this means that

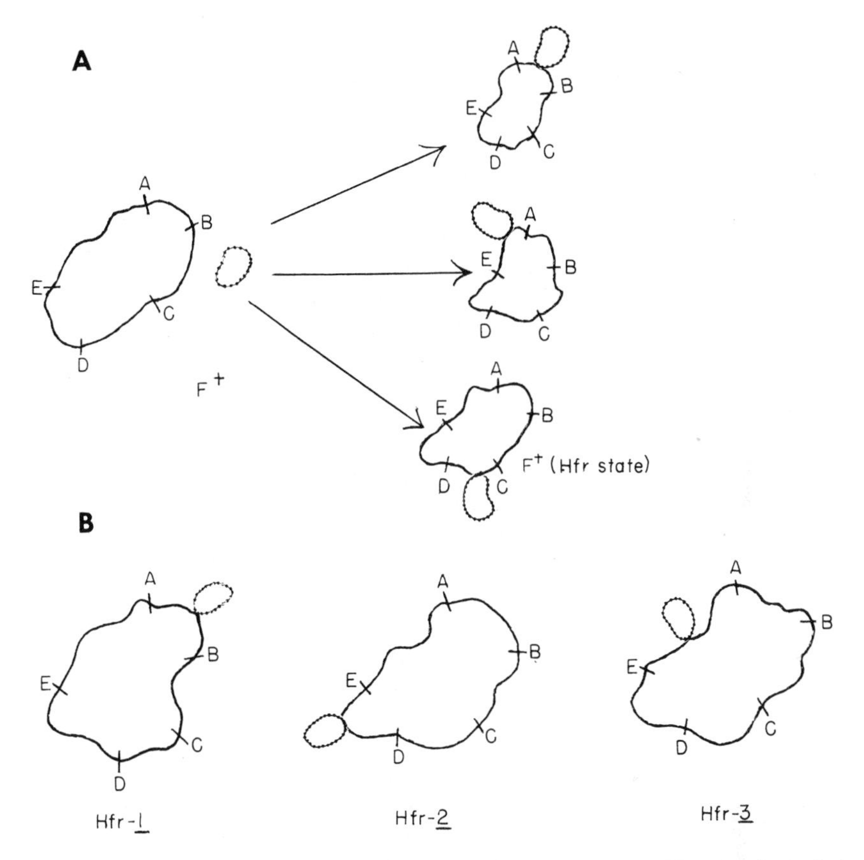

FIGURE 127. Diagrams illustrating (**A**) some of the many different possible sites of association of *F* with the chromosome in F^+ cells and (**B**) some of the specific sites of relatively permanent association of *F* with the chromosome in three different Hfr strains.

in each particular Hfr strain there exists a *specific* site of association of *F* with the chromosome* (Fig. 127B).

When a more detailed analysis was made of the actual frequency with which several markers (or linked genes) occurred in recombinants of a given Hfr strain, it was discovered that they appeared, in the totals of all recombinants, in a definitive decreasing order of frequency (e.g., A: 90%, B: 75%, C: 40%, D: 20%) (cf. Hayes, 1964). This suggested that these genes are arranged in the order A, B, C, D, E on the transferred chromosome and that it was more likely for A to enter the recipient F^- and to participate in recombinational events there, somewhat less likely for B, still less likely for C, etc. The understanding of the conjugation phenomenon and its genetic consequences gained greatly from the subsequent demonstration that the anticipated oriented (and partial) transfers of linked chromosomal genes of the donor parent did indeed occur.

*Remember, we have already indicated that this site represents the tail end of the migrating chromosome (Fig. 126).

Oriented, Partial Chromosome Transfer, as Revealed by Interrupted Matings. The Circular Chromosome Map

Two major experiments, both conducted by Jacob and Wollman (cf. Jacob and Wollman, 1961, for references), provided evidence for the oriented transfer of chromosomal genes from male to female *E. coli* cells. The first is the famous *interrupted mating experiment*; the second deals with the phenomenon of *zygotic induction*.

Let us discuss the interrupted mating test first. It has been known for some time prior to 1955 that bacteria can survive several minutes of violent agitation in a Waring blendor. In 1955 it was determined that two minutes of such treatment sufficed to separate bacteria undergoing the process of conjugation (Wollman and Jacob, 1955). Accordingly, to follow the kinetics of transfer of different donor markers to the zygote (detectable by their subsequent presence in recombinants), Hfr and F^- cells were mixed and samples from this mixture were placed at various periods thereafter into the blendor at 4° C. The agitated samples, in which mating had thus been interrupted at one of various periods after initiation of the Hfr and F^- mixture, were then plated on media permitting the growth of recombinants. In this way, evidence for the gradual transfer of linked genes from a male to a female cell was obtained. No recombinants were found in samples which had been agitated within the first eight minutes after the start of the mixed Hfr and F^- culture. Recombinants with donor gene A appeared in the progeny of samples agitated nine minutes after the mixed cultures were started, and in addition, donor gene B appeared in the progeny of samples that had been agitated after 10 minutes. In "17-minute samples" donor genes A, B and also C and D were found in the recombinants and donor gene E joined these in the "25-minute samples" (Fig. 128).

Let us now take a look at some actual data from such a test (Wollman and Jacob, 1958). In a mating between strain Hfr H (the H shows that this strain was isolated by Hayes) and F^- P678 the following markers were present:

$$\text{Hfr H: } T^+\ L^+\ Az^s\ T_1^s\quad Lac^+\ Gal^+\ S^{s*}$$
$$F^-\ :\ T^-\ L^-\ Az^r\ T_1^r\quad Lac^-\ Gal^-\ S^r$$

A mixture of these cells (Hfr: 2×10^7/ml; F^-: 4×10^8/ml) was placed into nutrient broth at 37° C and samples were removed and placed into the blendor at various intervals thereafter. Following the agitation required for interruption of conjugation, the samples were plated on minimal medium plus streptomycin, which permitted only the growth of T^+ L^+ S^r recombinants. The absence or presence of the unselected donor markers (Az^s, T_1^s, Lac^+) was then determined and plotted as shown in Figure 129. The order in which the unselected markers appeared in the progeny of

*Threonine- and leucine-independent, azide-sensitive, phage T_1-sensitive, lactose- and galactose-fermenting, and streptomycin-sensitive. This may also be written in the following preferred form: *thr*$^+$, *leu*$^+$, *azi-s*, T_1-*s*, *lac*$^+$, *gal*$^+$·*str-s*.

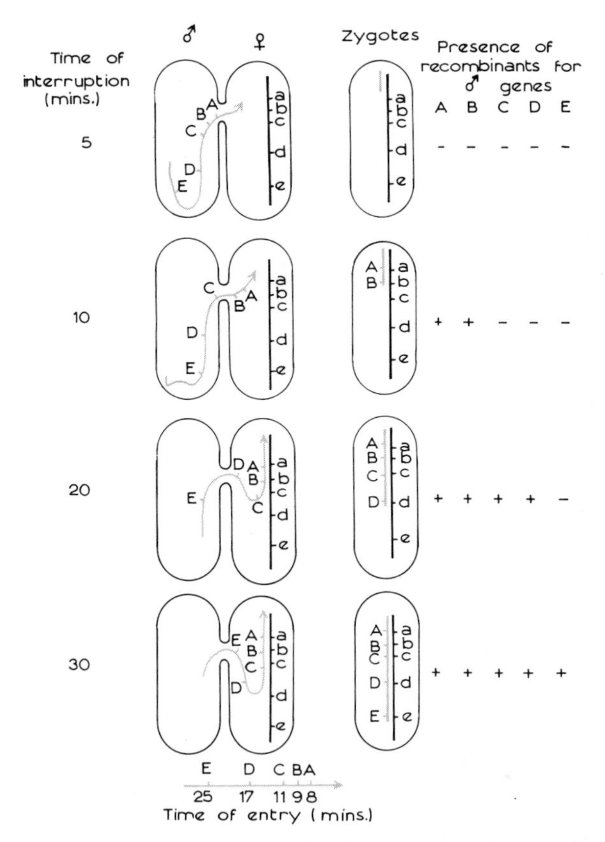

FIGURE 128. Diagrammatic representation of an interrupted mating experiment with *E. coli* strains. (From Hayes, 1964.)

recombinants from interrupted matings correlated perfectly with the order that had been established in prior mating experiments by the more conventional genetic techniques of recombination frequencies (p. 293) (Fig. 130).

It was therefore concluded that the penetration of the donor chromosome into the recipient cell must be an oriented process in which the male markers enter the recipient cell in the order in which they are arranged on the chromosome and at a rate that is proportional to their respective distance from each other. The latter correlation indicates that the speed of migration of the chromosomal material (the polydeoxynucleotide chain) from Hfr to F^- cell, once started, must continue at a constant rate, and that each chromosome piece, once it has entered the F^- cell, has an equal probability of participating in subsequent recombinations.

At optimal environmental conditions (37° C, in the presence of a good energy source) the transfer of the entire chromosome from the male to the female *E. coli* takes about 100 minutes.* However, as we have noted

*Since the *E. coli* chromosome contains about 10^7 base pairs, this means that under favorable conditions about 10^5 base pairs are transferred in one minute from the male to the female cell.

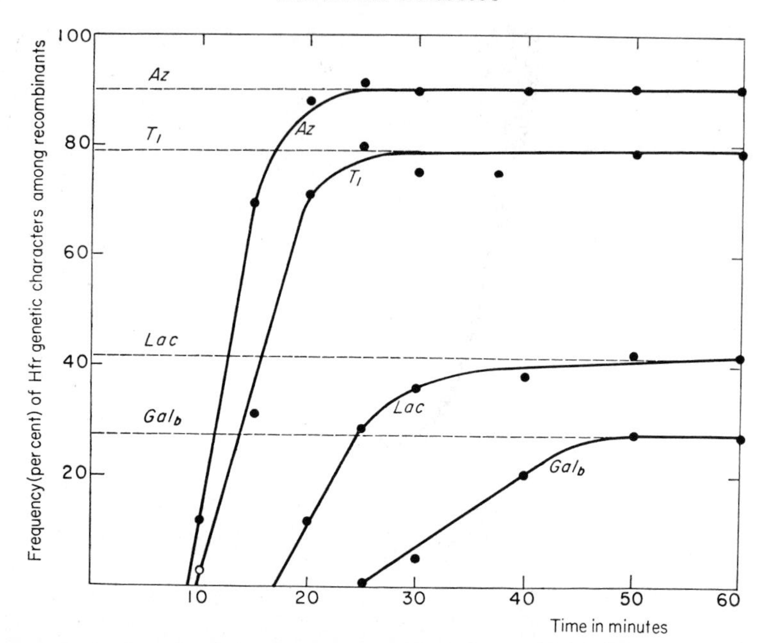

FIGURE 129. The order of penetration of various genetic determinants of Hfr H T^+ L^+ Az^s T_1^s Lac^+ Gal^+ S^s bacteria into F$^-$ *P678* T^- L^- Az^r T_1^r Lac^- Gal^- S^r bacteria during conjugation. The solid lines show the genetic constitution of the T^+ L^+ S^r recombinants from samples taken at various times and treated for 2 minutes in a Waring blendor prior to plating; the dotted lines show the genetic constitution of the same recombinants from untreated samples. Abcissa: Time of sampling. Ordinate: The frequency, per hundred T^+ L^+ S^r recombinants, of various genetic characters from the Hfr donors. (From Jacob and Wollman, 1961.)

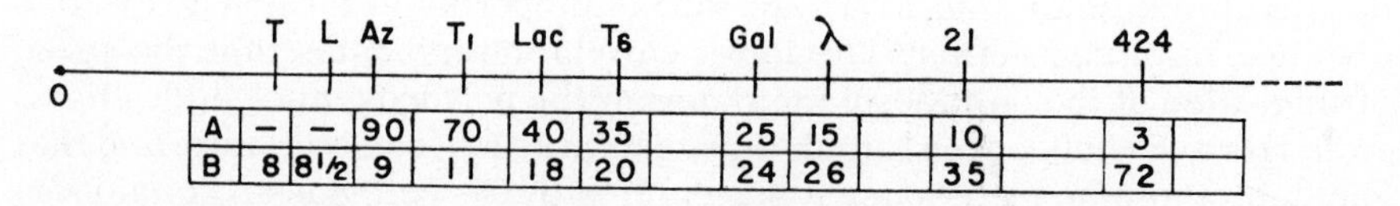

	T	L	Az	T1	Lac	T6		Gal	λ		21		424	
A	—	—	90	70	40	35		25	15		10		3	
B	8	8½	9	11	18	20		24	26		35		72	

FIGURE 130. The proximal segment of the migrating (from ♂ to ♀) chromosomal replicon of Hfr H bacteria. A, The frequencies with which various characters of Hfr H bacteria are recovered per hundred T^+ L^+ S^r recombinants formed in the cross indicated in Figure 129. B, The times (in minutes) at which the genetic determinants of these characters begin to enter the recipient bacteria as determined by interrupted matings. O (for origin) is the end that enters the F$^-$ cell first. (From Jacob and Wollman, 1961.)

before, even in the absence of agitation in the Waring blendor, certain donor markers, namely those located at the distal end of the migrating chromosome, fail to appear in most of the recombinant progeny. This means that even without experimental shaking, the migrating chromosome may break before its entire length has had an opportunity to pass through the conjugation bridge from the male to the female or, perhaps, the conjugation bridge itself may rupture, thus terminating chromosomal transfer prior to its completion. There is some evidence that the provision of a more solid substrate, such as a Millipore filter placed on nutrient agar, may prevent premature chromosome breakage and yield a higher frequency of recombinants involving genes (nucleotide sequences) located on the tail end of the migrating chromosome (Matney and Achenbach, 1962a, 1962b).

As we have mentioned before (p. 300), the Hfr state will be transferred from the donor to the recipient (in an Hfr × F^- mating) only when the distal markers are present in the progeny of the recombinant. This has served to indicate that the Hfr-determining factors may be located at the tail end of the migrating chromosome. Since both microscopic (p. 27) and genetic (p. 306) data have indicated that the bacterial chromosome is circular (a feature that is probably shared by all replicating genetic elements in bacteria), the conclusion was drawn that prior to migration the circular chromosome opens up at the site of the attachment of *F* to the chromosome.

In the example, Hfr H × F^-, which we have discussed in this section, we have noted that the nucleotide sequences determining the ability to synthesize threonine and leucine (T^+, L^+) enter the F^- cells first. When the frequency of appearance of donor markers in recombinants or the rate of transfers of such markers in interrupted mating experiments was determined for other, independently isolated Hfr strains, it developed that different Hfr strains tended to have different proximal markers, and sometimes even an opposite direction of marker transfer. Thus, while one strain would always transfer its markers in the order ZYX. . . .EDCBA →, another would always transfer markers in the order CBAZYX. . . .GFED →, still another in the order ONM. . . .BAZ. . . .RQP →, another one in the order CDE. . . .XYZAB →, and still another in the order QRS. . . .ZABC. . . . MNOP →. Some actual test data are shown in Table 21 in which the O

TABLE 21. *The linkage groups of different Hfr types and the order of transfer of the determinants**

TYPES OF Hfr	ORDER OF TRANSFER OF GENETIC CHARACTERS																		
Hfr H	O	T	L	Az	T_1	Pro	Lac	Ad	Gal	Try	H	S-G	Sm	Mal	Xyl	Mtl	Isol	M	B_1
1	O	L	T	B_1	M	Isol	Mtl	Xyl	Mal	Sm	S-G	H	Try	Gal	Ad	Lac	Pro	T_1	Az
2	O	Pro	T_1	Az	L	T	B_1	M	Isol	Mtl	Xyl	Mal	Sm	S-G	H	Try	Gal	Ad	Lac
3	O	Ad	Lac	Pro	T_1	Az	L	T	B_1	M	Isol	Mtl	Xyl	Mal	Sm	S-G	H	Try	Gal
4	O	B_1	M	Isol	Mtl	Xyl	Mal	Sm	S-G	H	Try	Gal	Ad	Lac	Pro	T_1	Az	L	T
5	O	M	B_1	T	L	Az	T_1	Pro	Lac	Ad	Gal	Try	H	S-G	Sm	Mal	Xyl	Mtl	Isol
6	O	Isol	M	B_1	T	L	Az	T_1	Pro	Lac	Ad	Gal	Try	H	S-G	Sm	Mal	Xyl	Mtl
7	O	T_1	Az	L	T	B_1	M	Isol	Mtl	Xyl	Mal	Sm	S-G	H	Try	Gal	Ad	Lac	Pro
AB 311	O	H	Try	Gal	Ad	Lac	Pro	T_1	Az	L	T	B_1	M	Isol	Mtl	Xyl	Mal	Sm	S-G
AB 312	O	Sm	Mal	Xyl	Mtl	Isol	M	B_1	T	L	Az	T_1	Pro	Lac	Ad	Gal	Try	H	S-G
AB 313	O	Mtl	Xyl	Mal	Sm	S-G	H	Try	Gal	Ad	Lac	Pro	T_1	Az	L	T	B_1	M	Isol

*From Jacob and Wollman, 1961.

("origine") designates the most proximal part of the migrating chromosome, i.e., the point that enters the F^- cell first.

The only logical conclusion from such data was that there is no definable beginning and end to the bacterial chromosome. The chromosome must be circular and the specific site of association of the F element with the chromosome must differ in different Hfr strains, thus giving rise to a specific starting point of the opened-up, migrating, linear, chromosomal structure that can be transferred during conjugation. Figure 131 shows the circular linkage group of *E. coli*, K-12, and also indicates the site at which *F* associates itself with the chromosomes in different Hfr strains, as well as the direction of migration of the opened-up chromosomal element of different Hfr strains.

The oriented transfer of DNA material from donor to recipient cells in conjugation has been supported by tests with radioactive tracers, including studies employing autoradiography or lysis of recipients following conjugation with radioactively labeled (H^3-thymidine- or C^{14}-thymidine-containing) donors (cf. Jacob and Wollman, 1961; Clark and Adelberg, 1962). Also, Hfr bacteria grown in P^{32}-containing media and subsequently stored for varying periods in liquid nitrogen at −196° C (in which P^{32} decay can take place) will show, with increasing time of storage at −196° C, an increasing inactivation of markers transferable to non-radioactive F^- cells (Jacob and Wollman, 1961). What is most significant, however, is the fact that in these tests the *rate* of decrease with which a given marker appears in the recombinant progeny differs decisively and consistently from marker to marker. This is in agreement with the conclusion that as P^{32} atoms disintegrate they have, with increasing time of P^{32} decay, an increasing probability of breaking the P-containing backbone of DNA in an increasing number of places. Thus, the likelihood that two marker (nucleotide) regions will be separated by P^{32} decay is proportional to the distance between them. The results of the P^{32} decay tests, therefore, can also be used to arrange the order of markers on the linkage map. The farther a genetic determinant lies from the proximal point of the migrating Hfr chromosome, the greater becomes the probability that following P^{32} decay and attendant chromosome breakage it will be excluded from transfer to the F^- bacterium. The effects of P^{32} decay on the process of chromosome transfer, therefore, are essentially similar to the effects of mechanical breakage following blendor agitation.*

*It should be noted that the oriented, partial transfer of donor chromosomes demands certain precautions in recombination analysis of the linkage relationships among genes. Thus, in a cross, Hfr a^+ b^+ c^- d^- e^+. . .x F^- a^- b^- c^+ d^+ e^-. . ., designed to establish the distances between *a*, *b*, *c* and *d* on the basis of recombinant frequencies (see p. 293) (with *a* being the proximal end of the opened-up chromosome), care must be taken that in the analysis only cells receiving all of the markers up to and including *d* from the donor are employed. This can be controlled in this cross through the presence of auxotrophic property e^- in the recipient, which assures the recovery on minimal medium of only recombinants that have received the entire piece from *a* to *e* from the donor (those that have received only *a* to *d* cannot grow because of the continued presence of e^-). The recombination values involving the unselected marker can then be used to calculate recombinations in cells that are known to have received the critical *a* to *d* piece from the donor. The situation would be quite different, and difficult to analyze, if nutrients permitting the growth of e^- cells were present in the medium, since this would permit the recovery of recombinants that received only the small piece *a* to *b*, or *a* only, from the donor.

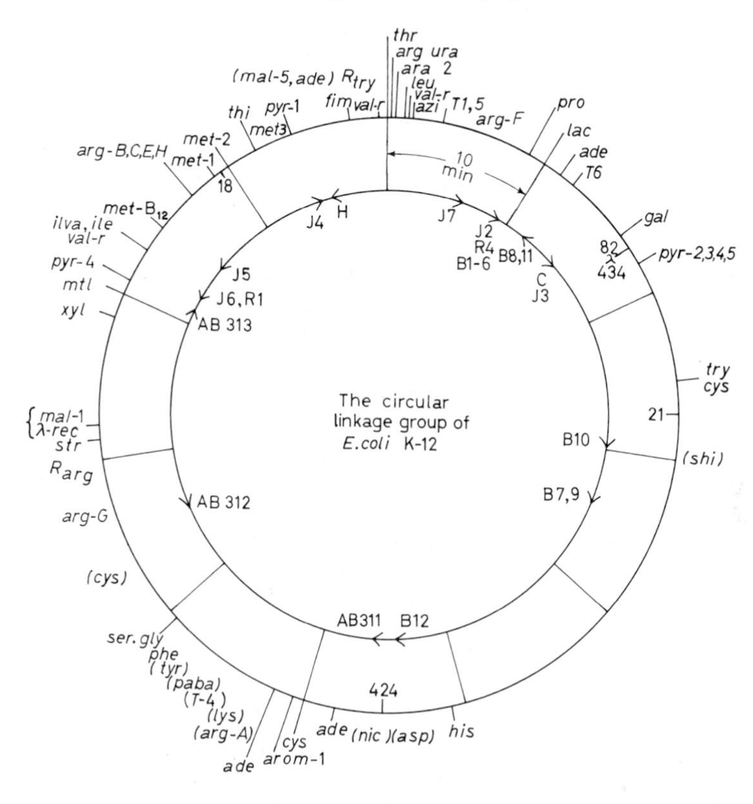

FIGURE 131. The circular linkage map of *E. coli*, K-12 showing, on the outer circle, the relative positions of markers. The approximate distances between markers is shown in time units (the entire map being divided into 11 segments, each equivalent to 10 minutes' transfer time as computed from interrupted mating experiments). The total length of the chromosome thus is equivalent to 110 minutes, which is the approximate time required for the transfer of the entire linkage group. The arrows on the inner circle indicate the leading extremities of various Hfr strains and the directions of their transfer. Prophage loci are indicated on the inside of the outer circle. (From Hayes, 1964.)

ade = adenine
ara = arabinose
arg = arginine
arg-ura = arginine + uracil requirement
arom = aromatic amino acids
asp = aspartate
azi = sodium azide resistance/ sensititivity
cys = cysteine
fim = fimbriation
gal = galactose
his = histidine
ile = isoleucine
ilva = isoleucine + valine requirement
lac = lactose
leu = leucine
lys = lysine
λ-rec = receptors for phage λ
mal = maltose
met = methionine
met-B_{12} = methionine + vitamin B_{12} requirement
mtl = mannitol
nic = nicotinamide
paba = *p*-aminobenzoic acid
phe = phenylalanine
pro = proline
pyr = pyrimidine
R_{arg} = regulator locus for arginine pathway
R_{try} = regulator locus for tryptophan pathway
ser-gly = serine + glycine requirement
shi = shikimic acid
str = streptomycin resistance/ sensitivity
T1, 5 = resistance/ sensitivity to phages $T_1 + T_5$
T4, T6 = phage T_4, phage T6, resistance/ sensitivity
thi = thiamine (vitamin B_1)
thr = threonine
try = tryptophan
tyr = tyrosine
val-r = valine resistance
xyl = xylose

Oriented, Partial Chromosome Transfer as Revealed by Zygotic Induction

It will be recalled that in the lysogenic state the maturation of the chromosome-associated prophage is prevented by the production of an immunity substance that represses vegetative growth of the phage (p. 161). This conclusion was derived in part from the intriguing phenomenon of *zygotic induction*, which takes place following conjugation between a lysogenic Hfr cell [Hfr $(ly)^+$] and a non-lysogenic F^- cell [F^- $(ly)^-$]. In this case, the recipient is lysed owing to the absence of the immunity substance in the F^-, which thus permits the maturation of lytic phage following the transfer of the chromosome-associated prophage into the F^- cell.

This zygotic induction, i.e., the conversion of the prophage to the vegetative state with eventual lysis of the zygote, can be recognized by the appearance of plaques ("lytic centers") on plates in which the zygote is plated with a large number of non-lysogenic cells (Jacob and Wollman, 1956). Zygotic induction only takes place in Hfr $(ly)^+ \times F^-$ $(ly)^-$ crosses; it does not occur in Hfr $(ly)^+ \times F^-$ $(ly)^+$ crosses and in Hfr $(ly)^- \times F^-$ $(ly)^+$ crosses. Naturally, zygotic induction can be employed to reveal the formation of a zygote in terms of chromosome transfer from the donor to the recipient cell, without the potentially possible subsequent integration of part of such transferred material into the recipient's chromosome, an event which is revealed by the appearance of recombinants (cf. Clark and Adelberg, 1962).

Different prophages have different specific sites of association* with the bacterial chromosome. Zygotic induction, therefore, has aided in the demonstration of the oriented transfer of the donor chromosome in conjugation as well as in the mapping of the specific chromosomal prophage sites (Wollman and Jacob, 1957). In Figures 130 and 131 it may be seen that the site of prophage λ is close to the *Gal* locus;† in Hfr H $(\lambda)^+ \times F^-$ $(\lambda)^-$ matings, the λ prophage therefore starts to enter the F^- cell about 26 minutes after the parental cells have been mixed. This means that in such a mating no lytic centers occur if mating is interrupted within the first 25 minutes, but lysis does ensue if matings are permitted to last 26 minutes or more. Similarly, zygotic induction of prophage 21 and consequent lysis of the zygote tend to occur in Hfr H $(21)^+ \times F^-$ $(21)^-$ matings 35 minutes after the start of the initial cell mixture (see Figs. 130 and 131). In Figure 131 it can also be seen that zygotic induction due to λ would occur very rarely in a Hfr C $(\lambda)^+ \times F^-$ $(\lambda)^-$ mating, since in this mating the λ prophage site lies close to the tail end of the migrating chromosome.

In experiments in which matings are not interrupted, the frequency of zygotic induction (as indicated by the number of lytic centers per 100 Hfr's) will decrease in direct proportion to the distance of the prophage site from the proximal site of the migrating opened-up chromosome. This again indicates that there is an increasing probability for a spontaneous

*The manner of this association has been a subject of much discussion, but it is now believed that the circular phage genome becomes inserted as a linear structure into the circular bacterial chromosome, similar to the process shown in Figure 134 (Campbell, 1962).

†Remember λ-*Gal* transductions, page 272.

and random break in the migrating chromosome as more and more of this DNA element is transferred from the donor into the recipient cell.

SEXDUCTION

By now the reader will probably have already noted some striking similarities between certain properties of the *F* element and some of the properties of temperate phages that we discussed earlier (p. 265). In both cases we are dealing with elements that can replicate autonomously or form an association with a specific site of the bacterial chromosome. Therefore, it may not come as a complete surprise that *F* elements, like prophage, occasionally have been found, following their dissociation from the chromosome-associated state, to have incorporated into themselves neighboring chromosomal regions. Thus, just as λ prophage can pick up neighboring *Gal* determinants and incorporate them into the mature phage following induction (p. 272), so-called F′ strains, derived from Hfr strains, have been found in which the *F* element carries the chromosomal determinants that it picked up, presumably by a process of exchange, from the chromosomal region with which it was previously associated (Adelberg and Burns, 1960; Sneath, 1962). Like F^+ strains, these F′ strains transfer their *F* element to F^- cells with very great efficiency, but in addition they transfer to these cells the bacterial marker that has become part of the *F* element (for example, *F-lac* can transfer the ability for lactose fermentation into lac^- F^- cells). This phenomenon has been labeled *sexduction* or *F-duction.*

The bacterial marker (or a group of closely linked markers) that migrates with the *F′* element into F^- cells persists and replicates in the recipient cell without necessarily recombining with the chromosomal structure. This means that the nucleotide regions involved are present in duplicate, one set in the recipient cell's chromosome and the other in the recipient cell's *F′* element. Such a cell, therefore, is a heterogenote and can serve in complementation analysis as efficiently as a transductional heterogenote (p. 287).

F′ cells resemble F^+ cells, but they have a much greater tendency than F^+ cells to transfer chromosomal markers (other than those that have become a permanent part of the *F′* element) into F^- cells, even though this tendency is not nearly as great as in Hfr cells. In the temporary conversion of some F′ cells to the chromosome-associated F′ state (which corresponds to the Hfr state and results in the opening up of the chromosome and its partial or total transfer into F^- cells) the *F′* element always associates itself with the site which matches the chromosomal piece carried by the *F′*. The presence of the small chromosomal region in the *F′* element thus has given it a "homing instinct" for a specific chromosomal site. In contrast, you will recall that the *F* element of F^+ cells shows no preferential site of association with the chromosome.

A homing instinct also appears to exist (but in this case for *F*) at the chromosomal site with which the *F′* tends to associate itself and where, prior to its original dissociation, it presumably left a bit of itself in exchange for the piece of chromosomal nucleotide sequence that it picked up. This is indicated by the following observation: When an F′ strain is cured by acridine-orange, and these F^- cells are reinfected (following conjugation) with a normal *F* element, they behave like F′ cells as far as frequency of transfer of chromosomes is concerned. This is believed to be due to the fact that the chromosomal site incorporating the bit of the previous *F* element has retained, by its homology with *F* material, a unique affinity ("memory") for the *F* element. This in turn may be held responsible for the more frequent association between *F* and the chromosome, a process that is believed to be prerequisite for chromosome transfer. It is not too difficult to visualize how the different Hfr types, with their specific site of *F* attachment (see Table 21), may have originated in a similar manner. The origin of their specificity may be sought in an exchange of chromosomal and *F* material at some time in the evolutionary history of these strains, which may have left each of these DNA elements with a piece of "foreign" material (in the sense of unique nucleotide sequences) which then provided a specific site of mutual attraction. This exchange of chromosomal and *F* material may not have been reciprocal; Adelberg (personal communication) believes that it may be the fact that *F* contains pieces of chromosome, rather than that the chromosome contains *F* pieces, which may be responsible for the homology of *F* with a specific chromosomal site.

INTERSPECIFIC *F*-MEDIATED CHROMOSOME TRANSFERS

Hfr strains of *E. coli* can conjugate with *Shigella* strains and yield recombinants at a frequency that is about 1/1000 of that typical for Hfr × F^- matings of *E. coli* strains. This lower efficiency of interspecific recombination does not seem to be due to a lesser frequency of transfer of the donor chromosome into the recipient cell, but rather appears to be due to a lack of perfect homology between *E. coli* and *Shigella* chromosomes. Such a lack of homology and its interference with chromosome exchanges in the merozygote (Luria and Burrous, 1957) were indicated by the fact that zygotic induction (p. 308) occurred in *E. coli* Hfr $(\lambda)^+$ × *Shigella* $(\lambda)^-$ matings at the same frequency as in *E. coli* matings, implying that conjugation itself, as well as the subsequent chromosome transfer, were just as efficient in the interspecific as in the intraspecific matings.* The poor homology between *E. coli* and *Shigella* chromosomes was further indicated by the absence of certain, presumably proximally transferred, donor markers in the recombinants.

Shigella × *Shigella* matings do not yield recombinants, even when *Shigella* cells which received *F* from *E. coli* F^+ are used. Such *Shigella* F^+ cells can transfer *F*, but cannot transfer chromosomal markers to F^- *E. coli*. This deficiency is possibly due to the lack of an appropriate region for *F* association in the *Shigella* chromosome (Luria and Burrous, 1957).

Recombinants are also formed, but at very low frequencies, in matings between *E. coli* Hfr and certain strains of *Salmonella* (Baron *et al.*, 1959; Miyaki and Demerec, 1959; Zinder, 1960). However, once obtained, re-

*Restriction, leading to a degradation of the transferred DNA, also may be responsible for the lower efficiency of interspecific (as well as some cases of intraspecific) recombination (see page 262).

combinants isolated from these crosses behave as very good recipients in further matings. This change in competence also appears to be due to non-homology between certain parts of the *E. coli* and *Salmonella* chromosomes and a removal of non-homologous sections in the fertile recombinants (cf. Marmur *et al.*, 1963).* Conjugation itself, as distinguished from subsequent recombinational events, appears to occur with equal frequency in *E. coli* Hfr × *E. coli* F⁻ and *E. coli* Hfr × *Salmonella* matings.

F can be transferred from *E. coli* to *Salmonella* and these *Salmonella* F^+ can now be mated with the usual *Salmonella* F^-, yielding recombinants at a frequency similar to that in *E. coli* F^+ × *E. coli* F^- matings (about 10^{-6}) (Zinder, 1960). The gene order obtained in such crosses corresponds to that found in *E. coli* crosses. Interspecific *Salmonella* crosses, using the same donor type as in intraspecific matings, yield lower frequencies of recombination, which is indicative of some degree of genetic non-homology among the *Salmonella* "species" (cf. Marmur *et al.*, 1963). A similar situation exists in the case of *Salmonella* × *Shigella* and *Salmonella* × *E. coli* crosses (Falkow *et al.*, 1962). Hfr mutants of *Salmonella typhimurium* have been isolated following UV-irradiation and replica plating on F^- lawns (see p. 300).

A high degree of efficiency of interspecific transfer of chromosomal markers among enterobacteriaceae, and even between *E. coli* and *Serratia marcescens*, *E. coli* and *Proteus* species, and *E. coli* and *Vibrio comma*, all of which have different GC ratios (see Table 1), can be achieved by sexduction (see Marmur *et al.*, 1963, for references). This means that the promiscuous *F* transfer, which can occur across species and family lines, can carry with it those chromosomal markers which in F′ have become a more or less permanent part of the *F* replicon. Thus *F-lac* (see p. 309) has permitted the transfer of lactose-fermenting capacities from *E. coli* into salmonellae, into *P. pestis*, and even into *Serratia marcescens*. The presence of the "foreign" *F* element in the *Serratia* cells was detectable in CsCl density gradient centrifugation of the cells' DNA, since the DNA of the *E. coli F-lac* element has a lower density than that of the *S. marcescens* DNA (Marmur *et al.*, 1961).† The foreign DNA apparently can function well in the new environment. This is revealed by the fact that *S. marcescens* cells that have received an *E. coli F* element carrying the gene for the enzyme alkaline phosphatase will form normal *S. marcescens* phosphatase, normal *E. coli* phosphatase, and a hybrid of the enzyme dimer in which one monomer is of the *E. coli* variety and the other has the *S. marcescens* specificity (Levinthal *et al.*, 1962).

It should be noted that the ability of the *F* element to cause conjugation among diverse members of the family Enterobacteriaceae, and the data on the occurrence of recombination among many of the member species of this family, testify to the phylogenetic relationship among these organisms. This relationship is further substantiated by the results obtained with

*The change of competence may also be the result of a selection of non-restricting mutants in the process of isolation of the recombinants.

†In sexduction across species lines the *F*-associated markers are not integrated with the chromosome, but always remain part of the *F* replicon. This absence of integration presumably reflects a lack of homology.

two other types of conjugation-mediating elements, the resistance transfer factor and the colicine factor, which we shall discuss next.

The Resistance Transfer Factor (*RTF*)

In studies with enteric gram-negative bacteria—studies that began in the late 1950's and were carried out principally by Japanese scientists including Watanabe, Fukasawa, Akiba, Harada, Hirota and Mitsuhashi (cf. Watanabe, 1963)—a genetic element capable of initiating conjugation and controlling the simultaneous transfer of resistance to several distinct antibiotics was recognized. Resistance to streptomycin (Sm), chloramphenicol (Cm), tetracycline (Tc) and sulfonamide (Su) can be transferred jointly, quickly and promiscuously by this genetic element between strains of *Shigella, E. coli* and *Salmonella,* from *Shigella* to *E. coli* and from *E. coli* to *Shigella*, etc., and even from enterobacteriaceae to other genera, including *V. coma, Proteus* and *Serratia.* Usually all four resistance properties are transferred together, but occasionally only three, two, or one of them may be transferred and all such transfers tend to occur independent of chromosomal genes. This unique situation was first recognized in epidemiological studies which revealed that since the late 1950's as many as 10 per cent of all *Shigella* strains isolated from outbreaks of bacillary dysentery in Japan showed multiple drug resistance that was readily transferred by cell contact, but not by cell-free culture filtrates, to appropriate recipient strains.

The genetic element responsible for such infectious multiple drug resistance has been named *RTF* (resistance transfer factor); it meets all of the specifications of an episome, replicon, or conjugon (see p. 291). This means it can exist as an independent replicating element, autonomous of the bacterial chromosome, or it can enter into direct association with a specific chromosomal site. When autonomous, it can replicate at a rate which may be, at least under certain conditions, higher than that of the chromosome and it can act as a sex factor, causing conjugation between RTF^+ and RTF^- cells. Subsequent to conjugation, the *RTF* element can migrate by itself from the RTF^+ donor to the RTF^- conjugant, or occasionally (10^{-6} to 10^{-8}), following association with the chromosome, chromosomal markers may be transferred with *RTF*. As in the case of the *F* factor, such transfers can be interrupted by agitation in a blendor. Also, as in the case of *F′*, when chromosomal markers have become more permanently associated with *F* following an apparent recombination with the chromosome, *RTF* appears to exchange occasionally some of its components for chromosomal components. The formation of *RTF* elements with resistance determinants for only three, two, or one therapeutic agent instead of the usual four is believed to be the result of such recombinational events. Like *F*, *RTF* can be eliminated by the exposure of RTF^+ cells to acridine.

The size of *RTF* seems to be similar to that of *F* and phage λ. The DNA nature of *RTF* is indicated by studies with radioactive tracers and by the fact that mitomycin C, which specifically inhibits DNA synthesis, also inhibits the transfer of multiple drug resistance. The location of the resistance determinants and the determinant of conjugation on this DNA structure appears to be distinct, since it has been possible to transfer the resistance determinants *by transduction* with the aid of phage LT-2 from *Shigella* into *Salmonella typhimurium* but such transductants cannot subsequently transfer these resistance determinants by conjugation. This suggests that the genetic determinants responsible for *RTF*-controlled conjugation cannot be picked up by the transducing phage, together with the resistance factors, the transduced *RTF* thus being deficient. Interestingly enough, introduction of an *F* element can restore the ability of such transductants to transfer, following conjugation, their resistance determinants (independently of the chromosome) to other strains.

As a rule, *RTF* competes with *F* when both are present in the same donor cell. F^+ strains containing *RTF* will not transfer their *F* factor, and even the efficiency of Hfr cells as chromosome donors is usually, but not in all strains, reduced to 1/100 by the presence of *RTF*. This epistatic (domineering) effect of *RTF* may be due, in part, to the fact that the periodate-sensitive surface antigen produced in the presence of *RTF* is different from that produced by *F*, as indicated by the loss of adsorption sites for the F-specific phage in RTF^+ cells (see p. 298). If, as some investigators suspect (cf. Jacob *et al.*, 1963), the site of formation of the conjugation-promoting antigen is localized near the site where the replicon (*F* or *RTF*, respectively) is attached to the cell membrane and if this site is also the place where the conjugation bridge is formed, then one might assume that the competition between *RTF* and *F* could involve a physical separation from the site of cell contact in conjugation. This means that in RTF^+ cells the conjugation bridge may be formed near the *RTF* element (which also may be circular in its non-migrating state); in F^+ and Hfr cells the conjugation bridge may be formed in close proximity to the *F* replicon.

RTF also can compete with the transfer of at least one type of colicinogenic factor (colicinogenic factors represent a third type of replicon, episome, or conjugon, which we shall discuss in the next section).

Little is known so far about the biochemical mechanisms responsible for the multiple drug resistance in RTF^+ cells. A reduced permeability of the cells for the drugs, specifically controlled for each of the different types of resistance, may be involved. It could not be a matter of generally reduced permeability, since, in addition to the most common type of strains which are resistant to Su, Sm, Cm and Tc, strains resistant to only one, two, or three of the drugs can be obtained in nature and in the laboratory. Little is known about the origin of the *RTF* replicon, but its importance for problems of public health should be obvious, since the *RTF* replicon and its constituent resistance determinants can be transferred so easily by non-pathogenic bacteria to every genus of the Enterobacteriaceae, and even to other genera such as *Vibrio*.

The Colicine Factor (*col*)

It has been known for a long time that some strains of Enterobacteriaceae can produce polypeptide antibiotics, called *colicines*, which can kill sensitive members of other strains of this family (Frédéricq, 1957).* The different colicines, which have different host specificities and different antigenic properties, have been labeled I, B, E_1, E_2, K, etc.; the factors responsible for their production (colicinogenic factors) are not linked to chromosomal markers and have been designated *col* I, *col* B, *col* E_1, etc. A given strain can produce more than one colicine and the production of colicine makes a cell immune to the cidal action of its own colicine.

Colicinogeny is in many respects similar to lysogeny: Colicine production increases after UV-irradiation (induction), and it can be lost spontaneously ($col^+ \rightarrow col^-$) but cannot be regained in col^- cells by means other than infection by *col*$^+$. The colicine factors (*col*) appear to be part of a distinct genetic element to which we shall refer as *Cf* and which is extremely similar in its properties to *RTF* and *F*.† Like the other replicons, conjugons, or episomes, *Cf* can be transmitted by cell contact from col^+ to col^-,‡ and it usually, but not always, is transferred independent of chromosomal markers. Thus, like *F* and *RTF*, *Cf* can exist and replicate autonomously as well as in apparent association with the chromosome. The speed of transmission of *Cf* is, however, in all the strains analyzed so far, much slower than that of *F* or *RTF*. Thus, while *RTF* is transferred to RTF^- cells within a few minutes after conjugation (as revealed by interrupted mating tests), transmission of *Cf* within a Cf^- population can take several hours (>five hours). However, retransmission of recently acquired *Cf* is quite rapid (<one hour) for seven to eight generations following the first acquisition of *Cf*. This indicates that the usual slow transmission may be a reflection of transmission by only a few cells in "old" col^+ populations, whereas high frequency transfer of colicogeny (HFCT) involves an ability of the majority of cells in a "new" col^+ population to participate in transfers (Stocker *et al.*, 1963).

The various *col* factors (e.g., *col* I, *col* E_1, *col* E_2, etc.) enable the possessor to conjugate with an enterobacterium lacking this *col* factor. Thus col I^+ will conjugate with col I^-, col E_1^+, or col E_2^+, etc. The *col* factor (presumably as a part of *Cf*) is transferred to the col^- recipient in such conjugations without a loss of col^+ characteristics in the donor cells. This implies that the carrier of *col* (the *Cf* element) must multiply autonomously either just prior to, or during, such transfers (Smith and Stocker, 1962).

Like *F* and *RTF*, *Cf* can occasionally transfer chromosomal markers, presumably after having associated itself temporarily with the chromosome (Ozeki and Howarth, 1961; Smith and Stocker, 1962). The frequency of *Cf*-mediated recombination of chromosomal markers in crosses between HFCT donors of *S. typhimurium* and col^- *S. typhimurium* recipients is approximately 1×10^{-8}. *Cf* also can be introduced into F^- *E. coli* cells which normally do not conjugate with other F^- cells (see p. 297). Such F^- *E. coli* cells yield recombinants at low frequency (10^{-8}) after having become col^+.

*Similar phenomena occur also in other bacterial groups (cf. Ivanovics, 1962) and the more general term "bacteriocine" has been applied to the entire group of such bacterial substances.

†Even though there is no evidence so far that any other genetic determinants are linked to *col*, it appears appropriate and conceptually helpful, to distinguish between *col* factors and a *Cf* element of which they are a part (and not necessarily the *sole* part).

‡In certain cases this requires the concurrent presence of *F* in the donor.

The linkage map (chromosome map) derived from col$^+$ × col$^-$ matings in *E. coli* is identical to that obtained from Hfr × F$^-$ or F$^+$ × F$^-$ matings. Also, the mapping of the *Salmonella* chromosome, with the aid of *Cf*-mediated transfers and subsequent analysis of recombinant classes, revealed that the order of loci in *S. typhimurium* is similar to that in *E. coli* (Smith and Stocker, 1962). As in *E. coli*, the data obtained with different selective markers showed that there is close linkage between the markers on opposite ends of any linkage map that can be constructed, which implies that the resident chromosome must be circular.

In cells that possess both *Cf* and *F*, transfer of *Cf* is reduced (Monk and Clowes, 1963).

Conjugation in *Pseudomonas* and *Vibrio* Species

Conjugation and recombination have been reported to occur in *Pseudomonas aeruginosa* (Holloway, 1955, 1956; Holloway and Fargie, 1960). The conjugon responsible for these events (*FP*) behaves very much like *F*, and in FP$^+$ × FP$^-$ matings involving seven markers, data reflecting the existence of a single linkage group have been obtained. Attempts to transfer *F* from *E. coli* into FP$^-$ strains have proved unsuccessful.

A strain of *Vibrio cholerae*, which produces a bacteriocin (see p. 314) killing other vibrios, has been found to yield recombinants when mixed with certain *V. cholerae* strains which lack the determinant for bacteriocin production (Bhaskaran, 1960). The conjugation-promoting element responsible for bacteriocin production has been labeled *P* and the properties of P$^+$ × P$^-$ matings are similar to those involving *Cf* in the Enterobacteriaceae.

Recombination has been claimed to occur between auxotrophic strains of *Serratia marcescens*, but it was a peculiar phenomenon from its very beginning because it involved the apparent transfer of only single markers from the presumed donor to the recipient (Belser and Bunting, 1956). More recently, it was shown that the events observed were not due to conjugation and recombination, but merely involved an increased frequency of residual growth and reversion to prototrophy in one auxotrophic strain under the influence of filtrable materials excreted by the other auxotroph strain (Dushman, 1963).

Current Concepts of the Nature of Conjugation and Cell-to-Cell Transfer of Information

On the basis of many suggestive experimental data, Jacob and his associates, and Adelberg and his associates arrived, in 1963, at comparable conclusions regarding the possible nature of conjugation and the transfer of informational DNA from a male donor cell to a female recipient cell in the various systems that promote conjugation. The following outline, which will repeat some of the general statements with which we opened this chapter, represents an attempt to combine and to summarize some of the essentially similar views expressed by these two groups of scientists.

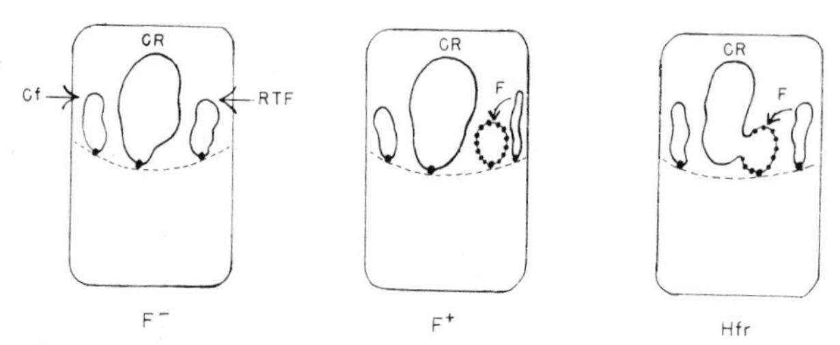

FIGURE 132. The probable organization of replicons in F$^-$, F$^+$ and Hfr cells of *E. coli*. All replicons are shown as attached to the membrane in the equatorial plane of the bacterial cell. *Cr*, chromosomal replicon; *F*, F replicon; *Cf*, colicinogenic replicon. (After Jacob.)

The principal elements of their unifying interpretation are: (1) the existence of sequentially replicating, circular DNA structures (*replicons*) of which the so-called bacterial chromosome is one,* the *F* factor another, and *RTF*, as well as *Cf*, still others; (2) the occurrence of associations and rare cross-overs leading to integrations and recombinations among such replicons; and (3) the ability of a freshly replicated copy of the opened up *F* replicon (or of the *Cf* or *RTF* replicons) to migrate from a male to a female cell through the conjugation bridge, sometimes carrying with it part, or even all, of the DNA from the chromosomal replicon with which it has become associated by integration, as a possible consequence of crossing-overs (Figs. 133 and 134).

A cell without an *F* replicon represents an F$^-$ cell, a cell with an *F* replicon is an F$^+$ cell, and a cell in which the *F* and chromosomal replicons have become one continuous structure by integration is an Hfr cell (Fig. 132). In F$^+$ × F$^-$ matings the *F* replicon may again dissociate itself from the chromosomal replicon after their joint cell-to-cell transfer; this separation of the two replicons may be caused by a reverse sequence of the events that led to the initial joining of the two replicons (Fig. 135). The process of separation sometimes may be imperfect and result in the "snipping off" of some of the material from the chromosomal replicon and the permanent incorporation of this material into the *F* replicon (Fig. 135). Such an *F* replicon carrying, more or less permanently, a piece of chromosomal replicon is apparently a typical component of so-called F′ cells, which will (in mating with F$^-$ cells) not only transfer the chromosomal markers that are now part of *F′*, but will also (with much higher frequency than *F*) undergo cross-overs with the chromosomal replicon (Fig. 136). The increased frequency of crossing-over between the *F′* replicon and the chromosomal replicon may be attributed to the easier pairing of matching DNA regions in *F′* and the chromosome (Fig. 136). The replicon determining colicin formation (*Cf*) and the *RTF* replicon may behave in a very similar way; this could explain why, for example, the colicinogenic factor

*To distinguish this replicon, carrying the majority of markers, from other replicons, we shall refer to it as a chromosomal replicon (*CR*).

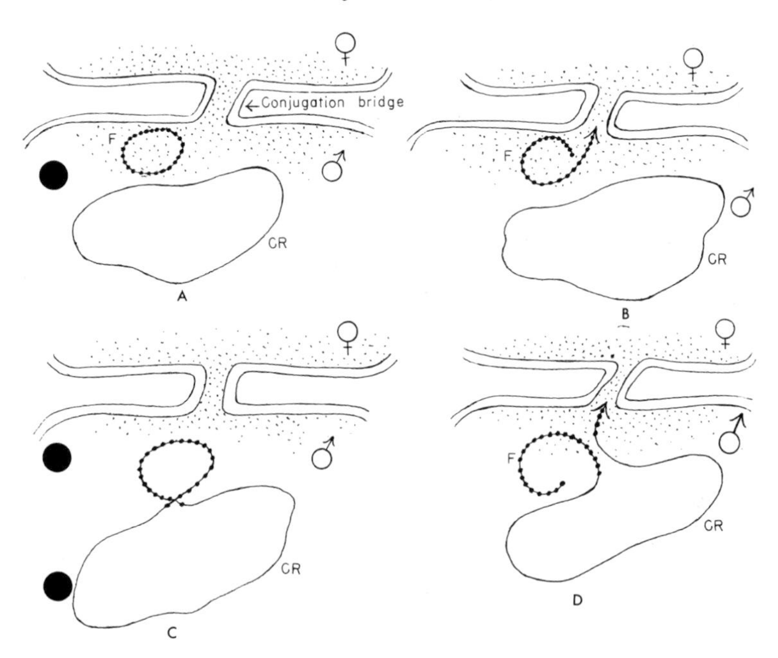

FIGURE 133. Stages in $F^+ \times F^-$ matings (A and B) and in Hfr $\times$ F^- matings (C and D). A, Chromosomal replicon (*CR*) and *F* in an F^+ cell. B. The opened-up, replicated *F* (the other *F* not shown) migrates from the F^+ to the F^- cell through the conjugation bridge. C, Part of an Hfr cell in which the *F* element is in association with the chromosomal replicon. D, The opened-up, replicated combination of *CR* and *F* in the process of migration from ♂ to ♀ cell.

can be used to transfer chromosomal DNA not only from col^+ to col^- cells of *E. coli*, but, as we have seen, even from *E. coli* col^+ to many other gram-negative cells. In the case of the more permanent association between *F* and *CR* which appears to characterize Hfr cells, *F* may remain associated (after transfer) with *CR*, but during the transfer a small *F* piece will be the proximal piece of the opened-up *CR-F* replicon and a much larger piece of *F* will be the distal piece, i.e., the piece that enters the F^- cells last (see Fig. 133).

Jacob *et al.* (1963) introduced the concept that the sequential replication of any replicon begins at a specific place in each replicon and is under the control of a specific, narrow DNA region (the "replicator"), which in turn may be activated by an "initiator" that is formed by a specific structural gene (Fig. 137).* There is evidence from studies by Nagata (1963) that in an F^- cell, replication of the chromosomal replicon may start at any one of several different sites in the circular structure, whereas after association with the *F* replicon, replication will begin immediately adjacent

*This model is patterned after the "operator" concept which has been used successfully to explain the control of modifiable gene activity. See page 352.

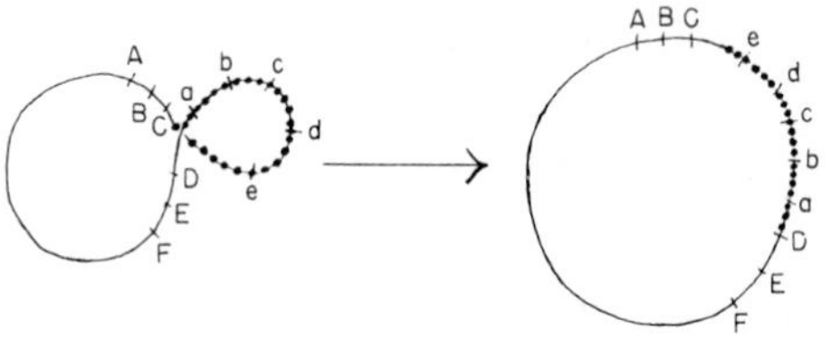

FIGURE 134. Probable mode of association between F (line with dots) and CR (solid line).

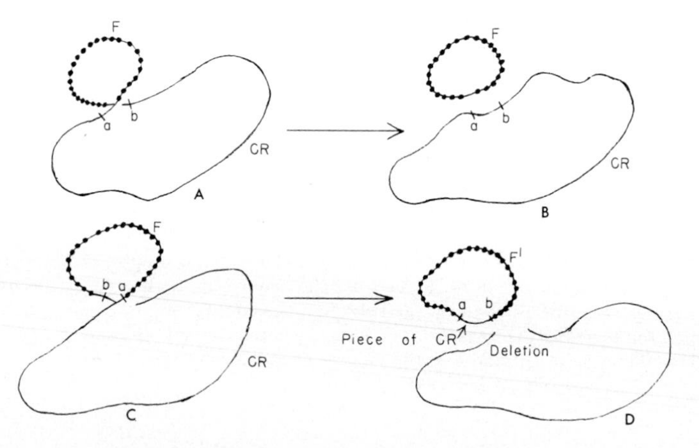

FIGURE 135. A possible mode of formation of F' (an alternate mode is indicated in Fig. 109). A and B, normal separation of F from its points of association with the chromosomal replicon. C and D, rare mode of separation resulting in the incorporation of a piece of chromosomal material into the F' element.

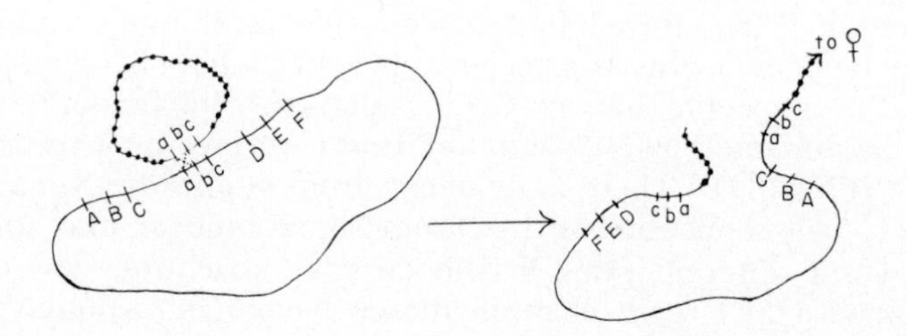

FIGURE 136. Probable modes of association and subsequent joint migration (from ♂ to ♀) of F' and CR.

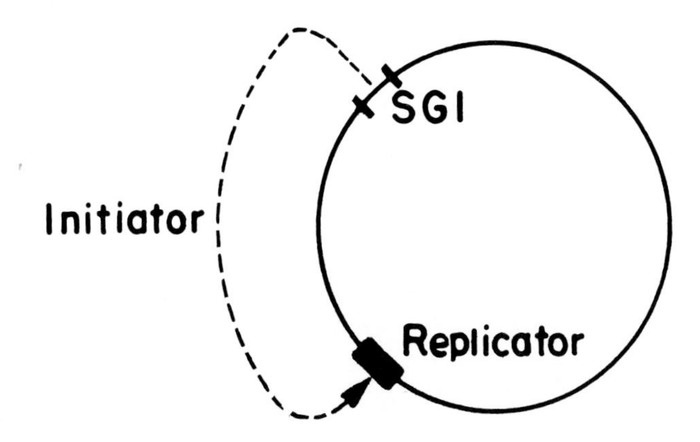

FIGURE 137. A model for the regulation of replication of a replicon. The circular replicon is assumed to carry two specific genetic determinants: (1) a structural gene (SGI) carrying the information for the synthesis of a diffusible initiator substance, and (2) the replicator that responds to the initiator and controls the beginning of the replication process, which proceeds sequentially along the circular replicon. (From Jacob *et al.*, 1963.)

to the site of *F* incorporation (D in Figure 134). The initiation point for replication of the *CR* after integration of *F*, and the driving force for male to female transfer of the *CR*-DNA, which has become associated with the *F*-DNA (Hfr), therefore, may be the replication process of *F* + *CR*; it has been assumed that the shift in the suggested initiation point of replication is due to a dominance of the activity of *F* replicators over *CR* replicators. As already mentioned in Chapter 3, it has also been suggested that the *F* replicon, and the other replicons as well, may be in intimate association with the cell membrane (see Fig. 22) and may cause the deposition of a specific localized antigen (see p. 298) on the cell surface near the site of attachment to the cell membrane. It is conceivable that the conjugation bridge is formed at this point and that the transfer of *F* and of *F*-associated materials from other replicons takes place at this point either during or immediately following DNA replication.

The fact that replication coincides with, or precedes, transfer of informative DNA during conjugation, is indicated by the finding that pulse-labeling of the male DNA just prior to conjugation leads to a recovery of one-half labeled and one-half unlabeled DNA from the transferred material. Jacob *et al.* (1963) have proposed that DNA replication coincides with transfer of DNA from the male to the female, whereas Adelberg, on the basis of studies involving inhibition of DNA synthesis (Bouck and Adelberg, 1963), has favored the idea that replication of the entire replicon precedes the transfer.

Finally, it should be emphasized that for the time being all of the thoughts expressed in this last section of Chapter 15 must be regarded as valuable working hypotheses rather than established facts.

[16]

INTRACELLULAR TRANSCRIPTION AND TRANSLATION OF GENETIC INFORMATION

In the preceding chapters we have occupied ourselves principally with the problem of transfer of information, in the form of DNA, from cell to cell. Now we shall focus our attention on the problem of how such information can control and regulate the vast variety of biochemical processes within the cell. This problem used to be referred to as the problem of "gene action," and in modern molecular biology is restricted principally to an inquiry into the mechanisms which control the formation of specific proteins. This restriction seems justified since metabolism, catabolism and biosynthesis, including the formation of structural elements of the cell, are all governed by enzymatically active proteins. The question of gene action, therefore, boils down to the question of how, within an individual cell, the genetic information in DNA is translated into the formation of polypeptides—the constituent of proteins. We have already touched on some general aspects of this problem in Chapters 1 and 2 but shall try to present some of the details in this chapter.

GENERAL ASPECTS OF THE INFORMATION FLOW FROM DNA TO PROTEIN

The experimental work which began in the 1950's has led to a good general picture of the manner in which the information specified by the sequence of nucleotides in DNA is first transcribed into *messenger RNA* (mRNA)* and then translated, with the help of *transfer RNA* (tRNA), into polypeptides. Figure 138 is a simple presentation of the recognized steps.

*Also referred to as *complementary RNA* (cRNA).

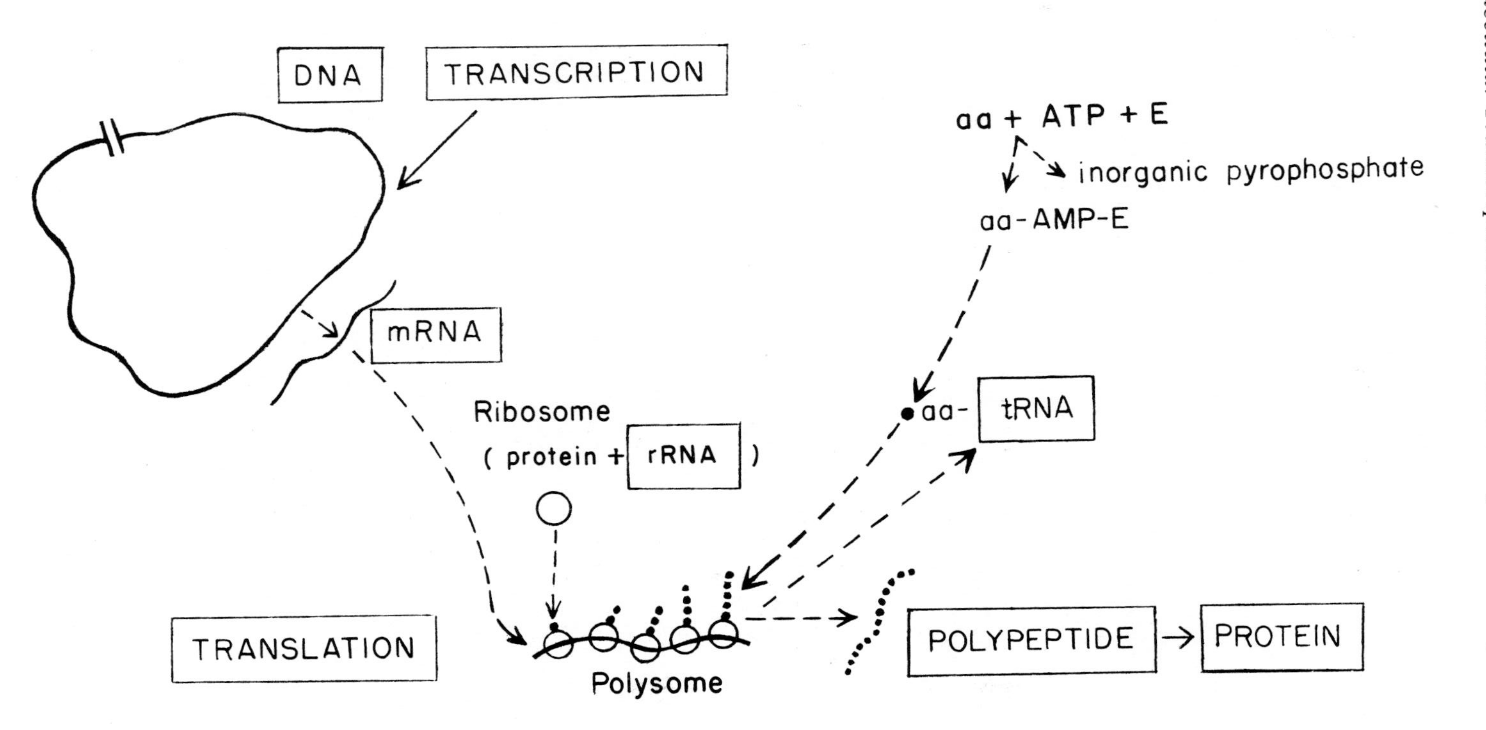

FIGURE 138. Diagram of some major steps in DNA-directed protein synthesis.

The information (deoxynucleotide sequence) contained in a limited region of one of the two strands of the circular DNA is transcribed first into a complementary single-stranded messenger RNA. This mRNA then associates itself with *ribosomes*. These are cytoplasmic particles which consist of protein and *ribosomal RNA* (rRNA) and which serve as assembly lines for polypeptide synthesis. To the ribosomes come complexes consisting of a given amino acid and its corresponding transfer RNA (there are at least 20 different tRNA's, differing in parts of their nucleotide sequence, for each of the 20 different amino acids). The tRNA serves as an adapter for the mRNA, bringing a given amino acid to its proper place in the polypeptide chain, the place being specified by the nucleotide sequence (codon). The polypeptide is assembled sequentially as the ribosome travels along the amino acid sequence-specifying mRNA (see Fig. 142 for details). Since the nucleotide sequence specifies the amino acid sequence (see pp. 337 and 343), each codon (see p. 7) on the mRNA attracts a specific tRNA and its associated amino acid. Although this attraction appears to involve weak hydrogen-bonding of complementary bases (A—U ; C—G), we could compare the mRNA with an assembly pattern having openings with 20 specific configurations (round, square, or triangular, etc.) into which (like a round, square, or triangular peg) a specific tRNA, and with it a specific amino acid, can fit. The newly arrived amino acid is then joined to the preceding amino acid in the evolving polypeptide chain.

The suggestion has been made that the lipoproteins may hold the amino acids together while the peptide bond (attachment of the amino group of one amino acid to the carboxyl group of the other, with the elimination of H_2O) is formed. There is also evidence that in the process of polypeptide formation amino acid subunits are incorporated into the growing protein chain one at a time, starting at the end of the chain with an NH_2 group and progressing toward the end that terminates in a COOH group (Dintzis, 1961; Schweet and Bishop, 1962). When completed, the polypeptide is released from the ribosome; in cases in which the protein consists of several polypeptide chains, the final assembly takes place, either on the ribosome or away from it, in an as yet undefined manner. The tRNA, having done its job of placing the specific amino acid into its proper position in the evolving polypeptide chain, is subsequently released intact to pick up more amino acid molecules.

A given mRNA also can serve more than once to specify the assembly of a polypeptide. Thus, a series of ribosomes attaches itself to a given messenger RNA to perform the job of putting specific amino acids together into a specific polypeptide chain; the resulting configuration of several ribosomes held together by one molecule of mRNA has been given the name polyribosome or *polysome*.

Figure 138 also shows the known steps in the formation of the aa-tRNA complex that brings the amino acids to the ribosomes. An amino acid is first activated by being coupled with energy-rich ATP through the aid of a specific enzyme (aminoacyl-tRNA synthetase), with a release of inorganic pyrophosphate. The amino acid-AMP-enzyme complex then interacts with the corresponding tRNA, the carboxyl group of the amino acid being esterified to a hydroxyl residue on a terminal adenosine moiety of tRNA. The enzyme and AMP are released during this esterification. Since there are 20 different amino acids and since these are bound in this activation process to at least 20 different tRNA's, it had to be concluded that there are also at least 20 different aminoacyl-tRNA synthetases.

We thus have a unidirectional intracellular flow of information, in the form of a *transcription* of specific nucleotide sequences, from DNA to mRNA and thence (with the aid of tRNA and ribosomes) a *translation* of these nucleotide sequences into specific amino acid sequences of specific polypeptides. Let us now examine some of these steps in more detail.

TRANSCRIPTION

The transfer of information from DNA to mRNA, i.e., the formation of an mRNA strand complementary to a part of one DNA strand, is known as the transcription step. Even prior to the experimental confirmation of this intermediary step in DNA-dependent protein synthesis, the involvement of RNA in the transfer of information from DNA to protein was suspected on the basis of a number of observations. Among these were the finding that enucleated (essentially DNA-free) algae and amoebae continued protein synthesis for a prolonged period of time, thus excluding DNA itself as a direct template for protein synthesis and pointing to the role of an intermediary (Hämmerling, 1953; Brachet and Chantrenne, 1956). RNA was suspected as being this intermediary, and cytochemical analyses revealed that indeed there was a close correlation between the RNA and protein content of these cells under different growth conditions.

This holds true for bacteria as well, in which under different growth conditions the amount of DNA may remain constant while the amount of RNA and protein may rise significantly (Maaløe, 1960). Furthermore, a depression of DNA synthesis (for example, in thymine-requiring mutants) is not accompanied by an immediate depression of protein synthesis (Barner and Cohen, 1957), whereas a depression of RNA synthesis (for example, in uracil-requiring mutants, or in the presence of uracil analogs) stops protein synthesis (Pardee, 1954; Naono and Gros, 1960).

In addition, studies on induced enzyme formation with conjugating *E. coli* cells had revealed that very shortly after the introduction of the appropriate gene for β-galactosidase into a recipient, the maximal rate of enzyme synthesis was attained and continued at a uniform rate (Riley *et al.*, 1960). This indicated that if DNA itself was not the template for protein synthesis, a rapid transfer of the DNA-carried information to protein-forming sites must have occurred and, since the rate of enzyme synthesis remained constant thereafter and did not increase with time, a constant number of active templates for protein synthesis must have been formed continuously. The simplest explanation for this was the formation of an unstable intermediate.

On the basis of these and other data, Jacob and Monod (1961) proposed the concept of the "messenger RNA" at a time when it had not yet been possible to isolate such a hypothetical RNA. We must point out one particular difficulty that existed in the earlier considerations regarding the role of RNA as an intermediary in DNA-controlled protein synthesis; this was the fact that the base content of cellular RNA did not seem to match that of DNA.* However, this apparent difficulty was resolved when it was discovered that there were actually several different types of RNA in the cell and that one of these, the messenger RNA, perfectly matched the base content of a given cell's DNA.

RECOGNITION OF DIFFERENT RNA'S

Differences in the physical properties of different types of cellular RNA first became apparent from the fact that following centrifugation of disrupted bacterial cells at 40,000 rpm for two to three hours, the sediment, rich in cytoplasmic RNA-protein particles known as ribosomes (see p. 331), contained about 80 per cent of the cells' RNA with molecular weights of 600,000 and 1,200,000, while the supernate contained a "soluble" RNA with a molecular weight of about 25,000. The soluble RNA fraction is now usually referred to as transfer RNA and it constitutes about 2 per cent of the cell's total RNA. From the ribosomal fraction containing the high molecular weight RNA it was possible to separate, after lowering the Mg^{++} concentration, an RNA fraction with a molecular weight of about 500,000 (Nomura *et al.*, 1960). This RNA is the messenger RNA and its $\frac{G + C}{A + U}$ ratio matches the $\frac{G + C}{A + T}$ ratio of the cell's DNA, while the other RNA's have an approximately equivalent content of each of the four bases. Messenger RNA represents about 20 per cent of a cell's total RNA.

The separation of these different types of RNA is routinely accomplished by prolonged centrifugation in a density gradient (sucrose, CsCl; see Fig. 36) or by high speed centrifugation in which the rate of sedimentation (S) is a function of the molecular weight and shape. Thus, ribosomal RNA has sedimentation constants of 23 S and 16 S; transfer RNA, 4 S; and messenger RNA, 8 S to 30 S (Spiegelman and Hayashi, 1963).

MESSENGER RNA

Now let us return to further discussion of the *messenger RNA*. This RNA, with a base composition resembling that of its corresponding DNA, was actually first observed in studies with T_2 phage-infected *E. coli*, in which (following infection) an RNA with a base composition similar to the phage DNA but different from the host cell DNA was detected (Volkin and Astrachan, 1956). The role of this RNA in protein synthesis was further indicated by the finding that such RNA was bound to the ribosomes of the phage-infected cells (Nomura *et al.*, 1960; Brenner *et al.*, 1961). Subsequently, it became possible through hybridization experiments to identify the existence of mRNA in normal *E. coli* cells uninfected by phage (Hayashi and Spiegelman, 1961; Gros *et al.*, 1961). The complementarity of this mRNA to one strand of the cell's DNA was demonstrated in so-called "hybridization tests" (Hall and Spiegelman, 1961; Hayashi and Spiegelman, 1961).

*Remember: except for uracil instead of thymine, and ribose instead of deoxyribose, RNA resembles DNA.

The basic principle of the hybridization test is relatively simple: A messenger RNA fraction, separated in a sucrose gradient from *E. coli* cells "pulse-labeled" with P^{32}, is incubated with heat-denatured (single-stranded) DNA at 55 to 60° C and then slow-cooled. When the DNA used is from the same species as the RNA, the mRNA will hybridize with the complementary DNA strand upon cooling. The non-hybridized RNA can then be destroyed by RNAase treatment, and the RNA-DNA hybrid, recognizable by its density (which is close to native DNA but very different from RNA) and by the presence of the P^{32} labeled RNA, is recoverable following centrifugation in a CsCl density gradient (Fig. 139). Hybrids are formed only when homologous DNA and RNA are used, which indicates that complementarity (corresponding sequences of complementary DNA and RNA bases) and not just similarity in base composition is required.

Subsequent to the discovery and use of the analytical method just cited, some preparatory methods for the *isolation of mRNA* were developed. In one of these, which served to isolate bacterial mRNA formed under the influence of phage DNA (Bautz and Hall, 1962), denatured (single-stranded) T_4 phage DNA was coupled to acetylated, phosphorylated cellulose in a column; the column was heated to 55° C, and phenol-extracted RNA from T_4-infected *E. coli* was added and left on the column for 8 to 12 hours. Following cooling, the bacterial mRNA, annealed to the single-stranded DNA, remained on the column while the non-mRNA was eluted by washing the column with solutions containing high salt concentrations. Subsequently, the mRNA could be eluted from the column by heating and washing with solutions containing low salt concentrations. Another method used is similar to the technique just described, but employs agar gel to trap the denatured DNA, which then, under appropriate conditions of temperature and ionic strength, can adsorb and subsequently release mRNA (Bolton and McCarthy, 1962).

PRIMING OF MRNA BY DNA. The ability of DNA to prime the synthesis of an mRNA complementary to DNA was demonstrated in cell-free bacterial systems almost simultaneously by several groups of investigators (Spiegelman, 1958; Stevens, 1960; Hurwitz *et al.*, 1961; Ochoa *et al.*, 1961; Weiss and Nakamoto, 1961).* They recognized a *DNA-dependent RNA polymerase* which (in the presence of DNA, Mg^{++}, and all four nucleoside triphosphates) catalyzes the formation of an RNA that has a base composition and base sequence identical to that of the DNA primer (except that in RNA, uracil takes the place of thymine). The primer DNA is not altered after RNA synthesis, as demonstrated by the fact that biologically active DNA from *D. pneumoniae* or *B. subtilis* retains its transforming activity after participating in the RNA polymerase reactions (Hurwitz *et al.*, 1963).

The basic technique employed in the cell-free studies of mRNA formation is relatively simple. It depends on the fact that single nucleotides

*Earlier work had led to the recognition of a *DNA-independent* enzyme (polynucleotide phosphorylase, see p. 64), which is able to catalyze the formation of polyribonucleotide chains from nucleoside diphosphates *in vitro* (Grunberg-Manago *et al.*, 1956). Also, RNA phages can induce an *RNA-dependent RNA polymerase*, a process which is independent of bacterial DNA (August *et al.*, 1963).

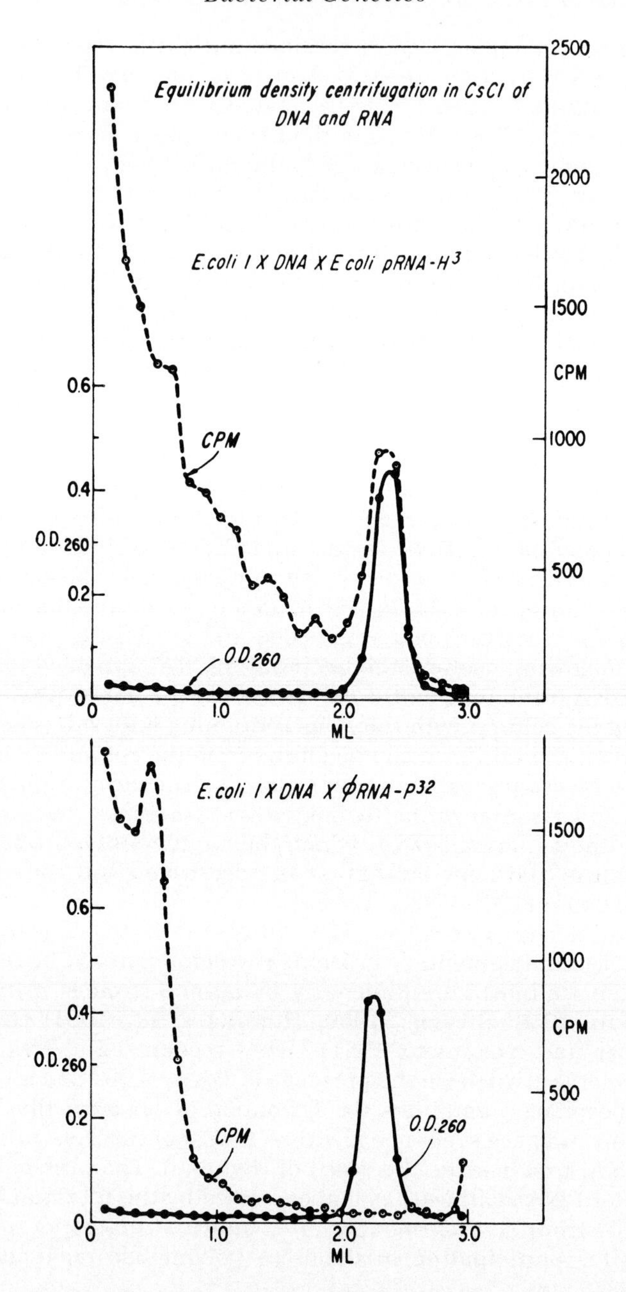

FIGURE 139. Cesium chloride density gradient centrifugation of incubated mixtures of heat-denatured *E. coli* DNA and *E. coli* ribosomal RNA (upper graph), and of heat-denatured *E. coli* DNA and RNA from bacteriophage MS ø 2 (lower graph). The peak in OD identifies the position of DNA in the density gradient which decreases from left to right. The ribosomal RNA was H^3-labeled, and the phage RNA was P^{32}-labeled. Mixtures of heated DNA and RNA were cooled slowly from 55° C to 30° C over a period of 17 hours and centrifuged, after addition of CsCl, for 72 hours at 33,000 rpm. Subsequent assays were performed as shown in Figure 36. (From Spiegelman and Doi, 1963.)

can be readily distinguished from RNA owing to their ability to dissolve in acid. In contrast, polyribonucleotides (RNA) are not soluble in acid. Therefore, the formation of RNA in a cell-free system can be followed by adding radioactively-labeled (P^{32} or C^{14}) nucleotides to various cell extracts and testing, after incubation, for the presence of radioactivity in acid-insoluble precipitates derived from the reaction mixture.

The early studies indicated that the DNA-dependent RNA polymerase can transcribe both strands of the DNA molecule (Geiduschek *et al.*, 1961; Chamberlin and Berg, 1962), but more recently it has been recognized that the *in vitro* conditions yielding such results represented artifacts, apparently due to the fact that the investigators utilized fragmented, linear DNA molecules. *In vivo*, where the DNA apparently exists as a circular structure, *only one strand of the DNA molecule is transcribed* into complementary mRNA (Hayashi *et al.*, 1963; Marmur and Greenspan, 1963), and when care is taken to isolate circular, rather than fragmented, phage DNA from infected *E. coli* cells, only one DNA strand is copied *in vitro* (Spiegelman and Hayashi, 1963). The experimental data leading to this conclusion employed hybridization tests between single-stranded phage DNA and mRNA formed in bacteriophage-infected bacterial cells.

In one series of such experiments the phage SP8 of *B. subtilis* was employed (Marmur and Greenspan, 1963). This phage is unique because its double-stranded DNA consists of two strands with different densities (the heavier strand is richer in pyrimidines), which results in banding at two distinct levels when heated single-stranded SP8 DNA is centrifuged in a CsCl density gradient. The two unlike strands can be separated by selective elution from columns containing methylated bovine albumin and Kieselguhr. Following such separation, the strands can be used for hybridization tests with mRNA isolated from SP8-infected bacteria. As shown in Figure 140, only the "heavy" strand hybridizes with the mRNA.

In another series of experiments (Spiegelman and Hayashi, 1963) the single-stranded bacteriophage ØX174 was used (Sinsheimer, 1959). It is known that immediately after infection of *E. coli* cells with this phage, a complementary strand of phage DNA is formed, giving rise to a temporarily double-stranded structure, which has been called the "replicating form" of the phage ØX (Sinsheimer *et al.*, 1962). In hybridization studies with mRNA from ØX174-infected cells it was demonstrated that only the complementary DNA strand of the "replicating" form" complexes with mRNA; neither the other strand nor the single strand of the mature virus hybridizes with appropriately purified mRNA.

As already stated, an *in vitro* transcription of both DNA strands does not occur when an unfragmented circular phage DNA, isolated by gentle extraction procedures from infected bacteria, is used. Under this condition, only one strand is copied, just as is the case *in vivo*. It can be assumed that the differences in the transcription process between fragmented linear and unfragmented circular DNA are due to the ability of the DNA-dependent RNA polymerase to start "reading" of both strands of an open ruptured DNA structure, whereas a circular DNA structure may have attachment sites for the enzyme on only one of the two DNA strands.

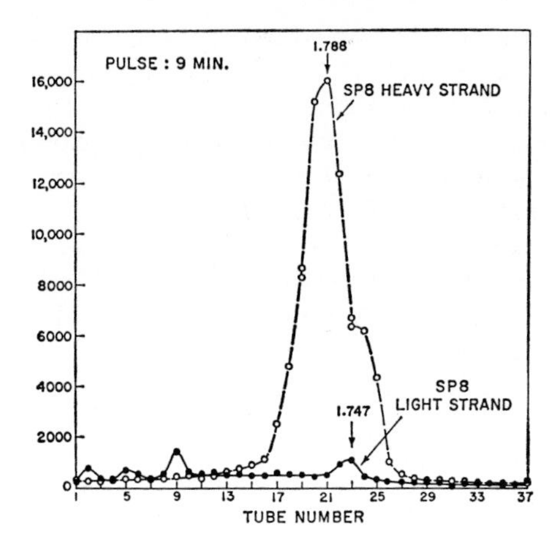

FIGURE 140. Specificity of hybridization of mRNA isolated from SP8-infected *B. subtilis* with the fractionated strands (heavy vs. light) of heated (denatured) SP8 DNA. The curves show the ribonuclease-resistant radioactivity of fractions, obtained after CsCl density gradient centrifugation from a hybridization mixture in which H^3-uridine-labeled RNA from infected bacteria was incubated with light and heavy strands of SP8 DNA for 10 hours at 57° C and then slowly cooled to room temperature. The heat-separated light and heavy phage DNA strands were fractionated by chromatography on a column containing methylated bovine serum albumin and Kieselguhr, from which they were selectively eluted with saline-phosphate. Abscissa: CsCl fractions collected after preparative centrifugation. Ordinate: Radioactivity (count/min) of H^3-uridine-labeled RNA of the CsCl gradient fractions after precipitation with trichloroacetic acid. (From Marmur and Greenspan, 1963.)

If only one strand of DNA is transcribed into mRNA under natural conditions, one may ask: What is the function of the complementary DNA strand? Recent data suggest that one of the functions of the non-transcribed second strand may be that of repairing faulty nucleotide sequences in the transcribed DNA strand (Spiegelman, unpublished observations)*.

THE SIZE OF THE TRANSCRIBED MESSAGE. What about the size of the mRNA messages that migrate from the DNA transcription site to the polypeptide-forming ribosomal site? It now appears that the mRNA may be sufficiently large (approximately 10^4 nucleotides) to contain the information for the assembly of several related proteins (Spiegelman and Hayashi, 1963; Martin, 1963; Ames and Hartman, 1963). These proteins are not related in structure but in function since they appear to be mem-

*The repairing function of the second DNA strand is also suggested by recent data obtained with *E. coli* mutants that lack one of the enzymes required for recombination. Such recombinationless mutants (which accept DNA donated by a male cell following conjugation, but fail to manifest recombinational events) also are very sensitive to the mutagenic effects of UV (Clark, 1965). This sensitivity suggests that the recombinationless mutants cannot repair the UV damage to one of the two DNA strands because the enzymes required for recombination probably are identical with those required for repair.

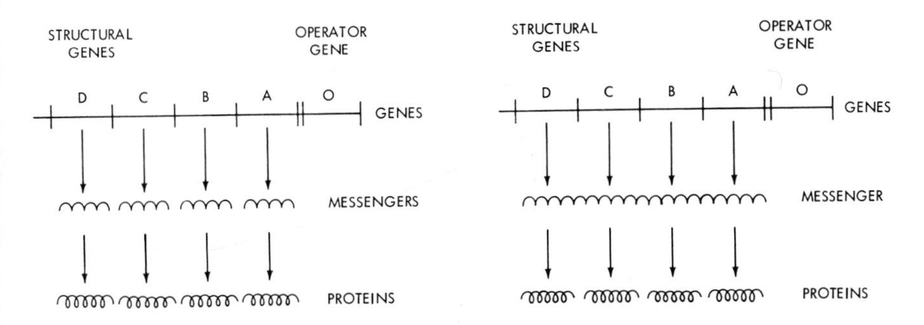

FIGURE 141. Two models for the transcription of an operon. (From Martin, 1963.)

bers of one "operon" (see p. 349); that is, they are members of a genetic unit controlling the function and regulation of several enzymes which are in the same biochemical pathway. Thus, the histidine operon (p. 286) contains seven cistrons (with about 13,000 nucleotides) controlling the formation of seven different biosynthetic enzymes. A variety of experimental data, including measurements on the molecular size and observations on functional behavior, indicate that one mRNA molecule is formed from the entire operon ("polycistronic messages"), rather than several mRNA's from each of the several cistrons of an operon (Fig. 141). However, available data do not rule out the possibility that smaller mRNA molecules may also be formed in the transcription of some of the DNA regions.

THE LIFETIME OF MRNA. The lifetime of mRNA is only a few minutes in bacteria (apparently it can be much longer in some mammalian cells) and the average mRNA appears to make approximately 15 protein molecules before it decays into acid-soluble nucleotides (Levinthal *et al.*, 1962). Data supporting this conclusion were obtained with the aid of actinomycin D, an antibiotic which interferes with mRNA synthesis by binding to dGMP-containing regions of DNA (Reich *et al.*, 1962; Hurwitz *et al.*, 1963). This antibiotic, incidentally, has been of unique usefulness for analytical studies in molecular biology, since it interferes only with DNA-dependent mRNA synthesis and not with RNA-dependent mRNA synthesis (see footnote, p. 325). It therefore does not affect, for example, the replication of RNA viruses and RNA bacteriophages.

In regard to structure, mRNA appears to be a single-stranded polynucleotide chain.

TRANSLATION

The principal participants in the translation of the four-letter language (4 nucleotides) of the mRNA into the 20-letter language (20 amino acids) of the polypeptides are the transfer RNA (tRNA) and the ribosomes.

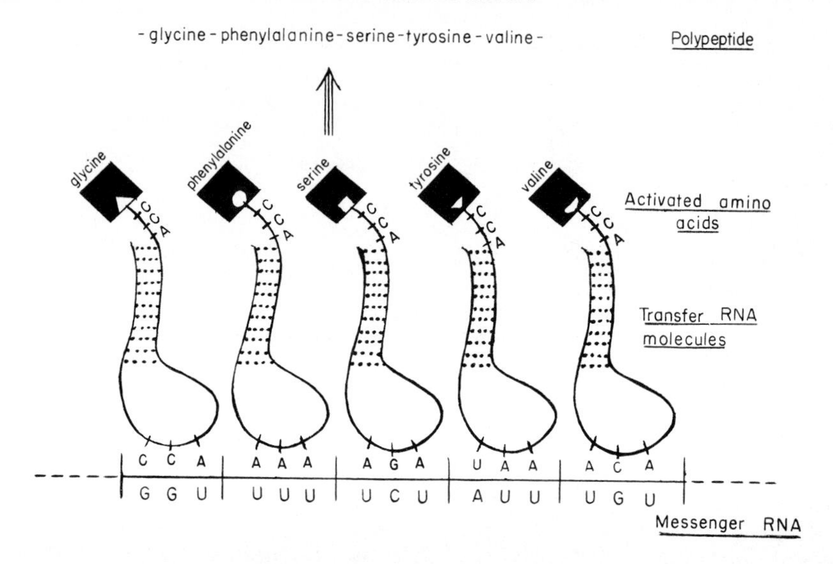

FIGURE 142. Schematic representation of some steps in the synthesis of a polypeptide chain. Note that in contrast to this simplified scheme, it is currently believed that only two transfer RNA molecules are attached to the messenger RNA-ribosome complex at any given time. The black boxes with the white geometric shapes are meant to represent the specific fit of a specific tRNA to a specific amino acid.

TRANSFER RNA

The *transfer RNA*, or soluble RNA, is both an amino acid carrier and an adaptor which, in a manner suggested by Figure 142, brings specific amino acids to the ribosome-associated mRNA template, holds them there while the amino acids are joined into a polypeptide structure, and then, having done its job, is released by enzymatic action from the polypeptide chain (Hoagland *et al.*, 1958; Zamecnik, 1960; Brown, 1962). We have already referred to the fact that an "activated" amino acid (p. 322) is coupled to the terminal adenosine moiety of the RNA (Berg and Ofengand, 1958); the final trinucleotide of *all* tRNA molecules contains cystosine-cytosine-adenine (see Fig. 142). Since each amino acid combines with a specific tRNA, a recognition mechanism between the activated amino acid and its specific tRNA must be assumed to exist; the nature of this recognition is as yet unknown. Recently, it has been discovered that about 2 per cent of the purine and pyrimidine bases in tRNA are methylated (Borek, 1963; Gold and Hurwitz, 1963) and this has given rise to the speculation that a special code involving methylated bases might play a role in the recognition of specific tRNA by specific activated amino acids.*

*Species-specific methylating enzymes methylate the conventional bases after their incorporation into tRNA. These methylating enzymes also can put methyl groups on some of the bases in DNA. The significance of such DNA methylation is still obscure; it may possibly provide the "periods" for the beginning and ends of message readings in transcription, or it might play a role in replication.

The tRNA molecules seem to be partially double-stranded (Fresco, 1963), and it is believed that the double-stranded regions originate from a hairpin-like doubling-back onto itself of an initially linear molecule; the double-strandedness is believed to result in regions where complementary bases (A—U, C—G) confront each other and can hydrogen-bond to each other. Figure 143 shows the sequence of nucleotides in a tRNA for alanine, the first tRNA to have been so analyzed (Holley *et al.*, 1965). Two of the several possible configurations, predictable on the basis of the known sequence, are also indicated in Figure 143. It will be noted that current speculations assume that there may be more than one unpaired (loop) region in tRNA. In any event, it is a nucleotide sequence in an unpaired region, presumably a triplet (see p. 337), that combines with a complementary region of the mRNA (see Fig. 142). The critical triplet base sequence of the tRNA, complementary to that of the codon in mRNA, has been referred to, perhaps with tongue in cheek, as a *nodoc*.

Transfer RNA molecules have a molecular weight of about 25,000 and a sedimentation constant of 4 S, contain about 80 nucleotides, have a purine to pyrimidine ratio of 1.0 and, unlike mRNA, have a uniform $\frac{A + U}{G + C}$ ratio of 0.6, regardless of source. They contain an unusually high percentage of pseudouridylic acid. Transfer RNA molecules are very stable and hybridize with a small part (0.023 per cent) of DNA from isologous cells, which indicates that their formation is under control of a specific DNA region (Spiegelman and Hayashi, 1963).

The hybridization studies just mentioned, in which tRNA from a given species hybridizes only with its homologous DNA have indicated that despite the uniformity of tRNA from different sources in respect to their G—C content, part of their nucleotide sequences must be uniquely different in different species (Spiegelman and Hayashi, 1963). Other functionally important parts of tRNA, however, must be uniform in all species, because tRNA from *E. coli* can participate in protein synthesis with ribosomes from rat liver cells (Nathans and Lipmann, 1961) and can also translate the genetic message of a rabbit into hemoglobin (von Ehrenstein and Lipmann, 1961). In such tests with species-foreign tRNA molecules, however, it has also been determined that functional cell-free systems require that both the ribosomes and the enzymes required for the transfer reactions come from the same source.

RIBOSOMES

About 85 per cent of a bacterial cell's RNA is found in the ribosome particles which, in turn, consist of 60 per cent ribosomal RNA (rRNA) and 40 per cent protein. Ribosomes can be separated from other cell components by centrifugation and they are visible globular structures in electron photomicrographs (Fig. 144). The size of the ribosomes varies in different types of cells; in *E. coli* most of them are 70 S (MW 2.5 to 4.5 × 10^6), but they can dissociate into two smaller particles of 30 S and 50 S (Tissières *et al.*, 1960; McQuillen, 1962; Roberts *et al.*, 1963). Two 70 S particles can unite to form 100 S particles. The 50 and 70 S particles contain two sizes of rRNA – the smaller, 15–18 S (MW 6 × 10^5), and the larger, 23–28 S (MW 12 × 10^5). The 30 S particles seem to contain only the smaller molecular weight rRNA.

(Text continued on page 334.)

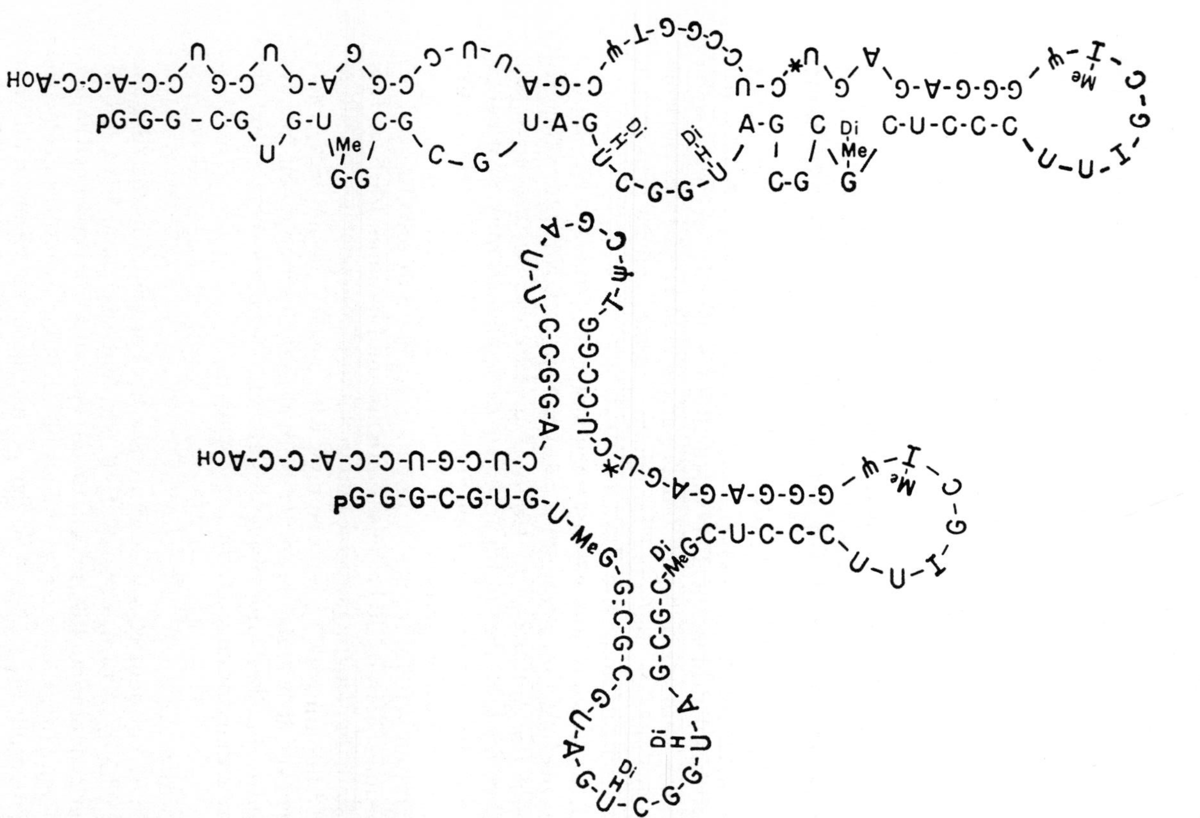

FIGURE 143. The sequence of nucleotides in alanine tRNA and two possible conformations of the molecule in solution. The conformations shown are speculative and may even vary under different conditions. Abbreviations: p and - are used interchangeably to represent a phosphate residue; A-, adenosine 3′-phosphate; C-, cytidine 3′-phosphate; DiHU-, 5,6-dihydrouridine 3′-phosphate; DiMeG-, N^2-dimethylguanosine 3′-phosphate; I-, inosine 3′-phosphate; MeG-, 1-methylguanosine 3′-phosphate; MeI-, 1-methylinosin 3′-phosphate; ψ-, pseudouridine 3′-phosphate; T-, ribothymidine 3′-phosphate; U-, uridine 3′-phosphate; U*-, a mixture of U- and DiHU-. (From Holley *et al.*, 1965.)

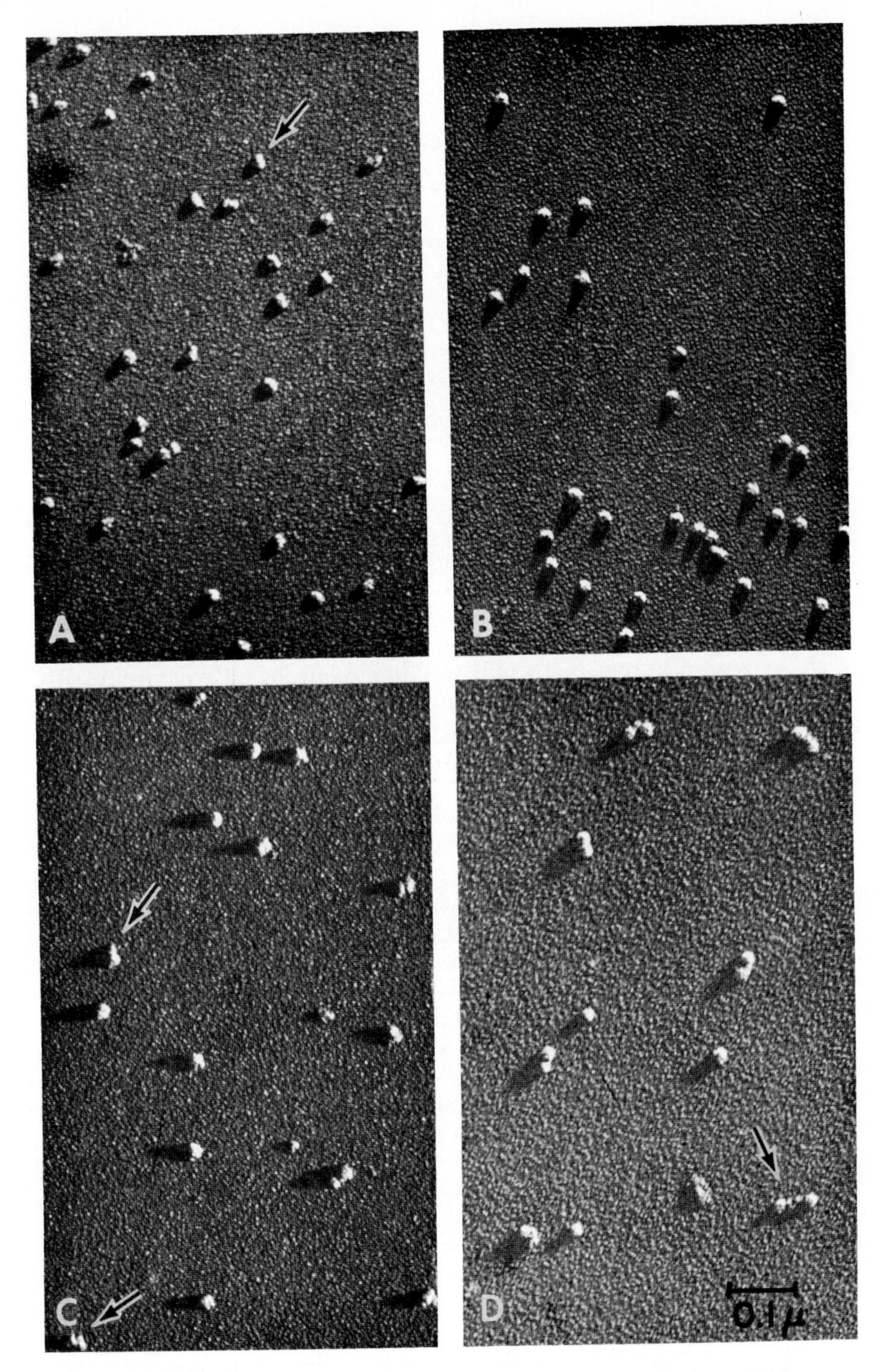

FIGURE 144. Ribonucleoprotein particles from *E. coli*. **A**, RNP particles from a 30 S preparation; the arrow indicates a typical asymmetrical particle. **B**, RNP particles from a 50 S preparation. **C**, RNP particles from a 70 S preparation indicated by arrows; 30 S and 50 S particles are also present. **D**, RNP particles from a 100 S preparation. (Magnification × 100,000.) (From Hall and Slayter, 1959.)

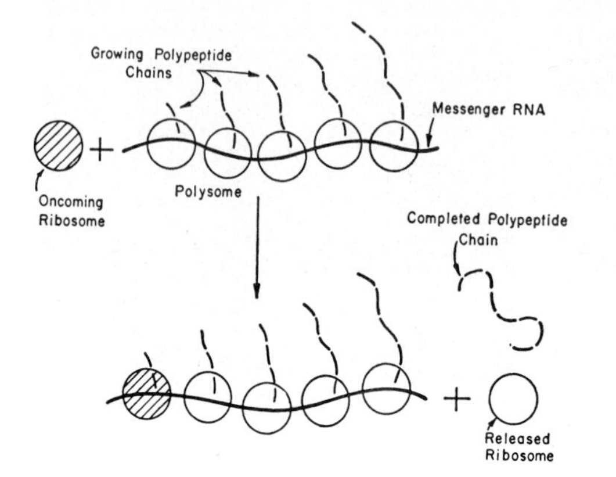

FIGURE 145. A schematic model of polysome function. (From Rich *et al.*, 1963.)

Again, hybridization tests (Yankofsky and Spiegelman, 1962, 1963) have shown that rRNA can hybridize with a small region of the cell's DNA (0.1 per cent); two separate DNA regions appear to be responsible for the information resulting in the formation of the two different types of rRNA with different molecular weights. As in the case of tRNA, rRNA has species-specific nucleotide sequences, yet it can function in the assembly of polypeptides with messages (mRNA) from other species. Also, like tRNA and unlike mRNA, rRNA from many different sources have a similar overall base composition. Like tRNA, rRNA also seems to have double-stranded regions as a result of folding back onto itself.

Although earlier studies had assumed that the mRNA attaches itself to ribosomes and there dictates the polymerization of specific polypeptide chains, more recent observations indicate that the ribosomes move along an mRNA molecule, helping to put on the next appropriate amino acid in a growing polypeptide chain (Fig. 145). The strings of ribosomes that are temporarily held together by mRNA are called *polyribosomes* or *polysomes* and they are visible in electron photomicrographs (Fig. 146).

Ribosomes are fairly stable structures and can be used as an assembly plant for more than just one type of polypeptide. This was demonstrated beautifully in some experiments by Brenner, Jacob and Meselson (Brenner *et al.*, 1961). They used a combination of radioactive (N^{15}, C^{14}) and non-radioactive isotopes to label ribosomes of *E. coli* before infection with bacteriophage T_4. After transfer of the bacteria to a medium free of N^{15} and C^{14}, they infected the bacteria with bacteriophage. They then labeled the mRNA produced in the phage-infected cells with P^{32} and the protein with S^{35} to localize the mRNA (containing P^{32}) and protein (containing S^{35}) formed after infection. After disrupting the bacteria and after centrifugation in a CsCl density gradient, they could now determine whether the new mRNA and protein were associated with the old, heavy (N^{15}, C^{14}) or new, light (N^{14}, C^{12}) ribosomes. It was found that the new mRNA and protein were associated with the old ribosomes, which prior to phage infection had been occupied with the synthesis of bacterial, rather than phage, proteins. The conclusion was that ribosomes are machines that can be

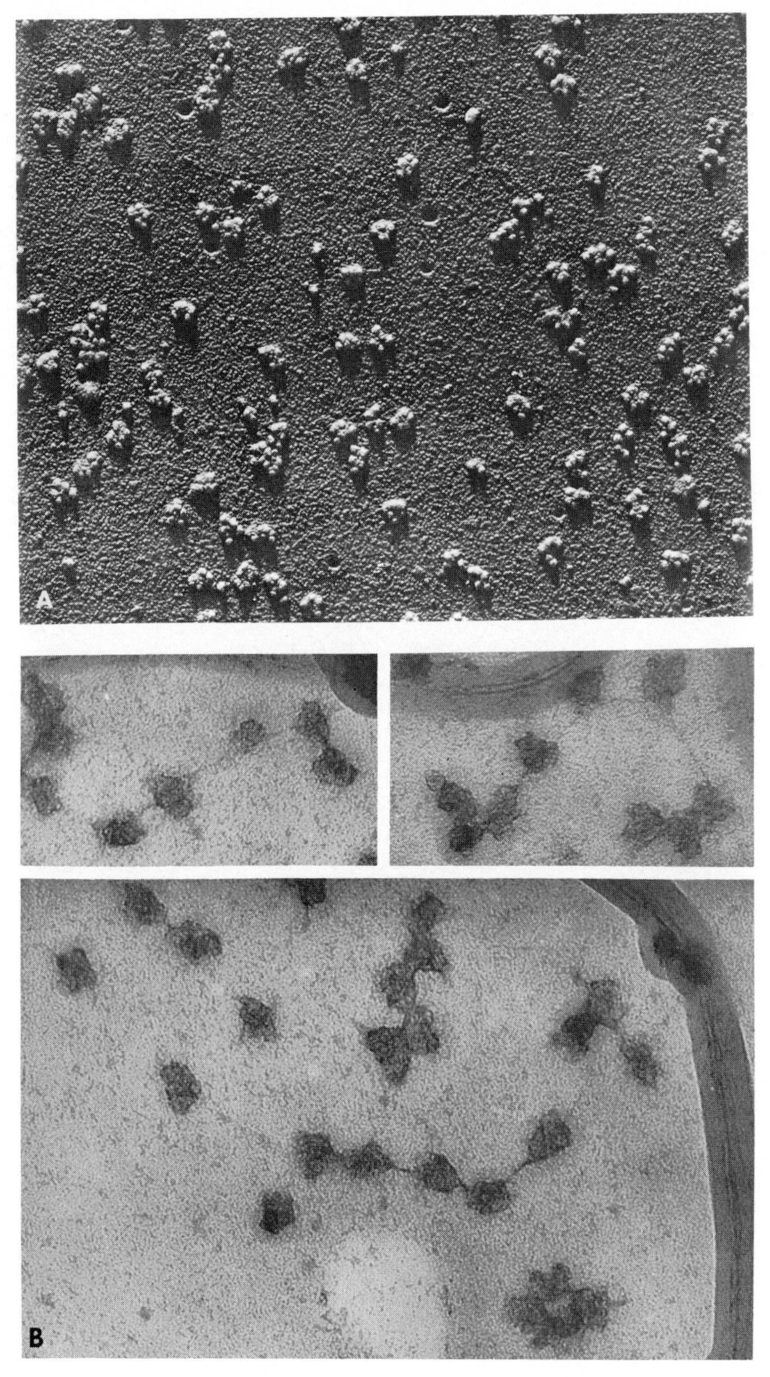

FIGURE 146. Electron micrographs of polysomes. A, Air-dried and platinum-shadowed preparation of HeLa polysomes. B, Reticulocyte polyribosomes stained positively with uranyl acetate. Note the thin strand (10–15 Å in diameter) between adjacent ribosomes; this is believed to be mRNA. (From Rich *et al.*, 1963.)

utilized for protein synthesis by different sets of instructions, i.e., by different messenger RNAs.

Streptomycin appears to be able to alter the relationships between ribosomes and mRNA, presumably by "distorting" the 30 S portion of the ribosome, resulting in a faulty translation process (Gorini *et al.*, 1964; Lederberg *et al.*, 1964). This expresses itself in the incorporation of the wrong amino acids into protein (a fact that can be demonstrated by adding streptomycin to a cell-free protein synthesizing system, as described on p. 339) and results in the same sort of excessive degeneration of the code that we have already mentioned as a possible mechanism by which some suppressor mutations act (see p. 285).

But let us return now to normal undisturbed polypeptide synthesis. Once the finished polypeptide comes off the ribosomes it may, in the case of proteins consisting of several distinct polypeptide chains, associate with the other polypeptide chains in a manner as yet poorly understood. The "native" protein then assumes its unique three-dimensional shape by folding in a manner that appears to be prescribed by the amino acid sequence and particularly by the location of cysteine, which can participate

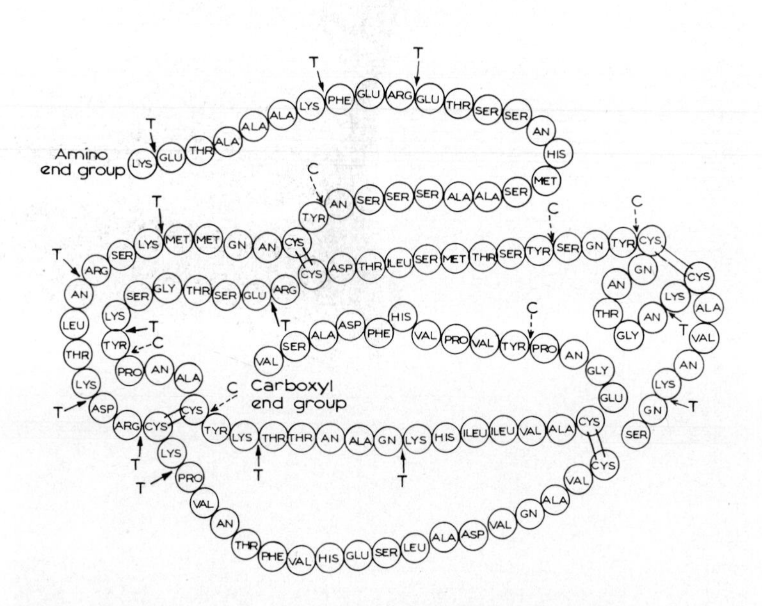

FIGURE 147. The structure of bovine pancreatic ribonuclease. The symbols represent:

ALA = alanine
AN = aspartic acid side-chain NH_2
ARG = arginine
ASP = aspartic acid
CYS = cysteine
GLU = glutamic acid
GLY = glycine
GN = glutamic acid side-chain NH_2
HIS = histidine
ILEU = isoleucine
LEU = leucine
LYS = lysine
MET = methionine
PHE = phenylalanine
PRO = proline
SER = serine
THR = threonine
TYR = tyrosine
VAL = valine

Disulfide linkages between cysteine residues are shown by double lines. T indicates sites cleaved by trypsin and C indicates sites cleaved by chymotrypsin. (From Hayes, 1964, after Anfinsen.)

in the formation of disulfide bridges between two cysteine residues (Fig. 147). Folding thus appears to be simply the function of the order of amino acids in a protein molecule, and whatever determines the order of amino acids can specify the complex final three-dimensional structure of proteins (Crick, 1958; Anfinsen, 1963; Epstein *et al.*, 1963).

THE GENETIC CODE

The problem of finding the nucleotide sequence that specifies the incorporation of a particular amino acid into the nascent protein has been referred to as the problem of the genetic code. It is, in its simplest form, the key to making at least 20 different words (20 amino acids) from an alphabet with only 4 letters (4 types of nucleotides). Thanks to the work of the Nirenberg and Ochoa groups, a considerable body of experimental information on the nature of the genetic code has been built up (cf. Nirenberg and Matthaei, 1961; Langyel *et al.*, 1961). But before we discuss such information we should consider some theoretical aspects of the coding problem (Gamow, 1954; Crick *et al.*, 1957).

As illustrated in Figure 148 (assuming that all code words are of the same length), a triplet code is required in order to provide information for the 20 common amino acids, a doublet code would provide information for only 16 words. If we assume a triplet code as the most economic device, we could have an overlapping code, i.e.,

...CATCATCAT...

could be read CAT, ATC, TCA, CAT, etc., or we could have a non-overlapping code in which, starting from a given point X and reading in one direction

...TXCATCATCATC... →

the triplets are read off sequentially in one direction in the manner CAT, CAT, CAT, etc.

The code could also be *degenerate*, which means that more than one type of triplet could code for the same amino acid. A series of experimental data has ruled out an overlapping code* and has supported the interpretation that the code is a degenerate triplet code.

The triplet nature of the code was indicated both in the cell-free amino acid incorporation studies, which we shall review shortly, and in a very ingenious experiment with phage mutants (Crick *et al.*, 1961). In this experiment advantage was taken of the fact that acridine can induce mutations in phage T_4 that appear to be due to either an addition or a deletion of a single base pair (see p. 95). Acridine-induced, so-called *r*II plaque-

*A change of one letter, i.e., one base, in such a code would lead to more than one altered signal, whereas the analysis of mutants with enzymatic alterations has shown that one base change leads to only one amino acid change.

SINGLET CODE (4 WORDS)
A
G
C
U

DOUBLET CODE (16 WORDS)			
AA	AG	AC	AU
GA	GG	GC	GU
CA	CG	CC	CU
UA	UG	UC	UU

TRIPLET CODE (64 WORDS)			
AAA	AAG	AAC	AAU
AGA	AGG	AGC	AGU
ACA	ACG	ACC	ACU
AUA	AUG	AUC	AUU
GAA	GAG	GAC	GAU
GGA	GGG	GGC	GGU
GCA	GCG	GCC	GCU
GUA	GUG	GUC	GUU
CAA	CAG	CAC	CAU
CGA	CGG	CGC	CGU
CCA	CCG	CCC	CCU
CUA	CUG	CUC	CUU
UAA	UAG	UAC	UAU
UGA	UGG	UGC	UGU
UCA	UCG	UCC	UCU
UUA	UUG	UUC	UUU

FIGURE 148. Chart of possible code-letter combinations as a function of the length of the code word. Note that since a minimum of 20 code words is required to specify the 20 common amino acids, a minimum code length would be a triplet (provided all code words are of equal length). (After Nirenberg, 1963.)

type mutants of T_4 phage can result from changes at any one of a large number of sites within one cistron of the phage DNA, but can revert spontaneously to the normal (wild) phenotype by a change (presumably an addition or deletion) at a different site in the same cistron. The production of the "pseudo-wild" type phage by a mutational event at a site *different* from the original *r*II mutation was proved by recombination tests. This finding then would be interpreted as an inability to read sense (CAT in our example) in a triplet code structure if one letter is deleted*

direction of reading →

......CATCATCATCATCAT......*r*II mutant

*Essentially the same considerations hold true if the original mutation adds a base and the subsequent suppressor mutation in the same cistron deletes a base.

But a return to partial sense reading could occur in the affected cistron when a new spontaneous mutation inserts an extra base pair

......CATCATCYATCATCAT......"pseudo-wild"

Furthermore, one could assume that three different mutational events (deletions or changes) at different sites in the same cistron would reestablish a correct reading frame

......CATCATCATCATCATCAT......

and yield a normal phenotype (provided the remaining, correctly read cistron region can impart enough of the required information). Through recombination between independently derived *r*II mutants, phage particles containing mutationally altered bases at three different (but not too distant) sites of the same cistron were produced and they did indeed show a normal phenotype.

Now let us look at the code data that developed from the studies of mRNA-guided polypeptide synthesis in cell-free systems. Again, the basic principle of this complex technique was relatively simple. The first requirement was an RNA with known nucleotide sequences. Such RNA could be, and was, synthesized from known ribonucleoside diphosphates with the aid of the enzyme polynucleotide phosphorylase (see p. 64 and footnote on p. 325). This DNA-independent enzyme is capable of producing RNA polymers by linking available bases together in random order. Thus, when uracil is provided, a synthetic RNA polymer containing only uracil is produced; this is called poly-U. When cytosine is provided, poly-C is produced. When an excess of U and a lesser amount of C are provided, copolymers containing U and C are formed in which the majority of triplets will be UUU, UUC, UCU, or CUU, since U was furnished in excess.

The next requirement was an effective, cell-free protein-synthesizing system in which mRNA could be replaced by the synthetic RNA polymer. Cell-free systems were available, though they were quite unstable; they had been developed in prior studies by Lamborg and Zamecnik (1960), Tissières *et al.* (1960), Kameyama and Novelli (1960) and others. These systems employed bacterial cell sap, which can be released, for example, by grinding *E. coli* cells with powdered alumina, and which is rich in ribosomes, DNA, RNA and enzymes. When enriched with amino acids, GTP, ATP (as energy sources) and salts, and particularly when the cell extracts are stabilized by the addition of mercaptoethanol (Nirenberg and Matthaei, 1961), the synthesis of polypeptides can be followed *in vitro*. Polypeptide synthesis stops when DNase is added to the system, or when the DNA required for mRNA production is removed by other means.

A frequently employed cell-free system consists of a washed particle (ribosome) fraction, a supernatant (enzyme-rich) freed of nucleic acid by protamine treatment, and a tRNA supplement. When a synthetic RNA polymer of proper size (more than 10 nucleotides) and proper shape (single-stranded) is now added to such a system, polypeptide synthesis resumes, the amino acids being incorporated into the polypeptide depending entirely upon the nature of the polynucleotide added to the system. Thus, in the initial tests of this nature, Nirenberg and Matthaei found that after addition of poly-U, only phenylalanine was incorporated into the polypeptide. The technique used to recognize that a polypeptide containing only polyphenylalanine was formed in the presence of poly-U, was to add to the cell-free system all 20 amino acids, with *one* of them being labeled with C^{14} in one reaction mixture, *another one* being labeled in another reaction mixture, etc. Thus each reaction mixture contained 19 unlabeled and 1 labeled amino acid. After incubation for 30 minutes at 37° C, the protein formed in the cell-free system was precipitated out by the addition of trichloroacetic acid and its constitution determined in respect to whether or not it was radioactive. Thus radioactivity appeared in the poly-U-containing system only in the precipitated protein of the mixture containing C^{14}-labeled phenylalanine and in none of the other 19 mixtures. It was therefore concluded that the code word for phenylalanine must be UUU (assuming a triplet code) in RNA, and that the corresponding deoxyribonucleotide sequence in DNA must be AAA.

These initial studies were soon followed by tests with other homopolymers, such as poly-A (controlling the incorporation of lysine) and poly-C (controlling the incorporation of proline), and with a large series of synthetic copolymers in which the calculated frequency of triplets, and the frequency of incorporation of a given amino acid in the presence of the copolymer, permitted tentative assignments of code triplet in the manner indicated in Table 22 (cf. Speyer *et al.*, 1963; Ochoa, 1963, Nirenberg and Jones, 1963). Additional matching of triplet frequency and amino acid

TABLE 22. *Examples of code triplet assignments derived from matching of triplet frequency and amino acid incorporation**

POLYNUCLEOTIDE	TRIPLETS	FREQUENCY OF EACH TRIPLET (%)	AMINO ACID INCORPORATION (%)	CODE TRIPLET COMPOSITION
UG (5:1)	UUU	100	Phe, 100	UUU
	UUG, UGU, GUU	20	Cys, 20;val, 20	2U1G
	UGG, GUG, GGU	4	Gly, 4;try, 4	1U2G
	GGG	0.8	—	—
AC (5:1)	AAA	100	Lys, 100	AAA
	AAC, ACA, CAA	20	AspN, 30;thr, 23	2A1C
	ACC, CAC, CCA	4	Pro, 5	1A2C
	CCC	0.8	—	—
CG (5:1)[a]	CCC	100	Pro, 100	CCC
	CCG, CGC, GCC	20	Ala, 22;arg, 19	2C1G
	CCG, GCG, GGC	4	Gly, 5	1C2G
	GGG	0.8	—	—

*For details see text (From Ochoa, 1963).
[a]Poly CI used in place of poly CG.

TABLE 23. *The amino acid code**

CODE TRIPLETS	AMINO ACID	CODE TRIPLETS	AMINO ACID
AAA	lysine	CAA	glutamine
AAG	lysine	CAG	glutamine
AAC	asparagine	CAC	histidine
AAU	asparagine	CAU	histidine
AGA	arginine	CGA	arginine
AGG	arginine	CGG	arginine?
AGC	serine	CGC	arginine
AGU	serine	CGU	arginine?
ACA	threonine	CCA	proline
ACG	threonine	CCG	proline?
ACC	threonine	CCC	proline
ACU	threonine	CCU	proline
AUA	isoleucine?	CUA	leucine
AUG	methionine	CUG	leucine
AUC	isoleucine	CUC	leucine
AUU	isoleucine	CUU	leucine
GAA	glutamic acid	UAA	gap (comma)
GAG	glutamic acid	UAG	gap (comma)
GAC	aspartic acid	UAC	tyrosine
GAU	aspartic acid	UAU	tyrosine
GGA	glycine?	UGA	tryptophan
GGG	glycine?	UGG	tryptophan
GGC	glycine?	UGC	cysteine
GGU	glycine	UGU	cysteine
GCA	alanine?	UCA	serine
GCG	alanine?	UCG	serine
GCC	alanine?	UCC	serine
GCU	alanine	UCU	serine
GUA	valine?	UUA	leucine
GUG	valine	UUG	leucine
GUC	valine?	UUC	phenylalanine
GUU	valine	UUU	phenylalanine

*The coding assignments shown are based on tests with synthetic trinucleotides, as reported by Leder *et al.*, 1965; Nishimura *et al.*, 1965; Smith *et al.*, 1965; Thach *et al.*, 1965; and Brenner *et al.*, 1965. (Table prepared by T. H. Jukes.)

incorporation, coupled with tests utilizing synthetic trinucleotides (Leder and Nirenberg, 1964), then led to a list of code triplet assignments, as shown in Table 23. It can be seen that the code is degenerate, which means that more than one word can code for the same amino acid; at least this is so *in vitro*. It is possible that the ability of one codon to cause the incorporation of more than one amino acid is less pronounced *in vivo*. However, in at least one case an actual physical basis for the degeneracy of the code exists, since it has been discovered in studies with *E. coli* that two different tRNA's, distinguishable by column chromatography, exist for leucine

(Weisblum *et al.*, 1962). The degeneracy of the code may account for the fact that even in organisms with strikingly different $\frac{G + C}{A + T}$ ratios the same basic code applies. Species within the high GC range may perhaps utilize triplets of high GC content to specify an amino acid that in species with a low GC content is directed by a triplet with a low or no GC content (cf. Speyer *et al.*, 1963).

The triplet nature of the code is supported not only by the studies of Crick *et al.*, which we reviewed earlier, but also by the *in vitro* studies just described on RNA-directed incorporation of amino acids into polypeptides in cell-free systems. It has been established that the highest number of different nucleotides in one copolymer coding for one amino acid is three (e.g., ACU) and that the addition of a fourth type of nucleotide (AGCU) leads to the incorporation of more than one amino acid.

Initially, the sequence of the bases in the code assignments was quite tentative since the data obtained in the *in vitro* tests with synthetic copolymers did not permit any decisions on whether, for example, the code for cysteine was GUU, UGU, or UUG. However, the newer tests with synthetic trinucleotides of known sequence have permitted more decisive conclusions regarding the proper sequence of bases in a codon. In addition, predictions regarding some probable sequences could be made (1) on the basis of known mutational amino acid replacements in the proteins of tobacco mosaic virus, *E. coli* (tryptophan synthetase) and mammals (myoglobin, hemoglobin) (Jukes, 1962), and (2) on the basis of recombination tests between *E. coli* mutants with known amino acid alterations (see p. 284). For example, Figure 149 shows the known mutational amino acid replacements at one specific position in tryptophan synthetase. It can be assumed that each such change involves a single nucleotide change, and this in turn imposes specific restrictions on the possible nucleotide composition and sequence in the coding units for these amino acids (Yanofsky, 1963).

By comparing Figure 149 with Table 23 it may be seen that the mutational data fit well with the code assignments obtained from the amino acid incorporation studies. An inspection of Table 23 also reveals that many of the several triplets that can code *in vitro* for the same amino acid (e.g., ACA, ACG and ACC in the case of the code assignments for threonine) share two of their bases (AC in our example). This has suggested that in these cases only two of the bases in the triplet may be meaningful from the standpoint of coding, and this could mean that a doublet as well as triplet code may function *in vivo*, thus reducing the extent of degeneracy suggested by current code word assignments (cf. Ochoa, 1963).

The code appears to be universal; similar coding words have been derived from studies with cell-free mammalian and bacterial systems. In addition, there are various demonstrations regarding the ability of foreign informational nucleic acids to function in unusual environments. For example, we have already mentioned earlier (p. 311) that an *E. coli* *F′* DNA can specify the production of an *E. coli* type of alkaline phosphatase in *Serratia marcescens*, and *E. coli* tRNA functions in the production of hemoglobin from rabbit reticulocytes.

Although most experimental tests on the coding problem have utilized RNA as the source of information, protein synthesis in cell-free systems

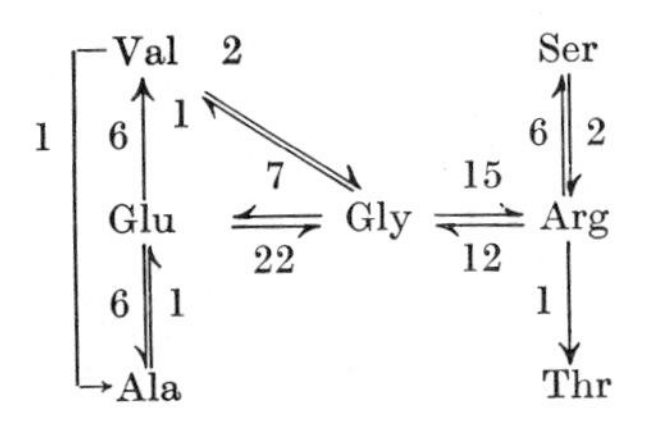

FIGURE 149. Amino acid replacements known to occur at a specific site of the A protein of tryptophan synthetase in different mutants of *E. coli*. The numbers next to the arrows indicate how frequently each replacement was observed in studies of forward and reverse mutations. (From Yanofsky, 1963.)

also has been carried out under conditions in which the instruction process originated from a known DNA, namely, an oligodeoxythymidilate (dTpdTpdT......). This polymer was used to prime the synthesis of poly A and this, in turn, directed the incorporation of lysine (Nirenberg *et al.*, 1963).

COLINEARITY OF BASE CHANGES AND AMINO ACID CHANGES

The most important support for the concept that the linear sequence of polydeoxyribonucleotides in DNA (or of their complementary polyribonucleotides in mRNA) specifies the linear sequence of amino acids in protein, comes from the demonstration that the relative position of mutational sites within a cistron (i.e., within a DNA region) corresponds to the relative position of altered amino acids in the corresponding protein (Fig. 150). Such colinearity of mutational sites (as determined by recombi-

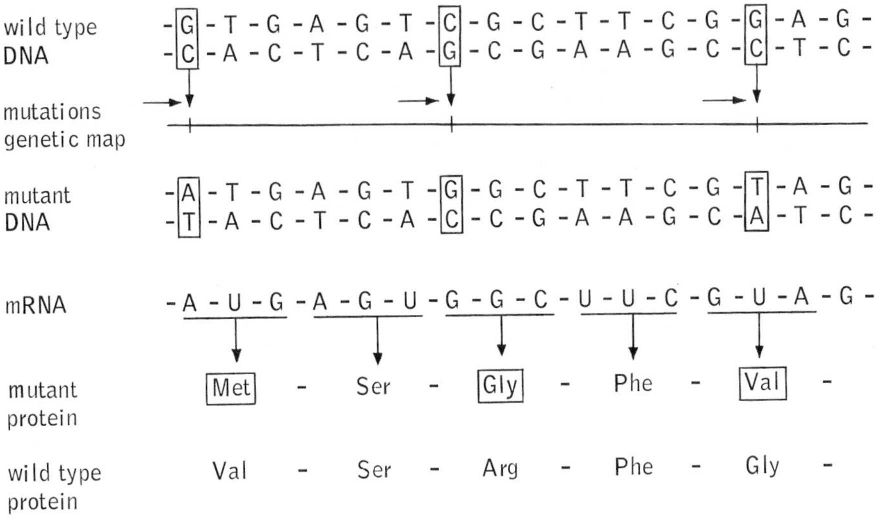

wild type DNA
-G-T-G-A-G-T-C-G-C-T-T-C-G-G-A-G-
-C-A-C-T-C-A-G-C-G-A-A-G-C-C-T-C-

mutations
genetic map

mutant DNA
-A-T-G-A-G-T-G-G-C-T-T-C-G-T-A-G-
-T-A-C-T-C-A-C-C-G-A-A-G-C-A-T-C-

mRNA
-A-U-G-A-G-U-G-G-C-U-U-C-G-U-A-G-

mutant protein
Met - Ser - Gly - Phe - Val -

wild type protein
Val - Ser - Arg - Phe - Gly -

FIGURE 150. Colinearity of sites of mutations, within part of a cistron, and sites of amino acid alterations in a portion of the protein controlled by this cistron. (After A. Yanofsky.)

nation and complementation) and of altered sites in the protein molecule (as determined by chemical analyses) has now been demonstrated both for bacteria, in which changes in part of the tryptophan synthetase protein were studied (Yanofsky *et al.*, 1964), and for the so-called *amber* mutants of bacteriophage (Sarabhai *et al.*, 1964). Such demonstrations lend support to the conclusion that the basic principles of genetic control over the specificity of enzyme production are now fairly well understood, and that a full elucidation of the details of these processes and their potential willful manipulation are merely a matter of time. Some of the implications of such knowledge for man's future have been, and should be, the subject of considerable discussion (cf. Braun, 1964).

[17]

REGULATION OF INTRACELLULAR TRANSCRIPTION AND TRANSLATION

In the preceding chapter we have stressed the functions of genetic material in specifying the sequence of amino acids which gives enzymatically active proteins their specificity of structure and function. The genes (deoxyribonucleotide sequences) responsible for specifying polypeptide structure are, therefore, known as *structural genes*. However, the presence and activity of structural genes alone would not suffice to initiate and to control the well-integrated processes of cellular function and the development, as well as maintenance, of cellular structures. Just as a factory filled with a multitude of molds and patterns, raw materials, and laborers, but devoid of flow charts and time directions would fail to turn out a properly finished product, a cell in which information is available without the dampers to control the availability of such information at the proper time would be a very poorly functioning, and probably even a non-functioning, structure. Therefore, what is needed in addition to structural genes are regulatory mechanisms that can control the activity of such genes.*

As we have seen, the major steps in the production of the enzymes (proteins) that control all biosynthetic, metabolic and catabolic processes are transcription (DNA → RNA), translation (RNA → polypeptide) and assembly (polypeptide → protein). Therefore, an *overall regulation* of the rate of cellular processes is dependent on factors that control the general rates of RNA synthesis and of the formation as well as assembly of polypeptides. We do not know too much as yet regarding the nature of these factors. Rates of polypeptide formation appear to be dependent on the

*For general reviews of regulation, see Jacob and Monod, 1961a, 1961b; Vogel, 1961a; Bonner, 1961; Riley and Pardee, 1962; Fincham, 1962; Fisher, 1962; Wagner and Mitchell, 1964.

availability of a properly balanced pool of amino acids, on the number of ribosomes, and on RNA (Berg, 1961). Rates of RNA synthesis, in turn, are dependent, in part, on the physical state of DNA, the size of the precursor pool, the presence of all common amino acids, and the extent of protein synthesis required for an appropriate supply of the enzymes involved in the synthesis of nucleic acids and their precursors (cf. Lark, 1963). Also, oligoribonucleotides can influence RNA synthesis through their stimulatory effects on RNA polymerase activity (Gros *et al.*, 1963).

Rates of RNA synthesis are very susceptible to changes in environmental conditions. A shift of bacteria from a minimal medium to a rich medium results in an immediate acceleration of RNA synthesis, and later in increased rates of protein and DNA syntheses, while a shift from a rich to a poor medium results in immediate inhibition of RNA synthesis (Kjeldgard *et al.*, 1958; Maaløe, 1960).

An overall control of synthetic rates, however, does not suffice to assure the availability of *specific* enzymes under particular conditions and at particular times. For this a *regulation of the activity of specific genes* (control of individual reactions), or of a block of genes with related functions (control of reaction pathways), is required. As we shall now see, such regulation may be inherent within the structural gene itself or it may be under the influence of specific *regulatory genes*. The latter type of gene represents a specific polynucleotide sequence which through the production of a cytoplasmic factor can control the activity of a specific structural gene.

REGULATION BY COMPONENTS OF THE STRUCTURAL GENE

To a certain extent, regulation can be a function of certain nucleotide sequences within the structural gene itself, i.e., within the polynucleotide sequence that specifies the structure of a given polypeptide. This is suggested by the fact that certain mutational changes in structural genes can alter the rate at which the corresponding enzyme is formed (Pardee and Beckwith, 1963). Such an effect might be due to an alteration of the starting point of reading of the DNA message by the RNA polymerase, or it might involve a change in the polymerase's affinity for the structural gene as the result of a base change in the affected polynucleotide region. Also, *mutants with conditional activity* are known, which means that such mutants fail to show enzyme activity under all of the environmental conditions that permit functioning of the wild-type enzyme; for example, they function only at certain temperatures or in the presence of certain ion concentrations (Fincham, 1962). It has been suggested that such changes are configurational in character, which means that they may affect the folding of the protein and thus its activity under environmental conditions that influence protein configuration.

Another regulatory mechanism that appears to be more or less "built into" the structural gene can influence the reading of the mRNA in the translation step. The existence of such a control was discovered in studies with the complex histidine locus in which, as in other complex loci of bacteria (p. 283), a series of enzymes controlling histidine biosynthesis is controlled by a series of linked structural genes (see Fig. 121). It was observed that about 50 per cent of all mutational changes in this genetic region of *S. typhimurium* result not only in the loss of activity of the corresponding enzyme, but also in the lowering of the activities of all the enzymes which are involved in histidine synthesis and which lie on the linkage map *to the left* of the site of mutation (Ames and Hartman, 1963). In contrast, the enzymes that are controlled by nucleotide sequences located on the other side (to the right) of the mutated nucleotide remain unaffected. Mutants that produce this sort of effect have become known as *polarity mutants* (Jacob and Monod, 1961), and the quantitative alteration of function of the determinants on one side of the mutated site in a genetic region concerned with one particular pathway has become known as *modulation*.

It has been suggested that modulation may involve (a) an increased likelihood of the "falling off" of ribosomes from the messenger RNA, (b) a slowing down of reading as the ribosome travels along the mRNA in one direction and reaches the altered *modulating* nucleotide sequence which corresponds to the altered deoxyribonucleotide sequence in the DNA of the polarity mutant (Ames and Hartman, 1963), or (c) a change in the availability of specific tRNAs (Stent, 1964). Apart from the histidine example which we have cited here, polarity mutants have been recognized in quite a number of different systems.

REGULATORY GENES

Many factors must be involved both in controlling the reading of specific DNA regions in transcription and in regulating the reading of the mRNA in the process of translation. So far we do not have too much information regarding the specific nature of these factors, but we have evidence indicating that specific genes may regulate both the formation and the function of mRNA, i.e., both transcription and translation steps. The evidence for the existence and activity of such *regulatory* or *controlling genes*, which may or may not be linked to the structural gene (or the block of genes) whose activity they control, has come from a combination of biochemical and genetic studies.

As we discussed earlier (p. 136), it has long been known that certain enzymes are *inducible*; that is, they are formed in appreciable amounts only in the presence of their specific substrate (or in the presence of certain non-utilizable analogues of such substrates, which are referred to as gratuitous inducers) (Cohn and Monod, 1953). It also has been known for an equally long time that some strains can form the very same enzymes at a relatively constant rate in the absence of the inducing substrate; in such strains enzyme production is said to be *constitutive*. Constitutive mutants can be isolated from inducible strains, and vice versa, and the extent to which enzyme production can vary in different types of inducible and constitutive strains is indicated by Figure 151. Some examples of bacterial enzymes that are produced either constitutively or inducibly are:

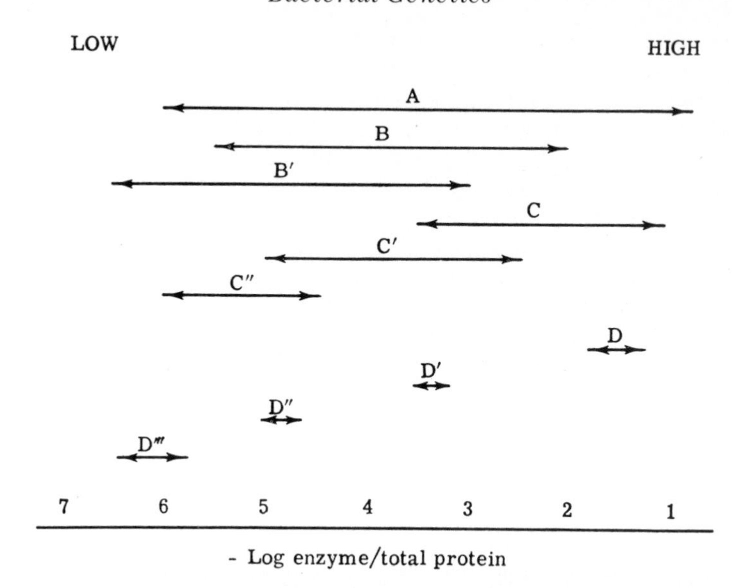

FIGURE 151. Modes of enzyme production: A, super-inducible; B, highly inducible or repressible; C, moderately inducible or repressible; D, constitutive. (From Pardee and Beckwith, 1963.)

penicillinase, β-galactosidase, alkaline phosphatase, galactose enzymes, and enzymes involved in arginine, tryptophan and histidine biosynthesis.

Exactly opposite to the phenomenon of enzyme induction is the phenomenon of *enzyme repression*, in which the product of an enzymatic reaction, or the final product of a biosynthetic pathway of which the constitutive enzyme is a member, can interfere with the continued *formation* of the enzyme.* Thus, for example, the formation of acetylornithinase, an enzyme catalyzing a step in the arginine pathway, is repressed after the addition of arginine to the culture medium (Vogel, 1957, 1961). Many examples of enzyme repression by an excess of an end product of the biosynthetic sequence are known. To cite just a few, we can refer to the repression of enzymes involved in the synthesis of histidine, methionine, valine, tryptophan, alkaline phosphatase, purines and pyrimidines.

Most investigators now regard most cases of enzyme induction as being due to enzyme *derepression*, thus placing both induction and repression at the opposite ends of one basic spectrum of enzyme control. In this unified concept the formation of a single enzyme, or the formation of related enzymes active in the same pathway, can be blocked (either at the level of transcription or translation) by a repressor which usually is the end product of the pathway. The addition of an inducer may then lead to a loss of repression and the renewed formation of an enzyme or a block

*It is important to differentiate between repression, in which the *formation* of an enzyme is affected, and the phenomenon of feedback inhibition to be discussed subsequently (p. 356), in which the *action* of an enzyme is affected.

of related enzymes (see also p. 352). On a biochemical level this concept finds some support in the fact that both induction and repression tend to act on a pathway-wide basis; i.e., they shut off or turn on all of the related enzymes in a pathway or all the several enzymes that may be involved in the utilization of one given substrate (Vogel, 1957; Pardee *et al.*, 1959).

The most suggestive support for the relationship between induction and repression, however, has come from studies in which genetic analysis was combined with biochemical assays. It was demonstrated, for example, that the same regulatory gene can simultaneously control both repression and induction of enzymes involved in arginine synthesis (Bacon and Vogel, 1963). But the most detailed and impressive analysis of the probable relationships between repression and induction on the genetic level has been furnished by the work of Jacob and Monod (1961a, 1961b, 1963) on lactose fermentation in mutants of *E. coli*, K-12.

THE LACTOSE OPERON

The enzyme β-galactosidase, controlled by the *lac* locus of *E. coli*, hydrolyzes lactose to glucose and galactose. However, even in the presence of the normal structural gene for β-galactosidase formation (the so-called *z* gene), lactose cannot be fermented (although β-galactosidase is formed "cryptically") unless a linked gene *y*, which specifies the synthesis of an enzyme called galactoside permease, needed for the uptake of the galactoside lactose, is also functioning.*

In addition, two other genes play an important part in the function of the *lac* region (Fig. 152): (1) a nearby gene *i*, which in its normal form (i^+) suppresses the formation of both β-galactosidase and permease, but in its mutant form (i^-) permits the constitutive formation of these enzymes even in the absence of the inducer (lactose or certain other galactosides, and (2) a gene *o* (for *operator*), which is linked to *y* and *z*, appears to respond to a hypothetical repressor substance produced by *i* and may also represent the site at which the reading (transcription) of the *lac* locus begins.† The assumption has been made that in the presence of the repressor produced by *i*, the operator is "clogged" and transcription of the structural information cannot take place; however, when the repressor substance is tied up by preferential association with the inducer, the operator region is free to operate.

Jacob and Monod (1959) proposed that the complex of related structural genes serving a coordinated function (*y* and *z* genes in the case of the *lac* region) plus the adjacent operator region controlling the transcription of the related structural genes, be called an *operon*. The operon, according to this concept, represents a genetic unit of coordinated transcription in which the contiguous arrangement of nucleotide sequences

*The formation of a third enzyme, galactoside-acetylase, is also controlled by the *lac* region, but its function is poorly understood and unimportant to our present discussion.

†Recent data suggest that the operator region is actually not the region where reading starts; rather an adjacent nucleotide sequence, called *promoteur* and influenced by the function of the operator, appears to be the region where transcription of the genetic region begins (Jacob *et al.*, 1964).

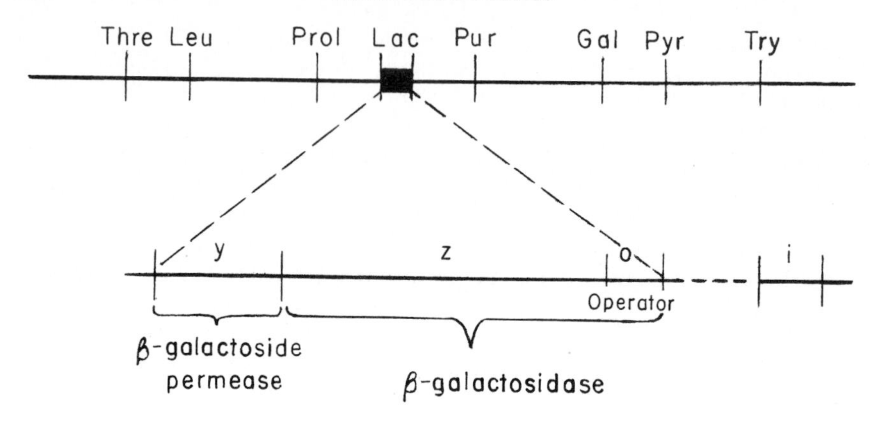

FIGURE 152. Operon for the utilization of lactose. The upper line shows the position of the *lac* region in the *E. coli* chromosome; the lower line shows an enlargement of this region. The direction of reading (mRNA formation) appears to be from right to left. (After Jacob and Monod, 1963.)

(genes) controlling *different* enzymes of a biosynthetic pathway, or of a metabolic reaction, can be under coordinated control of *one* operator. Or, to put it into still different terms, the operon seems to encompass a DNA region, of usually more than one functional unit, which is simultaneously transcribed into one single mRNA molecule (see Fig. 154). The different enzymes controlled by one operon can, within limits, be repressed and derepressed to the same extent; this phenomenon has been referred to as *coordinate repression* (Ames and Garry, 1959).

Before engaging in a further analysis of some of the virtues of the operon model, let us first say something about the way in which it has been possible to postulate the existence of the i (regulator) and o (operator) genes, and to map their position in the linkage map of *E. coli*. Remember that in the case of lactose fermentation we are dealing with the following four determinants, each of which can mutate independently and can be mapped by conjugation:

z = structural gene for β-galactosidase

y = structural gene for permease

i = regulator gene for the *lac* operon (i^- = constitutivity; i^+ = inducibility)

o = operator and presumed combining site for the product of i.

Mutants of z and y were recognized by testing of a number of strains that remained lac^- even in the presence of inducer. They were mapped as discussed in Chapter 15. Constitutive (i^-) mutants, which produce both permease and β-galactosidase in the absence of inducer, were isolated from inducible (i^+) strains, and the determinant for constitutivity was found to occur in the order $y \cdot z \cdot i$ on the linkage map.

The production of a repressor substance by i^+ was indicated by the fact that matings between Hfr i^+z^+ and F^- i^-z^- (using glycerol rather than lactose as carbon source) resulted in a cessation of constitutive formation of β-galactosidase in the female shortly after the introduction of the i^+ gene, but enzyme formation resumed when inducer was added (Fig. 153). The testing of the properties of the merozygote was made possible in this case by the use of streptomycin-sensitive males and streptomycin-resistant

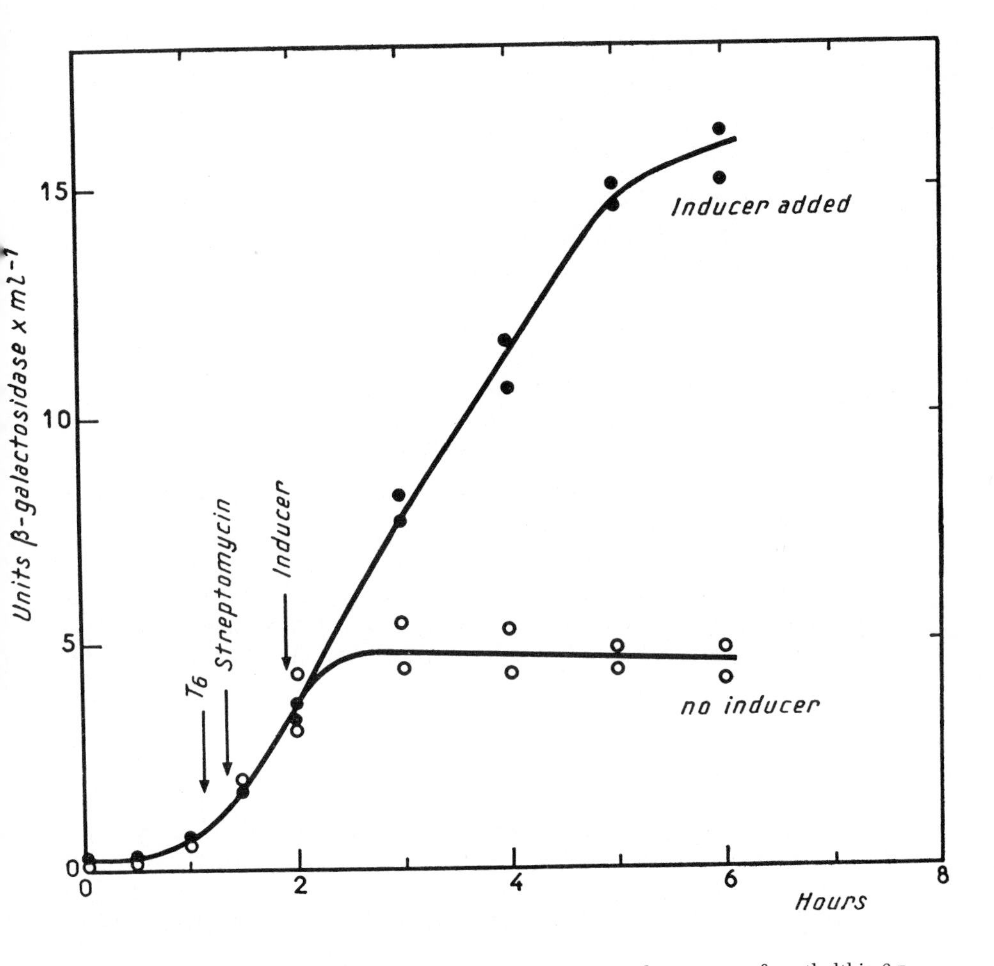

FIGURE 153. Synthesis of β-galactosidase in the absence and presence of methylthio-β-D-galactoside (inducer) following mating of inducible, galactosidase-positive males (Hfr $i^+z^+T_6^sStm^s$) and constitutive, galactosidase-negative females (F^- $i^-z^-T_6^rStm^r$). In this mating the first merozygotes which receive the *lac* region from the male are formed from the twentieth minute on. Streptomycin and phage T_6 are added at the times indicated by arrows to prevent further formation of recombinants and induction of the male parent. It can be seen that in the absence of inducer, enzyme synthesis stops about 80 minutes after transfer of the first i^+z^+ segment, but continues in the presence of inducer. (From Pardee *et al.*, 1959.)

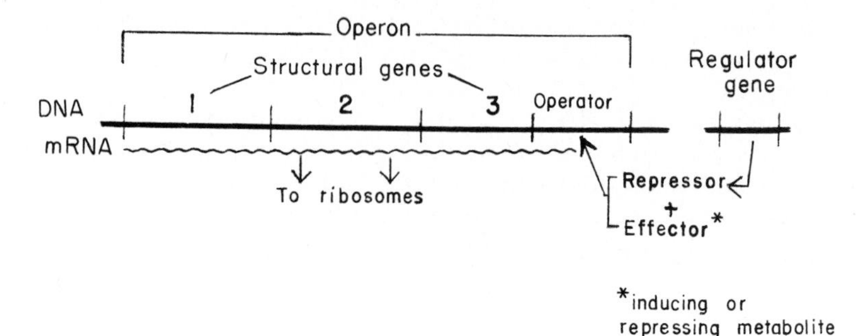

FIGURE 154. The Jacob-Monod model for the regulation of enzyme synthesis at the level of transcription.

females, which permitted the elimination of all i^+ males by adding streptomycin about 60 minutes after the start of conjugation (Pardee *et al.*, 1959).

Constitutivity was also found to result when another region, the so-called *o* region, of the *lac* locus mutated, but these *o* mutants behaved quite differently from the *i* mutants in several respects: First of all, a mutant labeled o^c (leading to constitutive formation of permease and β-galactosidase) proved to be dominant to o^+, while, as we have just seen, i^- (leading to constitutivity) is recessive to i^+ in the merozygote. Also, in a heterogenote (see p. 266) o^c produces constitutivity only when it is on the same chromsome as z^+ and y^+, in other words when it is in the *cis* position (i.e., $\frac{y^-z^-o^+}{y^+z^+o^c}$). In the *trans* position (i.e., $\frac{y^+z^+o^+}{y^-z^-o^c}$) o^c is inactive. In contrast, the *i* gene is active and causes repression, relievable by induction, whether or not it is in the *cis* or *trans* position in a heterogenote. Finally, if o^+ really controls the transcription of the structural genes *z* and *y*, one should also expect that *o* mutants can be isolated that will block this transcription under any known conditions by interfering with the start of reading. Such o^0 mutants were found.*

A MODEL FOR REGULATION AT THE TRANSCRIPTION LEVEL

These and many other data (cf. Hayes, 1964) have led to a model of regulation of enzyme synthesis at the transcription level as shown in Figure 154. This model assumes that a specific, but so far unidentified, repressor substance is produced by a specific regulatory gene. This substance, by combining with *o*, prevents the transcription of the structural

*However, the assumption that these o^0 mutants are due to a lack of regional transcription of DNA has been questioned following the more recent finding that suppressor mutations at several *distant* genetic loci are capable of restoring the function of o^0 mutants (Beckwith, 1963). Such a phenomenon would be more in line with regulation at the translation level (p. 354).

genes in the operon controlled by this particular regulator gene. In enzyme *induction* the inducer will inactivate the repressor, possibly by combining with it, and thus will relieve the repression of the operator; transcription and enzyme formation can now proceed.

When the inducer is removed, the half-life of the enzyme-forming capacity coincides with the half-life estimated for mRNA (Magasanik, 1963), which supports the belief that induction has permitted the temporary formation of a particular mRNA (see also p. 355). In the case of *enzyme repression*, it is assumed that another type of regulator gene produces an inactive aporepressor which, in the presence of an excess of the end product of the pathway controlled by the operon, will be converted into an active repressor.

SIMULTANEOUS REPRESSION OF SIMILAR CHARACTERISTICS CONTROLLED BY NON-LINKED GENES

While most enzymes controlling a single biosynthetic pathway in bacteria are clustered in one operon, as in the case of histidine synthesis, exceptions to this rule also are found. Thus, the eight structural genes for the enzymes controlling arginine synthesis are scattered throughout the bacterial chromosome, rather than forming a single operon. Nevertheless, they are all simultaneously repressed by arginine, which suggests that a single aporepressor can combine with arginine and can affect all the genes at their different locations (Gorini *et al.*, 1961; Vogel, 1961b).

MULTIVALENT REPRESSION

Some enzymes are active in biosynthetic pathways that yield more than one end product. For example, there are branched pathways, as in the case of the biosynthesis of aromatic compounds in which a series of end products arise from common intermediates. Also, a unique situation exists in the formation of isoleucine and valine in which the last four steps in the production of valine are catalyzed by the very same enzymes that catalyze the last four steps of isoleucine formation (Fig. 155).* In addition, the precursor of valine is also a precursor for leucine (Fig. 155).

Obviously, if repression by an excess of end products were to act as usual in a multiple pathway such as that illustrated in Figure 155, an excess of one end product (valine, for example) would be expected to interfere simultaneously with the formation of the other end products (isoleucine and leucine in our example). It was recently shown (Freundlich *et al.*, 1963) that a unique situation does exist in a pathway like the one pictured in Figure 155, insofar as an excess of all three end products (valine, isoleucine and leucine) is required for repression of the enzymes in this pathway. Such *multivalent repression*, involving possibly three sites on the aporepressor or on the operator for repression, may be typical for all pathways in which more than one end product is formed, since it avoids the possibility that an excess of one end product will prevent the formation of enzymes required for the other end product(s).

*This is the reason for the requirement for both valine and isoleucine for the growth of either valine or isoleucine auxotrophs.

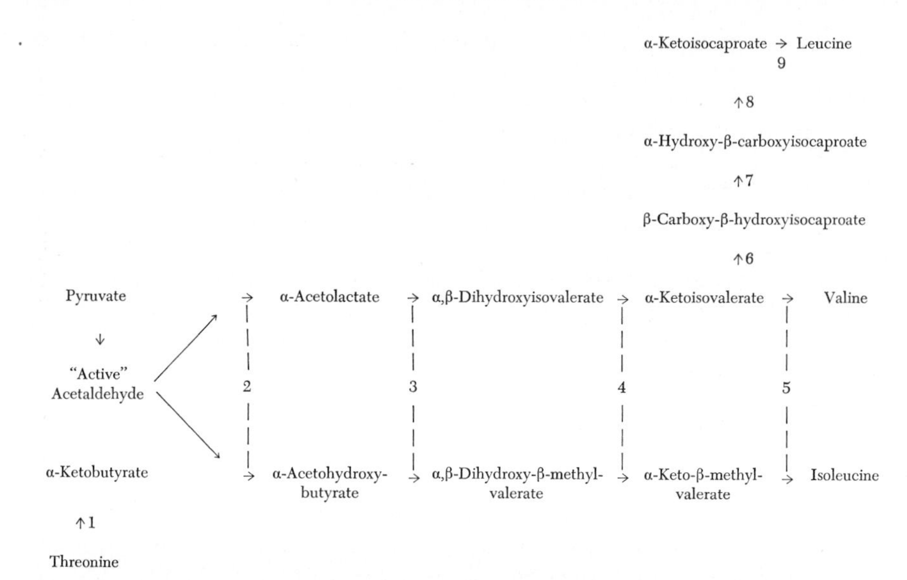

FIGURE 155. Pathways leading to the formation of valine, isoleucine, and leucine, and enzymes (1 to 9) involved. (From Freundlich *et al.*, 1963.)

NATURE OF THE REPRESSOR

As to the nature of the repressor, little factual information is available. It is suspected of being a protein, possibly an *allosteric protein*, which is a protein that presumably possesses two distinct sites: one reacting with the specific metabolite and the other reacting with the operator (Jacob and Monod, 1963). The general definition for an allosteric enzymatic protein is that of a protein which can react at one site with substances unrelated to its substrate; as the result of this reaction the activity of the other active site on the allosteric protein can be altered (Changeux, 1961; Gerhart and Pardee, 1962). Since only a very few molecules of any given repressor would be required per cell, no means for isolating and identifying the postulated repressor has so far been devised.

REGULATION AT THE TRANSLATION LEVEL

While some direct evidence supports the assumption that repressors act at the level of DNA, interfering with the transcription from DNA to mRNA, the possibility that repressors act at other levels, e.g., by interfering with the translation from mRNA to polypeptide or by influencing the removal of the finished polypeptide from the ribosome, has not been ruled out. It has, in fact, found growing support in recent speculations (Ames and Martin, 1963; Ohtaka and Spiegelman, 1963; Stent, 1964). For example, Stent (1964) has suggested that some repressors may represent specific enzymes that can inactivate specific tRNAs.

WHICH ARE THE REAL SITES OF REGULATION?

At this time it is impossible to decide between the various possibilities, and the probability that regulation occurs at many different levels cannot be excluded. Available experimental data can be cited in support of regulation at the level of transcription and at the level of translation, and we shall cite some examples of each.

Evidence that appears to support *regulation at the transcription level*, as originally proposed by Jacob and Monod, comes from certain hybridization tests between DNA and mRNA (see p. 325) in which the presence of a specific mRNA in the derepressed cell, and its absence in the repressed cells, has been demonstrated (Attardi *et al.*, 1963; Hayashi *et al.*, 1963). Again *E. coli* strains displaying inducible synthesis of β-galactosidase (*lac*$^+$) were used in some of these tests and attempts were made to detect hybrids between *lac*$^+$ DNA and its corresponding mRNA in induced cells. In order to identify the hybrids, certain tricks had to be used to reduce the background of extraneous (non-*lac*) DNA-mRNA hybrids. This was accomplished in one case by employing *F-lac* DNA [which was separable by CsCl density centrifugation from *F-lac*-infected *Serratia marcescens* (see p. 311)] and mRNA preparations from induced and non-induced *E. coli* following absorption with a denatured (single-stranded) DNA from *E. coli* with a *lac* deletion. In these and other tests (Guttman and Novick, 1963) an mRNA complementary to the *lac* region of DNA was detected in induced (derepressed) but not in non-induced (repressed) cells. It has been pointed out, however, that such a difference in mRNA in repressed and derepressed cells also could occur if regulation were operating at the level of reading of mRNA (i.e., at the transcription level). In this case, one would have to assume that the rate of mRNA formation is controlled, via a sort of "feedback control," by the extent of functioning of mRNA in the translation process (Stent, 1964).

Support for *regulation at the level of mRNA function* has come, for example, from the following observation: Again using the β-galactosidase system of *E. coli* but carrying out all the tests in a cell-free, sRNA- and ribosome-containing system, Novelli and Eisenstadt (1963) noted that mRNA, produced *in vitro* from *lac*$^+$ DNA of pre-induced cells, can, in the presence of inducer (galactoside), control the cell-free synthesis of β-galactosidase. However, mRNA obtained from DNA in the absence of the inducer, when added to functional mRNA, can inhibit the formation of β-galactosidase at the polypeptide-synthesizing stage. This finding indicates that mRNA from non-induced cells can have a repressing action at the translation level, which is inhibited by addition of the inducer. The inducer, however, also must be present at the transcription level, even in this cell-free system.

It should be clear that even though we have learned a great deal about the regulation of protein formation, we are still quite far from a full understanding of the intricacies of the control mechanisms,* and we certainly have not yet recognized all the various levels at which they may act. However, even existing models, especially the operon model, lend themselves to the construction of complex schemes, such as the one shown in Figure 156 in which the presence of two different regulator

*To mention one additional famous mystery, we may refer to the so-called *glucose effect*: It has been known since the early 1940's that glucose can inhibit the synthesis of quite a number of enzymes, but the way in which this phenomenon operates is still not understood (cf. Riley and Pardee, 1962).

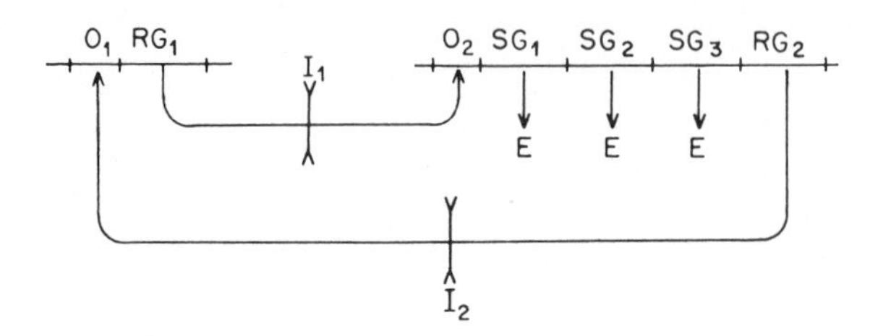

FIGURE 156. A model of possible interactions between two operons, each of which contains a regulator gene for the other. See text for details. (From Monod and Jacob, 1961.)

genes in two different interdependent operons can explain how an initial environmental stimulus can determine two different *irreversible* consequences for a cell with such regulation.

The assumption is made that the regulator gene RG_1 represses an operon consisting of O_2, three structural genes (SG_1, SG_2, and SG_3) and a regulator gene RG_2. RG_2, in turn, controls the operator, O_1, of the operon containing RG_1. The addition of the inducer I_1 will inhibit the action of the product of RG_1, thereby permitting the synthesis of enzymes E_1, E_2, and E_3, as well as an activation of RG_2, which now inhibits the function (reading) of RG_1. Once this state has been achieved, it should be maintained even in the absence of I_1. Similarly, if I_2 is the first inducer presented to such a cell, RG_1 would be activated and the transcription of the operon containing O_2, SG_1, SG_2, SG_3 and RG_2 would fail to occur, even after the removal of I_2. It is evident that a scheme of this sort presents some intriguing possibilities for mechanisms that might operate in cellular differentiation of higher organisms, regardless of whether the actual site of regulation is in transcription or translation, or at the stage of the release of the finished product from the ribosome.

FEEDBACK INHIBITION AND ALLOSTERIC PROTEINS

All the regulatory mechanisms discussed so far operate by interfering with the *formation* of a protein. There is, however, also a sort of regulatory "fine adjustment," in which the *function* of an enzyme participating in an early step of a biosynthetic pathway can be inhibited by an excess of the end product (Umbarger, 1961). An example of such control by *feedback inhibition* is shown in Figure 157. The inhibition pictured appears to be due to the binding of the end product to the "regulatory site" of the enzyme. This is supported by the fact that certain treatments can alter this site (preventing the binding of CTP, in the example in Figure 157) without affecting the catalytic activity of the treated enzyme (Gerhart and Pardee, 1962).

Comparable inhibition of an early enzyme by the end product of the pathway has been described in the biosynthesis of threonine, histidine,

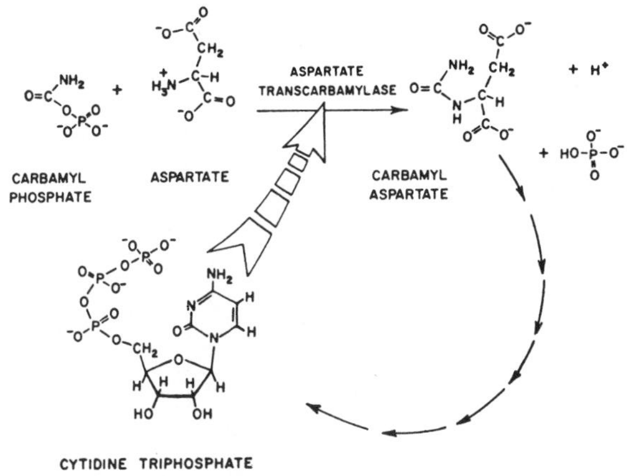

FIGURE 157. Diagram of feedback inhibition in the pyrimidine pathway of *E. coli*. Aspartate transcarbamylase, the first enzyme in the pathway leading (through six subsequent steps) to the pyrimidine nucleotide CTP (and also to UTP) is inhibited by accumulating CTP. CTP will accumulate when it is not rapidly utilized for nucleic acid synthesis. (From Gerhart and Pardee, 1963.)

arginine, tryptophan, purines and other essential metabolites (see Riley and Pardee, 1962). The phenomenon was noted first by Novick and Szilard (1954) in studies with the chemostat, in which the addition of tryptophan to the growth medium of *E. coli* resulted in a prompt cessation of tryptophan synthesis by the bacteria. Since this phenomenon involves an inhibition, by the end product, of one particular early enzyme in the pathway, and since it does not involve interactions with a substrate of the affected enzyme, the effects can be explained best by assuming that the *affected enzyme is an allosteric protein* (Jacob and Monod, 1963). Such a protein, as we have stated earlier (p. 354), is assumed to possess two distinct sites. One of these two sites may react with the end product of the biosynthetic pathway and the other, the enzymatically active site, may react with the substrate of the enzymatic activity. It can now be assumed that the enzymatically active site may lose its activity as the result of interactions between the protein and the end product.

In this manner enzyme proteins may alter their specific activity, or their affinity to the substrate, by reacting with agents that are neither analogs of the substrate nor intermediary participants in the reaction (Jacob and Monod, 1963). Obviously, the concept of allosteric proteins with two distinct reactive and active sites provides unique flexibility for the regulation of biological systems, but its validity in this and other phenomena is only suggested by the experimentation of the past and must be confirmed by the investigations of the future.

REFERENCES

Adelberg, E. A. (1953), Bact. Rev., *17*:253.

Adelberg, E. A., and Burns, S. N. (1960), J. Bact., *79*:321.

Adelberg, E. A., and Myers, J. W. (1952), Microb. Genet. Bull., No. 6.

Alexander, H. E., and Leidy, G. (1951), J. Exp. Med., *93*:345.

Allessandrini, A., and Sabatucci, M. (1931), Ann. d'Igiene, *41*:853.

Alloway, J. L. (1933), J. Exp. Med., *55*:91.

Altenbern, R. A., and Housewright, R. D. (1951), J. Bact. *62*:97.

Altenbern, R. A., and Landman, O. E. (1960), J. Bact., *79*:510.

Altenbern, R. A., Williams, D. R., and Ginoza, H. S. (1959), J. Bact., *77*:509.

Altenbern, R. A., Williams, D. R., Kelsh, J. M., and Mauzy, W. L. (1957), J. Bact., *73*:697.

Amano, T., Goebel, W. F., and Smidth, E. M. (1958), J. Exp. Med., *108*:731.

Ambler, R. P., and Rees, M. W. (1959), Nature, *148*:56.

Ames, B. N., and Garry, B. (1959), Proc. Nat. Acad. Sci., U.S., *45*:1453.

Ames, B. N., and Hartman, P. E. (1962), in *The Molecular Basis of Neoplasia*, University of Texas Press, Austin.

Ames, B. N., and Hartman, P. E. (1963), Cold Spr. Harb. Symp. Quant. Biol., *28*:349.

Anderson, E. H. (1944), Proc. Nat. Acad. Sci., U.S., *30*:397.

Anderson, T. F., Wollman, E. L., and Jacob, F. (1957), Ann. Inst. Pasteur, *93*:450.

Anfinsen, C. B. (1959), *The Molecular Basis of Evolution*, John Wiley and Sons, Inc., N. Y.

Anfinsen, C. B. (1963), in *Informational Macromolecules*, H. J. Vogel, V. Bryson, and J. O. Lampen, eds., Academic Press, N. Y.

Arber, W. (1960), Virology, *11*:273.

Arber, W. (1964), Virology, *23*:173.

Arber, W., and Dussoix, D. (1962), J. Mol. Biol., *5*:18.

Arber, W., and Morse, M. L. (1965), Genetics, *51*:137.

Armitage, P. (1952), J. Roy. Statist. Soc., Ser. B., *14*:2.

Attardi, G., Naono, S., Ronvière, J., Jacob, F., and Gros, F. (1963), Cold Spr. Harb. Symp. Quant. Biol., *28*:363.

Atwood, K. C., Schneider, L. K., and Ryan, F. J. (1951), Proc. Nat. Acad. Sci., U.S., *37*:146.

August, J. T., Cooper, S., Shapiro, L., and Zinder, N. D. (1963), Cold Spr. Harb. Symp. Quant. Biol., *28*:95.

Austrian, R. (1952a), Bact. Rev., *16*:31.

Austrian, R. (1952b), Bull. Johns Hopkins Hosp., *91*:189.

Austrian, R. (1953), J. Exp. Med., *98*:21.

Austrian, R., Bernheimer, H. P., Smith, E. E. B., and Mills, G. T. (1959), J. Exp. Med., *110*:585.

Austrian, R., and MacLeod, C. M. (1949), J. Exp. Med., *89*:451.

Avery, O. T., MacLeod, C. M., and McCarty, M. J. (1944), J. Exp. Med., *79*:137.

Bacon, G. A., Burrows, T. W., and Yates, M. (1950), Brit. J. Exp. Path., *31*:714.

Bacq, Z., and Alexander, P. (1961), *Fundamentals in Radiobiology*. 2nd Ed., Pergamon Press, N. Y.

Bailey, W. R. (1956), Canad. J. Microb., *2*:555.

Baldwin, R. L. (1964), in *The Bacteria*, vol. 5, I. C. Gunsalus and R. Y. Stanier, eds., Academic Press, N. Y.

Barksdale, L. (1959), Bact. Rev., *23*:202.

Barner, H. D., and Cohen, S. S. (1957), J. Bact., *74*:350.

Baron, L. S., Formal, S. B., and Spilman, W. (1953), Proc. Soc. Exper. Biol. Med., *83*:292.

Baron, L. S., Spilman, W. M., and Carey, W. F. (1959), Science, *130*:566.

Baskett, A. C., and Hinshelwood, C. (1951), Proc. Roy. Soc., Ser. B, *139*:58.

Bauman, N., and Davis, B. D. (1957), Science, *126*:170.

Bautz, E., and Freese, E. (1960), Proc. Nat. Acad. Sci., U. S., *46*:1585.

Bautz, E., and Hall, B. D. (1962), Proc. Nat. Acad. Sci., U. S., *48*:400.

Beadle, G. W. (1959), Science, *129*:1715.

Beale, G. H., and Wilkinson, J. F. (1961), Ann. Rev. Microbiol., *15*:263.

Beckwith, J. (1963), Biochim. Biophys. Acta, *76*:162.

Beijerinck, M. W. (1901), Versl. Afd. Natuurkunde Kon. Akad. Wetensch. Amsterdam, *9*:310.

Beijerinck, M. W. (1912), Folia Microb., *1*:4.

Beiser, S., and Davis, B. D. (1957), J. Bact., *74*:303.

Belser, W. L., and Bunting, M. I. (1956), J. Bact., 72:582.

Benkers, R., and Berends, W. (1961), Biochim. Biophys. Acta, *49*:181.

Benzer, S. (1957), in *The Chemical Basis of Heredity,* W. D. McElroy and B. Glass, eds., Johns Hopkins Press, Baltimore.

Benzer, S. (1961), Proc. Nat. Acad. Sci., U. S., *47*:403.

Berg, P. (1961), Ann. Rev. Biochem., *30*:293.

Berg, P., and Ofengand, E. J. (1958), Proc. Nat. Acad. Sci., U. S., *44*:78.

Bertani, G. (1951), Genetics, *36*:598.

Bertani, G. (1958), Adv. Virus Res., 5:151.

Bhaskaran, K. (1958a), J. Gen. Microbiol., *18*:315.

Bhaskaran, K. (1958b), J. Gen. Microbiol., *19*:71.

Bhaskaran, K. (1960), J. Gen. Microbiol., *23*:47.

Bisset, K. A., ed. (1950), *The Cytology and Life History of Bacteria,* Williams and Wilkins Co., Baltimore.

Böhme, H. (1961a), Z. Vererbgsl., *92*:197.

Böhme, H. (1961b), Biol. Zbl., *80*:5.

Bolton, E. T., and McCarthy, B. J. (1962), Proc. Nat. Acad. Sci., U. S., *48*:1390.

Bonner, D. M. (1961a), *Heredity,* Prentice-Hall, Inc., Engelwood Cliffs, N. J.

Bonner, D. M., ed. (1961b), *Control Mechanisms in Cellular Processes,* Ronald Press, N. Y.

Bonner, D. M., Suyama, Y., and DeMoss, J. A. (1960), Fed. Proc., *19*:926.

Borek, E. (1963), Cold Spr. Harb. Symp. Quant. Biol., *28*:139.

Bornschein, H., Dittrich, W., and Höhne, G. (1951), Naturwissensch., *38*:383.

Bouck, N., and Adelberg, E. A. (1963), Biochem. Biophys. Res. Comm., *11*:24.

Boyer, H. (1964), J. Bact., *88*:1652.

Bracco, R. M., Krauss, M. R., Roe, A. S., and MacLeod, C. M. (1957), J. Exp. Med., *106*:247.

Brachet, J., and Chantrenne, H. (1956), Cold Spr. Harb. Symp. Quant. Biol., *21*:329.

Bragg, P. D., and Polglase, W. J. (1962), J. Bact., *84*:370.

Braun, W. (1946), J. Bact., *51*:327.

Braun, W. (1947), Bact. Rev., *11*:75.

Braun, W. (1949), J. Bact., *58*:299.

Braun, W. (1950), in *Brucellosis,* A.A.A.S., Washington, D. C.

Braun, W. (1958), J. Cell. Comp. Phys., suppl. 1, *52*:337.

Braun, W., ed. (1960), Ann. N. Y. Acad. Sci., *88*:1021.

Braun, W. (1964), in *Molecular and Cellular Basis of Antibody Formation,* J. Sterzl, ed., Academic Press, N. Y.

Braun, W., Altenbern, R., Kelsh, J., and Sandoval, H. (1956), J. Bact., *71*:417.

Braun, W., and Bonestell, A. (1947), Amer. J. Vet. Res., *8*:386.

Braun, W., and Ciaccio, E. (1952), Bact. Proc., p. 41.

Braun, W., Firshein, W., and Whallon, J. (1957), Science, *125*:445.

Braun, W., Goodlow, R. J., Kraft, M., Altenbern, R., and Mead, D. (1951), J. Bact., *62*:45.

Braun, W., Gorelick, A., Kraft, M., and Mead, D. (1951), J. Inf. Dis., *89*:286.

Braun, W., Kraft, M., Mead, D. D., and Goodlow, R. J. (1952), J. Bact., *64*:41.

Braun, W., and Lewis, K. H. (1950), Genetics, *35*:97.

Braun, W., Plescia, O., Kohoutová, M., and Grellner, J. (1965), Microb. Genet. Bull., 22.

Braun, W., Pomales-Lebrón, A., and Stinebring, W. R. (1958), Proc. Soc. Exp. Biol. Med., *97*:393.

Braun, W., Pootjes, C., and Plescia, O. J. (1962), Microb. Genet. Bull., *18*:6.

Braun, W., and Whallon, J. (1954), Proc. Nat. Acad. Sci., U. S., *40*:162.

Brenner, S. (1955), Proc. Nat. Acad. Sci., U. S., *41*:862.

Brenner, S., *et al.* (1958), Nature, *181*:1713.

Brenner, S., Barnett, L., Crick, F. H. C., and Orgel, A. (1961), J. Mol. Biol., *3*:121.

Brenner, S., Jacob, F., and Meselson, M. (1961), Nature, *190*:576.

Brenner, S., Stretton, A. O. W., and Kaplan, S. (1965), Nature, 205.

Bresch, C. (1962), Z. Vererbgsl., *93*:476.

Brinton, C. C. (1959), Nature, *183*:782.

Brinton, C. C., Jr., Gemski, P., Jr., Falkow, S., and Baron, L. S. (1961), Biochem. Biophys. Res. Comm., *5*:293.

Brodie, J., and Shepherd, W. (1949), J. Gen. Microbiol., *3*:74.

Brown, G. L. (1962), Brit. Med. Bull., *18*:10.

Brubaker, R. R., and Surgalla, M. J. (1962). J. Bact., *84*:615.
Bryson, V. (1952), Science, *116*:48.
Bryson, V., and Davidson, H. (1951), Proc. Nat. Acad. Sci., U. S., *37*:784.
Bryson, V., and Demerec, M. (1950), Ann. N. Y. Acad. Sci., *53*:283.
Bryson, V., and Demerec, M. (1955), Amer. J. Med., *18*:723.
Bunting, M. I. (1942), J. Bact., *43*:593.
Bunting, M. I. (1946), Cold Spr. Harb. Symp. Quant. Biol., *11*:25.
Buonomini, G. (1938), Bull. Assoc. Diplomes Microbiol. Faculté Pharm. Nancy, *16*:17.
Burrows, T. W. (1962), Brit. Med. Bull., *18*:69.
Burrows, W., Porter, R. J., and Moulder, J. W. (1959), *Textbook of Microbiology*, 17th Ed., W. B. Saunders Co., Philadelphia.
Burton, K. (1962), Brit. Med. Bull., *18*:3.

Cairns, J. (1963), J. Mol. Biol., *6*:208.
Campbell, A. (1957), Virology, *4*:366.
Campbell, A. (1962), Adv. Genetics, *11*:101.
Campbell, A. (1964), in *The Bacteria*, vol. 5, I. C. Gunsalus and R. Y. Stanier, eds., Academic Press, N. Y.
Cantoni, G. L., Ishikura, H., Richards, H., and Tanaka, K., (1963), Cold Spr. Harb. Symp. Quant. Biol., *28*:123.
Carey, W. F., Spilman, W., and Baron, L. S. (1957), J. Bact., *74*:543.
Catcheside, D. G. (1960), in *Microbial Genetics*, Cambridge University Press, Cambridge.
Catlin, B. W. (1953), J. Bact. *65*:413.
Catlin, B. W. (1960), J. Bact., *79*:579.
Catlin, B. W., and Cunningham, L. S. (1961), J. Gen. Microbiol., *26*:303.
Cavalli, L. L. (1952), Bull. W.H.O., *6*:185.
Cavalli-Sforza, L. L. (1950), Boll. Ist. Sieroterap. Milan, *29*:281.
Cavalli-Sforza, L. L., and Lederberg, J. (1953), in *Symposium on Growth Inhibition and Chemotherapy*. VI Int. Congr. Microbiol. Rome, suppl. rend. Ist. Superiore di Sanita, pp. 108-142.
Cavalli-Sforza, L. L., and Lederberg, J. (1956), Genetics, *41*:367.
Cavalli-Sforza, L. L., Lederberg, J., and Lederberg, E. M. (1953), J. Gen. Microbiol., *8*:89.
Chamberlin, M., and Berg, P. (1962), Proc. Nat. Acad. Sci., U. S., *48*:81.
Changeux, J. P. (1961), Cold Spr. Harb. Symp. Quant. Biol., *26*:313.
Chargaff, E., and Davidson, J. N., eds. (1955), *The Nucleic Acids*, Academic Press, N. Y.
Chatterjee, B. R., and Williams, R. P. (1962), J. Bact., *84*:340.
Clark, A. J., and Adelberg, E. A. (1962), Ann. Rev. Microbiol., *16*:289.
Clark, A. J., and Margulies, A. D. (1965), Proc. Nat. Acad. Sci., U. S., *53*:451.
Clark, J. B., and Webb, R. B. (1955), J. Bact., *70*:454.
Clark, P. F. (1950), Ann. Rev. Microbiol., *4*:343.
Clowes, R. C. (1960), in *Microbial Genetics*, Cambridge University Press, Cambridge.
Clowes, R. C., and Rowley, D. (1955), J. Gen. Microbiol., *13*:461.
Coetzee, J. N., and Sacks, T. G. (1960), J. Gen. Microbiol., *23*:445.
Cohen, G. N., and Monod, J. (1957), Bact. Rev., *21*:169.
Cohen, S. S., and Barner, H. D. (1954), Proc. Nat. Acad. Sci., U. S., *40*:885.
Cohn, M., and Monod, J. (1953), Symp. Soc. Gen. Microbiol., *3*:132.
Cole, L. J., and Braun, W. (1950), J. Bact., *60*:283.
Cole, L. J., and Wright, W. H. (1916), J. Inf. Dis., *19*:209.
Colwell, C. A. (1946), J. Bact., *52*:417.
Cooper, S., and Zinder, N. D. (1962), Virology, *18*:405.
Coughlin, C. A., and Adelberg, E. A. (1956), Nature, *178*:531.
Crick, F. H. C. (1958), Symp. Soc. Exper. Biol., *13*:138.
Crick, F. H. C., Barnett, L., Brenner, S., and Watts-Tobin, R. J. (1961), Nature, *192*:1227.
Crick, F. H. C., Griffith, J. S., and Orgel, L. E. (1957), Proc. Nat. Acad. Sci., U. S., *43*:416.
Crossley, V. M., Ferguson, M., and Brydson, L. (1946), J. Bact., *52*:367.

Davies, D. A. L. (1957), Biochim. Biophys. Acta, *26*:151.
Davis, B. D. (1948), J. Am. Chem. Soc., *70*:4267.
Davis, B. D. (1950a), Experientia, *6*:41.
Davis, B. D. (1950b), J. Bact., *60*:507.
Davison, P. F., Freifelder, D., Hede, R., and Levinthal, C. (1961), Proc. Nat. Acad. Sci., U. S., *47*:1123.
Dawson, M. H., and Sia, R. H. P. (1931), J. Exp. Med., *54*:681.
De Kruif, P. H. (1921), J. Exp. Med., *33*:773.
Delaporte, B. (1950), Adv. Genetics, *3*:1.
Delwiche, E. A., Fukui, G. M., Andrews, A. W., and Surgalla, M. J. (1959), J. Bact., *77*:355.
Demain, A. L., and Newkirk, J. F. (1960), J. Bact., *79*:783.
Demerec, M. (1946), Proc. Nat. Acad. Sci., U. S., *32*:36.
Demerec, M. (1948), J. Bact., *56*:63.
Demerec, M. (1949), Hereditas, *35* Suppl.:201.
Demerec, M. (1954), Proc. Amer. Phil. Soc., *98*:318.
Demerec, M. (1956), in *Genetic Studies with*

Bacteria, publication 612, p. 5, Carnegie Institute of Washington, Washington, D. C.
Demerec, M. (1960), Proc. Nat. Acad. Sci., U. S., *46*:1075.
Demerec, M., Bertani, G., and Flint, J. (1951), Amer. Nat., *85*:119.
Demerec, M., Goldman, I., and Lahr, E. L. (1958), Cold Spr. Harb. Symp. Quant. Biol., *23*:59.
Demerec, M., and Hanson, J. (1951), Cold Spr. Harb. Symp. Quant. Biol., *16*:215.
Demerec, M., and Hartman, P. E. (1959), Ann. Rev. Microbiol., *13*:377.
Demerec, M., and Ozeki, H. (1959), Genetics, *44*:269.
Deskowitz, M. W. (1937), J. Bact., *33*:349.
Dienes, L., and Weinberger, H. J. (1951), Bact. Rev., *15*:245.
Dintzis, H. M. (1961), Proc. Nat. Acad. Sci., U. S., *47*:247.
Dodson, E. O. (1956), *Genetics: The Modern Science of Heredity*, W. B. Saunders Co., Philadelphia.
Doty, P., Marmur, J., and Sueoka, N. (1959), Brookhaven Symp. Biol., *12*:1.
Doudney, C. O., and Haas, F. L. (1960), Genetics, *45*:1481.
Doudoroff, M., Hassid, W. Z., Putnam, E. W., Potter, A. L., and Lederberg, J. (1949), J. Biol. Chem., *179*:921.
Driskell, P. J., and Adelberg, E. A. (1961), Bact. Proc., p. 186.
Dubos, R. (1958), *Bacterial and Mycotic Infections of Man*, 3rd Ed., J. B. Lippincott, Philadelphia.
Dubos, R., Davis, B. D., Middlebrook, G., and Pierce, C. (1946), Am. Rev. Tuberc., *54*:204.
Duguid, J. P. (1959), J. Gen. Microbiol., *21*:271.
Dunn, D. B., and Smith, J. D. (1954), Nature, *174*:304.
Dunn, D. B., and Smith, J. D. (1955), Nature, *175*:336.
Dushman, M. B. (1963), J. Bact., *86*:1173.

Eagle, H., Levy, M., and Fleischman, R. (1952), Antib. and Chemotherapy, *2*:563.
Ecker, R. E., and Lockhart, W. R. (1961), J. Bact., *82*:80.
Eigelsbach, H. T., Braun, W., and Herring, R. D. (1951), J. Bact., *61*:557.
Eisenberg, P. (1914), Zbl. Bakt. I. Abt. Orig., *73*:449.
Enderlein, G. (1925), *Bakterien-Cyclogenie*, W. de Gruyter & Co., Berlin.
Englesberg, E. (1961), J. Bact., *81*:996.
Englesberg, E., and Baron, L. S. (1959), J. Bact., *78*:675.
Englesberg, E., and Ingraham, L. (1957), Proc. Nat. Acad. Sci., U. S., *43*:369.
English, A. R., and McCoy, E. (1951), J. Bact., *62*:19.
Ephrussi, B. (1953), *Nucleo-Cytoplasmic Relations in Microorganisms*, Clarendon Press, Oxford.
Ephrussi-Taylor, H. (1951a), Exp. Cell Res., *2*:589.
Ephrussi-Taylor, H. (1951b), Cold Spr. Harb. Symp. Quant. Biol., *16*:445.
Ephrussi-Taylor, H. (1955), Adv. Virus Res., *3*:275.
Ephrussi-Taylor, H. (1960a), Symp. Soc. Gen. Microbiol., *10*:132.
Ephrussi-Taylor, H. (1960b), in *Microbial Genetics*, Cambridge University Press, Cambridge.
Epstein, C. J., Goldberger, R. F., and Anfinsen, C. B. (1963), Cold Spr. Harb. Symp. Quant. Biol., *28*:439.

Falkow, S., and Baron, L. S. (1962), J. Bact., *84*:581.
Falkow, S., Rownd, R., and Baron, L. S. (1962), J. Bact., *84*:1303.
Ferreira, A. J. (1942), Arch. Inst. Bact. Camara Pestana, *8*:133.
Fildes, P., and Whitaker, K. (1948), Brit. J. Exp. Path., *29*:240.
Fincham, J. R. S. (1962), Brit. Med. Bull., *18*:14.
Firshein, W. (1961), J. Bact., *82*:169.
Firshein, W., and Braun, W. (1958), Proc. Nat. Acad. Sci., U. S., *44*:918.
Firshein, W., and Braun, W. (1960), J. Bact., *79*:246.
Fisher, K. W. (1962), Brit. Med. Bull., *18*:19.
Fitz-James, P. C. (1960), J. Biophys. Biochem. Cytol., *8*:507.
Foster, J. W., and Pittillo, R. F. (1953), J. Bact., *66*:478.
Fox, M. S. (1955), J. Gener. Physiol., *39*:267.
Fox, M. S. (1960), Nature, *187*:1004.
Fox, M. S., and Hotchkiss, R. D. (1957), Nature, *179*:1322.
Franklin, N. C., and Luria, S. E. (1961), Virology, *15*:299.
Franklin, R. E., and Gosling, R. G. (1953), Nature, *171*:740.
Frédéricq, P. (1957), Ann. Rev. Microbiol., *11*:7.
Freese, E. (1959), Brookhaven Symp. Biol., *12*:63.
Freese, E. B. (1961), Proc. Nat. Acad. Sci., U.S., *47*:540.
Freese, E. (1963), in *Molecular Genetics*, vol. 1, J. H. Taylor, ed., Academic Press, N. Y.
Freese, E., Bautz, E., and Freese, E. B. (1961), Proc. Nat. Acad. Sci., U. S., *47*:845.

Freese, E., and Strack, H. B. (1962), Proc. Nat. Acad. Sci., U. S., *48*:1796.
Fregnan, G. B., Smith, D. W., and Randall, H. M. (1961), J. Bact., *82*:517.
Fresco, J. (1963), in *Informational Macromolecules*, H. J. Vogel, V. Bryson, and J. O. Lampen, eds., Academic Press, N. Y.
Freundlich, M., Burns, R. O., and Umbarger, H. E. (1963), in *Informational Macromolecules*, H. J. Vogel, V. Bryson, and J. O. Lampen, eds., Academic Press, N. Y.
Fukasawa, T., and Nikaido, H. (1960), Virology, *11*:508.
Fukui, G. M., Lawton, W. D., Ham, D. A., Janssen, W. A., and Surgalla, M. J. (1960), Ann. N. Y. Acad. Sci., *88*:1146.
Furness, G., and Rowley, D. (1956), J. Gen. Microbiol., *15*:140.

Gamow, G. (1954), Nature, *173*:318.
Garber, E. D. (1960), Ann. N. Y. Acad. Sci., *88*:1187.
Garber, E. D., Hackett, A. J., and Franklin, R. (1952), Proc. Nat. Acad. Sci., *38*:693.
Garber, E. D., Shaeffer, S. G., and Goldman, M. (1956), J. Gen. Microbiol., *14*:261.
Garen, A., and Garen, S. (1963), J. Mol. Biol., *7*:13.
Gause, G. F., and Kochetkova, G. V. (1962), J. Gen. Microbiol., *29*:317.
Geiduschek, E. P., Nakamoto, T., and Weiss, S. B. (1961), Proc. Nat. Acad. Sci., U. S., *47*:1405.
Gerhart, J. C., and Pardee, A. B. (1963), J. Biol. Chem., *237*:891.
Gierer, A. (1960), in *Microbial Genetics*, Cambridge University Press, Cambridge.
Gierer, A., and Mundry, K. W. (1958), Nature, *182*:1457.
Giles, N. H., Partridge, C. W. H., and Nelson, N. J. (1957), Proc. Nat. Acad. Sci., U. S., *43*:305.
Gillespie, W. A. (1952), J. Path. Bact., *64*:551.
Glass, E. A., and Novick, A. (1959), J. Bact., *77*;10.
Gold, M., and Hurwitz, J. (1963), Cold Spr. Harb. Symp. Quant. Biol., *28*:149.
Goldschmidt, E. P., and Landman, O. E. (1962), J. Bact., *83*:690.
Goldstein, A. (1954), J. Pharmacol. Exptl. Therap., *112*:326.
Goodgal, S. H., and Herriott, R. M. (1957a), in *Chemical Basis of Heredity*. W. D. McElroy, and B. Glass, eds., Johns Hopkins Press, Baltimore.
Goodgal, S. H., and Herriott, R. M. (1957b), Records Genet. Soc. Am., *26*:372.
Goodgal. S. H., and Herriott, R. M. (1961), J. Gener. Physiol., *44*:1201.
Goodlow, R. J., Braun, W., and Mika, L. A. (1951a), Arch. Biochem., *30*:402.
Goodlow, R. J., Braun, W., and Mika, L. A. (1951b), Proc. Soc. Exp. Biol. Med., *76*:786.
Goodlow, R. J., Mika, L. A., and Braun, W. (1950), J. Bact., *60*:291.
Goodlow, R. J., Tucker, L., Braun, W., and Mika, L. A. (1952), J. Bact., *63*:681.
Gorini, L., Gundersen, W., and Burger, M. (1961), Cold Spr. Harb. Symp. Quant. Biol., *26*:173.
Gorini, L., and Kaufman, H. (1960), Science, *131*:604.
Gould, J. C. (1957), Nature, *180*:282.
Gowen, J. W., Stadler, J., Plough, H. H., and Miller, H. N. (1951), Genetics, *36*:553.
Green, D. (1959), Exp. Cell Res., *18*:466.
Greer, S. (1958), J. Gen. Microbiol., *18*:543.
Greer, S., and Zamenhof, S. (1962), J. Mol. Biol., *4*:123.
Griffith, F. (1928), J. Hyg., *27*:113.
Groman, N. B. (1961), Ann. Rev. Microbiol., *15*:153.
Groman, N. B., and Lockart, R. Z. (1953), J. Bact., *66*:178.
Gros, F., Dubert, J.-M., Tissières, A., Bourgeois, S., Michelson, M., Soffer, R., and Legault, L. (1963), Cold Spr. Harb. Symp. Quant. Biol., *28*:299.
Gros, F., Hiatt, H., Gilbert, W., Kurland, C. G., Riseborough, R. W., and Watson, J. D. (1961), Nature, *190*:581.
Gross, J. (1964), in *The Bacteria*, vol. 5, I. C. Gunsalus and R. Y. Stanier, eds., Academic Press, N. Y.
Grunberg-Manago, M., and Ochoa, S. (1955). J. Am. Chem. Soc., *77*:3165.
Grunberg-Manago, M., Ortiz, P. J., and Ochoa, S. (1956), Biochem. Biophys. Acta, *20*:269.
Guild, W. R. (1961), Proc. Nat. Acad. Sci., U. S., *47*:1560.
Guild, W. R. (1963), J. Mol. Biol., *6*:214.
Guthrie, R. (1949), J. Bact., *57*:39.
Guttman, B. S., and Novick, A. (1963), Cold Spr. Harb. Symp. Quant. Biol., *28*:373.

Haas, G. J., and Sevag, M. G. (1953), Arch. Biochem., Biophys., *43*:11.
Hadley, P. (1927), J. Inf. Dis., *40*:1.
Hadley, P. (1937), J. Inf. Dis., *60*:129.
Hall, B. D., and Spiegelman, S. (1961), Proc. Nat. Acad. Sci., U. S., *47*:137.
Hall, C. E., and Slayter, H. S. (1959), J. Mol. Biol., *1*:329.
Hämmerling, J. (1953), Intern. Rev. Cytol., *2*:475.
Hartman, P. E., (1957), in *The Chemical Basic of Heredity*, W. D. McElroy, and B. Glass, eds., Johns Hopkins Press, Baltimore.
Hartman, P. E., and Goodgal, S. H. (1959), Ann. Rev. Microbiol., *13*:465.

Hartman, P. E., Hartman, Z., and Šerman, D. (1960), J. Gen. Microbiol., *22*:354.

Hartman, P. E., Loper, J. C., and Šerman, D. (1960), J. Gen. Microbiol., *22*:323.

Hashimoto, K. (1960), Genetics, *45*:49.

Hayakawa, K. (1937), Japan J. Exp. Med., *15*:197.

Hayashi, M., Hayashi, M. N., and Spiegelman, S. (1963), Proc. Nat. Acad. Sci., U. S., *50*: 664.

Hayashi, M., and Spiegelman, S. (1961), Proc. Nat. Acad. Sci., U. S., *47*:1564.

Hayashi, M., Spiegelman, S., Franklin, N. C., and Luria, S. E. (1963), Proc. Nat. Acad. Sci., U. S., *49*:729.

Hayes, W. (1952), Nature, *169*:118.

Hayes, W. (1953a), Cold Spr. Harb. Symp. Quant. Biol., *18*:75.

Hayes, W. (1953b), J. Gen. Microbiol., *8*:72.

Hayes, W. (1962), Brit. Med. Bull., *18*:36.

Hayes, W. (1964), *The Genetics of Bacteria and their Viruses,* John Wiley and Sons, Inc., N. Y.

Henry, B. S. (1933), J. Inf. Dis., *52*:374.

Herriott, R. M. (1961), Proc. Nat. Acad. Sci., U. S., *47*:146.

Herskowitz, I. H. (1962), *Genetics,* Little, Brown and Co., Boston.

Hinshelwood, C. N. (1947), *The Chemical Kinetics of the Bacterial Cell,* Oxford University Press, London.

Hirota, Y. (1960), Proc. Nat. Acad. Sci., U. S., *46*:57.

Hirsch, H. M. (1961), J. Bact., *81*:448.

Hoagland, M. B., Stephenson, M. L., Scott, J. F., Hecht, R. J., and Zamecnik, P. C. (1958), J. Biol. Chem., *231*:241.

Hoerlein, B. F. (1948), J. Bact., *56*:139.

Hollaender, A., Baker, W. K., and Anderson, E. H. (1951), Cold Spr. Harb. Symp. Quant. Biol., *16*:315.

Hollaender, A., and Kimball, R. F. (1956), Nature, *177*:726.

Holley, R. W., Apgar, J., Everett, G. A., Madison, J. T., Marquisee, M., Merrill, S. H., Penswick, J. R., and Zamir, A. (1965), Science, *147*:1463.

Holloway, B. W. (1955), J. Gen. Microbiol., *13*:572.

Holloway, B. W. (1956), J. Gen. Microbiol., *15*:221.

Holloway, B. W., and Fargie, B. (1960), J. Bact., *80*:362.

Holloway, B. W., and Monk, M. (1959), Nature, *184*:1426.

Hotchkiss, R. D. (1948), *Colloques sur "Les unités biologiques douées de continuité génétique."* Centre Nat. Rech. Sci., Paris, *8*:57.

Hotchkiss, R. D. (1951), Cold Spr. Harb. Symp. Quant. Biol., *16*:457.

Hotchkiss, R. D. (1952), Bull. N. Y. Acad. Med., *28*:346.

Hotchkiss, R. D. (1954a), Proc. Nat. Acad. Sci., U. S., *40*:49.

Hotchkiss, R. D. (1954b), J. Cell. Comp. Phys. *45*:1.

Hotchkiss, R. D. (1955), in *The Nucleic Acids.* vol. 2, E. Chargaff, and J. N. Davidson, eds. Academic Press, N. Y.

Hotchkiss, R. D. (1956), in *Enzymes: Units of Biological Structure and Function,* O. H. Gaebler, ed., Academic Press, N. Y.

Hotchkiss, R. D., and Ephrussi-Taylor, H. (1951), Fed. Proc., *10*:200.

Hotchkiss, R. D., and Marmur, J. (1954), Proc. Nat. Acad. Sci., U. S., *40*:55.

Hubacek, J. (1960), Folia Microb., *5*:171.

Hurwitz, J., and August, J. T. (1963), in *Progress in Nucleic Acid Research,* J. N. Davidson and W. E. Cohn, eds., Academic Press, N. Y.

Hurwitz, J., Evans, A., Babinet, C., and Skalka, A. (1963), Cold Spr. Harb. Symp. Quant. Biol., *28*:59.

Hurwitz, J., Furth, J. J., Anders, M., Ortiz, P. J., and August, J. T. (1961), Cold Spr. Harb. Symp. Quant. Biol., *26*:91.

Iino, T. (1959), Ann. Rept. Natl. Inst. Genetics (Japan), *10*:112.

Iino, T. (1962), J. Gen. Microbiol., *27*:167.

Ingram, V. M. (1961), *Hemoglobin and Its Abnormalities*, Charles C Thomas, Springfield.

Ingram, V. M. (1962), in *The Molecular Control of Cellular Activity,* J. M. Allen, ed., McGraw-Hill, N. Y.

Iseki, S., and Sakai, T. (1954), Proc. Japan. Acad., *30*:143.

Ivanovics, G. (1962), Bact. Rev., *26*:108.

Iyer, N. (1960), J. Bact., *79*:309.

Jacob, F. (1955), Virology, *1*:207.

Jacob, F., Brenner, S., and Cuzin, F. (1963), Cold Spr. Harb. Symp. Quant. Biol., *28*:329.

Jacob, F., and Monod, J. (1959), C. R. Acad. Sci. (Paris), *249*:1282.

Jacob, F., and Monod, J. (1961), J. Mol. Biol., *3*:318.

Jacob, F., and Monod, J. (1963a), in *Cytodifferentiation and Macromolecular Synthesis,* M. Locke, ed., Academic Press, N. Y.

Jacob, F., and Monod, J. (1963b), Cold Spr. Harb. Symp. Quant. Biol., *26*:193.

Jacob, F., Schaeffer, P., and Wollman, E. L. (1960), in *Microbial Genetics,* Cambridge University Press, Cambridge.

Jacob, F., and Wollman, E. L. (1956a), Ann. Inst. Pasteur, *91*:486.

Jacob, F., and Wollman, E. L. (1956b), C. R. Acad. Sci. (Paris), *242*:303.

Jacob, F., and Wollman, E. L. (1958), C. R. Acad. Sci. (Paris), *247*:154.
Jacob, F., and Wollman, E. L. (1961), *Sexuality and the Genetics of Bacteria,* Academic Press, N. Y.
Jacob, F., Ulman, A., and Monod, J. (1964), C. R. Acad. Sci. (Paris), *258*:3125.
James, T. W. (1961), Ann. Rev. Microbiol., *15*:27.
Jawetz, E., Gunnison, J. B., and Coleman, V. R. (1954), J. Gen. Microbiol., *10*:191.
Jenkin, C. R. (1962), J. Exp. Med., *115*:731.
Jinks, J. L. (1964), *Extranuclear Inheritance,* Prentice-Hall, Inc., Englewood Cliffs, N. J.
Jones, L. M., and Berman, D. T. (1951), J. Inf. Dis., *89*:214.
Jones, L. M., McDuff, C. R., and Wilson, J. B. (1962), J. Bact., *83*:860.
Jordon, R. C., and Jacobs, S. E. (1944), J. Bact., *48*:579.
Josse, J., Kaiser, A. D., and Kornberg, J. (1961), J. Biol. Chem., *236*:864.
Jukes, T. H. (1962), Proc. Nat. Acad. Sci., U. S., *481*:1809.
Jukes, T. H. (1963), Amer. Scientist, *51*:127.

Kalckar, H. M., Kurahashi, K., and Jordan, E. (1959), Proc. Nat. Acad. Sci., U.S., *45*:1776.
Kameyama, T., and Novelli, G. D. (1960), Biochem. Biophys. Res. Comm., *2*:393.
Kandler, O., and Zehender, C. (1957), Z. Naturforsch., *12b*:725.
Kaplan, H. S., and Zavarine, R. (1962), Biochem. Biophys. Res. Comm., *8*:432.
Kaplan, R. W. (1948), Naturwissensch., *35*:127.
Kaplan, R. W., Winkler, U., and Wolf-Ellmauer, H. (1960), Nature, *186*:330.
Karlson, J. L. (1956), J. Bact., *72*:813.
Kaudewitz, F. (1959), Z. Naturforsch., *146*:528.
Kauffmann, F. (1953). Acta Path. Microb. Scand., *33*:409.
Kauffmann, F. (1961), *Die Bakteriologie der Salmonella Species,* Munksgaard, Copenhagen.
Kauffman, F., Kruger, L., Lüderitz, O., and Westphal, O. (1961), Zbl. Bakt., I. Abt. Orig. *182*:57.
Kauffman, F., Lüderitz, O., Stierlin, H., and Westphal, O. (1960), Zbl. Bakt., I. Abt. Orig., *178*:442.
Kellenberger, E. (1960), in *Microbial Genetics,* Cambridge University Press, Cambridge.
Kelner, A. (1949), J. Bact., *58*:511.
Kjeldgard, N. O., Maaløe, O., and Schaechter, M. (1958), J. Gen. Microbiol., *19*:607.
Kjems, E. (1957), Acta Path. Microb. Scand., *42*:56.
Klein, D. T., and Klein, R. M. (1956), J. Bact., *72*:308.
Kleinschmidt, A. K., Burton, A., and Sinsheimer, R. L. (1963), Science, *142*:961.
Kleinschmidt, A. K., Lang, D., and Zahn, R. K. (1961), Z. Naturforsch., *166*:730.
Klieneberger, E. (1935), J. Path. Bact., *40*:93.
Knaysi, G. (1951), *Elements of Bacterial Cytology,* 2nd Ed., Comstock Publishing Co., Ithaca, N. Y.
Kohiyama, M., and Ikeda, Y. (1960), Nature, *187*:168.
Kohn, A. (1960), J. Bact., *79*:679.
Kohoutová, M. (1962), Folia Microb., *7*:33.
Korman, R. Z., and Berman, D. T. (1962), J. Bact., *84*:137.
Kornberg, A. (1960), Science, *131*:1503.
Kornberg, A. (1961), *Enzymatic Synthesis of DNA,* Ciba Lectures in Microbial Biochemistry, John Wiley & Sons, N. Y.
Kornberg, A. (1962), in *The Molecular Control of Cellular Activity.* J. M. Allen, ed., McGraw-Hill, N. Y.
Kozinski, A. W. (1961), Virology, *13*:373.
Kraft, M., and Braun, W. (1952), Bact. Proc., p. 78.
Kraft, M., and Braun, W. (1954), Bact. Proc., p. 51.

Lacks, S. (1962), J. Mol. Biol., *5*:119.
Lacks, S., and Hotchkiss, R. (1960), Biochim. Biophys. Acta, *45*:155.
Lamborg, M., and Zamecnik, P. (1960), Biochim. Biophys. Acta, *42*:296.
Landman, O. E., and Burchard, W. (1962), Proc. Nat. Acad. Sci., U. S., *48*:219.
Landman, O. E., and Ginoza, H. S. (1961), J. Bact., *81*:875.
Landman, O. E., and Halle, S. (1963), J. Mol. Biol., *7*:721.
Langvad-Nielsen, A. (1944), Acta Path. Microb. Scand., *21*:362.
Langyel, P., Speyer, J. F., and Ochoa, S. (1961), Proc. Nat. Acad. Sci., U. S., *47*:1936.
Lanni, F. (1960), Perspectives in Biol. and Med., *3*:418.
Lark, K. G. (1963), in *Molecular Genetics,* vol. 1, J. H. Taylor, ed., Academic Press, N. Y.
Lea, D. E., and Coulson, C. A. (1949), Genetics, *49*:264.
Leder, P., and Nirenberg, M. (1964), Proc. Nat. Acad. Sci., U. S., *52*:420.
Leder, P., Rottman, F., Brimscombe, R., Trupin, J., O'Neal, C., and Nirenberg, M. W. (1965), Fed. Proc., *24*:408.
Lederberg, E. M. (1960), in *Microbial Genetics,* Cambridge University Press, Cambridge.
Lederberg, E. M., Cavalli-Sforza, L. L., and Lederberg, J. (1964), Proc. Nat. Acad. Sci., U. S., *51*:678.
Lederberg, J. (1946), J. Bact., *71*:497.
Lederberg, J. (1947), Genetics, *32*:505.

Lederberg, J. (1949), Proc. Nat. Acad. Sci., U. S., *35*:178.

Lederberg, J. (1950a), J. Bact., *59*:211.

Lederberg, J. (1950b), Methods in Med. Res., *3*:5.

Lederberg, J. (1956a), Genetics, *41*:845.

Lederberg, J. (1956b), Proc. Nat. Acad. Sci., U. S., *42*:574.

Lederberg, J., Cavalli, L. L., and Lederberg, E. M. (1952), Genetics, *37*:720.

Lederberg, J., and Edwards, P. R. (1953), J. Immunol., *71*:232.

Lederberg, J., and Iino, T. (1956), Genetics, *41*:743.

Lederberg, J., and Lederberg, E. M. (1952), J. Bact., *63*:399.

Lederberg, J., Lederberg, E. M., Zinder, N. D., and Lively, E. R. (1951), Cold Spr. Harb. Symp. Quant. Biol., *16*:413.

Lederberg, J., and St. Clair, J. (1958), J. Bact., *75*:143.

Lederberg, J., and Tatum, E. L. (1946), Nature, *158*:558.

Lederberg, J., and Zinder, N. (1948), J. Am. Chem. Soc., *70*:4267.

Lee, N., and Englesberg, E. (1962), Proc. Nat. Acad. Sci., U. S., *48*:335.

Lehman, I. R. (1960), J. Biol. Chem., *235*: 1479.

Leidy, G., Hahn, E., and Alexander, H. E. (1959), Proc. Soc. Exp. Biol. Med., *102*:86.

Leifson, E., Carhart, S. R., and Fulton, M. D. (1955), J. Bact., *69*:73.

Leifson, E., and Palen, M. I. (1955), J. Bact., *70*:233.

LeMinor, L., LeMinor, S., and Nicole, P. (1961), Ann. Inst. Pasteur, *101*:571.

Lennox, E. S. (1955), Virology, *1*:190.

Lerman, L. S. (1963), Proc. Nat. Acad. Sci., U. S., *49*:94.

Lerman, L. S., and Tolmach, L. J. (1957), Biochim. Biophys. Acta, *26*:68.

Lerman, L. S., and Tolmach, L. J. (1959), Biochim. Biophys. Acta, *33*:371.

Lester, G., and Bonner, D. M. (1957), J. Bact., *73*:544.

Levine, H. G., and Maurer, R. L. (1958), J. Immunol., *81*:433.

Levinthal, C. (1959), Brookhaven Symp. Biol., No. 12.

Levinthal, C., and Crane, H. R. (1956), Proc. Nat. Acad. Sci., U. S., *42*:436.

Levinthal, C., and Davison, P. F. (1961), Ann. Rev. Biochem., *30*:641.

Levinthal, C., Keynan, A., and Higa, A. (1962), Proc. Nat. Acad. Sci., U. S., *48*:1631.

Levinthal, C., Signer, E. R., and Fetherolf, K. (1962), Proc. Nat. Acad. Sci., *48*:1230.

Lewis, I. M. (1934), J. Bact., *28*:619.

Li, K., Barksdale, L., and Garmise, L. (1961), J. Gen. Microbiol., *24*:355.

Lieb, M. (1960), Biochim. Biophys. Acta, *37*:155.

Lincoln, R. E. (1947), J. Bact., *54*:745.

Lindegren, C. C. (1935), Zbl. Bakt. II Abt., *93*:113.

Lissouba, P., Mousseau, J., Rizet, G., and Rossignol, J. L. (1962), Adv. Genetics, *11*:343.

Litman, R. (1961), J. Chim. Phys., *58*:997.

Litman, R., and Ephrussi-Taylor, H. (1959), C. R. Acad. Sci. (Paris), *249*:838.

Litt, M., Marmur, J., Ephrussi-Taylor, H., and Doty, P. (1958), Proc. Nat. Acad. Sci., U. S., *44*:144.

Loeb, T., and Zinder, N. D. (1961), Proc. Nat. Acad. Sci., U. S., *47*:282.

Loper, J. C., Grabnar, M., Stahl, R. C., Hartman, Z., and Hartman, P. E. (1964), Brookhaven Symp. Biol., *17*.

Loutit, J. S. (1958), J. Gen. Microbiol., *18*:315.

Loveless, A., and Howarth, S. (1959), Nature, *184*:1780.

Lowe, G. H. (1960), J. Gen. Microbiol., *23*:127.

Lubin, M. (1959), Science, *129*:838.

Luria, S. E. (1945), Genetics, *30*:84.

Luria, S. E. (1947), Bact. Rev., *11*:1.

Luria, S. E. (1960a), in *The Bacteria,* vol. 1, I. C. Gunsalus, and R. Y. Stanier, eds., Academic Press, N. Y.

Luria, S. E. (1962), Science, *136*:685.

Luria, S. E. (1960b), Cancer Res., *20*:677.

Luria, S. E. (1963), Recent Progr. in Microbiol., *8*:604.

Luria, S. E., Adams, J. N., and Ting, R. C. (1960), Virology, *12*:348.

Luria, S. E., and Burrous, J. W. (1957), J. Bact., *74*:461.

Luria, S. E., and Delbrück, M. (1943), Genetics, *28*:491, 1943.

Lwoff, A. (1953), Bact. Rev., *17*:269.

Maaløe, O. (1960a), in *Microbial Genetics,* Cambridge University Press, Cambridge.

Maaløe, O. (1960b), Symp. Soc. Gen. Microbiol., *10*:272.

Maccacaro, G. A., and Comolli, R. (1956), J. Gen. Microbiol., *15*:121.

MacLeod, C. M. (1958), in *Bacterial and Mycotic Infections of Man,* 3rd Ed., R. J. Dubos, ed., J. B. Lippincott Co., Philadelphia.

MacLeod, C. M., and Kraus, M. R. (1947), J. Exp. Med., *86*:439.

Magasanik, B. (1963), in *Informational Macromolecules,* H. J. Vogel, V. Bryson, and J. O. Lampen, eds., Academic Press, N. Y.

Malek, I. (1958), *Continuous Cultivation of Microorganisms,* Čsekoslov. Acad. Ved., Prague.

Manten, A., and Rowley, D. (1953), J. Gen. Microbiol., *9*:226.

Manwaring, W. H. (1934), Science, *79*:466.
Marmur, J., and Doty, P. (1959), Nature, *183*:1426.
Marmur, J., and Doty, P. (1962), J. Mol. Biol., *5*:109.
Marmur, J., Falkow, S., and Mandel, M. (1963), Ann. Rev. Microbiol., *17*:329.
Marmur, J., and Greenspan, C. M. (1963), Science, *142*:387.
Marmur, J., and Grossman, L. (1961), Proc. Nat. Acad. Sci., U. S., *47*:778.
Marmur, J., Rownd, R., Falkow, S., Baron, L. S., Schildkraut, C., and Doty, P. (1961), Proc. Nat. Acad. Sci., U. S., *47*:972.
Marmur, J., Rownd, R., and Schildkraut, C. L. (1963), in *Progress in Nucleic Acid Research,* J. N. Davidson, and W. E. Cohn, eds., Academic Press, N. Y.
Marmur, J., Schildkraut, C. L., and Doty, P. (1962), in *The Molecular Basis of Neoplasia,* University of Texas Press, Austin.
Marmur, J., Seaman, E., and Levine, J. (1963), J. Bact., *85*:461.
Martin, R. G. (1963), Cold Spr. Harb. Symp. Quant. Biol., *28*:357.
Massini, R. (1907), Arch. Hyg., *61*:250.
Matney, T. S. (1955), J. Bact., *69*:101.
Matney, T. S., and Achenbach, N. E. (1962a), Biochem. Biophys. Res. Comm., *9*:285.
Matney, T. S., and Achenbach, N. E. (1962b), J. Bact., *84*:874.
Matney, T. S., and Goldschmidt, E. P. (1962), J. Bact., *84*:874.
Matney, T. S., Shankel, D. M., and Wyss, O. (1958), J. Bact., *75*:180.
Matsushiro, A. (1961), Biken's J., *4*:141.
McCarty, M., and Avery, O. T. (1946), J. Exp. Med., *83*:89.
McCarty, M., Taylor, H. E., and Avery, O. T. (1946), Cold Spr. Harb. Symp. Quant. Biol., *11*:177.
McDonough, M. W. (1962), Biochem. J., *84*: 114.
McElroy, W. D., and Farghaly, A. H. (1948), Arch. Biochem., *17*:379.
McKee, J. J., and Braun, W. (1962), Proc. Soc. Exp. Biol. Med., *109*:166.
McQuillen, K. (1962), Progress in Biophys. *12*:67.
Mellon, R. R. (1926), J. Bact., *11*:203.
Mellon, R. R. (1942), J. Bact., *44*:1.
Meselson, M. S., and Stahl, F. W. (1958), Proc. Nat. Acad. Sci., U. S., *44*:671.
Meselson, M. S., and Weigle, J. J. (1961), Proc. Nat. Acad. Sci., U. S., *47*:847.
Meyer, A. (1912), *Die Zelle der Bakterien.* Gustav Fischer, Jena.
Meynell, G. G. (1961), Symp. Soc. Gen. Microbiol., *11*:174.
Michael, J. G., and Braun, W. (1959a), Proc. Soc. Exp. Biol. Med., *100*:422.
Michael, J. G., and Braun, W. (1959b), Proc. Soc. Exp. Biol. Med., *102*:486.
Mika, L. A., Goodlow, R. J., and Braun, W. (1952), Bact. Proc., p. 77.
Miller, I. L., and Landman, O. E. (1963), Bact. Proc., p. 34.
Mills, G. T., Austrian, R., and Bernheimer, H. P. (1961), in *Immunochemical Approaches to Problems in Microbiology,* M. Heidelberger, and O. J. Plescia, eds., Rutgers University Press, New Brunswick, N. J.
Mills, G. T., and Smith, E. E. B. (1962), Brit. Med. Bull., *18*:27.
Mitchison, D. A. (1953), J. Gen. Microbiol., *8*:168.
Mitchison, D. A. (1954), Brit. Med. J., *1*:128.
Mitchison, D. A. (1962), Brit. Med. Bull., *18*:74.
Miyake, T. (1960), Genetics, *45*:11.
Miyake, T., and Demerec, M. (1959), Nature, *183*:1586.
Monod, J. (1947), Growth Symposium, *11*:223.
Monod, J., and Jacob, F. (1961), Cold Spr. Harb. Symp. Quant. Biol., *26*:389.
Morse, M. L. (1959), Proc. Nat. Acad. Sci., U. S., *45*:722.
Morse, M. L., and LaBelle, J. W. (1962), J. Bact., *83*:775.
Morse, M. L., Lederberg, E. M., and Lederberg, J. (1956a), Genetics, *41*:142.
Morse, M. L., Lederberg, E. M., and Lederberg, J. (1956b), Genetics, *41*:758.
Moser, H. (1958), *The Dynamics of Bacterial Populations Maintained in the Chemostat,* publication No. 614, Carnegie Institute of Washington, Washington, D. C.
Mundry, K. W., and Gierer, A. Z. (1958), Z. Vererbgsl., *89*:614.
Murray, R. G. E. (1960), in *The Bacteria,* vol. 1, I. C. Gunsalus and R. Y. Stanier, eds., Academic Press, N. Y.

Nagata, T. (1963), Proc. Nat. Acad. Sci., U. S., *49*:551.
Nakada, D., Strelzoff, E., Rudner, R., and Ryan, F. J. (1960), Z. Vererbgsl., *91*:210.
Naono, S., and Gros, F. (1960), C. R. Acad. Sci. (Paris), *250*:8527.
Nathans, D., and Lipmann, F. (1961), Proc. Nat. Acad. Sci., U. S., *47*:497.
Neisser, L. M. (1906), Zbl. Bakt., I. Abt. Ref., *38*:98.
Nester, E. W., and Lederberg, J. (1961), Proc. Nat. Acad. Sci., U. S., *47*:52.
Nester, E. W., and Stocker, B. A. D. (1963), J. Bact., *86*:785.
Newcombe, H. B. (1948), Genetics, *33*:447.
Newcombe, H. B. (1949), Nature, *164*:150.
Newcombe, H. B., and Whitehead, H. A. (1951), J. Bact., *61*:243.

Nikaido, H. (1962), Proc. Nat. Acad. Sci., U. S., *48*:1337.
Nikaido, H., Nikaido, K., Subbaiah, T. V., and Stocker, B. A. D. (1964), Nature, *201*: 1301.
Nirenberg, M. W. (1963), Scientific Amer., *208*(3):80.
Nirenberg, M. W., and Jones, O. W. (1963), in *Informational Macromolecules*, H. J. Vogel, V. Bryson, and J. O. Lampen, eds., Academic Press, N. Y.
Nirenberg, M. W., Jones, O. W., Leder, P., Clark, B. F. C., Sly, W. S., and Pestka, S. (1963), Cold Spr. Harb. Symp. Quant. Biol., *28*:549.
Nirenberg, M. W., and Matthaei, J. H. (1961), Proc. Nat. Acad. Sci., U. S., *47*:1588.
Nishimura, S., Jones, D. S., Wells, R. D., Jacob, T. M., and Khorana, H. G. (1965), Fed. Proc., *24*:409.
Nomura, M., Hall, B. D., and Spiegelman, S. (1960), J. Mol. Biol., *2*:306.
Northrop, J. H., and Kunitz, M. (1957), J. Gener. Physiol., *41*:119.
Novelli, G. D., and Eisenstadt, J. M. (1963), in *Informational Macromolecules*, H. J. Vogel, V. Bryson, and J. O. Lampen, eds., Academic Press, N. Y.
Novick, A. (1956), Brookhaven Symp. Biol., *8*:201.
Novick, A., and Szilard, L. (1951), Cold Spr. Harb. Symp. Quant. Biol., *16*:337.
Novick, A., and Szilard, L. (1954), in *Dynamics of Growth Processes*, E. J. Boell, ed., Princeton University Press, Princeton, N. J.
Nyberg, C. (1938), Zbl. Bakt., I. Abt. Orig., *142*:178.

Ochoa, S. (1963), in *Informational Maccromolecules*, H. J. Vogel, V. Bryson, and J. O. Lampen, eds., Academic Press, N. Y.
Ochoa, S., Burma, D. P., Kroger, H., and Weill, J. D. (1961), Proc. Nat. Acad. Sci., U. S., *47*:670.
Ochoa, S., and Heppel, L. A. (1957), in *The Chemical Basis of Heredity*, W. D. McElroy, and B. Glass, eds., Johns Hopkins Press, Baltimore.
Ogg, J. E., Adler, H. I., and Zelle, M. R. (1956), J. Bact., *72*:494.
Ogg, J. E., and Humphrey, R. D. (1963), J. Bact., *85*:801.
Ogg, J. E., and Zelle, M. R. (1957), J. Bact., *74*:477.
Ogur, M., St. John, R., Ogur, S., and Mark, A. M. (1959), Genetics, *44*:483.
Ohtaka, Y., and Spiegelman, S. (1963), Science, *142*:493.
Okada, T., Yanagisawa, K., and Ryan, F. J. (1961), Z. Vererbgsl., *92*:403.
Okubo, S., Stodolsky, M., Bott, K., and Strauss, B. (1963), Proc. Nat. Acad. Sci., U. S., *50*:679.
Ørskov, F., and Ørskov, I. (1961), Acta Path. Microb. Scand. *51*:280.
Ørskov, I., and Ørskov, F. (1960), Acta Path. Microb. Scand., *48*:37.
Osborn, M. J. (1963), Proc. Nat. Acad. Sci., U. S., *50*:499.
Osborn, M. J., Rosen, S. M., Rothfield, L., and Horecker, B. L. (1962), Proc. Nat. Acad. Sci., U. S., *48*:1831.
Ottolenghi, E., and Hotchkiss, R. D. (1960), Science, *132*:1257.
Ottolenghi, E., and MacLeod, C. M. (1963), Proc. Nat. Acad. Sci., U. S., *50*:417.
Ozeki, H. (1956), in *Genetic Studies with Bacteria*, publication 612, p. 97, Carnegie Inst. of Washington, Washington, D. C.
Ozeki, H., and Howarth, S. (1961), Nature, *190*:986.

Page, L. A., Goodlow, R. J., and Braun, W. (1951), J. Bact., *62*:639.
Pakula, R. (1962), Abh. Deut. Akad. Wissensch. Berlin, *1*:178.
Pallade, G. E. (1964), Proc. Nat. Acad. Sci., U. S., 52:613.
Pardee, A. B. (1954), Proc. Nat. Acad. Sci., U. S., *40*:263.
Pardee, A. B., and Beckwith, J. R. (1963), in *Informational Macromolecules*, H. J. Vogel, V. Bryson, and J. O. Lampen, eds., Academic Press, N. Y.
Pardee, A. B., Jacob, F., and Monod, J. (1959), J. Mol. Biol., *1*:165.
Parr, L. W., and Robbins, M. L. (1941), J. Bact., *43*:661.
Parr, L. W., and Simpson, W. F. (1940), J. Bact., *40*:467.
Pasteur, L. (1881), C. R. Acad. Sci. (Paris), *92*:429.
Pickarski, G. (1937), Arch. Microb., *8*:428.
Pizzura, M., and Szybalski, W. (1959), J. Bact., *77*:614.
Plescia, O. J., Braun, W., and Palczuk, N. C. (1964), Proc. Nat. Acad. Sci., U. S., *52*:279.
Ponnamperuma, C. A., Lemmon, R. M., and Calvin, M. (1962), Science, *137*:605.
Pontecorvo, G. (1962), Brit. Med. Bull., *18*:81.

Ramsey, H., and Padron, J. L. (1954), Antib. and Chemotherapy, *4*:537.
Raffel, S. (1961), *Immunity*, 2nd Ed., Appleton-Century-Crofts, N. Y.
Rappaport, H. P., and Guild, W. R. (1959), J. Bact., *78*:203.
Ravin, A. W. (1957), Ann. N. Y. Acad. Sci., *68*:335.
Ravin, A. W. (1959), J. Bact., *77*:296.
Ravin, A. W. (1960), Genetics, *45*:1387.
Ravin, A. W. (1961), Adv. Genetics, *10*:61.

Ravin, A. W., and Iyer, V. N. (1961), J. Gen. Microbiol., *66*:1.
Reed, G. B. (1937), J. Bact., *34*:255.
Reich, E., Franklin, R. M., Shatkin, A. J., and Tatum, E. L. (1962), Proc. Nat. Acad. Sci., U. S., *48*:1238.
Reimann, H. A. (1937), J. Bact., *33*:513.
Rich, A., Warner, J. R., and Goodman, H. M. (1963), Cold Spr. Harb. Symp. Quant. Biol., *28*:269.
Richmond, H. M., and Maaløe, O. (1962), J. Gen. Microbiol., *27*:285.
Rickenberg, H. V. (1960), J. Bact., *80*:421.
Riley, M., and Pardee, A. B. (1962), Ann. Rev. Microbiol., *16*:1.
Riley, M., Pardee, A. B., Jacob, F., and Monod, J. (1960), J. Mol. Biol., *2*:216.
Ritzki, M. T. M. (1950), J. Bact., *80*:305.
Robbins, P. W., and Uchida, T. (1962), Biochemistry, *1*:323.
Roberts, R. B., Britten, R. J., and McCarthy, B. J. (1963), in *Molecular Genetics*, vol. 1, J. H. Taylor, ed., Academic Press, N. Y.
Robinow, C. F. (1942), Proc. Roy. Soc. Ser. B., *130*:299.
Robinow, C. F. (1945), in *The Bacterial Cell*, R. J. Dubos, ed., Harvard University Press, Cambridge, Mass.
Robinow, C. F. (1960a), in *The Cell*, J. Brachet, and A. E. Mirsky, eds., Academic Press, N. Y.
Robinow, C. F. (1960b), in *The Bacteria*, vol. 1, I. C. Gunsalus and R. Y. Stanier, eds., Academic Press, N. Y.
Roger, M., and Hotchkiss, R. D. (1961), Proc. Nat. Acad. Sci., U. S., *47*:653.
Rogosa, M., and Mitchell, J. A. (1950), J. Bact., *59*:303.
Rolfe, R., and Ephrussi-Taylor, H. (1961), Proc. Nat. Acad. Sci., U. S., *47*:1450.
Romantsova, V. (1963), Fed. Proc., *22*:T1025.
Rosenberg, B. H., Sirotnak, F. M., and Cavalieri, L. F. (1959), Proc. Nat. Acad. Sci., U. S., *45*:144.
Rothfels, K. H. (1952), Genetics, *37*:297.
Rountree, P. M. (1959), J. Gen. Microbiol., *20*:620.
Rubenstein, I., Thomas, C. A., Jr., and Hershey, A. D. (1961), Proc. Nat. Acad. Sci., U. S., *47*:1113.
Rudner, R. (1960), Biochem. Biophys. Res. Comm., *3*:275.
Rudner, R. (1961), Z. Vererbgsl., *92*:336.
Rupert, C. S. (1960), J. Gen. Physiol., *43*:573.
Rupert, C. S., and Goodgal, S. H. (1960), Nature, *185*:556.
Rupert, C. S., Goodgal, S. H., and Herriott, R. M. (1958), J. Gen. Physiol., *41*:451.
Ryan, F. J. (1953), VI Int. Congr. Microb. Rome, *1*:649.
Ryan, F. J. (1954), Proc. Nat. Acad. Sci., U. S., *40*:178.
Ryan, F. J. (1959), J. Gen. Microbiol., *21*:530.
Ryan, F. J., Fried, P., and Schwartz, M. (1954), J. Gen. Microbiol., *11*:380.
Ryan, F. J., Nakada, D., and Schneider, M. J. (1961), Z. Vererbgsl., *92*:38.
Ryan, F. J., and Schneider, L. K. (1948), J. Bact., *56*:699.
Ryan, F. J., and Schneider, L. K. (1949a), J. Bact., *58*:181.
Ryan, F. J., and Schneider, L. K. (1949b), J. Bact., *58*:191.
Ryan, F. J., and Schneider, L. K. (1949c), J. Bact., *58*:201.
Ryan, F. J., Schwartz, M., and Fried, P. (1955), J. Bact., *69*:552.
Ryan, F. J., and Wainwright, L. K. (1954), J. Gen. Microbiol., *11*:364.
Ryter, A., and Jacob, F. (1963), C. R. Acad. Sci. (Paris), *257*:3060.

Sager, R. (1960), Science, *132*:1459.
Sager, R., and Ryan, F. J. (1961), *Cell Heredity*, J. Wiley and Sons, N. Y.
Salton, M. R. J. (1960), in *The Bacteria*, vol. 1, I. C. Gunsalus and R. Y. Stanier, eds., Academic Press, N. Y.
Sarabhai, A. S., Stretton, A. O. W., Brenner, S., and Bolle, A. (1964), Nature *201*:13.
Saz, A. K., and Eagle, H. (1953), J. Bact., *66*:347.
Schaeffer, P. (1957), C. R. Acad. Sci. (Paris), *245*:230.
Schaeffer, P. (1958a), Ann. Inst. Pasteur, *94*:167.
Schaeffer, P. (1958b), Symp. Soc. Exper. Biol., *12*:60.
Schaeffer, P. (1964), in *The Bacteria*, vol. 5, I. C. Gunsalus and R. Y. Stanier, eds., Academic Press, N. Y.
Schaeffer, P., Ionesco, H., and Jacob, F. (1959), C. R. Acad. Sci. (Paris), *249*:577.
Schildkraut, C. L., Marmur, J., and Doty, P. (1961), J. Mol. Biol., *3*:595.
Schildkraut, C. L., Marmur, J., and Doty, P. (1962), J. Mol. Biol., *4*:430.
Schlesinger, M. J., and Levinthal, C. (1963), J. Mol. Biol., *7*:1.
Schneider, H. A. (1949), Am. J. Pub. Health, *39*:57.
Scholes, G., Ward, J. F., and Weiss, J. (1960), J. Mol. Biol., *2*:379.
Schuster, H. (1960), Biochem. Biophys. Res. Comm., *2*:329.
Schweet, R., and Bishop, J. (1962), in *Molecular Genetics*. vol. 1, J. H. Taylor, ed., Academic Press, N. Y.
Seiffert, W. (1936), Zbl. Bakt., I. Abt. Ref., *121*:143.
Seppilli, A. (1939), 3rd Intern. Congr. Microb., New York, Rept. Proc., 162.

Setlow, R. B., and Carrier, W. L. (1964), Proc. Nat. Acad. Sci., U. S., *51*:226.

Shah, K. K., and Iyer, V. N. (1961), J. Bact., *81*:887.

Shedden, W. I. H. (1962), J. Gen. Microbiol., *28*:1.

Shinn, L. E. (1939), J. Bact., *38*:5.

Shugar, D. (1960), in *The Nucleic Acids,* vol. 3, E. Chargaff and J. N. Davidson, eds., Academic Press, N. Y.

Siddigi, O. H. (1963), Proc. Nat. Acad. Sci., U. S., *49*:589.

Sinai, J., and Yudkin, J. (1959), J. Gen. Microbiol., *20*:373 and 384.

Sinkovics, J. (1957), Acta Microb. Acad. Sci. Hung., *4*:61.

Sinsheimer, R. L. (1959), J. Mol. Biol., *1*:43.

Sinsheimer, R. L. (1962), Scientific Amer. *207*:109.

Sinsheimer, R. L., Starman, B., Nagler, C., and Guthrie, S. (1962), J. Mol. Biol., *4*:142.

Sirotnak, F. M., Lunt, R. B., and Hutchison, D. J. (1960), J. Bact., *80*:648.

Sirotnak, F., Lunt, R. B., and Hutchison, D. J. (1963), J. Bact., *86*:735.

Skaar, P. D. (1956), Proc. Nat. Acad. Sci., U. S., *42*:245.

Smith, M. A., Salas, M., Stanley, W. M., Jr., and Wahba, A. J. (1965), Fed. Proc., *24*:409.

Smith, S. M., and Stocker, B. A. D. (1962), Brit. Med. Bull., *18*:46.

Sneath, P. H. A. (1962), Brit. Med. Bull., *18*:41.

Sneath, P. H. A., and Lederberg, J. (1961), Proc. Nat. Acad. Sci., U. S., *47*:86.

Soffer, R. L. (1961), J. Bact., *82*:471.

Speyer, J. F., Lengyel, P., Basilio, C., Wahba, A. J., Gardner, R. S., and Ochoa, S. (1963), Cold Spr. Harb. Symp. Quant. Biol., *28*:559.

Spiegelman, S. (1959), in *Progress in Microbiology,* VIIth Int. Congr. f. Microbiol., Almqvist and Wiksell, Stockholm.

Spiegelman, S., and Doi, R. H. (1963), Cold Spr. Harb. Symp. Quant. Biol., *28*:109.

Spiegelman, S., and Hayashi, M. (1963), Cold Spr. Harb. Symp. Quant. Biol., *28*:161.

Spizizen, J. (1958), Proc. Nat. Acad. Sci., U. S., *44*:1072.

Spizizen, J. (1959), Fed. Proc., *18*:957.

Spizizen, J. (1961), in *Spores,* vol. 2, H. O. Halvorson, ed., Burgess Publishing Co., Minneapolis.

Srb, A. M., and Owen, R. D. (1958), *General Genetics,* W. H. Freeman, San Francisco.

Stahl. F. W. (1964), *The Mechanics of Inheritance,* Prentice-Hall, Inc., Englewood Cliffs, N. J.

Stamp, L. (1953), Brit. J. Exp. Path., *34*:347.

Stanier, R. Y. (1947), J. Bact., *54*:339.

Stanier, R. Y. (1951), Ann. Rev. Microbiol., 5:35.

Staub, A.-M. (1960), Ann. Inst. Pasteur, *98*:814.

Staub, A.-M. (1964), in *Bacterial Endotoxins,* M. Landy, and W. Braun, eds., Rutgers University Press, New Brunswick, N. J.

Staub, A.-M., and Forest, N. (1963), Ann. Inst. Pasteur, *104*:371.

Staub, A.-M., and Tinelli, R. (1960), Bull. Soc. Chim. Biol., *42*:1637.

Steiner, R. F., and Beers, R. F. (1961), *Polynucleotides,* American Elsevier Publishing Co., N. Y.

Stent, G. (1960), Advances Biol. Med. Phys., 7:2.

Stent, G. (1964), Science, *144*:816.

Sterne, M. (1938), Onderstepoort J. Vet. Sci., *10*:245.

Stevens, A. (1960), Biochem. Biophys. Res. Comm., *3*:92.

Stinebring, W. R., Braun, W., and Pomales-Lebrón, A. (1960), Ann. N. Y. Acad. Sci., *88*:1230.

Stocker, B. A. D. (1949), J. Hyg., *47*:398.

Stocker, B. A. D. (1956), J. Gen. Microbiol., *15*:575.

Stocker, B. A. D., McDonough, M. W., and Ambler, R. P. (1961), Nature, *189*:556.

Stocker, B. A. D., Smith, S. M., and Ozeki, H. (1963), J. Gen. Microbiol., *30*:201.

Stocker, B. A. D., Staub, A.-M., Tinelli, R., and Kopacka, B. (1960), Ann. Inst. Pasteur, *98*:505.

Stocker, B. A., Zinder, N. D., and Lederberg, J. J. (1953), J. Gen. Microbiol., *9*:410.

Strauss, B. S. (1960), *Chemical Genetics,* W. B. Saunders Co., Philadelphia.

Strauss, B., and Okubo, S. (1960), J. Bact., *79*:464.

Strelzoff, E. (1961), Biochem. Biophys. Res. Comm., 5:384.

Stuy, J. H. (1962), Biochem. Biophys. Res. Comm., *6*:328.

Subbaiah, T. V., and Stocker, B. A. D. (1964), Nature, *201*:1298.

Subramaniam, M. K., and Prahlada Rao, L. S. (1951), Experientia, 7:98.

Suskind, S. R., and Yanofsky, C. (1961), in *Control Mechanisms in Cellular Processes,* D. Bonner, ed., Roland Press Co., N. Y.

Szybalski, W. (1960), in *Developments in Industrial Microbiology,* B. M. Miller, ed., Plenum Press, N. Y.

Szybalski, W., and Bryson, V. (1952), J. Bact., *64*:489.

Szybalski, W., and Bryson, V. (1953a), J. Bact., *66*:468.

Szybalski, W., and Bryson, V. (1953b), Am. Rev. Tuberc., *68*:280.

Szybalski, W., and Lorkiewicz, Z. (1962), Abh. Deut. Akad. Wissensch. Berlin, *1*:63.

Tabor, C. W. (1962), J. Bact., *83*:1101.
Talmadge, M. B., and Herriott, R. M. (1960), Biochem. Biophys. Res. Comm., *2*:203.
Tatum, E. L. (1959), Science, *129*:1711.
Tatum, E. L., and Lederberg, J. (1947), J. Bact., *53*:673.
Taubeneck, U. (1962), Zeitschr. f. Allg. Mikrob., *2*:132.
Taylor, H. E. (1949a), C. R. Acad. Sci. (Paris), *228*:1258.
Taylor, H. E. (1949b), J. Exp. Med., *89*:399.
Taylor, M. J., and Thorne, C. B. (1963), J. Bact., *86*:452.
Thach, R. E., Sundararajan, T. A., and Doty, P. M. (1965), Fed. Proc., *24*:409.
Thomas, C., and Wilson, J. B. (1960), Proc. Soc. Exp. Biol. Med., *103*:292.
Thorne, C. (1961), in *Spores*, vol. 2, H. D. Halvorson, ed., Burgess Publishing Co., Minneapolis.
Tissières, A., Schlesinger, D., and Gros, F. (1960), Proc. Nat. Acad. Sci., U. S., *46*:1450.
Thornley, M. J., and Horne, R. W. (1962), J. Gen. Microbiol., *28*:51.
Tomcsik, J., and Guex-Holzer, S. (1952), Schweiz. Ztschr. Allg. Path., *15*:517.
Trantner, T. A., Swartz, M. N., and Kornberg, A. (1962), Proc. Nat. Acad. Sci., U. S., *48*:449.
Treffers, H. P., Spinelli, V., and Belser, N. O. (1954), Proc. Nat. Acad. Sci., U. S., *40*:1064.

Uetake, H. (1959), Virology, *7*:253.
Uetake, H., and Hagiwara, S. (1961), Virology, *13*:500.
Uetake, H., Luria, S. E., and Burrows, J. W. (1958), Virology, *5*:68.
Umbarger, H. E. (1961), Cold Spr. Harb. Symp. Biol., *26*:301.

van Loghem, J. J. (1929), Z. Hyg. Infektionskrankh, *110*:382.
Vogel, H. J. (1957a), Proc. Nat. Acad. Sci., U. S., *43*:491.
Vogel, H. J. (1957b), in *The Chemical Basis of Heredity*, W. D. McElroy, and B. Glass, eds., Johns Hopkins Press, Baltimore.
Vogel, H. J. (1961a), in *Cellular Control Mechanisms*, D. M. Bonner, ed., Ronald Press, N. Y.
Vogel, H. J. (1961b), Cold Spr. Harb. Symp. Quant. Biol., *26*:163.
Vogel, H. J. (1961c), in *Control Mechanisms in Cellular Processes*, D. M. Bonner, ed., Ronald Press, N. Y.
Vogel, H. J., and Davis, B. D. (1952), Fed. Proc., *11*:485.
Volkin, E., and Astrachan, L. (1956), Virology, *2*:433.
Voll, M. J., and Goodgal, S. H. (1961), Proc. Nat. Acad. Sci., U. S., *47*:505.
von Ehrenstein, G., and Lipmann, F. (1961), Proc. Nat. Acad. Sci., U. S., *47*:941.

Wachsman, J. T., and Mangalo, R. J. (1962), J. Bact., *83*:35.
Wacker, A. (1963), Progr. Nucl. Acid Res., *1*:369.
Wainwright, S. D., and Mullaney, J. (1954), J. Bact., *67*:504.
Wardlaw, A. C. (1964), in *Bacterial Endotoxins*, M. Landy, and W. Braun, eds., Rutgers University Press, New Brunswick, N. J.
Wagner, R. P., and Mitchell, H. K. (1964), *Genetics and Metabolism*, 2nd Ed., J. Wiley and Sons, Inc., N. Y.
Watanabe, T. (1963), Bact. Rev., *27*:87.
Watanabe, T., and Fukasawa, T. (1961), J. Bact., *81*:669 and 679.
Watanabe, T., Fukasawa, T., and Ushiba, D. (1957), J. Bact., *73*:770.
Watanabe, T., and Watanabe, M. (1959), J. Gen. Microbiol., *21*:16.
Watson, J. D., and Crick, F. H. C. (1953a), Cold Spr. Harb. Symp. Quant. Biol., *18*:123.
Watson, J. D., and Crick, F. H. C. (1953b), Nature, *171*:737.
Weatherwax, R. S., and Landman, O. E. (1960), J. Bact., *80*:528.
Weibull, C. (1953), J. Bact., *66*:668.
Weigle, J. J., Meselson, M., and Paigen, K. (1959), J. Mol. Biol., *1*:379.
Weil, E., and Felix, A. (1917), Wien. Klin. Wchnschr., *30*:1509.
Weinberg, R., and Latham, A. B. (1956), J. Bact., *72*:570.
Weiner, L. M., and Swanson, R. E. (1960), J. Bact., *79*:863.
Weisblum, B., Benzer, S., and Holley, R. W. (1962), Proc. Nat. Acad. Sci., U. S., *48*:1449.
Weiss, S. B., and Nakamoto, T. (1961), Proc. Nat. Acad. Sci., U. S., *47*:694 and 1400.
Welsch, M., and Osterrieth, P. (1958), Antonie van Leeuwenhoek, *24*:257.
White, A., Foster, F., and Lyan, L. (1962), J. Bact., *84*:815.
Wilkins, M. H. F., Stokes, A. R., and Wilson, H. R. (1953), Nature, *171*:738.
Witkin, E. M. (1947a), Cold Spr. Harb. Symp. Quant. Biol., *12*:256.
Witkin, E. M. (1947b), Genetics, *32*:221.
Witkin, E. M. (1950), Methods in Med. Res., *3*:23.
Witkin, E. M. (1951), Cold Spr. Harb. Symp. Quant. Biol., *16*:357.
Witkin, E. M. (1956), Cold Spr. Harb. Symp. Quant. Biol., *21*:123.
Witkin, E. M. (1959), Proc. 10th Intern. Congr. Genet., *1*:280.

Witkin, E. M. (1961), J. Cell. Comp. Phys., Suppl. 1, *58*:135.
Witkin, E. M., and Theil, E. C. (1960), Proc. Nat. Acad. Sci., U. S., *46*:226.
Wollman, E. L., and Jacob, F. (1955), C. R. Acad. Sci. (Paris), *240*:2449.
Wollman, E. L., and Jacob, F. (1957), Ann. Inst. Pasteur, *93*:223.
Wollman, E. L., and Jacob, F. (1958), Ann. Inst. Pasteur, *95*:641.
Won, W. D. (1950), J. Bact., *60*:102.
Wyss, O., Clark, J. B., Haas, F., and Stone, W. S. (1948), J. Bact., *56*:51.
Wyss, O., and Wyss, M. B. (1950), J. Bact., *59*:287.

Yankofsky, S. A., and Spiegelman, S. (1962), Proc. Nat. Acad. Sci., U. S., *48*:1069.
Yankofsky, S. A., and Spiegelman, S. (1963), Proc. Nat. Acad. Sci., U. S., *49*:538.
Yanofsky, C. (1960), Bact. Rev., *24*:221.
Yanofsky, C. (1963a), Cold Spr. Harb. Symp. Quant. Biol., *28*:581.
Yanofsky, C. (1963b), in *Informational Macromolecules,* H. J. Vogel, V. Bryson, and J. O. Lampen, eds., Academic Press, N. Y.
Yanofsky, C., Carlton, B. C., Guest, J. R., Helinski, D. R., and Henning, U. (1964), Proc. Nat. Acad. Sci., U. S., *51*:266.
Yoshikawa, H., and Sueoka, N. (1963a), Proc. Nat. Acad. Sci., U. S., *49*:559.
Yoshikawa, H., and Sueoka, N. (1963b), Proc. Nat. Acad. Sci., U. S., *49*:806.
Young, F. E., and Spizizen, J. (1963), J. Bact., *86*:392.

Zamecnik, P. C. (1960), Harvey Lectures, *54*:526.
Zamenhof, S. (1946), Heredity, *37*:273.
Zamenhof, S. (1946), J. Bact., *51*:351.
Zamenhof, S. (1961), J. Bact., *81*:111.
Zamenhof, S., and Griboff, G. (1954), Nature, *174*:306.
Zamenhof, S., Leidy, G., Greer, S., and Hahn, E. (1957), J. Bact., *74*:194.
Zelle, M. (1942), J. Inf. Dis., *71*:131.
Zelle, M. R., and Hollaender, A. (1955), in *Radiation Biology,* vol. 2, A. Hollaender, ed., McGraw-Hill, N. Y.
Zelle, M. R., and Lederberg, J. (1951), J. Bact., *61*:351.
Zelle, M. R., Ogg, J. E., and A. Hollaender (1958), J. Bact., *75*:190.
Zinder, N. D. (1955), J. Cell. Comp. Phys., Suppl. 2, *45*:23.
Zinder, N. D. (1957), Science, *126*:1237.
Zinder, N. D. (1960), Science, *131*:924.
Zinder, N. D., and Lederberg, J. (1952), J. Bact., *64*:679.

INDEX

Extended discussions are indicated by bold face figures